DAVID KRAUS

Upper Saddle River,
New Jersey

THE AUTHOR

DAVID KRAUS, B.S., M.S. in Education; former Chairman of the Science Department, Far Rockaway High School, New York City. Member of the New York State Biology Syllabus Committee and President of the Biology Chairmen's Association of New York City. Member of the Committee on Social Implications of Biology Teaching of the National Association of Biology Teachers. Winner of the NSTA STAR Teaching Award and designated as Teacher of the Year by the New York Biology Teachers Association. Served on curriculum project at Sloan-Kettering Institute and did research on *Hydra* at Adelphi University and at Boyce Thompson Institute. Founding member of New York Council for Evolution Education. Contributor to *The American Biology Teacher*, *The Science Teacher*, *Adaptation*, and *Creation/Evolution*.

Printed in the United States of America
2 3 4 5 6 7 8 9 10 04 03 02 01 00

ISBN 0-835-94841-2 (case bound)

ISBN 0-835-94839-0 (paperback)

Globe Fearon

CONTENTS

UNIT FOUR

REPRODUCTION AND DEVELOPMENT

UNIT FIVE

GENETICS

ACKNOWLEDGEMENTS

ONTENT CONSULTANTS

arren Rosenberg
ssociate Professor of Biology
na College, New Rochelle NY

Roger Anderson
enior Research Scientist
olumbia University, Palisades NY

Joseph Novak
Professor of Biological Sciences
Cornell University, Ithaca NY

Ann M. Willey
Director, Laboratory of Human Genetics
New York State Department of Health,
Albany NY

EVIEWERS

eona Freeman
iology Teacher
nion—Endicott High School, Endicott NY
irector-At-Large/Biology
cience Teachers Association of New York State

ichard Plass
ssistant Principal, Biology
tuyvesant High School, New York NY

ichard Goodman
cience Teacher
Iorace Greeley High School, Chappaqua NY

Randy Barbarash
Assistant Principal, Science
Port Richmond High School, Staten Island NY

Imelda Gallagher
Science Supervisor
Harborfields High School, Greenlawn NY

Estella Abel
Science Administrator
Mount Vernon High School, Mount Vernon NY

ONTRIBUTORS

ichard Goodman
cience Teacher
Iorace Greeley High School, Chappaqua NY

eoffrey Schwartz
hairman, Science Department
alhoun High School, Merrick NY

Theresa Nason
Science Writer
Voorhees NJ

Randy Barbarash
Assistant Principal, Science
Port Richmond High School, Staten Island NY

Ann M. Willey
Director, Laboratory of Human Genetics
New York State Department of Health,
Albany NY

Dan Kunkle
Science Supervisor
Freedom High School, Bethlehem PA

HOW TO USE THIS BOOK

- *Concepts In Modern Biology* is designed to help you learn all of the importan concepts necessary for a complete course in Biology. This text is organized int units, chapters, and chapter sections. Each chapter section has a title in th margin that tells you what the section is about.
- To help you check your own learning, you'll find many questions at the end of eac chapter. The end-of-chapter questions are organized by a system of letters in a square or circle that matches the organization of the chapter text. The end-of chapter questions are of two kinds. There are **Reasoning Exercises** to help yo organize your knowledge by writing brief essays. There are also numerous shor answer **Completions Questions** and **Multiple Choice Questions**. They provid review and drill of smaller bits of information. You'll also find a **Chapter Test** at th end of each chapter.
- *Concepts In Modern Biology* has illustrations and photographs to clarify the text. Read the captions; you'll find important information there.
- *Concepts In Modern Biology* has charts that organize important information fo study and for fast reference.
- *Concepts In Modern Biology* has lab skills within the chapters. The page margin are color keyed to indicate sections on lab skills. These skills will help you see th relationship lab methods have to the study of biology. It is through the carefu observation and recording of data that the broad concepts of science are devel- oped. There is also an **Appendix** with a Review of Laboratory Skills and question about them.
- *Concepts In Modern Biology* helps you with science vocabulary. *Italicized* word are special terms or are ideas that need emphasis. As you read, pay attention to th words in italics.
- *Concepts In Modern Biology* has a **Glossary** of biology terms used in the text. Use it often to help you fully understand the science vocabulary that makes the meaning of this text more precise.
- *Concepts in Modern Biology* has a **Classification of Organisms** that gives a sum- mary of the five kingdoms.

UNIT ONE UNITY AND DIVERSITY AMONG LIVING THINGS

Living things exhibit a variety of features. Some are able to move with incredible speed, and others remain stationary. Some organisms can live deep within the oceans, and others live at very high elevations. Living things can be large or tiny in size—some too minute to be seen with the naked eye. Most living organisms are found in or near the water, but some live in very dry places, such as the desert, and can exist without water for long periods of time. There is great diversity in the ways life on earth exists.

All living things carry on essential life functions. They all require energy, they are all composed of the same chemical materials, and they all carry out basically the same chemical reactions. There are also patterns of *similarity* among living things.

In this unit you learn how the existence and life functions of all living things demonstrate both unity and diversity.

Chapter 1 The Concept of Life

Biology is the study of living things (*bios* = life, *logia* = study). Although many books have been written on the subject of biology, biologists still cannot provide a satisfactory and complete definition of life. Scientists do know that life itself consists, in part, of a continuous series of interrelated chemical reactions that require a source of energy from the environment. This chapter briefly introduces the characteristics of life.

A Definition of Life

Compare a living thing, such as a dog, with a nonliving thing, such as a rock. How can you determine the basic differences between something that is living and something that is not living? Most living things *do* something: they move, they take in food, they grow. In simplest terms, we can define life by saying that living things carry on certain life processes. These processes are common to all living things, no matter how different they may seem. A giraffe, a maple tree, and a bacterium all carry on similar life functions. This fact provides some evidence that there is a basic unity of life.

B Life Processes

The many ways in which living things are interrelated with each other exist in the specific life processes they all share.

Nutrition. Most living things perform various kinds of work: many animals move from place to place—they may fly, swim, run, or burrow; they chew and swallow their food; they respond to changes in their environment. To do this work, all organisms must obtain energy from an energy source. Just as a car engine uses gasoline as its energy source, living things use food as the source of energy to do work. The process by which organisms obtain and use food is called *nutrition.* Most animals take in food by the process of *ingestion.* Eating is a form of ingestion. Green plants make their own food from simpler materials in the environment. The process by which green plants use energy from sunlight to make their own food is called *photosynthesis.*

Transport. The process by which ingested materials are distributed within an organism is called *transport.* On the cellular level, transport includes the passage of materials into and out of cells and the distribution of materials throughout the cell. Complex animals generally have a circulatory system, in which materials are carried by the blood to and from the various parts of the body. Among the materials transported by the circulatory system are dissolved foods, oxygen, minerals, and waste products. Many plants have a system of tubes that transport water and food up and down the stem.

Respiration. The energy required for an organism to perform its life functions is supplied by its food in chemical form. In order to be used, this energy must be released from the food molecules by the process of *respiration.* Chemically, respiration is the oxidation of food materials. Oxidation occurs by a complex series of chemical reactions within one-celled organisms and within the individual cells of a multicellular plant or animal. Breathing is only one of the steps in the respiration process and occurs in some but not all animals.

Excretion. The chemical reactions by which cells carry on the life processes produce waste materials. These waste materials may be harmful if they accumulate within the organism. *Excretion* is the removal of cellular waste products.

Synthesis. *Synthesis* consists of the chemical reactions by which cells combine small molecules to form larger ones. Sometimes those larger molecules are used to build the microscopic structures from which cells are made. In this way, synthesis can help form new cells for an organism's growth and for the repair of worn or lost parts.

Regulation. In an emergency situation your heart beats faster, your air passages open wide, and your muscle cells obtain more glucose for energy. This is an example of how parts of your body work together to respond to challenges from any changes in the environment. The control and coordination of the various activities of an organism is known as *regulation.* In higher animals, regulation is carried on by the nervous system and the endocrine system. Plants have chemical methods for regulating such activities as turning toward the light and producing flowers.

Growth. *Growth* is the life process by which organisms increase in size. Single-celled organisms grow because synthesis causes an increase in the cell's volume. Many-celled organisms grow mainly through an increase in the number of cells.

Reproduction. *Reproduction* is the life process by which an organism produces new individuals of the same kind. This is the only one of the life processes which is not essential for the life of an individual organism. Reproduction, however, is essential for the survival of that species.

Life Processes of Living Things

Process	Definition
Nutrition	The obtaining and processing of food materials
Transport	The intake and distribution of materials throughout an organism
Respiration	The release of energy from food by oxidation
Excretion	The removal of metabolic wastes from an organism
Synthesis	The combining of simple substances to form more complex substances, thereby forming more living matter
Regulation	The coordinated response of an organism to a changing environment in order to maintain stability
Growth	The increase in size of an organism that results from the synthesis and organization of materials into new substances and structures
Reproduction	The ability of living things to produce more of their own kind. This process is essential to the species, but not to the individual organism

The sum total of all the life processes required to sustain life is called *metabolism*. All of these processes require food, which in turn supplies the energy that is needed for carrying on life activities. The proper functioning of the many chemical reactions within the cells of an organism requires delicate control of the internal environment. This internal environment must remain relatively stable even during extreme variations in the activity of the organism or in the external environment. The stability of the internal environment is called *homeostasis* (*homeo* = same, *statis* = condition). Life processes must be coordinated in a manner that maintains homeostasis, or serious problems may result.

Reasoning Exercises

1. Define biology.
2. Is breathing the same as respiration? Explain.
3. Describe what is meant by homeostasis.
4. List eight life functions that are common to living things.

Laboratory Skills

Gather, Process, and Record Data

Biologists continue to investigate the nature of living things. Scientists are always trying to find the answers to new questions. The *scientific method* is an organized approach that scientists use in solving problems. The basic steps in the scientific method are as follows:

1. **Clearly define the problem.** Identifying the problem helps determine the ways to find out the answer or solution to the problem.
2. **Research and collect data.** Asking questions and making careful observations are ways of collecting evidence. The information that comes from measuring, comparing, and experimenting is called

data. The data that are collected must be recorded, organized, analyzed, and finally presented in a way that will help others understand the experimental test studies. These are important scientific processes in laboratory investigations.

3. **Formulate a generalization, or scientific hypothesis.** On the basis of research collected, a trial idea or *hypothesis* is constructed that can be used to explain certain events.
4. **Conduct an experiment to test the hypothesis.** Devise an experiment that would test the hypothesis. An experiment must contain a *control* group. The control provides the basis of comparison for the *variable*, or *experimental factor* that is being tested.
5. **Draw a conclusion based upon the results.** Upon repeated experimentation, results are studied and a conclusion is formed that supports or disproves the hypothesis. If the hypothesis is not supported, the experiment must be redesigned to test an altered or completely new hypothesis.

Completion Questions

A

1. The study of living things is called . . . . . .
2. You can simply define life by saying that living things carry on certain . . . . . .
3. No matter how different living things are, the life processes are common to . . . . . . (all, most, none) living things.

B

4. The process by which living things obtain and use food is called......
5. The process by which green plants use energy from sunlight to make their own food is called......
6. The process by which ingested materials are distributed within living things is called......
7. Complex animals have a......to distribute materials within the animal.
8. The release of energy from food molecules so it can be used by living things is by the process of . . . . . .
9. The removal of cellular waste from living things is called . . . . . .
10. The control and coordination of the various activities of living things is called . . . . . .
11. The sum total of all the life processes required to sustain the life of living things is called . . . . . .
12. During extreme variations in the activities of an organism, the internal environment must remain stable. This process is called . . . . . .

• 13. The organized approach that scientists use to solve problems is called the . . . . . .

• 14. Information that comes from measuring, comparing, and experimenting is called . . . . . .

• 15. In laboratory investigations, measuring, comparing, and recording information are important . . . . . . in scientific investigation.

Multiple-Choice Questions

A-B

1. People who study biology are concerned with (1) everything on earth, (2) all living things, (3) only animals, (4) only plants.
2. To do work of different kinds, living things must have (1) energy, (2) growth, (3) oxygen and minerals, (4) green plants.
3. Nutrition is the process by which living things (1) breathe, (2) take in food, (3) obtain and use food, (4) give off nutrients.
4. Moving materials in and out of cells as well as throughout the cell is called (1) nutrition, (2) transport, (3) growth, (4) respiration.
5. The removal of cellular waste from living things is called (1) nutrition, (2) transport, (3) excretion, (4) respiration.
6. The life process by which living things increase in size is called (1) nutrition, (2) growth, (3) reproduction, (4) excretion.
7. The process by which animals take in food is called (1) ingestion, (2) reproduction, (3) growth, (4) transport.
8. In complex animals, a circulatory system is responsible for the process of . . . . . . in the organism. (1) respiration, (2) excretion, (3) transport, (4) nutrition
9. In the process of respiration, food must be chemically (1) excreted, (2) transported, (3) oxidized, (4) reacted.
10. The chemical reactions by which cells carry on the life processes produce (1) waste products, (2) synthesis, (3) respiration, (4) circulation.
11. The nervous system and the endocrine system in higher animals carry on the process of (1) reproduction, (2) respiration, (3) excretion, (4) regulation.
12. The term most closely associated with homeostasis is (1) growth, (2) stability, (3) regulation, (4) ingestion.
13. • The trial idea that scientists construct so that they can test certain events leading up to the answer of a problem is called a(n) (1) data, (2) hypothesis, (3) control, (4) variable.
14. • The basis of comparison in testing an hypothesis is called a(n) (1) data, (2) variable, (3) control, (4) experimental factor.
15. • The scientific method is (1) a way to define a problem, (2) used to record, organize, and collect data, (3) an organized approach used in solving problems, (4) used by all scientists in an identical way.

Base your answers to questions 16 and 17 on the chart on p. 3.

16. Which is the only life process that is not necessary for survival of an individual organism? (1) nutrition, (2) respiration, (3) regulation, (4) reproduction.
17. Which life process takes place when small molecules of sugar combine to form large molecules of starch? (1) transport, (2) excretion, (3) synthesis, (4) growth.

Chapter Test

1. The sum total of all the life functions is called (1) respiration, (2) nutrition, (3) homeostasis, (4) metabolism.
2. The energy present in food molecules is released by the process of (1) reproduction, (2) ingestion, (3) respiration, (4) excretion.
3. The process by which living things obtain and use food is (1) nutrition, (2) transport, (3) regulation, (4) synthesis.
4. Making more complex substances from simpler ones is (1) regulation, (2) synthesis, (3) reproduction, (4) digestion
5. A life process that is not essential for the life of an individual but is essential for the survival of the species is (1) transport, (2) reproduction, (3) nutrition, (4) excretion.

For the following questions, choose the letter corresponding to the correct answer:

6. An organism increases in size by the process of (a) development, (b) growth, (c) reproduction, (d) synthesis.
7. Ingested materials are distributed within an organism by the process of (a) transport, (b) circulation, (c) digestion, (d) locomotion.
8. The control and coordination of the various activities of an organism is known as (a) feedback, (b) metabolism, (c) regulation, (d) respiration.
9. The stability of an organism's internal environment is called (a) homeostasis, (b) *Homo sapiens*, (c) synthesis, (d) stabilization.
10. The removal of cellular waste products from an organism is called (a) sweating, (b) filtration, (c) regulation, (d) excretion.

Chapter 2 The Diversity of Life

More than five million different kinds of organisms inhabit the earth. More than 1.5 million have already been described and named, and each year several thousand more are found and added to the list. How can this huge number of living things be organized into a meaningful system of classification? You can classify a stamp collection to serve any purpose you wish—by countries, shapes, colors, or topics. What should be the basis for the biologists' scheme for classifying and naming living things?

A

ecessity for lassification

Biologists classify organisms to study unity and diversity in an organized manner. Similarity in physical structure is an important criterion for classifying organisms. If you are told that a strange organism is classified as a mollusk, for example, you already know much about its internal structure. The division of biology that deals with the classification and naming of living and extinct organisms is *taxonomy.* A recognized, international system of taxonomy permits biologists from different countries to locate information about organisms in museums and libraries and to communicate with each other about the organisms.

B

xonomy and Evolution

Most biologists today seek to classify organisms in a way that shows how they are related by evolution. According to the theory of *organic evolution,* living things have changed over many generations from common ancestors. Similarity in physical structure is only one of the ways to determine the closeness of relationships.

The pathway of evolution may be considered as a branching tree, as shown in Figure 2–1.

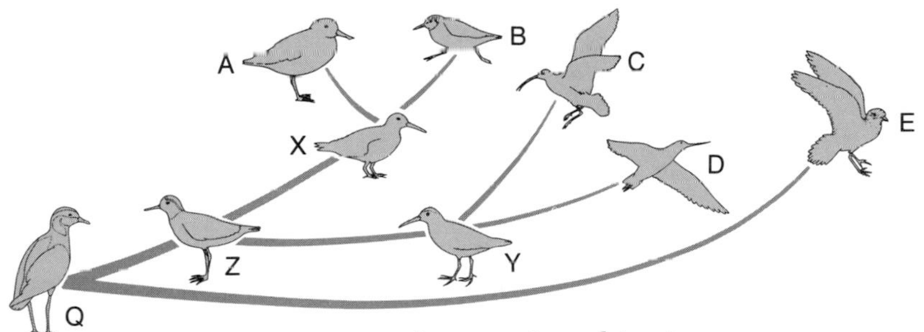

Fig. 2–1. Evolution: a branching tree

In this diagram, each letter goes with a different kind of bird. A and B are *closely* related because they came from a common ancestor, X. C and D are *closely* related for they too came from a common ancestor, Y.

Are A and C related? Yes, but they are more distantly related. They are like cousins. Their common ancestor (Z) is in the remote past. Is A related to E? Yes, but their relationship is still more distant. What is their common ancestor?

C The Classification Scheme

Living things do not come in neat packages labeled Plant or Animal. These two groupings are artificial categories designed by humans. Like other human endeavors, taxonomy is subject to change in light of new knowledge.

The Two-Kingdom System

From earliest times, organisms were divided into two major groups: the plant kingdom and the animal kingdom. Distinguishing members of the two kingdoms was easy. Plants made their own food and grew in one place; animals depended upon other organisms for food and moved about. With the invention of the microscope came additional criteria for classification. For example, plant cells were found to have cell walls, but animal cells do not.

The Three-Kingdom System

Additional studies of simple microscopic organisms revealed, however, that some were neither definitely plants nor animals. *Euglena* (Fig. 2–2) is a one-celled organism that has a whip-like flagellum with which it moves like an animal, yet it can make its own food like a plant cell. To meet this problem, a third kingdom, the *Protista,* was suggested and generally accepted. The algae and protozoa were removed from the plant and animal kingdoms and included in the Protista. Ancient protists are regarded as the ancestors of today's plants and animals, as well as of today's protists.

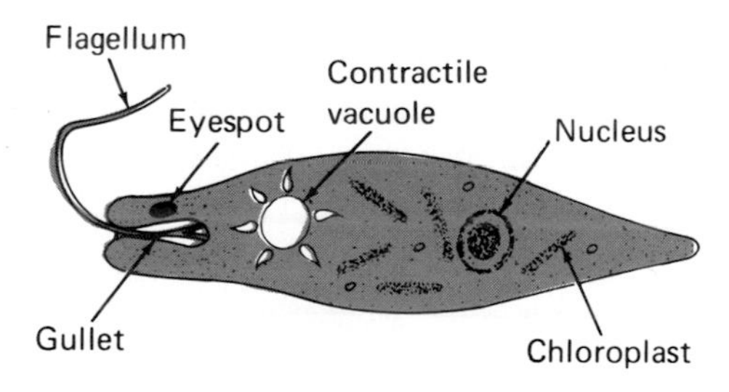

Fig. 2–2. *Euglena*—Plant or Animal?

One Four-Kingdom System

Bacteria are cells that differ from other living things in that they lack a nucleus. Their hereditary material is a single circular chromosome that is not enclosed within a nuclear membrane. Biologists consider the development of a nuclear membrane and other cell organelles to be so important an evolutionary step that they group bacteria into a separate kingdom, the *Monera.* Some biologists propose that some kinds of bacteria-like cells known as Archaebacteria be classified separately from the Monera.

The Five-Kingdom System

Bread molds, mushrooms, and yeasts resemble plants in that they have cell walls. Unlike plants, however, they cannot make their own food. Yeasts are one-celled. Bread molds and mushrooms are considered multicellular. Nonetheless, these organisms resemble each other in other respects. They are assigned to a fifth kingdom, the *Fungi.*

A System of Classification			
King-dom	**Partial List of Phyla**	**Characteristics**	**Examples**
Monera	Bacteria	All monera have a primitive cell structure that lacks a nuclear membrane. Most bacteria live on other organisms or other food from their environment, but a few have chloroplasts, structures with chlorophyll that enables them to make their own food.	*Streptococcus, E. coli*
	Blue-green Bacteria	Unicellular or forming filaments; carry on photosynthesis (make their own food) but lack chloroplasts	*Nostoc*
Protista	Protozoa	The protists are animallike or plantlike in their mode of nutrition. The protozoa are animallike; unicellular or multicellular; divided into four major groups based upon their method of movement. One group forms spores.	*Amebu, Paramecium,* (*Euglena* may be classified with the protozoa or algae)
	Algae	Plantlike in their mode of nutrition (photosynthesis); unicellular or multicellular	*Spirogyra Chlorella*
Fungi		Cells usually organized into branched, multinucleated filaments which absorb digested food from their environment.	yeast, bread mold, mushrooms
Plant	Bryophytes	The plant kingdom consists of multicellular, photosynthetic organisms. Bryophytes are low-growing, green plants that lack vascular (conducting) tissue and true roots, stems, and leaves.	moss
	Tracheophytes	Have vascular tissue that allows them to grow tall; have true roots, stems, and leaves	fern, geranium, bean, pine tree, maple tree, corn
Animal	Coelenterates ("cup animals")	The animal kingdom contains multicellular organisms that ingest their food. Coelenterates have a body wall composed of two cell layers forming a cup-shaped, hollow body cavity.	hydra, jellyfish
	Annelids ("segmented worms")	Have segmented body walls composed of three cell layers; digestive tract forms a continuous tube with two openings.	earthworm, sandworm
	Arthropods	Exoskeleton (on the outside of the body); jointed appendages	grasshopper, lobster, spider
	Chordates	Dorsal notochord (stiff supporting rod); dorsal, hollow nerve cord. (A major subphylum, the vertebrates, have supporting column of bone or cartilage called vertebrae and an endoskeleton.)	shark, flounder, frog, turtle, robin, cow, human

The Species

The basic unit in taxonomy is the *species*. A species is defined as a group of interbreeding organisms that do not normally breed with members of other groups. Although this definition is useful for animals, it is not so useful for organisms such as protozoa that reproduce only by cell division. In plants, also, reproduction can take place sometimes between different kinds.

The horse and the donkey can mate to produce the mule. The mule offspring, however, are usually nonfertile. Since the horse and the donkey do not generally produce fertile offspring, they are classified into different species.

D

Nomenclature

The Higher Categories

Categories of classification are known as ranks. The highest rank is the Kingdom. We shall use a system of five kingdoms.

Following the kingdom, the successively lower ranks are Phylum, Class, Order, Family, Genus, and Species.

Binomial Nomenclature

The scientific name for an organism consists of the names of its genus and species; for example, *Homo sapiens*. This two-name system is called *binomial nomenclature*. For example, a genus of catlike animals known as *Felis* includes the species *Felis leo* (the lion), *Felis tigris* (the tiger), and *Felis domesticus* (the house cat). Note that the first word of the name has a capital letter and the second word has a small first letter. The scientific name should be italicized or underlined.

Frequently, the Latin and Greek names given to organisms are descriptive. For example, the scientific name of the fruit fly, *Drosophila melanogaster*, means "black-bellied sugar lover" (*Dros* = sugar, *phil* = like, *melano* = black, *gaster* = stomach). The description humans took for themselves, *Homo sapiens*, means "wise man."

Comparing Cat and Human Classification

	Cat	Human
Kingdom	Animalia	Animalia
Phylum	Chordata	Chordata
Class	Mammalia	Mammalia
Order	Carnivora	Primates
Family	Felidae	Hominidae
Genus	*Felis*	*Homo*
Species	*Felis domesticus*	*Homo sapiens*

A microscopic organism commonly studied in biology is *Paramecium*. This, however, is only the genus name. Two species, under the genus, are *Paramecium caudatum* and *Paramecium aurelia*.

The scientific name may also include a third name, indicating the subspecies. The name or initial of the person who first described and named the organism is often added. In 1753, the Swedish naturalist Carolus Linnaeus (originally Karl von Linné) published a book in which he classified and named all plants and animals then known in Europe. Linnaeus took credit for naming the organisms in his system of classification and, therefore, his initial is included in many scientific names. For example, the red maple is *Acer rubrum, L.*

Reasoning Exercises

1. What is the value of having an international system for classifying and naming organisms?
2. What is taxonomy? How is taxonomy based on evolution?
3. What is the basis for a three-kingdom and four-kingdom classification system? Why is the two-kingdom system rarely used today?
4. Why is a mule not considered to be a species?
5. What is binomial nomenclature? How is it used?

Ⓔ

The Roll Call of Living Things

Living things inhabit the seas, the forests, the prairies, and the deserts. They occupy frozen mountain peaks and the waters of hot springs. They come in all sizes, from bacteria to the whale. Their shapes vary from the eight-armed octopus to the long-necked giraffe. Some are delicate like the jellyfish; others are massive like the rhinoceros. They fly like the gull, swim like the porpoise, crawl like the centipede, burrow like the mole, or float like the Portuguese man-of-war. They remain in one place like the rosebush or hitch a ride on sharks like the remora fish. We can be bewildered by the sheer number of living things, by their varied shapes, and by their many modes of life.

Kingdom Monera

Bacteria are so different from other organisms that they have been set apart in a separate kingdom, called the Monera. The main difference between cells of the Monera and cells of other kingdoms is that monerans lack a distinct, membrane-bound nucleus. (See Fig. 2–3.) Cells that lack a distinct, membrane-bound nucleus, like those of the Monera, are called

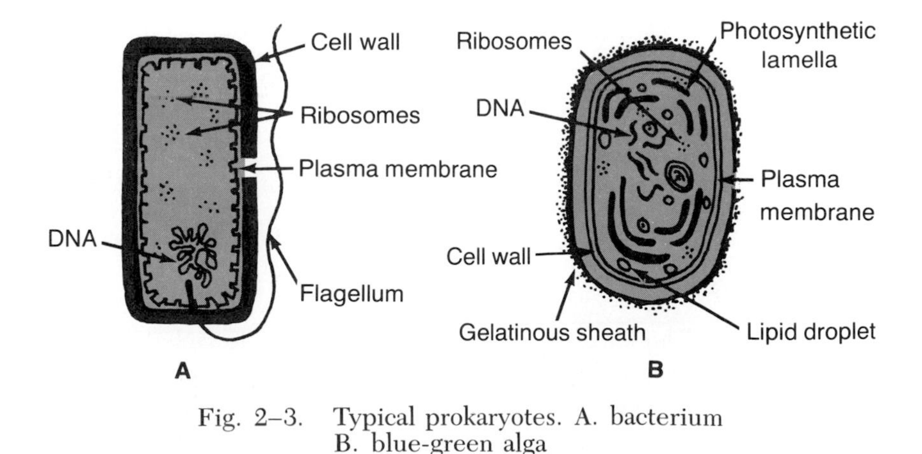

Fig. 2–3. Typical prokaryotes. A. bacterium B. blue-green alga

prokaryotes (Greek *pro* = before, *karyon* = nucleus). Those having a distinct nucleus are called *eukaryotes* (Greek *eu* = good, *karyon* = nucleus) Thus, one could establish two super-kingdoms: the *prokaryotes*, consisting only of the monerans, and the *eukaryotes*, consisting of all other living things.

Moneran cells also lack other membrane-bounded cell organelles, such as mitochondria, the endoplasmic reticulum, and chloroplasts. Although they lack a formed nucleus, they do have DNA *(deoxyribonucleic acid)* which transmits hereditary information.

Blue-green Algae and Bacteria

The blue-green bacteria, also known as cyanobacteria, have a blue pigment along with green chlorophyll and carry on photosynthesis. Such organisms that can produce their own food from simple materials are called *autotrophs* (*auto* = self, *trophe* = nourishment). The blue-green bacteria are simple autotrophs. Most bacteria, however, are *heterotrophs* (*hetero* = other). This means that their food is preformed high-energy molecules obtained from dead or living things.

Bacteria are found practically everywhere on Earth. Although many kinds are disease-producing, some bacteria are essential to human welfare: in the process of decay, they return to the environment the chemicals locked in the bodies of dead organisms.

What is meant by a "strep" or a "staph" infection? These terms refer to the arrangement of some bacteria. Bacteria are divided by shape into three basic kinds. (See Fig. 2–4.) A spherical bacterium is a *coccus*, a rod-shaped one is a *bacillus*, and a spiral or coiled one is a *spirillum*. When daughter cells do not separate after cell division, a chain of cells may form. This arrangement is called a *Streptococcus* or *Streptobacillus*. A mass of cocci is called a *Staphylococcus*.

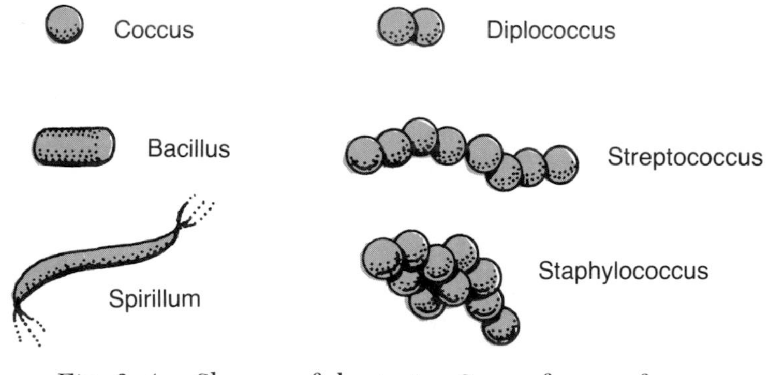

Fig. 2–4. Shapes of bacteria. Some forms of sore throat and blood poisoning are caused by a streptococcus. Boils are sometimes caused by a staphylococcus.

Kingdom Protista

The kingdom Protista was established to include microscopic organisms that could not be classified with certainty as plants or animals. Some forms are autotrophic, others are heterotrophic. Most are unicellular. The protists include algae, protozoans, and slime molds.

Euglena. *Euglena* is an unusual organism that possesses characteristics of both animal and plant cells. *Euglena* resembles an animal in that it lacks a cell wall, possesses a flagellum for rapid locomotion, and has a light-sensitive, red-pigmented eyespot. Under certain conditions, it can live on food materials taken in from its watery environment. However, like a plant, *Euglena* possesses chloroplasts which are used for photosynthesis.

Algae. Unlike the blue-green algae, the algae have true nuclei and specialized organelles. The *green algae* have chlorophyll that can easily be seen, but this pigment is masked in the *brown algae* and *red algae* which contain other pigments in addition to chlorophyll. Some algae form large, many-celled structures. Algae live in the ocean, fresh water, and moist places on land. *Protococcus* (Fig. 2–5) is a green alga that lives on the moist bark of trees and moist surfaces of rocks.

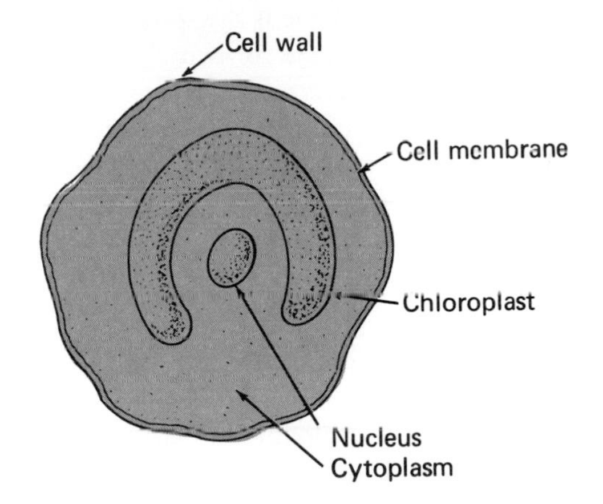

Fig. 2–5. *Protococcus*, a green alga. Note the definite nucleus with its nuclear membrane.

Spirogyra, shown in Figure 2–6, is a green alga found in freshwater ponds. Its cells are attached to form long filaments or threads. Although

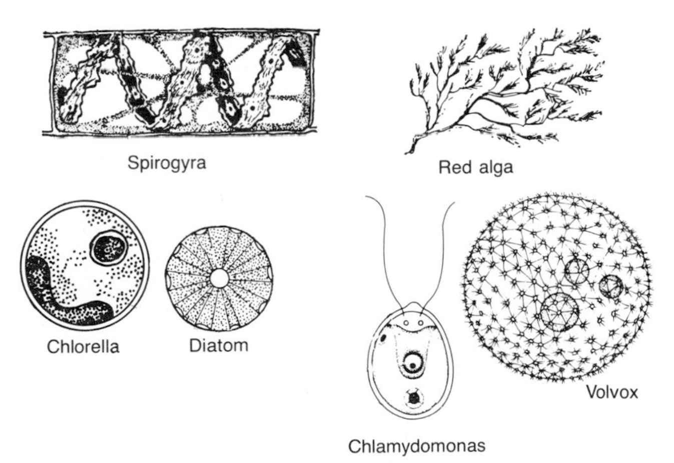

Fig. 2–6. Common algae

its spiral-shaped chloroplast is not typical of algae, its shape makes this genus interesting to study under the microscope.

Chlorella is a common single-celled green alga, used extensively in experiments on the chemistry of photosynthesis.

Chlamydomonas is a one-celled freshwater alga that has two flagella. The colonial alga, *Volvox,* is a hollow sphere of cells, each resembling the single cell of *Chlamydomonas.* The many-celled colony is regarded as a single individual since some cells are specialized.

Diatoms (Fig. 2–6) have a hard silica cell wall that consists of two overlapping halves. When diatoms die, their silica shells deposit on the bottom of the sea as diatomaceous earth, used as a fine abrasive. Diatoms constitute a large portion of the *plankton,* the mass of minute organisms floating near the surface of the sea. They are a major food source for nonphotosynthetic organisms in the sea.

One of the red algae is the source of agar that is used to grow bacteria in biological laboratories. Brown algae include kelps and rockweeds. Rockweeds grow in the form of dense mats close to the shore. *Algin,* obtained from algae, is used as a thickener for ice cream and puddings.

Researchers in 1980 studied a primitive alga that lives in hot springs. Studies indicate that this alga is a "missing link" between cells that lack a nucleus and those that have a nucleus.

Protozoa

Protozoa are unicellular, complex, animallike protists that lack chlorophyll. In the two-kingdom classification they are described as one-celled animals. They live in fresh water, salt water, and moist soil. Some live as parasites within other organisms. The protozoa are classified by their method of movement.

Among the freshwater protozoa are *Ameba* and *Paramecium,* single-celled organisms large enough to be seen with the naked eye. The foraminifera are saltwater protozoa that have an external skeleton of calcium carbonate (a rocklike substance). Undersea deposits of shells of these protozoa resulted in chalk that later rose to form the white cliffs of Dover, England. Radiolaria also live in salt water; they have pseudopods that protrude from their external skeletons, which are made of silica.

Plasmodium is a spore-forming protozoan that causes malaria. The *Plasmodium* spends part of its life in the female *Anopheles* mosquito. If an infected mosquito "bites" a human, the mosquito may transfer protozoa into the human's bloodstream. When this happens, the protozoa cause malaria by producing poisons and destroying red blood cells. People with malaria are weakened and may have chills and fever.

Trypanosoma gambiense causes the often fatal disease called African sleeping sickness. This protozoan has a *flagellum*—a whiplike tail that propels it. Many other protozoa also have flagella.

Ameba

Ameba is an irregularly shaped organism classified with the protozoa—the one-celled animallike organisms. It can be seen with the naked eye and appears under the microscope as a translucent mass of protoplasm that slowly changes shape. It lives in water and may be found on the underside of the leaves of plants which grow near the bottom of freshwater ponds. Some types live in the sea and some are parasites.

The ameba moves by means of its *pseudopods* (Greek *pseudes* = false, *pod* = foot). The cell membrane bulges at any point, and cytoplasm flows into the gradually extending pseudopod (Fig. 2–7). This type of movement is known as *ameboid movement.*

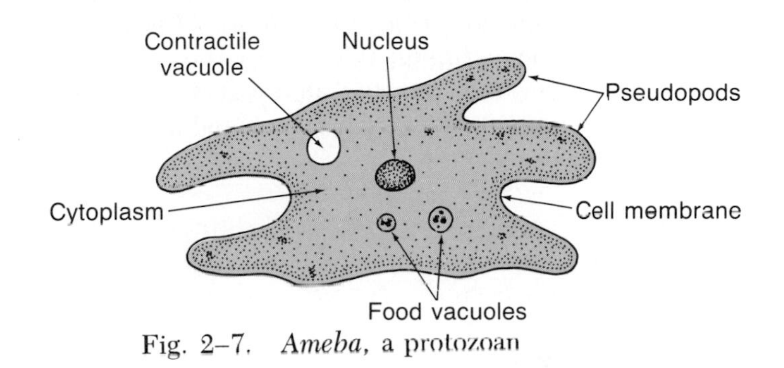

Fig. 2–7. *Ameba,* a protozoan

Paramecium

Another protozoan, *Paramecium,* is smaller than the ameba, and it can not be seen with the naked eye. Paramecia live in freshwater ponds and lakes. The *pellicle,* or outer covering, is flexible but stiff enough to give the organism a definite shape. (See Fig. 2–8.) Viewed in two dimensions, the shape is like a slipper.

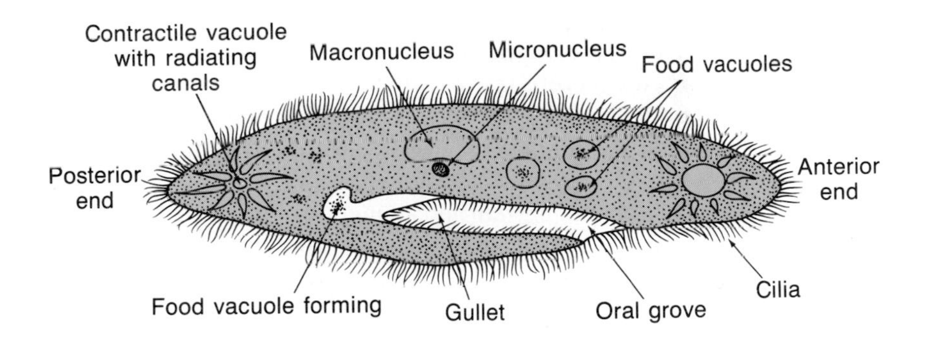

Several thousand hairlike projections, the *cilia,* protrude through the pellicle and are used for locomotion. Inside the pellicle is a layer of numerous boxlike structures, the *trichocysts,* each of which can discharge a hairlike thread. These seem to be used for attaching the paramecium to decaying matter. In the central portion of the cell are two nuclei, a *macronucleus* (large nucleus) and a *micronucleus* (small nucleus). The micronucleus contains chromosomes and functions mainly in reproduction. The macronucleus seems to be more involved in controlling other metabolic processes.

Slime Molds Slime molds are so named because at one stage of their existence they are like a slimy mass of protoplasm. During this period in their life cycle, they spread over damp, decaying vegetation. Some slime molds have a plant-animal life cycle. During one stage, they are animal-like flagellated cells; at another stage, they have amebalike cells. At other times, they have a moldlike structure that forms spore cases, a plant characteristic. Slime molds are a good example of protists because they cannot clearly be defined as plants or animals. A common type of slime mold that is often studied in school laboratories is *Physarum*.

The plantlike stage can also be called the plasmodium stage. A *plasmodium* is a spreading mass that is not separated into individual cells. This stage of *Physarum* can be found in woods growing on rotting logs.

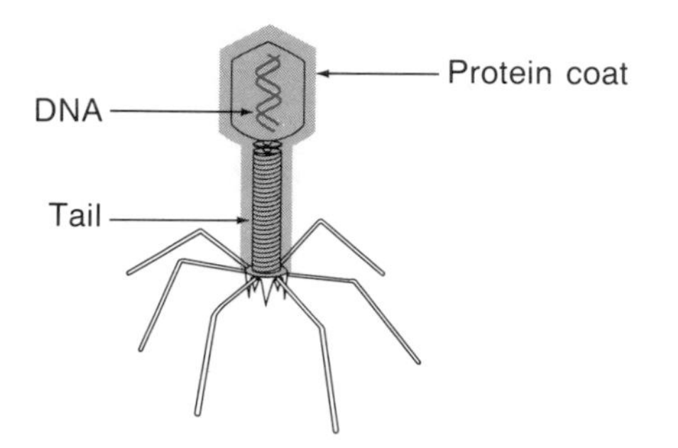

Fig. 2–9. The structure of a virus that attacks bacteria.

Viruses Viruses are much smaller than bacteria. The first biologists to study viruses merely knew that they were some kind of disease-causers that could pass through pores of the finest filter. They called them "filterable viruses"—filterable poisons. The electron microscope and biochemical studies revealed that a virus particle is composed of two chemicals: an outer coat of protein and an inner coil of either DNA or RNA (*ribonucleic acid*). Many biologists do not consider viruses to be organisms, and do not include them in either the Protista or the Monera.

Viruses live only within living cells of a host. Here a virus particle directs the host cell's chromosomes to cause the production of additional virus particles instead of carrying on the cell's normal metabolism.

Viruses cause a number of human diseases, including lethal illnesses such as AIDS, and forms of cancer such as T-cell leukemia. Viruses cause influenza, or the flu, and the common cold. Children are vaccinated for protection from dangerous viral diseases such as polio and measles.

A great step toward understanding the nature of viruses occurred in 1935 when Wendell M. Stanley was able to obtain the virus causing tobacco mosaic disease in the form of crystals. These could be stored in a bottle on a shelf. When this "nonliving chemical" was placed on fresh tobacco leaves, it began to reproduce like a living thing and caused a new infection. Viruses that attack bacteria are called *bacteriophages*.

Kingdom Fungi

The fungi are a group of plantlike organisms lacking chlorophyll. Since they do not carry on photosynthesis, they are *heterotrophs.* Some obtain their food from living things and are *parasites.* Others obtain their food from dead organisms or from the waste products of living things and are *saprophytes.*

The common *bread mold* consists of a mass of tiny threads called *hyphae.* Specialized upright hyphae produce masses of black spores. A spore that lands on moist, warm bread gives rise to a new mass of threads. Storing bread in a refrigerator is one way to prevent the bread from becoming moldy.

Other molds form green, yellow, or black areas on fruits and vegetables. The gray fuzz that develops on wet leather shoes stored in a closet is a mold. *Mildew* is a mold that forms black spots on damp towels jammed into a hamper.

The edible part of a *mushroom* consists of thin sheets of tissue whose hyphae produce spores. Underground hyphae of this saprophyte obtain food from decaying matter in the rich soil. Because some mushrooms are poisonous, a person who is unskilled in identifying mushrooms should not eat wild mushrooms found growing in the woods. Poisonous mushrooms are commonly known as toadstools.

Truffles are prized European delicacies, the size of a walnut or potato, that grow in clusters below ground. A specially trained pig can smell a truffle from a distance of six meters and will run quickly to the spot and dig it out.

Yeasts obtain energy by the fermentation of sugars. The carbon dioxide and alcohol produced are the basis for the baking and brewing industries. These one-celled fungi reproduce by budding, a process whereby new yeast cells form directly on the parent cell.

In the same class with the yeasts is *Penicillium notatum,* a fungus that produces the life-saving antibiotic penicillin. Useful molds add flavor to Camembert, Roquefort, and other cheeses.

The fungi that cause ringworm and athlete's foot are also classified with the yeasts. The ringworm fungus causes a raised ring to form under the skin, giving the appearance of a worm under the skin—yet it is caused by a fungus. Athlete's foot usually occurs between the toes and causes itching. Cleanliness and keeping the toes dry are preventives.

Lichens

A lichen looks like a thin, gray crustlike pancake growing on rocks or trees. It is a combination of a fungus and an alga. (See Fig. 2–10.) Growing together as a unit, each helps the other in a relationship called *mutualism.* The cells of the alga seem to produce food for both organisms, and the tough *mycelium* (mass of hyphae) of the fungus holds water and protects the alga. This combination of alga and fungus can grow in hostile places such as on rocks and in very cold regions. Acids produced by the fungus cause lichens to decompose rocks, leading to the formation of soil. The death and decay of lichens enriches soil by the addition of organic matter.

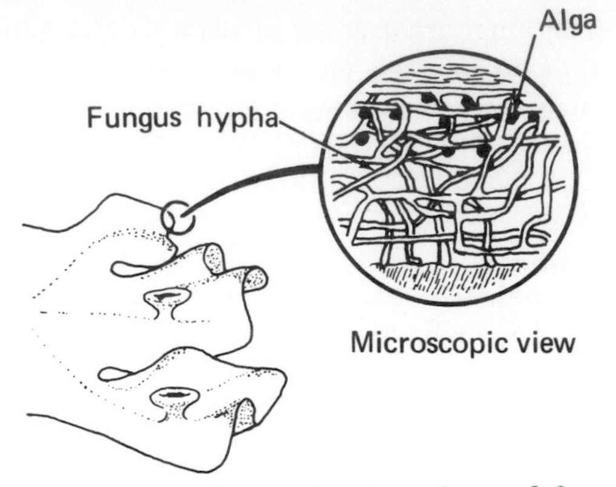

Fig. 2–10. Lichen—showing alga and fungus

Kingdom Plantae The plant kingdom has only two phyla—the bryophytes and the tracheophytes. Most of these are land plants.

Phylum—Bryophyta The bryophytes are small green plants that grow in moist places. They have no true leaves and lack a stem or have a very simple stem. In their reproductive cycle, bryophytes alternate from one generation to the next between two types of plants. One generation reproduces sexually (by gametes) and is called the *gametophyte*. The next generation reproduces asexually (by spores) and is called the *sporophyte*. This alternation between an asexual reproductive stage and a sexual reproductive stage is called *alternation of generations*. In the bryophytes, the gametophyte generation is the larger of the two and the more easily seen.

The bryophytes are divided into two classes: the liverworts and the mosses. Their name is derived from *bryon*, the Greek word for moss.

Class—liverworts. The plant body of a liverwort consists of simple branching leaves that grow flat on moist soil or water. (See Fig. 2–11.)

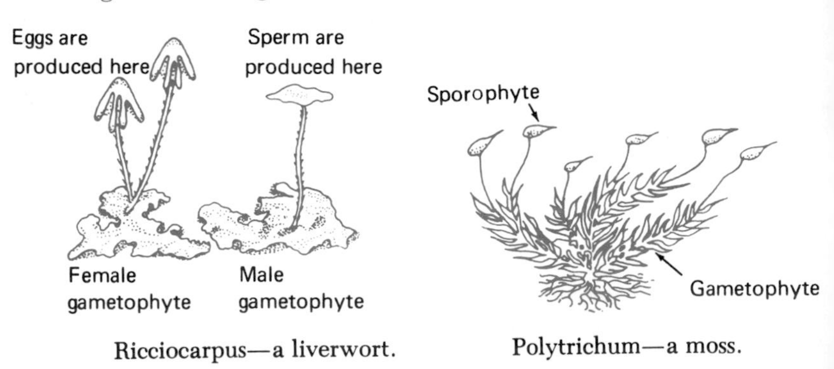

Ricciocarpus—a liverwort. Polytrichum—a moss.

Fig. 2–11. Examples of Bryophytes

Class—mosses. The mosses have simple stems that bear tiny leaflets arranged in spirals. Rootlike structures, called *rhizoids*, anchor the plant to the soil and absorb water and minerals. Sphagnum, a peatforming moss, grows in swamps and bogs. When dried, it is used to keep the soil from becoming too tightly packed and to retain moisture.

Fossil evidence indicates that the bryophytes arose from green algae as an adaptation to life on land. But the bryophytes are only partly free of dependence on water. Moisture is still needed for sperm to reach egg cells. Mosses cannot grow tall for they lack vascular tissue to carry water up a stem. They have rootlike structures but not true roots for absorbing water.

Phylum—Tracheophyta

The tracheophytes (tube plants) have a *vascular* (conducting) system of tubes for conducting water. This system of vessels allows these plants to grow taller than the low-lying liverworts and mosses. Furthermore, the more advanced tracheophytes have true roots, stems, and leaves.

Classes of Tracheophytes

The tracheophytes include primitive ferns such as the club mosses and *equisetum,* the horsetail. (See Fig. 2–12.) The branching stem of a horsetail resembles the tail of a horse. Because of the hard silica in their stems they were formerly used in the home as an abrasive. We shall limit

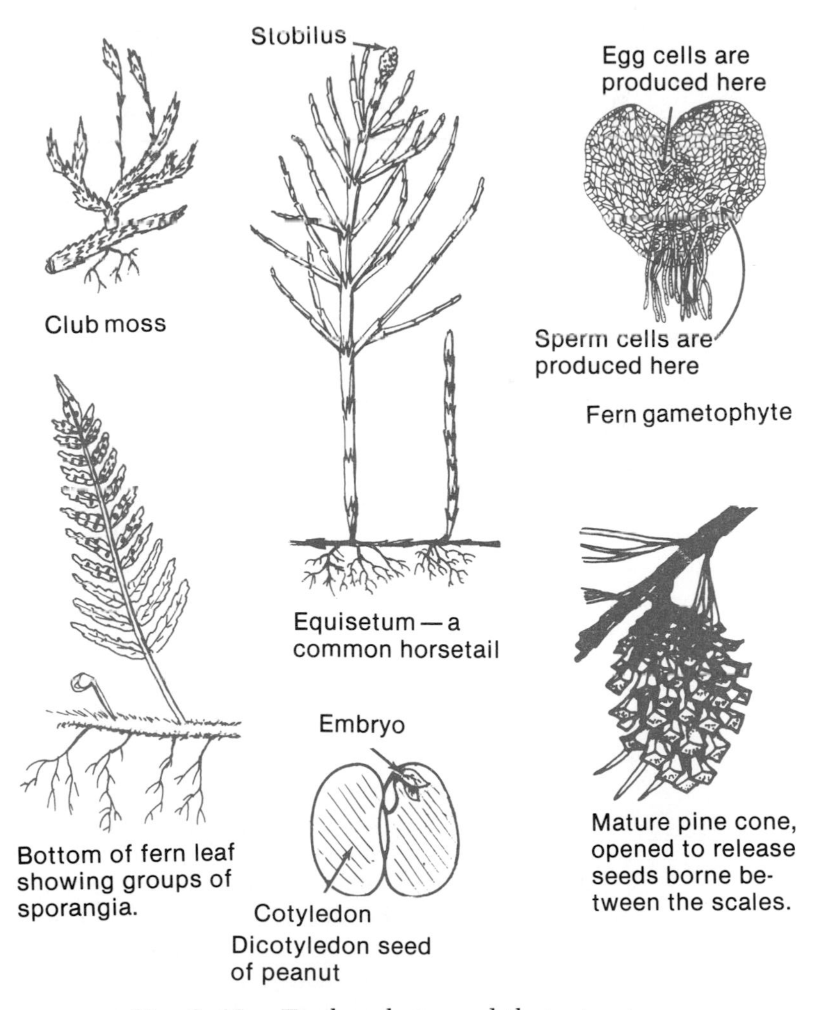

Fig. 2–12. Tracheophytes and their structures

our discussion of tracheophytes to the classes shown below. These are the ferns, evergreens, and flowering plants that people usually have in mind when they speak of a plant.

Class: Filicineae. The ferns
Class: Gymnosperms. Evergreen conifers (pines, spruces, and others)
Class: Angiosperms. Flowering plants
  Subclass: dicotyledons
    Bean, peanut, maple, rose
  Subclass: monocotyledons
    Grasses such as blue-grass, corn, oats, wheat

Filicineae (ferns). When you examine a fern closely, you can see that both its roots and stems (rhizomes) grow underground. Each spring, the familiar many-branched leaves called *fronds* appear above ground. The roots, stems, and fronds of a fern have well-developed vascular tissue for conducting water. The undersurface of some fern leaves (Fig. 2–12) has brown spots called *sori,* these are clusters of spore-producing sporangia, or spore cases. The sporangia are the spore cases containing spores for the reproduction of the plant. Fern spores develop into an inconspicuous *gametophyte* generation. This produces gametes (sex cells) that unite to produce the large plant, commonly considered by the layman to be the fern. Actually, this large, visible structure is only one of the generations of the fern's life cycle. It is the conspicuous *sporophyte* generation. As you can see, ferns undergo an alteration of generations. Some tropical ferns are tree-sized. Coal came mainly from the remains of prehistoric tree ferns.

Ferns require water for fertilization and thus are usually found in moist places. But the next two classes of tracheophytes are true land plants. Their sperm cells do not swim through water to the egg cells. Furthermore, their embryos are enclosed in a *seed.* A seed can survive long periods of dryness without losing the capacity to give rise to a new plant of the next generation. These *seed plants* are divided into the *gymnosperms* (naked-seeded plants) and the *angiosperms* (hidden-seeded plants).

Gymnosperms (naked seeds). Gymnosperm seeds are produced in cones such as the pine cone. (See Fig. 2–12.) Because they bear cones, gymnosperms are called *conifers.* When the cone dries, its thick, hard scales spread out, and the seeds are exposed and carried away by the wind.

The gymnosperms include "evergreen" conifers, such as pines, spruces, hemlocks, and cedars. They also include the cycads and the *ginkgo.* The ginkgo is popular in cities because of its exotic shape and its ability to survive under the adverse conditions of city life. The ginkgo is called a "living fossil" because it is the last of a once prominent group of plants.

Most gymnosperms have leaves that are needlelike in shape. They have well-developed roots and stems. Their vascular tissue enables them to grow to great heights. An example is the giant redwood *(Sequoia gigantea)* of California which grows over 100 meters (300 ft.) high. The coniferous forests are sources of lumber and paper.

Angiosperms (hidden seeds). Angiosperms have this name because their seeds are hidden within a fruit, as in the apple. The angiosperms are also called the "flowering plants." The flowers of many angiosperms are large and showy (tulip, gladiolus), but the flowers of others are relatively inconspicuous (maple tree, privet hedge, lawn grasses). Some angiosperms have lost the ability to produce chlorophyll and are saprophytes, like the colorless Indian Pipe that lives on the humus of the forest floor. Although the angiosperms generally are adapted to terrestrial life, many (such as the water lily, *Elodea,* and the duckweed) have returned to a watery environment.

The angiosperms are divided into two subclasses: the *dicotyledons* (or dicots) and the *monocotyledons* (or monocots). This division is based upon the number of cotyledons present in the seeds. A *cotyledon* is an organ that supplies food to the developing embryo plant. A familiar example of a dicotyledonous seed is the peanut. Each half of the nut is a cotyledon (Fig. 2–12). A corn kernel is a monocotyledonous seed.

Comparison of Dicots and Monocots

Dicots	Monocots
Two cotyledons	One cotyledon
Veins of leaves form a network	Veins of leaves are parallel
Vascular bundles of stem in a radial pattern	Vascular bundles of stem scattered
Flower parts (such as petals) in fours or fives, or their multiples	Flower parts in threes, or their multiples

Many of our edible fruits such as the apple, peach, and cherry are dicots. Monocot grasses such as corn, wheat, rye, and oats are major sources of food for humans.

Kingdom Animalia

Placing the protozoa in the protist kingdom leaves the animal kingdom only with multicellular organisms. Animals have neither chlorophyll nor cellulose cell walls. Most of them can move their bodies by means of contracting fibers. We shall consider nine main phyla of the animal kingdom.

Phylum—Porifera (Sponges)

The porifera, or sponges, are simple animals that spend their lives attached to solid objects under water. Most sponges are marine, but a few are freshwater types. Their bodies have many pores, hence their phylum name, porifera (pore-bearers). Sponges feed by drawing water through their pores and filtering out food particles. The movement of water through the sponge is accomplished by flagellated cells that create a current. The filtered water passes out through the *osculum.* (See Fig. 2–13.)

Sponges have two layers of cells with a jellylike layer between. Many sponges have radial symmetry—parts of the body radiate from a central axis, similar to the spokes of a wheel.

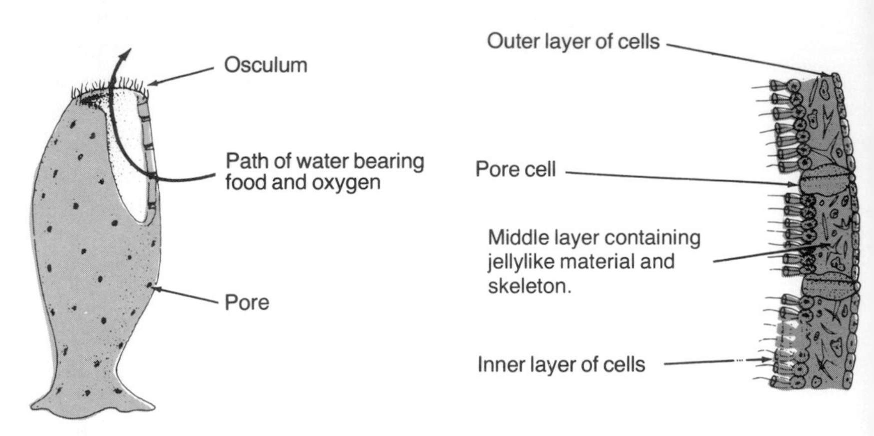

Fig. 2–13. Structure of a sponge.

The skeletons of sponges are made of tiny, pointed granules of lime or silica, or of a soft material called spongin. The adult sponge is *sessile* (nonmoving), but the larval form is free swimming.

The sponges are the least complex of the animal phyla. Although sponges have specialized groups of cells for moving water, these cells are not organized into real tissues. Lacking nerve cells, sponges cannot coordinate action by different regions of the body. If you separate the cells of the sponge in a small container of water, the cells rejoin to form a complete individual. A sponge is little more than a colony of protozoa.

Sponge divers remove the common bath sponge from the bottom of shallow waters off the coasts of Florida and Greece. The sponges are hung to decay, leaving the skeleton of absorbent spongin.

Phylum—Coelenterata

The coelenterates include the hydra, jellyfish, sea anemones, and corals. Their bodies consist of a cuplike digestive sac with a wall composed of two layers of cells. The outer layer is the *ectoderm* and the inner layer is the *endoderm.* Between the two cell layers is a jellylike layer which is thin in some representatives of the phylum, but greatly enlarged in others, such as the jellyfish. The opening in the cylindrical body of the hydra serves as both a mouth and anus. This opening is surrounded by a crown of tentacles. All coelenterates have radial symmetry. They also have stinging cells, known as *nematocysts,* that they use to paralyze their prey. Most coelenterates are marine, but the hydra lives in freshwater ponds and lakes. As shown in Figure 2–14, the basic pattern of the hydra and the jellyfish are the same.

The Portuguese man-of-war is a colony of coelenterate organisms with specialized functions. It looks like a gas-filled bag floating in the sea. Hanging from the animal's body are streamers which have stinging cells that are used to paralyze its prey. The sting can be very painful to people.

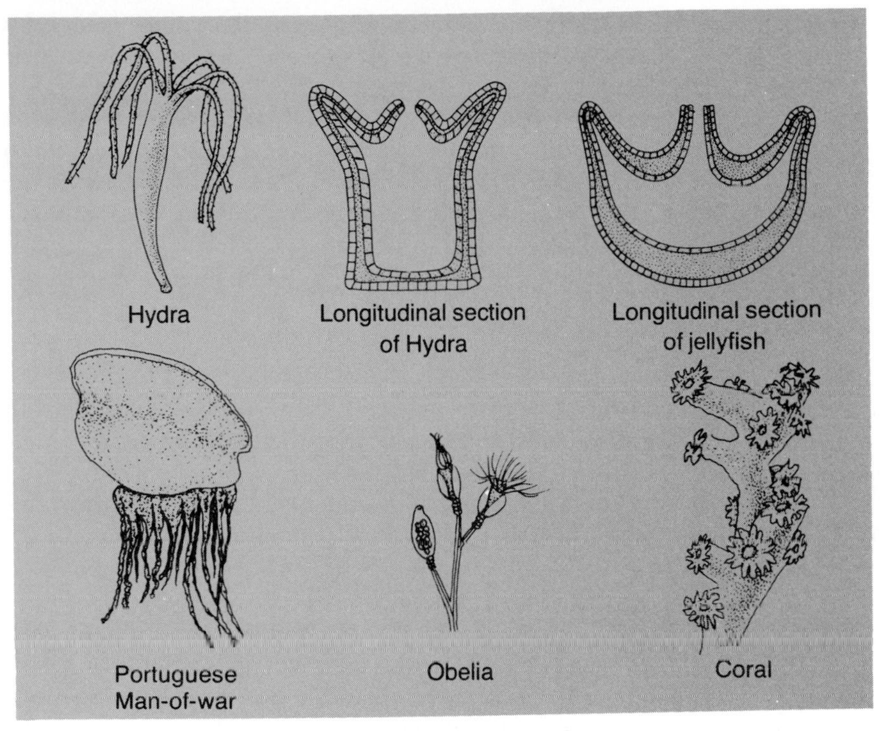

Fig. 2–14. Examples of Coelenterates

Coral is common in tropical waters. Coral rock is formed in layers by the exterior skeletons of millions of tiny *Hydra*-like animals. Some corals are used as jewelry. The most primitive coelenterates suggest a relationship to colonial protozoa.

Phylum—Platyhelminthes (Flatworms)

The platyhelminthes are the simplest of the three phyla of wormlike animals. They are called flatworms (*platy* = flat, *helminth* = worm) because their bodies are flat in cross section. Some of the flatworms are shown in Figures 2–15 and 2–16.

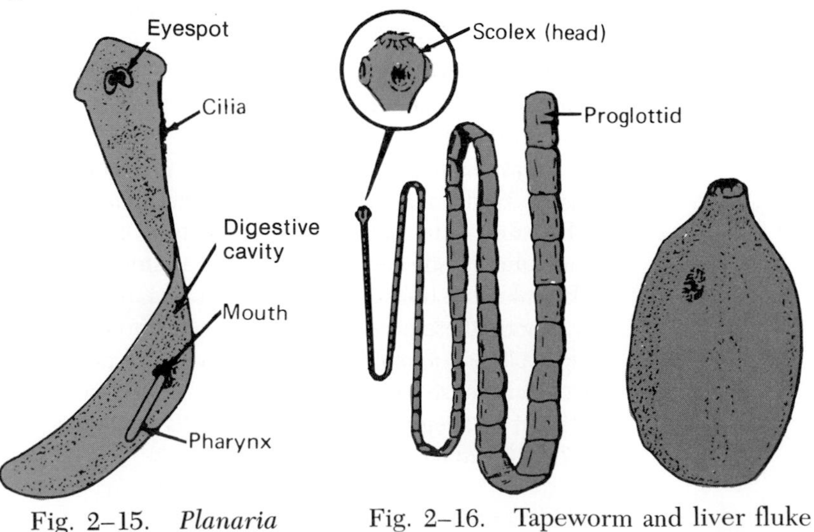

Fig. 2–15. *Planaria*

Fig. 2–16. Tapeworm and liver fluke

This is the first phylum whose members show *bilateral symmetry*. This means that they have a right side and a left side that are alike. They have a dorsal (top) surface and a ventral (bottom) surface, as well as anterior and posterior ends. The flatworms are more advanced than animals discussed before in that the body is composed of three layers of cells instead of two. The layers are the *ectoderm* (outer layer), the *endoderm* (inner layer), and a new layer called the *mesoderm* (middle layer). Flatworms have definite tissues, organs, and organ systems. However, the presence of a single body opening that serves as both mouth and anus suggests that flatworms evolved from the coelenterates.

Planaria, a common freshwater flatworm, secretes a slimy mucus layer, glides over underwater objects by the beating of cilia on its ventral surface, and swims by undulating body movements. As representatives of a simpler form of life with a simple nervous system, planarians are used for experiments to test their ability to learn.

Although *Planaria* is free-living, many flatworms are parasites that cause great damage to humans and other higher animals. In the life cycle of flukes and tapeworms, certain stages alternate between several hosts. For example, the liver fluke, which is a dangerous parasite of sheep and cattle, also lives in snails during one stage of its life cycle.

A tapeworm grows as a long flat ribbon consisting of rectangular sections called *proglottids*. The tapeworm lacks a digestive system and a sensory system. These were presumably lost during evolution from free-living (nonparasitic) ancestors. The minute head of a tapeworm attaches to the lining of the small intestine of the host (human, cow, pig, or other animal) by means of hooks and suckers. Lying within the intestinal cavity, the tapeworm absorbs predigested food and may grow to a length of over 20 feet. Humans may acquire tapeworm larvae by eating undercooked meat from infected animals such as the pig.

Phylum—Nematoda (Roundworms)

The nematodes, or roundworms, have bodies that are round in cross section. They show a great advance over their flatworm ancestors in having a one-way digestive system that runs from an anterior mouth to a posterior anus.

Nematodes have bilateral symmetry and three layers of cells. Most of them are no larger than bits of thread and can be identified by their whiplike, thrashing movements. They are found in rich soil, fresh water, and salt water. Most roundworms are free living, but there are also many parasitic kinds such as those shown in Figure 2–17.

The cause of trichinosis is the nematode *Trichinella.* These roundworms enter human bodies when people eat undercooked, infected meat, mainly pork. Unless there is strict local inspection, people should assume that pork may contain these parasites and this meat should be cooked thoroughly until it is gray. The *Trichinella* larvae live in a cyst (protective covering) in human muscle and cause pain and sometimes death. Cooking pork at a temperature of at least 170 degrees F until the meat is no longer pink will usually destroy any *Trichinella* larvae that may be present.

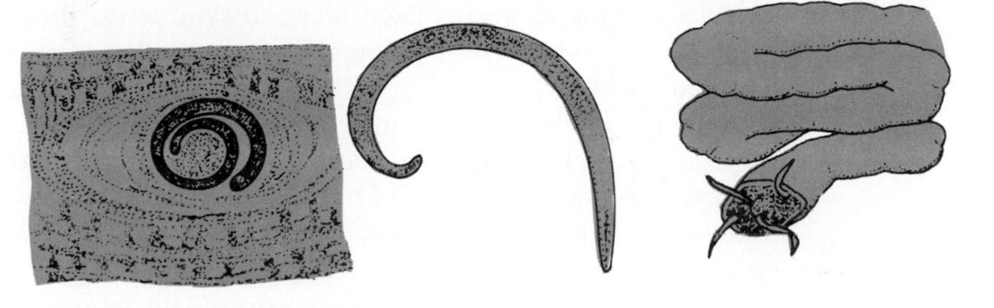

Trichinella encysted in muscle.

Necator americanus (hookworm)

Ascaris in human intestine. Children are frequently infected with *Ascaris*.

Fig. 2–17. Examples of Nematodes

The hookworm *(Necator americanus)* is a parasite that usually enters the human body through the feet. If a person walks barefoot on soil contaminated with human excrement, tiny hookworm larvae may penetrate the soles of the feet. The hookworm travels through the body to the walls of the small intestine. Here it attaches and lives off blood. A large number of these worms in the human body makes a person weak and lethargic. Although hookworm disease was formerly common in remote areas of the southeastern part of the United States, it has been controlled by increasing use of shoes and by improvements in methods of sanitation and waste disposal.

Elephantiasis is a disease, prevalent in tropical countries, caused by the minute nematode, *Filaria*. These worms cause enormous swelling of the feet, legs, hands, or other parts of the body. Other parasitic nematodes in the soil cause severe losses to the orange, tobacco, and strawberry crops.

Plylum—Annelida (Segmented worms)

The annelid worms are the segmented worms. (See Fig. 2–18.) The visible sign of segmentation is the series of rings encircling the body, as seen in the common earthworm. These rings on the outside of the earthworm indicate partitions that separate the body into segments. In most of the body segments the same internal body organs are repeated again and

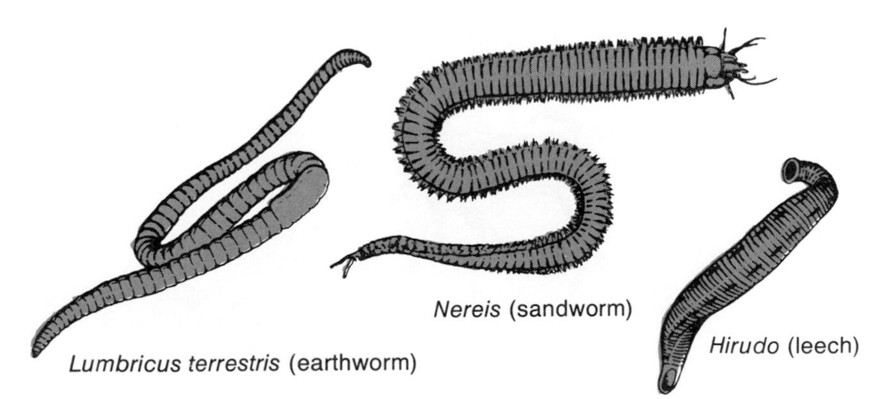

Nereis (sandworm)

Lumbricus terrestris (earthworm)

Hirudo (leech)

Fig. 2–18. Examples of Annelids

again. The annelid worms have bilateral symmetry, three cell layers, a body cavity, and a well-developed closed circulatory system. Annelids have excretory organs and a well-defined central nervous system. The body of an annelid suggests many roundworms placed end to end, but there is no real information about the relationship of the two phyla.

Earthworms are *hermaphrodites*. This means that each worm possesses both male and female sex organs. The sperm cells of one worm, however, do not fertilize its own eggs. Instead, at copulation, each worm transfers sperm cells to a pouch of the other worm. The transferred sperm cells then fertilize each worm's own egg cells. The young worms develop inside a cocoon. As in the nematodes, the digestive tract is a long tube with a mouth and anus. Although the earthworm lives on land, most of the annelid worms live in tiny tubes in the sea, or under rocks close to shore.

Leeches, which live in freshwater ponds and streams, are in a separate group of the annelid phylum. They have suckers at each end of their bodies so that the posterior sucker can anchor the leech temporarily while the anterior one sucks the blood of the host animal. In some parts of the world, people still apply leeches to the body because they believe bloodletting is good treatment for many illnesses. Turtles and fishes, as well as humans, are commonly attacked by these external parasites.

Phylum—Mollusca

The mollusks are soft-bodied, unsegmented animals that have three layers of tissue and well-developed organ systems. The bodies of many mollusks are protected by shells of calcium carbonate. The mantle, a body fold of the animal, forms these shells. (See Fig. 2–19.)

Clams, oysters, mussels, and scallops are called *bivalves* because they have two shells. Most of these mollusks are marine although some live in fresh water. They feed by filtering food particles from the mouth. Clams move by pulling on a thick hatchet-shaped foot that they extend from between their shells.

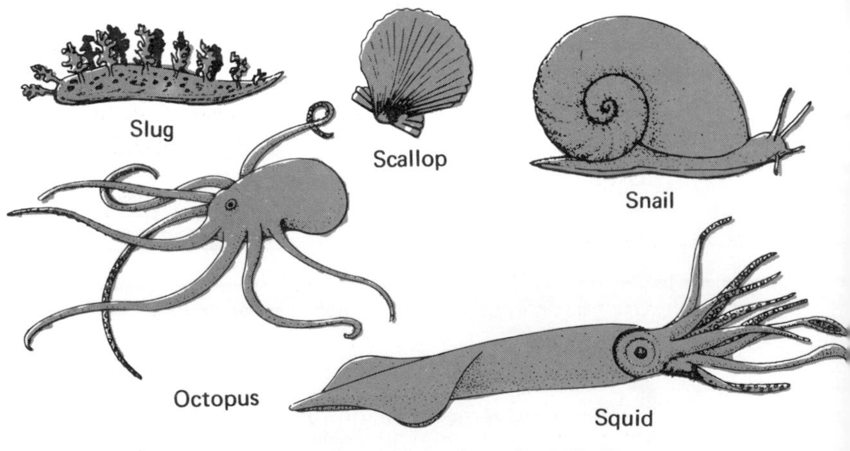

Fig. 2–19. Examples of Mollusks

Snails are called *univalves* because they have only one shell. They feed by scraping their food to bits with a rasping tongue. Their thick, flat foot, used for locomotion, bears tentacles that serve as sensory organs.

Octopuses and squids are active shell-less mollusks with complex nervous systems. Their eyes function almost like the human eye but have a different evolutionary development and structure. The octopus has eight arms, or tentacles, covered with suction disks, that are used for locomotion and grasping. The squid has ten arms that are used in the same manner. The squid moves by "jet propulsion" as it ejects a stream of water. It protects itself by giving off a screen of inky fluid when escaping from an enemy.

Many mollusks (clams, oysters, scallops, and mussels) are used as food by humans, but some cause us trouble. For example, the *shipworm* bores holes into the sides of wooden boats. The *oyster drill*, a univalve snail, bores through the oyster's shell and eats its flesh. A shell-less relative of the snail, the *garden slug*, causes great economic loss by eating vegetable crops.

The anatomy of mollusks differs greatly from that of other phyla. But since the larvae of mollusks and annelid worms are nearly identical, these two phyla are probably closely related.

Plylum—Arthropoda

The arthropods are "the joint-legged animals" (*arthro* = jointed, *poda* = leg). This phylum contains over 90 percent of the species of the animal kingdom. More than 900,000 species have been identified, and the number of species is estimated to be in the millions. They are the most complex and successful of the animals without backbones. One class, the insects, are the most serious competitors of humans for food. Arthropods have segmented bodies, and there is little doubt that they have evolved from annelids.

Several advanced features distinguish arthropods from annelids. The body of the arthropod is covered with a thick, flexible exoskeleton composed of *chitin*. Instead of the segments being nearly alike, as in the annelids, they are specialized in various ways, and form specific body divisions. Their chief distinction is their *jointed appendages*. These are highly modified for locomotion, food getting, sensation, reproduction, and protection. Arthropods have a ventral nerve cord as in annelid worms. The circulatory system is open so that the blood does not always travel through a system of tubes. They breathe through gills or by a system of tubes known as tracheae.

One group of fossil arthropods, called trilobites, were a group of arthropods that died out leaving no known living descendants. As shown in Figure 2–20, trilobites had jointed appendages. Every segment had a pair of appendages, and all were much alike except in size. Much of the later evolution of the arthropods consisted in specialization of appendages in different parts of the body for different functions.

Arthropods inhabit most places on earth—in fresh water, salt water, on the surface of the land, in the soil, and on or inside animals and plants. The living arthropods are divided into five main classes.

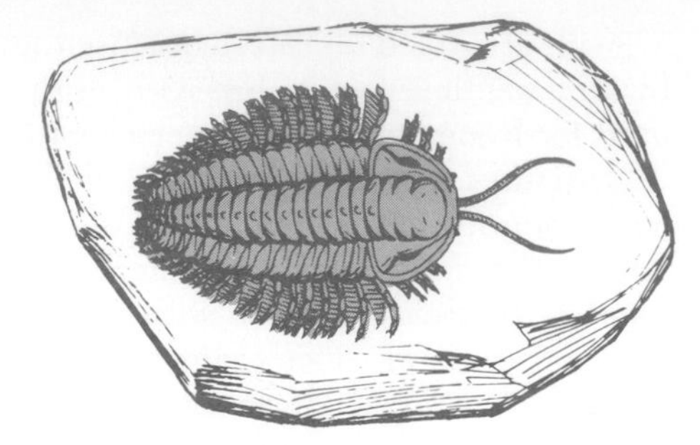

Fig. 2–20. A fossil trilobite

Class—Chilopoda. The *centipedes* (hundred leggers) are elongated, flattened wormlike arthropods with little external difference in the numerous segments. (See Fig. 2–21.) Each segment of the abdomen, except for the first segment and the last two segments, has *one* pair of walking legs. The first body segment bears a pair of poison claws. Since most of the appendages do not show specialization for different functions, this class is considered primitive.

Class—Diplopoda. The *millipedes* (thousand leggers) are rounder than the centipedes, and they have *two pairs* of walking legs for each segment except the first one and the last two. Millipedes are vegetarians often found under logs and stones and in damp basements.

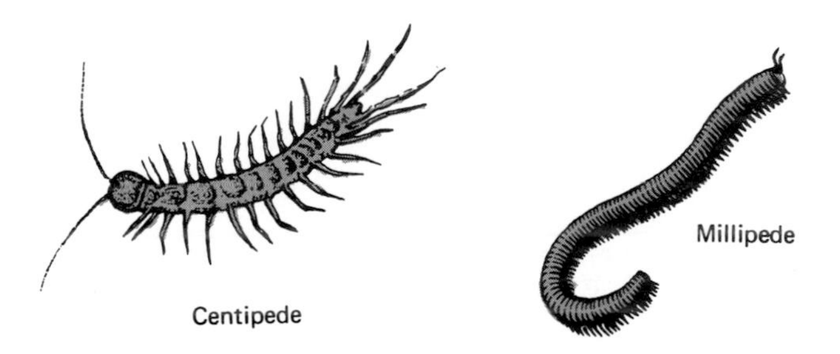

Fig. 2–21. The centipede and millipede. Which moves faster? The one with fewer legs—the centipede.

Class—Crustacea. Most crustaceans are water-dwelling animals that breathe by means of gills and have two pairs of antennae. The segments are commonly fused into two distinct body regions, the cephalothorax (fused head and thorax) and the abdomen. Specialized appendages are used for chewing, for walking, for swimming, and for reproduction. Some crustaceans are shown in Figure 2–22. This class includes the pill bug, *Daphnia,* barnacle, shrimp, brine shrimp, crayfish, lobster, and crab.

The barnacle might be mistaken for a mollusk because of its rocklike shell. The barnacle is sedentary in its adult stage but develops from a shrimplike larva that attaches itself to ships or wooden pilings. If you remove a barnacle with its underlying wood and place it in a pail of sea water, the shell will open. Inside you will see what looks like a tiny

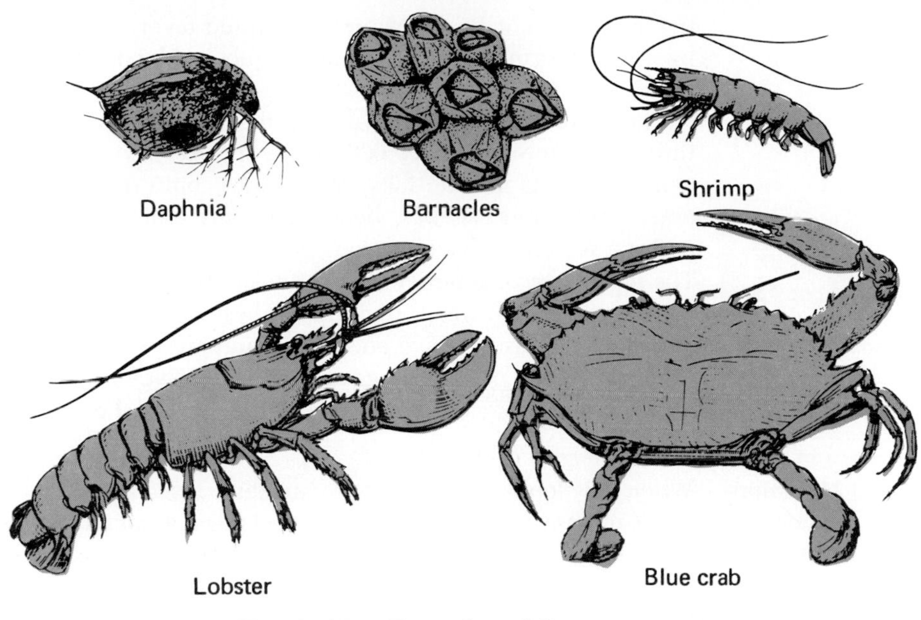

Fig. 2–22. Examples of Crustaceans

shrimp kicking its legs. Ships must periodically be scraped of barnacles because their collective weight and water resistance greatly slow the vessels.

Lobsters, crabs, and shrimp are valuable foods for humans. Minute crustaceans in the oceans serve as food for fish and for the giant blue whale.

Class—Arachnida. The arachnids include ticks, mites, spiders, daddy longlegs, and scorpions. One way to distinguish spiders from insects is that arachnids have eight legs but insects have only six. Count the legs in Figure 2–23. Most arachnids are land-living and breathe through fills or "book-lungs." Their bodies are divided in a cephalothorax and an abdomen.

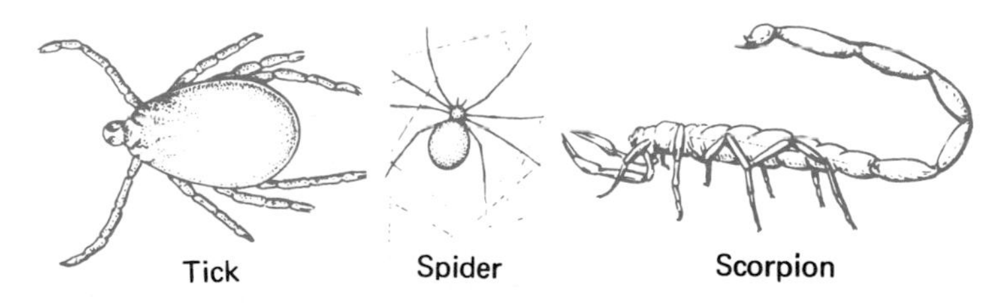

Fig. 2–23. Examples of Arachnids

Most spiders are helpful to humans because they consume destructive insects. The bite of the black widow spider, however, can be fatal to humans. The sting of a scorpion is painful but seldom fatal to humans. Mites and ticks cause discomfort to humans and to other animals when they live as parasites on the skin. The bite of an infected Rocky Mountain tick may transmit Rocky Mountain spotted fever. This disease is caused by a microorganism injected into the host's bloodstream when the tick bites.

Class—Insecta. Insects make up the largest class of the phylum arthropoda. More than 700,000 living species have been classified and named. Insects include flies, mosquitoes, butterflies, moths, grasshoppers, wasps, ants, beetles, bees, and many others.

Because insects have six legs, this class is also known as *hexapoda.* The name *insecta* is derived from the fact that the body is "insected" (or cut) into three distinct divisions. These are the *head, thorax,* and *abdomen.* All insects have one pair of antennae on the head. Most adult insects have two pairs of wings on the thorax. They breathe by a system of tubes, called *tracheae.* The external openings of the tracheae are called *spiracles.*

Metamorphosis in Different Insects

When developing from an egg to an adult, insects undergo a remarkable series of transformations in body form known as *metamorphosis.* Some of these stages have different names in different insects, as shown in the table:

Examples of Stages in Complete Metamorphosis

Stage	Fly	Mosquito	Moth	Butterfly
Egg	egg	egg	egg	egg
Larva	maggot	wriggler	caterpillar	caterpillar
Pupa	pupa	pupa	cocoon	chrysalis
Adult	adult	adult	adult	adult

Complete metamorphosis occurs if an insect passes through all four stages listed above. Grasshoppers pass through an *incomplete metamorphosis* in which the young, called nymphs, greatly resemble the adults but are smaller versions. As they grow, nymphs split their exoskeleton and discard it—a process called *molting.* Grasshoppers molt several times during their development.

The class Insecta has been divided into about twenty orders based on differences in metamorphosis, mouth parts, and wing structure. Some of the orders of insects are illustrated in Figure 2–24.

Insects are our chief nuisance and competitor for food. Every crop that humans plant for their own use feeds an army of insects. Grasshoppers eat plant parts, while other insects (such as aphids and scale insects) suck juices from plants. In moths and butterflies, it is the voracious caterpillar stage that is most destructive. During this stage, the caterpillar stores food to be used in the pupa stage when it does not feed. The "worm" in an apple is the caterpillar of the coddling moth. The European corn borer and the chinch bug are notorious destroyers of crops. It is the larval stage of the clothes moth that eats holes in woolens.

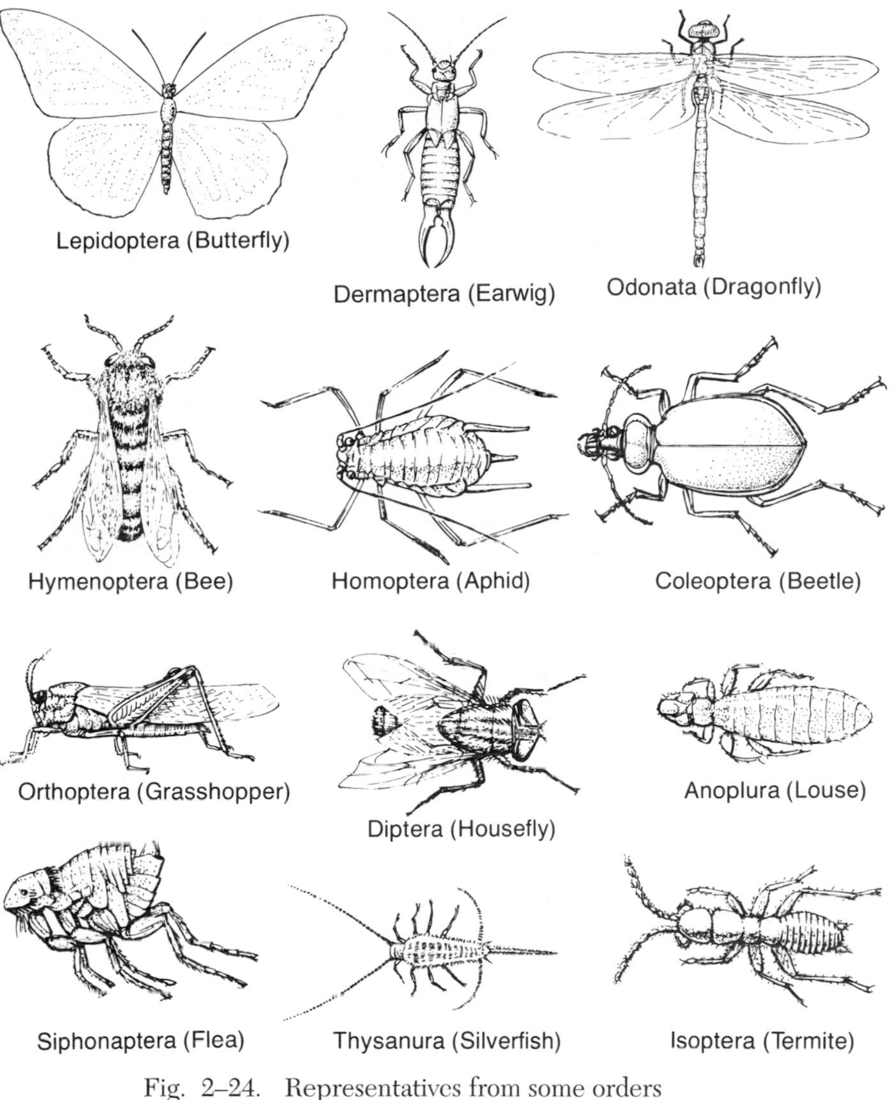

Fig. 2–24. Representatives from some orders of insects

Insect bites spread the microorganisms causing malaria, yellow fever, African sleeping sickness, elephantiasis, and typhus fever. Although humans use chemical insecticides to control harmful insects, our best allies are birds, other insects, fishes, small mammals, and other natural enemies of insects.

Many insects are useful to us. The silkworm moth produces silk in its cocoon. The honeybee produces beeswax and honey and pollinates plants that supply us with fruits and seeds for food.

Phylum—Echinodermata

The echinoderms are called the "spiny-skinned animals" because of the spines that cover their skins (*echino* = spine, *derm* = skin). The starfish (or seastar), a common example of this phylum, has five arms radiating from a central disk. It appears to be radially symmetrical, but experiments show that all of its arms do not function in the same manner. Moreover, its larva is bilaterally symmetrical. The starfish's body is supported by an internal skeleton of hard plates. This is quite different from the external skeleton of an arthropod.

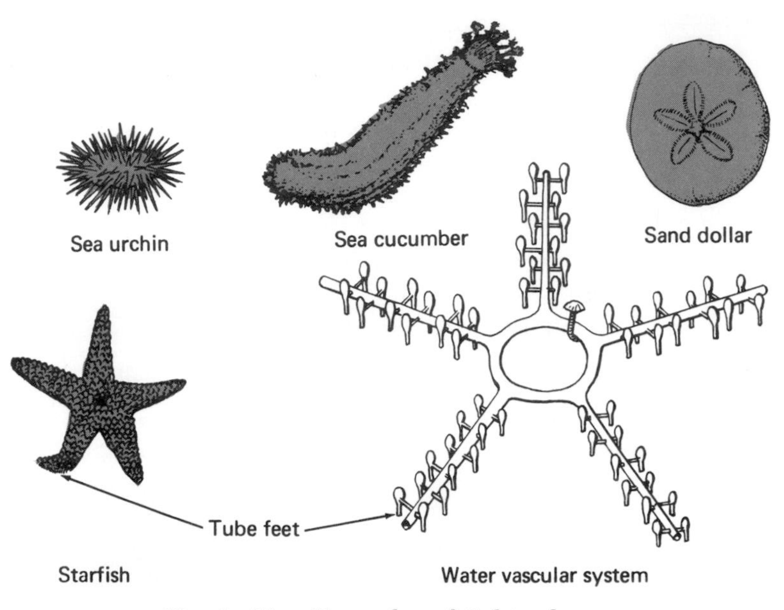

Fig. 2–25. Examples of Echinoderms

The vascular system of a starfish (Fig. 2–25) draws sea water into a system of canals that end in many *tube feet* at the ventral surface of the radiating arms. The tube feet act as suction cups. Water drawn from these cups creates a suction, enabling the animal to attach itself to solid objects. The starfish feeds on a bivalve (such as a clam or an oyster) by encircling it with its arms, attaching its suction cups to each half of the shell, and pulling. The oyster's muscles for keeping its shell closed are stronger than those of the starfish, but they tire sooner. With a long, steady pull, the starfish succeeds in parting the shells. Then it everts its mouth and stomach into the opening to obtain its meal.

Oysterfishers who found starfish used to hack them up with a knife and toss the parts into the sea. Then they learned that starfish have great powers of *regeneration*. Any arm containing a portion of the central disk can become a complete new starfish.

The sea urchin, the sea cucumber, the brittle star, and the sand dollar are other echinoderms. Nothing in the structure, embryology, or chemistry of the echinoderms suggests a relationship to the annelids, mollusks, or roundworms. The only clue is that their larvae, their internal skeleton, and some aspects of their body chemistry seem to suggest that they are related to the chordates.

Phylum—Chordata The chordates take their name from the *notochord*. This stiff supporting rod of cartilage in the dorsal (upper) part of the body is present at some stage in their lives. In higher chordates, the notochord is replaced in the adult by the vertebral column, or backbone. Because most chordates have vertebrae, the term *vertebrates* is loosely applied to the chordates. All the previous phyla that we have studied lack vertebrae and are called *invertebrates*.

A few primitive marine chordates have no backbones and are, therefore, not true vertebrates. They are called primitive chordates, or protochordates. Chordates of this type are the acorn worm, the sea squirt, and the lancelet (Amphioxus). (See Fig. 2–26.) Fossil records, such as those of the Burgess Shale, indicate that the first chordates were probably similar to the primitive chordates of today.

All chordates, including the primitive ones, have the following characteristics at some stage of their life:

- A dorsal notochord
- Paired gill slits connecting the pharynx to the outside
- A dorsal, tubular nerve cord
- A tail extending beyond the anus

Vertebrates, the more advanced chordates, also have:

- Vertebrae which surround or replace the notochord (Vertebrae are composed of bone or of cartilage. The column of vertebrae is called the spinal column, or backbone.)
- The cranium or skull, a boxlike structure that protects the brain

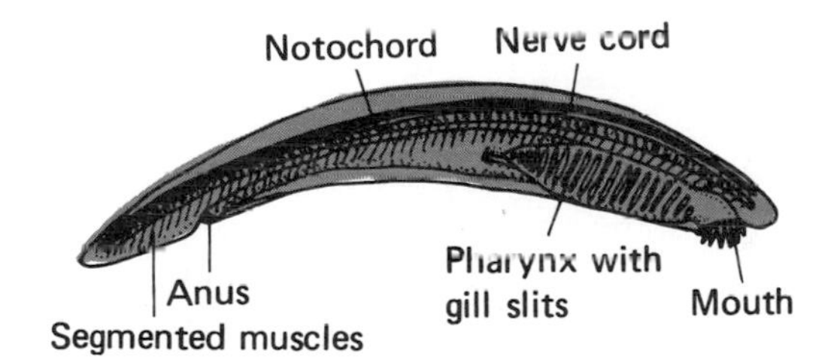

Fig. 2–26. The lancelet, *Amphioxus*, is a primitive chordate whose notochord remains throughout its life. Since it lacks vertebrae, jaws, or paired appendages, it is not truly a vertebrate. Such animals are sometimes called prevertebrate chordates or protochordates.

The seven classes of the chordates, not including the primitive chordates, are the jawless fishes, cartilage fishes, bony fishes, amphibia, reptiles, birds, and mammals.

Class—Pisces. In simplified schemes of classification, all the fish are grouped in the class Pisces, but specialists consider the fish as three separate classes: the jawless fishes, the cartilage fishes, and the bony fishes.

Fish are *ectotherms*, or cold-blooded animals, that inhabit fresh or salt water. The body temperature of ectotherms depends upon the temperature of the environment. *Endotherms*, by contrast, maintain a constant body temperature despite variations in their environment. Fish have two-chambered hearts and scales on their bodies. In addition, they have gills with many filaments that present a large surface area to the water. Gills have many microscopic blood vessels that absorb dissolved oxygen from the water. Many fish have air bladders that help them to move higher or lower.

Fish swim by paired appendages called *fins* and by undulations of the body and tail. Biologists think that the fins of certain prehistoric fish evolved into the legs of land-dwelling vertebrates—the amphibia, reptiles, birds, and mammals. The paired fins of fish are, therefore, homologous to the arms and legs of humans.

Jawless Fishes. The earliest vertebrates (early Paleozoic era) were free-swimming fishes that had no movable jaw. They fed by sucking in mud and nourishing themselves on the microorganisms therein. The only survivors of this class are two species that live as parasites, lamprey eels and hagfish.

Although the lamprey eel has cartilage, it is listed with the jawless fishes. The lamprey eel causes great economic loss in the Great Lakes by attacking the bodies of other fish. Its jawless mouth is modified as a round sucker with many hooklike, horny teeth and a rasping tongue used for boring. After attaching itself to another fish, it extracts blood and other body fluids from a hole that it bores.

At one time, lampreys were so numerous that long-distance swimming contests in the lake near Toronto were cancelled because of attacks on swimmers. But studies of the lamprey's life history have enabled biologists to devise effective means for their control. The lamprey's larval stage greatly resembles the basic structure of the adult *Amphioxus*.

Cartilage Fishes. The sharks, dogfish, and sting rays have no bones in their bodies. Their skeletons are composed of cartilage and their scales are of the same materials that compose teeth. Their five to seven pairs of gill openings (see Fig. 2–27) and the enormous amount of urea in their blood further distinguish them from the other fishes.

Fig. 2–27. Lower forms of fish. A. Unlike modern fishes, the shark has separate openings for each of its gills. B. The jawless, round mouth of the lamprey has hooks and a rasping tongue.

Bony Fishes. This is the largest group of marine and freshwater vertebrates and includes the trout, seahorse, catfish, perch, bass, pickerel, flounder, and swordfish. The skeletons of these fishes are made of bone. Their gills are covered so that there is a single opening for the gills on each side.

Class—Amphibia. The amphibia (*amphi* = on both sides, *bios* = life) get their name from the fact that nearly all of them go through a metamorphosis involving a water-dwelling stage followed by a land-dwelling stage.

The amphibians are derived from the bony fishes through a group of lobe-finned fishes, a transition that is well-documented by fossils. The fossil series shows a gradual change from a bony fin to legs with toes and rearrangements to permit air breathing. The lung is an ancient structure, found in some of the earliest fishes, but the amphibians have developed a special circulation of blood to the lung to use this structure effectively as an oxygen supply. These changes include the development of a third chamber in the heart. Fishes have only two heart chambers. Modern amphibians have lost much of their ancient skeleton. They have no scales in the skin, as had the earliest amphibians. Their naked, moist skin can be used to absorb oxygen from air or water.

Amphibians such as the frog (Fig. 2–28) and the toad begin life in the water. Their tadpoles have gills and a tail, but their adult stage has lungs for breathing on land and no tail. Another amphibian, the mud puppy, remains in the water all of its life. It retains both its gills and its tail.

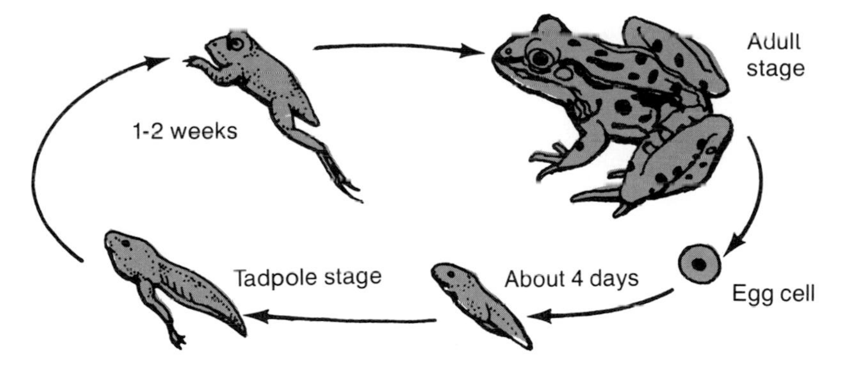

Fig. 2–28. The frog—an amphibian

Frogs deposit their eggs in water. When fertilized, these develop into larvae—the tadpoles. The tadpole breathes by gills, swims with its tail, and feeds on plants. When a tadpole metamorphoses into an adult frog, it absorbs its gills and tail, develops lungs and legs, and changes to a diet consisting mainly of insects.

Class—Reptilia. The modern reptiles are the turtles, lizards, snakes, crocodiles, and alligators—not an especially prominent group today. In the Mesozoic era, however, this class dominated the earth. There were giant dinosaurs, flying reptiles—creatures of the sea, the swamps, and the deserts. Fossils of the earliest reptiles are scarcely distinguishable from those of an early amphibian. The reptiles arose from the amphibia soon after the latter emerged from the water.

In the transition from amphibian to reptile, the following changes occurred: a dryer skin, an improved skeleton and musculature for walking on land, and a further partitioning of the heart. Of the reptiles, the crocodile and alligator have achieved a four-chambered heart. This partitioning of the heart and its blood vessels provides better separation of the circulating blood into oxygenated and unoxygenated portions.

Reptiles do not have a larval stage, as do amphibians. They lay eggs that are covered with a leathery shell on land, usually in the soil or beneath vegetation. Young have the same body form as the adult.

As you know, turtles have a hard shell. The shell is not an exoskeleton like that of arthropods; instead, it consists of many greatly enlarged ribs that have fused into bony plates. Although snakes have no limbs, vestigial remnants of hind limb bones are present in the boa constrictor and python. Some snakes' jaws stretch apart to swallow large prey.

Most snakes in America are nonpoisonous, but some species deadly to humans are the copperhead, the water moccasin, the rattlesnake, and the coral snake. The Gila monster and the beaded lizard of Mexico are the only poisonous lizards. One difference between the American alligator and the American crocodile is that the crocodile's snout is more pointed.

Lizards of the world range in size from the Komodo monitor lizard, which can attain a length of 10 feet, to small anoles and geckos only a few inches long. Some lizards, most notably the chameleons, are known for their ability to make rapid color changes that camouflage them in their surroundings.

Reptiles are not popular animals though many are valuable to humans. Some species of snakes and turtles are eaten as a delicacy. The skins of lizards, snakes, alligators, and crocodiles have been used to make shoes, belts, and handbags. Concern for protecting species that are in danger of extinction, however, has led many people to cease buying such animal products. Land snakes aid the farmer by consuming large numbers of destructive insects and rodents.

Fig. 2-29. Examples of Reptiles

Class—Aves (Birds). The most characteristic feature of birds is their feathers. This covering provides the insulation that a warm-blooded creature needs and airflow surfaces like the wings of a plane. Birds have a highly efficient lung system and a four-chambered heart. A special adaptation for flight are the bird's hollow bones.

Birds are important to humans in many ways. Chickens and their eggs are such an important part of our diet in this country that chickens are now raised in highly mechanized factories. Wild birds are important to people because they eat harmful insects and the seeds of weeds. Owls and hawks are valuable because they eat rats and mice.

Class—Mammalia. The characteristics that set mammals apart from other vertebrates are: (1) the females nurse, or provide their newborn young with milk secreted by the mammary glands; (2) mammals have hair on their bodies; (3) in most mammals, the developing embryo in the female reproductive tract is supplied with nourishment from the mother's bloodstream. Except in a few kinds of egg-laying mammals, mammalian birth consists of the separation of the young from the uterus of the mother, where it had been attached. Some fish and snakes give birth to young, instead of laying eggs outside the body. They differ from mammals in that their young were never attached to the mother, but developed inside eggs kept in the female's body.

Mammals arose from a fairly primitive reptile in the early Mesozoic era. They are warm-blooded, like birds, but they have entirely different adaptations to provide the necessary conditions for their style of life. Their hearts are four-chambered, but the arrangement of blood vessels differs from that of birds. Insulation is provided by hair not feathers. Air is pumped in and out of the lungs by a muscular *diaphragm* stretched across the bottom of the chest and by movement of the ribs.

Mammals are widely distributed. Most mammals live on the land, but some (whales, dolphins) have returned to water. Bats are mammals that fly with wings, but these wings have hair (fur) unlike the wings of birds.

Some vertebrates that are classified as mammals do not have all of the common characteristics of mammals. For example, the duckbilled platypus of Australia (Fig. 2–30) is an egg-laying mammal. It lays eggs much like those of reptiles. The marsupials, such as the kangaroo and the opossum, bear their young in such an immature state that they climb into their mother's pouch (the marsupium) on the abdomen and fasten to the mammary glands. The opossum is the only marsupial native to this country. Others, such as the koala bear and the wombat, are native to Australia.

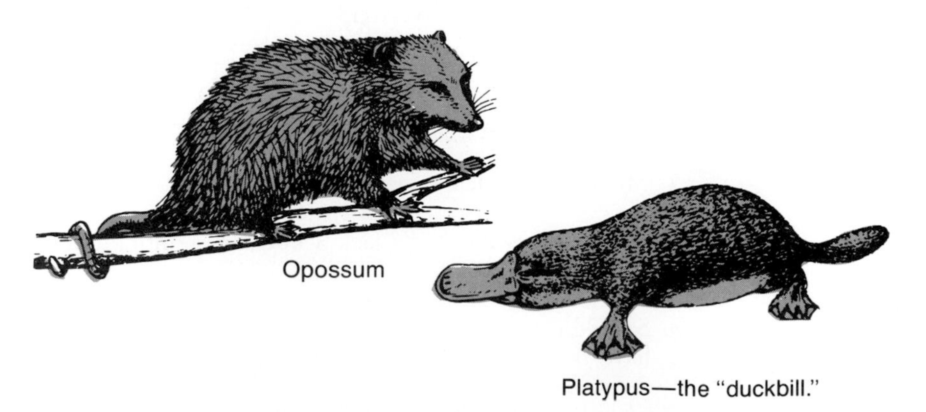

Fig. 2–30. Primitive mammals

Representative Orders of the Class Mammalia	
Rodents	These are the gnawing mammals, such as the rat, mouse, squirrel, and beaver.
Bats	The wing of the bat is a modified arm.
Cetacea	Note that whales, dolphins, and porpoises are mammals, not fish.
Carnivora	These meat eaters include the lion, cat, dog, walrus, and sea lion.
Hoofed Animals	Some have an odd number of toes, and others have an even number. Most are vegetarians. Examples of these animals are the horse, zebra, rhinoceros, camel, giraffe, sheep, and hippopotamus.
Primates	Most possess digits specialized for grasping and manipulating objects in the environment. This is especially true of the forelimb digits. The opposable thumb of many primates gives them great dexterity. These mammals generally have a highly developed brain, social life, and means of communication. In humans, the combination of the large brain and opposable thumb permitted tool use and tool making to develop. Other examples of primates are monkeys, lemurs, and great apes such as the gorilla.

Reasoning Exercises

1. What are the main differences between the prokaryotes and the eukaryotes?
2. Why can the tracheophytes grow taller than the bryophytes?
3. Name eight phyla of the animal kingdom and give an example of each.
4. What are the characteristics of the chordates?
5. Give three characteristics of the mammals that distinguishes them from all other animals.

Completion Questions

A-B

1. The branch of biology that deals with the classification and naming of living things is called . . . . . .
2. A system of taxonomy should embrace living and . . . . . . organisms.
3. Modern classification is based upon the concept of . . . . . .

C

4. Organisms whose cells lack a nuclear membrane are classified in the kingdom . . . . . .
5. The kingdom Monera includes the bacteria and . . . . . .
6. Simple organisms that cannot be considered as plants or animals have been grouped in the kingdom . . . . . .

7. The animal phylum that includes human beings is the......
8. Multicellular organisms that can carry on photosynthesis are in the ...... kingdom.
9. Many taxonomists divide living things into five kingdoms: monerans, protists, plants, animals, and......
10. Organisms that interbreed in nature are considered to be in the same......

D

11. In our scheme of taxonomy, each phylum is divided into a number of......
12. The genus name and the species name make up an organism's ...... name.
13. Using two words for the scientific name of an organism is known as...... nomenclature.

E

14. Cells that lack a distinct membrane-bounded nucleus are called ......
15. Spherical bacteria in a mass are called......
16. A lichen is a combination of a fungus and a(n)......
17. Plants with a well-developed vascular system for transport of water are placed in the phylum......
18. Angiosperms with parallel-veined leaves are classified as......
19. Flatworms and roundworms have...... symmetry.
20. In a single earthworm, the body organs in one...... may be repeated again in the next.
21. Starfish can reproduce by the process of...... as well as by sperm and eggs.
22. At some time in their lives, chordates have a dorsal...... for support

Multiple-Choice Questions

A-B

1. An important basis for classifying organisms together is similarity in (1) color, (2) habitat, (3) basic structure, (4) outward appearance.
2. Most modern biologists agree that an ideal classification system should reflect (1) nutritional similarities among organisms, (2) habitat requirements of like groups, (3) distinctions between organisms based on size, (4) evolutionary relationships among species.

C

3. Organisms whose cells lack a nuclear membrane are placed in the kingdom (1) Monera, (2) Protista, (3) Plant, (4) Animal.
4. The animallike protists are the (1) algae, (2) annelid worms, (3) protozoa, (4) coelenterates.
5. Bread mold is in the kingdom (1) Monera, (2) Protista, (3) Fungi, (4) Plant.
6. The Monera include the bacteria and (1) mushrooms, (2) protozoa, (3) algae, (4) blue-green algae.
7. *Euglena* is a single-celled organism that possesses chlorophyll but has no cell wall. It carries on photosynthesis, but it has a mouth and swims by means of a flagellum. Therefore, it is most reasonable to classify it among the (1) protists, (2) plants, (3) animals, (4) protozoa.

D

8. Low-growing plants that lack a vascular system are the (1) bryophytes, (2) algae, (3) tracheophytes, (4) mushrooms.
9. Chordates all have (1) an exoskeleton, (2) a notochord, (3) a two-cell-layered body wall, (4) chloroplasts.
10. The organism *Acer rubrum* is most closely related to (1) *Rubrum acer*, (2) *Rubrum cordis*, (3) *Acer cordis*, (4) *Cordis rubrum*.
11. Two animals belong to the same species if they (1) have similar nutritional requirements, (2) show a very close resemblance, (3) can mate and produce fertile offspring, (4) can live together in a similar environment.
12. Which is the correct classification arrangement? (1) phylum, genus, class, species, (2) genus, species, phylum, class, (3) species, genus, phylum, class, (4) phylum, class, genus, species.

E

13. Which green plant does *not* reproduce by means of seeds? (1) fern, (2) conifer, (3) grass, (d) ginko
14. Which type of bacteria is represented by the diagram below? (1) coccus, (2) bacillus, (3) streptococcus, (4) staphylococcus.

Chapter Test

1. The binomial system for naming living things originated with the work of (1) Charles Darwin, (2) Carolus Linnaeus, (3) E. Haeckel, (4) Aristotle.
2. A group of organisms capable of interbreeding and producing fertile offspring under natural conditions is known as a (1) species, (2) genus, (3) phylum, (4) kingdom.
3. Bacteria and blue-green algae are in the kingdom (1) Animalia, (2) Protista, (3) Plantae, (4) Monera.
4. Which is the correct way to indicate the scientific name of the human? (1) Homo sapiens, (2) *Homo Sapiens*, (3) homo Sapiens, (4) *Homo sapiens*
5. The scientific name of any organism consists of (1) its family and order, (2) its phylum and class, (3) its species and variety, (4) its genus and species.
6. In attempting to classify a newly discovered organism the following characteristics were noted: multicellular specialized organs and tissues, cell walls, chlorophyll-containing plastids. The kingdom into which this organism should be placed is (1) animal, (2) plant, (3) protist, (4) monera.
7. An example of an invertebrate is the (1) guinea pig, (2) salamander, (3) sponge, (4) eel.
8. The presence of well-developed vascular tissue for conducting liquids is characteristic of (1) ferns, (2) mosses, (3) algae, (4) slime molds.
9. Which protists do *not* have true roots, stems, or leaves but do contain chlorophyll? (1) algae, (2) fungi, (3) molds, (4) ferns
10. To which organism is the whale most closely related? (1) horse, (2) turtle, (3) dinosaur, (4) fish

Chapter 3 Unity of Life

Despite vast differences in appearance and ways of life, all living things have a unity of life. They are all composed of cells that are similar in structure and function. Some organisms, such as *Paramecium* and *Euglena,* are made up of only one cell. In more complex, multicellular organisms, the cells may perform more specialized functions, but all have certain features in common.

In this chapter the discovery of cells and what biologists found out about their similarities and differences will be discussed. Since most cells cannot be seen with the naked eye what was learned about the cell depended on the development of the instrument used to see them—the microscope.

A Historical View of the Cell Theory

Developments in all fields of science have led to improvements in scientific instruments. In turn, more accurate methods and instruments have resulted in new discoveries. The mass of new information that resulted from the development of the microscope is an example of how new instruments help to advance human knowledge.

About 1590, Zacharias Janssen, a Dutch lens maker, built the first simple microscope. (A *simple microscope* is a microscope with only one set of lenses.)

In the 1670s, Anton van Leeuwenhoek, a Dutch naturalist and lens maker, constructed a simple microscope that could magnify objects as much as 270 times. With his simple microscope, Leeuwenhoek saw objects that had never been seen before because they were invisible to the naked eye. Among his discoveries were bacteria, protozoa, sperm cells, red blood cells, and yeast cells.

Robert Hooke, an English physicist, combined two sets of lenses and produced a *compound microscope.* In 1665, while examining a thin piece of cork with his microscope, Hooke discovered that it was not solid as had been believed, but was made up of walled compartments. These looked like the honeycomb of a beehive. Hooke called these hollow boxes "cells." We know now that Hooke saw the walls of empty dead plant cells. He concluded that the cell was an empty box.

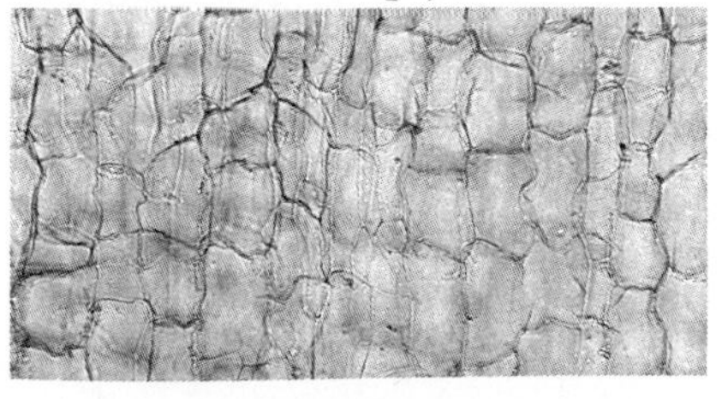

Fig. 3–1. A thin slice of cork, magnified 100 times.

In 1831, Robert Brown, a Scottish botanist, described a small, spherical structure in the center of living plant cells. He called this central structure the *nucleus* (plural: *nuclei*).

In 1838, Matthias Schleiden, a German botanist, concluded that all plants are composed of cells. About the same time, Theodor Schwann, a German zoologist, was studying animal tissues under the microscope. Because animal cells do not have cell walls as plant cells do, they are more difficult to see. However, by concentrating his search on the nuclei that Robert Brown had earlier described, Schwann concluded that all animals are also composed of cells. Thus, Schleiden and Schwann jointly established the concept that *all living things are composed of cells.*

In 1839, Johannes Purkinje, a Czech physiologist, used the word *protoplasm* to refer to the living material within the cell. At the same time in Germany, Hugo von Mohl and Max Schultze were studying the functions of protoplasm. Schultze called protoplasm "the physical basis of life," and the idea developed that living things carry on their life activities because of the activity of their cells. This idea was stated as: *The cell is the unit of function of living things.*

The German scientist, Rudolf Virchow, is called the "father of pathology" (the study of disease). In 1858, Virchow explained that an organism becomes sick because its cells do not function properly. Through his study of microorganisms, Virchow contributed the important concept that *cells arise only from previously existing cells.*

By the end of the 19th century, the cell theory was widely accepted. This recognition resulted from the development of better stains for observation of cells, from improvement in lenses, from the development of methods for slicing sections of tissue thin enough for observation under the microscope, and from the spread of information by scientific societies through their meetings and journals.

Summary of the Cell Theory

1. *The cell is the unit of structure of plants and animals.* Plants and animals are composed of cells and of products made by cells.
2. *The cell is the unit of function of plants and animals.* Living things carry on their activities because of the activity of their component cells.
3. *All cells arise from preexisting living cells.*

B Methods Used in the Study of Cells

As you may already know, most cells are too small to be seen with the naked eye. With the aid of various types of microscopes, scientists have developed detailed concepts of cell structure and function. The microscope that is most commonly used is the *light microscope.* This type of microscope focuses light on an object whose image is then magnified by the lens system of the microscope.

Laboratory Skill

The Compound Microscope: Parts and Function

The compound microscope (Figure 3-2) contains a combination of two lens systems. The *eyepiece,* or *ocular,* is a system of lenses closest to the observer's eye. The *objective* is the system of lenses closest to the specimen or object. The objective produces a magnified image of the specimen, and this image is further magnified by the eyepiece.

The compound microscope commonly used in the high-school laboratory has two interchangeable objectives. The shorter objective is low power in its magnification, and the longer one is high power. The magnifying power is always marked on the objective. If the two objectives are 10x and 43x and the eyepiece has a magnifying power of 10x, the specimen can be magnified to 100 times using the low-power objective and 430 times under the high-power objective. The objectives are fastened to the *nosepiece*, which may be rotated to bring either of the two objectives into position below the body tube.

The specimen to be observed is usually placed on a glass microscope slide over the opening in the *stage* and held in place by *stage clips*.

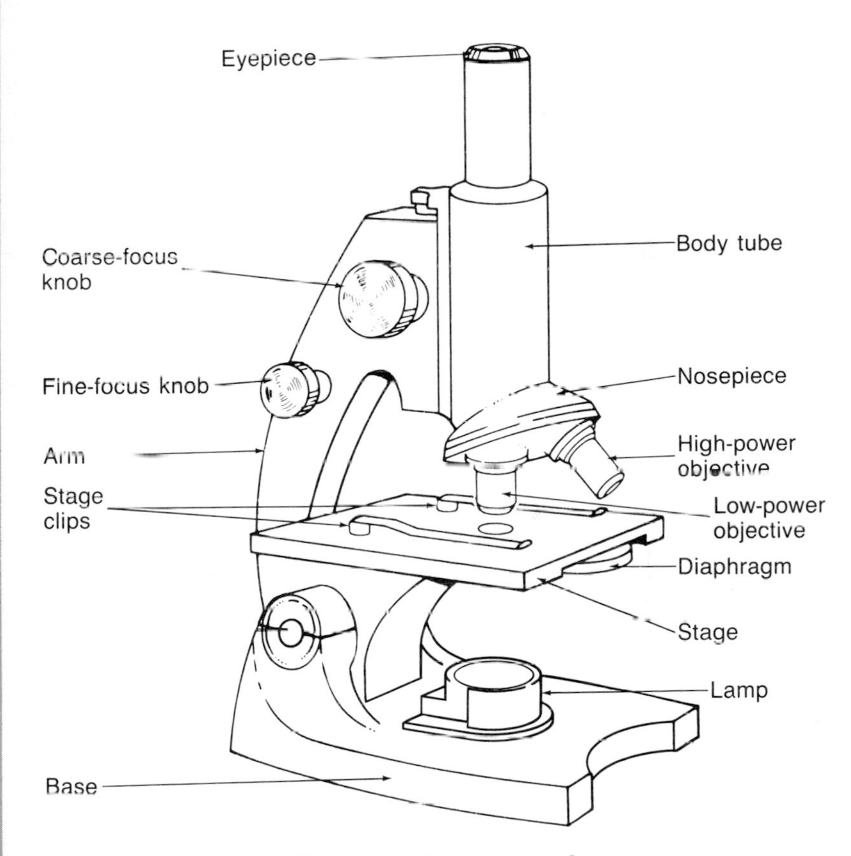

Fig. 3–2. The parts of a compound microscope

In order to observe the specimen, light must pass through the specimen on the slide and travel up through the objective, the body tube, and the eyepiece to the eye of the observer. In some microscopes, daylight or the light in a room is focused through the microscope lens system by a *mirror.* Other microscopes have an electric light attached below the stage to provide the required illumination. Illumination of the specimen is improved in some microscopes by a *condenser* (lens) placed in the opening in the stage, or below the stage.

A *diaphragm*, mounted below the stage, regulates the light reaching the objective lens. One type of diaphragm, the *disc diaphragm*, has a series of holes of various sizes in a flat disc. The disc is rotated to select the proper size opening. Another type of diaphragm is the *iris diaphragm*. This diaphragm permits the size of a single opening to change, like the iris of the eye. This regulation is accomplished by a circle of flat, thin strips of metal.

The heavy *base* supports the microscope and is attached to the *arm* which holds the body tube and acts as a carrying handle. A *coarse-focusing knob* and a *fine-focusing knob* can be turned to vary the distance between the objective and the specimen in order to produce a sharp image. For the object to be in focus under high power, the objective lens must be closer to the object than under low power.

At higher magnifications (for example, 970x), more light is necessary. Therefore, when a higher power objective (usually 97x) is used, steps must be taken to avoid the loss of light in the air space between the microscope slide and the objective lens. This is done by placing a drop of a special oil on the slide and very carefully lowering the objective lens into it. Then focus away from the slide, as with every other objective. (Focusing upward prevents damage to the objective and slide.) An objective designed to be used with oil is known as an *oil-immersion objective*.

A microscope reverses and inverts the image of an object seen under it. Therefore, a microorganism viewed under the microscope will appear to move in the opposite direction from which it is actually moving.

Magnification and Resolving Power

We have noted that a microscope can produce a magnified image. Another point to be considered is the amount of *resolution*, or the *resolving power* of a microscope. The resolving power of an optical system is its ability to distinguish clearly and in detail between two points which lie very close to each other. Two microscopes may have the same magnifying power but may differ in resolving power. Remember the best image is not the largest but is the clearest.

The Stereomicroscope

The stereomicroscope is sometimes called the binocular microscope because it has two eyepieces and two objectives. With this instrument the two eyepieces and the two objectives are used at the same time (one set for each eye). Thus the object is seen in three dimensions (3-D). Since a stereomicroscope does not have high power, it is used to observe relatively large objects, such as minute insects and small crystals. It may be used with light which is either reflected from the object or transmitted through it, if the object is thin enough.

The Phase-Contrast Microscope

The ordinary compound microscope does not differentiate well between structures within a cell. They appear about equally transparent. Contrast between structures is usually obtained by using stains. For example, certain dye combinations stain the nucleus blue and the cytoplasm pink. But the process of staining may kill the cell or distort the shape of its contents.

The phase-contrast microscope permits us to distinguish the structures within *living* cells. How is this done? Various structures within a cell have differing effects upon the speed of light waves passing through them. As a result, the transmitted light waves are out of step, or *out of phase* (Figure 3–3). These phase differences are then converted to differences in brightness or in color, so that you can distinguish the separate parts.

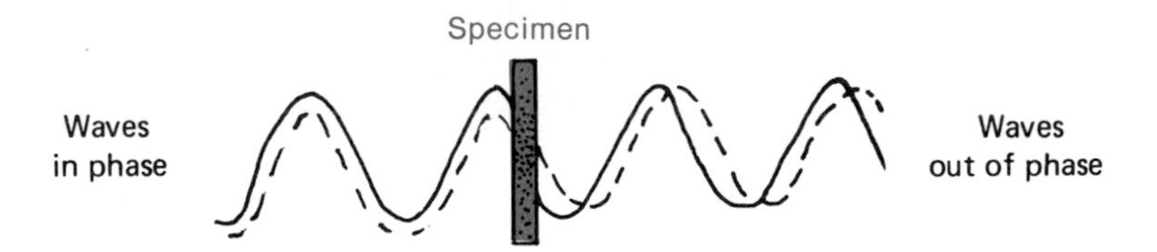

Fig. 3–3. Light waves in a phase-contrast microscope

The Electron Microscope

The electron microscope uses a beam of electrons instead of light rays. Having an extremely short wavelength, the electron beam provides greater resolution and, therefore, greater clarity at higher magnifications. Focusing is accomplished not by glass lenses (which do not affect an electron beam) but by means of electromagnets. The image appears on a photographic plate or on a screen. The electron microscope can provide magnifications of 200,000 times. Tissues being studied with an electron microscope must be sliced extremely thin. They also must be dry and in a vacuum chamber, since water and air absorb electrons. Therefore, the electron microscope cannot be used with living material.

The scanning electron microscope is often used today to provide images with a three-dimensional quality. In the scanning electron microscope, a moving (scanning) electron beam causes the surface of the specimen to yield a photograph in which the low parts appear dark and the high ones light. The resulting three-dimensional effect provides a new understanding of microstructures.

Micro-dissection Apparatus

Knowledge of cells has also been increased by the manipulation and dissection of living cells. For example, biologists can remove the nucleus from a living ameba to find out whether the cell can live and reproduce without this organelle. The *micromanipulator*, the instrument used for this purpose, permits the user to control the movement of very delicate instruments under the compound microscope.

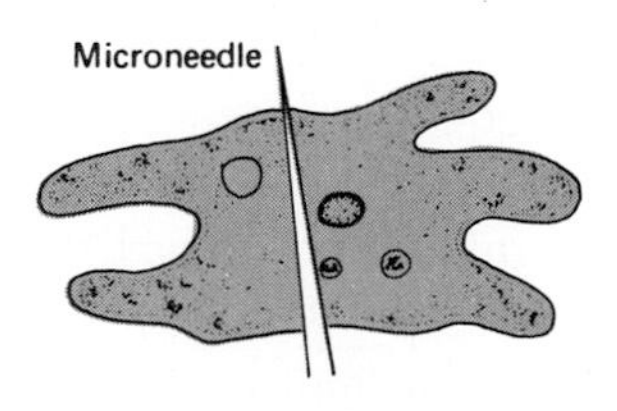

Fig. 3–4. An ameba being dissected by a microneedle. When separation is complete, the part without the nucleus will die after a while; the part with the nucleus will live.

High-Speed Centrifuge

Cytologists (biologists who study cells) usually try to avoid distorting the cells being studied. However, cytologists want to study the parts of cells separately. They do this by grinding tissues so that cell contents are released. When the liquid containing the cell fragments is placed in a tube and spun at high speed in a centrifuge, cell components sort out in different layers according to their density. Batches of mitochondria, ribosomes, and nuclei, separated by this method, can then be studied with the electron microscope and by biochemical methods.

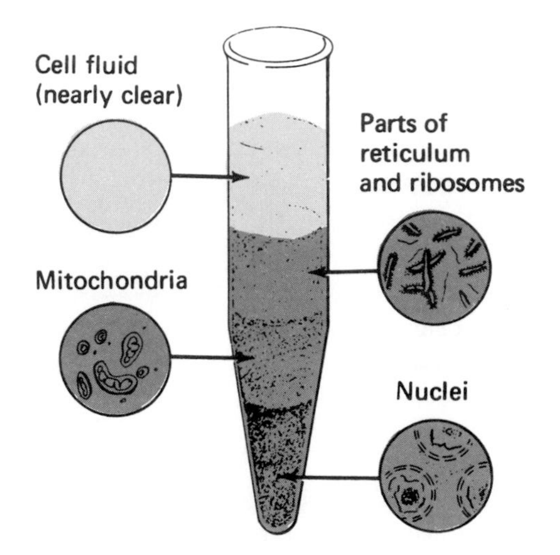

Fig. 3–5. Centrifuge tube showing various layers

Laboratory Skill

Microscopic Measurement

Objects seen under the microscope are so small that they are measured in a special unit. This is the *micrometer* (μm) formerly called the *micron* (μ).

Let us see what this is. The smallest unit on your metric rule is the millimeter (mm). A micrometer is 1/1,000 of a millimeter. One thousand micrometers would fit across the edge of a thin dime. The diameter of a red blood cell is about 8.5 μm. An average-sized bacterium is about 2 μm long.

To compare metric units, let us start with the *meter* which is a little more than a yard long (actually 39.37 inches).

1/100 meter	=	1 centimeter (cm)
1/1000 meter	=	1 millimeter (mm)
1/1000 millimeter	=	1 micrometer (μm) or 1 micron (μ)
1/10,000 millimeter	=	1 Angstrom unit (Å)

The Ångstrom unit is often employed for indicating the wavelength of light. For example, red light has a wavelength of about 6500 Å. The thickness of the cell membrane of a red blood cell is about 200 Å. Use of this minute unit indicates the sensitivity of modern instruments.

How can you convert millimeters to micrometers? Since the micrometer is the smaller of these units, you *multiply* by one thousand. This can be accomplished by moving the decimal point three places to the *right*. Examples:

4.56 mm = 4560 μm (or 4.56×10^3 μm)

0.0378 mm = 37.8 μm (or 3.78×10^1 μm)

To convert micrometers to millimeters, *divide* by 1,000, or move the decimal point three places to the *left:*

A tiny worm is 2,500 μm long. How can you express this measurement in millimeters?

2500 μm = 2.5 mm

Convert 0.15 μm to millimeters.

Answer: 0.00015 mm. (or 1.5×10^{-4} mm)

Estimating the size of a specimen can be done in the following way: Place a transparent plastic metric ruler in the field of your *low-power objective* as shown in the diagram. Then estimate the diameter of the field in millimeters. For example, 1.3 mm. Finally, convert the millimeters to micrometers; 1.3 mm = 1300 μm. The diameter of the low power field, therefore is 1300 μm.

An object that is about one-half the length of the diameter of the field, as seen under low power, has an approximate length of 650 μm.

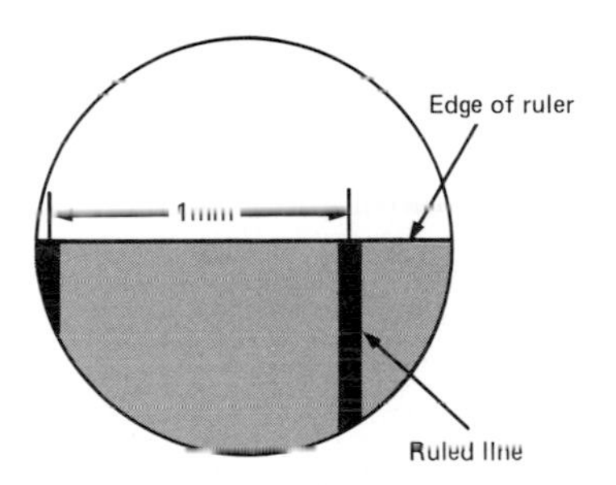

Fig. 3–6. The field of view under low power measured with a transparent ruler.

Reasoning Exercises

1. Explain the difference between a simple microscope and a compound microscope.
2. What are the three concepts of the cell theory?
3. What damage can result if you focus downward while looking through the eyepiece of a microscope? How can you prevent this from happening?
4. What is meant by the resolving power of a microscope?
5. The low power field of a microscope is 1.4 mm in diameter. The length of a cell, as viewed under low power, is one-fourth of the diameter of the field. What is the length of the cell in micrometers?

C

Cell Organelles

The term *protoplasm* was first used to refer to the living substance in the cell. It was then believed that protoplasm was the same in all living things. Today we know that the cell is made up of many substances and structures, not just a single substance. All of these substances together are responsible for the characteristics of life. Just as an automobile is not made up of a basic "automobile substance," a cell is not made up of a basic "cell substance." Instead, it is a complex organization of many parts. Nevertheless, today the term *protoplasm* is still widely used to designate the living contents of the cell, and we use it this way for convenience. *Cytoplasm* refers to the contents of the cell between the nucleus and the cell membrane. Cytoplasm often flows in a circular motion through the cell. This streaming motion is called *cyclosis*.

We now know that the cells of plants and animals contain well-defined structures called organelles. An organelle often seen through the microscope is the cell nucleus. Organelles, which are often bound by membranes, perform specialized functions such as building important biological substances, transport, and energy release.

Cells of the kingdom Monera, which includes bacteria and blue-green algae, are distinguished by the lack of cell organelles bound by membranes. These organisms also lack a cell nucleus. Cells without a distinct nucleus are called prokaryotic cells, or prokaryotes. Cells with a nucleus are called eukaryotic cells, or eukaryotes. Therefore, all members of the kingdom Monera are prokaryotes; all other organisms are eukaryotes.

Plasma membrane. Every cell is enclosed by a *plasma membrane*, or cell membrane, that separates the cell from its environment.

Since the plasma membrane permits some materials but not others, to pass through readily it is said to be a *selectively permeable membrane*. The plasma membrane controls the transport of material into and out of the cell. The fluid-mosaic model of the plasma membrane is described in Chapter 6.

Extensions of the cell membrane probably help cells cling together and increase the surface for passage of materials between cells. *Pinocytic vesicles* are saclike enfoldings of the cell membrane. The process by which these vesicles form and discharge their liquid contents into the cell is called *pinocytosis*.

The endoplasmic reticulum. The cytoplasm has within it an extensive network of tubelike structures called the *endoplasmic reticulum* (reticulum = "network"). The tubes of the endoplasmic reticulum have a membrane which appears double under the electron microscope. Some of the tubes join with the nuclear membrane. The endoplasmic reticulum forms a passageway that functions in the transport of materials throughout the cell, and is the site of fat and protein synthesis.

Ribosomes. *Ribosomes* are tiny dense particles that are attached to the walls of the endoplasmic reticulum or that move freely in the cytoplasm. Composed of ribonucleic acid (RNA) and protein, they are the site for the synthesis of proteins.

The Golgi bodies. As seen under the electron microscope, *Golgi bodies* usually appear as a cuplike stack of tiny, flattened, saclike tubes. Golgi bodies function in the process of *secretion*. They package a large number of protein molecules in a membrane and send the package to the cell's surface, where they can be released from the cell.

Mitochondria. *Mitochondria* appear as short rods or tiny spheres and are found in all plant and animal cells. The number of mitochondria varies with the amount of cellular activity being performed. Very active cells may contain more than a thousand mitochondria.

Each mitochondrion is enclosed by a double membrane. An inner membrane is folded into a system of shelflike ridges. These increase the interior surface area of the membrane. The mitochondria have been called the "powerhouses of the cell" because it is here that much of cellular respiration takes place.

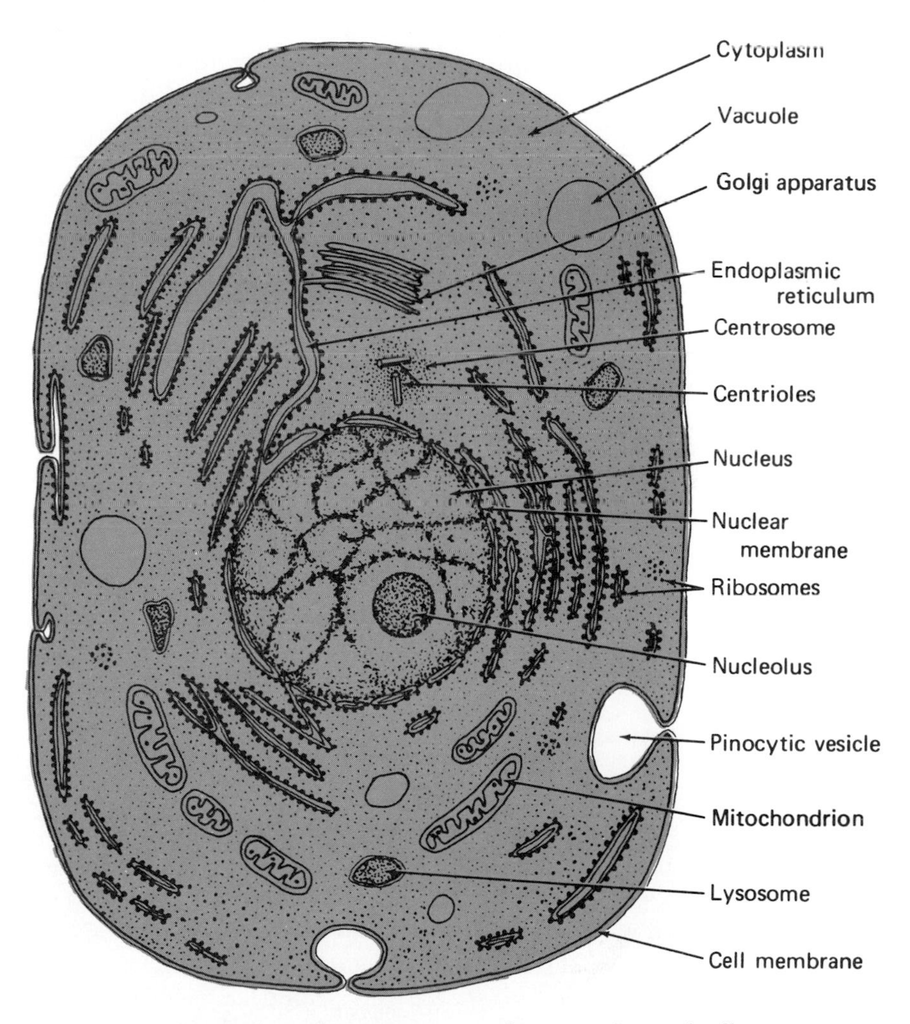

Fig. 3–7. The structures inside a typical animal cell.

Microtubules. *Microtubules* are long, slender tubes that serve as support for the cell. Sometimes they function as fairly rigid rods and sometimes as flexible ropes. In a moving ameba, microtubules are disassembled and reassembled to assist in movement. A sliding action by bundles of microtubules causes the bending of cilia and flagellae.

Microtubules compose the fibers that join centrioles and attach them to chromosomes as a cell divides. They also assist in the discharge of secretions from cells.

Microfilaments. *Microfilaments* are long, thin threads attached to cell membranes. Containing the same two proteins that cause muscle contraction, they play a role in movement, such as the streaming of cytoplasm in *Ameba*.

Lysosomes. *Lysosomes* are small, oval bodies that contain chemicals used in digestion. When a lysosome fuses with a food vacuole its chemicals digest the food into small molecules. Lysosomes also digest other cell structures and in this way dispose of old, wornout cells.

Cell Organelles and Their Functions

Organelle	Function
Cell wall	Protects and supports plant cell and maintains shape
Cell membrane	Controls transport of material into and out of cell
Nuclear membrane	Controls transport of material into and out of the nucleus
Cytoplasm	Provides an organized watery environment in which life functions take place by means of organelles contained in it
Endoplasmic reticulum	Provides channels through which transport of material occurs in cytoplasm
Golgi bodies	Package secretions for discharge from the cell
Ribosomes	Sites for protein synthesis
Vacuoles	Storage sacs for water, dissolved materials, and wastes; maintain internal pressure of cell
Chloroplasts	Contain chlorophyll in green plant cells; act as sites for food manufacture
Nucleolus	Contains centrioles that function during reproduction of animal cells
Nucleus	The information center for cell reproduction and control of cell functions
Chromosomes	Contain the hereditary material (DNA); are the agents for distribution of hereditary information.
Mitochondria	Sites of cellular respiration and ATP production
Microtubules	Serve as support of the cell
Microfilaments	Aid in cell movement
Lysosomes	Have chemicals used in cellular digestion

The nucleus. This structure of eukaryotes regulates all the cell's activities. It does so by controlling the synthesis of chemicals essential for life. A double-layered membrane separates the nucleus from the cytoplasm. Pores in the nuclear membrane permit certain chemicals to pass from the nucleus to the cytoplasm. The nucleus contains the *chromosomes,* which are long, coiled fibers that carry the material of heredity. During cell division, the chromosomes shorten and thicken into rod-like shapes. The number of chromosomes in the nucleus is characteristic of each species (46 in human cells). Usually a cell has one nucleus, but a *Paramecium* is an example of a single-celled organism with two nuclei.

The nucleus contains two types of nucleic acids: *deoxyribonucleic acid* (DNA) and *ribonucleic acid* (RNA). Chromosomes are made of DNA and protein. DNA controls cell growth and development, and passes on the cell's traits to the next generation of cells. For a further discussion of RNA and DNA, see Chapters 4, 17, and 21.

Within the nucleus is a smaller body called a *nucleolus.* The nucleolus is composed mainly of RNA, and is involved in the passage of RNA to the cytoplasm. A nucleus may contain more than one nucleolus.

The centrioles. Most animal cells have tiny structures in the cytoplasm called centrioles. Each centriole, which is a cylinder containing tiny tubules, appears to play an important role in cell division.

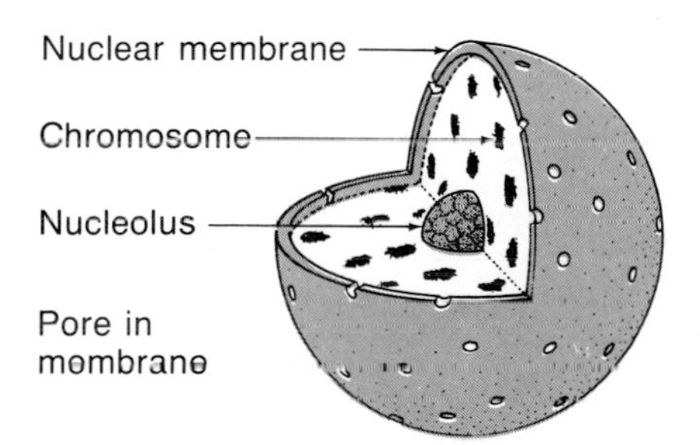

Fig. 3–8. The structure of a cell nucleus, with a portion cut away to show smaller structures.

Cilia and flagella are outward projections from the cell membrane and are bounded by an outfolding of the membrane. Cilia are short structures whereas flagella are longer ones. They are used for locomotion or for moving liquids or objects past stationary cells. Cilia and flagella are formed from centrioles and their internal structure greatly resembles that of the centriole.

Plastids are small structures in the cytoplasm of cells of higher plants and a few one-celled organisms. Some *plastids* are colorless, and some contain pigments that give them color. *Chloroplasts* are plastids containing the green pigment *chlorophyll* which is used in manufacturing food by plants.

Vacuoles. Many cells have spherical, bubblelike storage sacs called *vacuoles*. In plants, these may be filled with a fluid called *cell sap*. Plant cells generally have large vacuoles but those of animals are usually small. Some single-celled organisms have specialized vacuoles. Ameba, for example, has food vacuoles and a contractile vacuole.

The cell wall. This is a fairly rigid envelope of nonliving material that surrounds the cell membrane of plant cells. It is composed mainly of cellulose. Unlike the cell membrane, which controls the passage of materials into and out of the cell, the *cell wall* permits most molecules to pass through.

The presence of a cell wall is an important characteristic used by biologists in deciding whether to classify an organism as a plant or an animal. The cell wall is the plant skeleton that protects and supports the individual cell and helps to support an entire tree made up of many cells. The wood of a tree consists mainly of its cellulose walls.

Comparison of Plant and Animal Cells

Cells vary greatly in size, shape, and function. However, they have certain characteristic features. We have already noted some structures that can be seen under the electron microscope. Now we are ready to compare a typical animal cell and a typical plant cell as they would appear under the compound microscope. (See Fig. 3–9.)

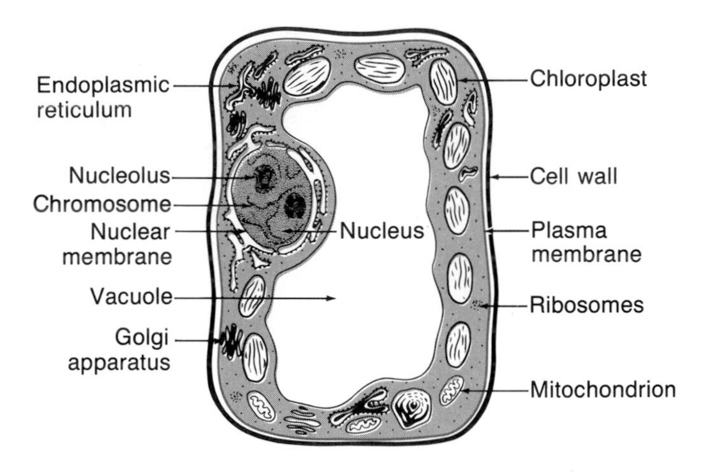

Fig. 3–9. Structure of a generalized cell of a green plant.

Structures present in both plant and animal cells are the cell membrane, nucleus, mitochondria, and cytoplasm. Differences between the two kinds of cells are compared in the following table:

Comparison of a Generalized Plant and Animal Cell

Structure	Green Plant Cell	Animal Cell
Cell wall	present	absent
Chloroplasts	present	absent
Centrosome	absent	present
Vacuoles	usually large	usually small

Laboratory Skills

Identifying Cell Organelles

It is easy to study a piece of onion skin under the microscope because the tissue is thin enough for light to pass through readily. Cut a wedge from an onion, remove one of the thick leaves, and then remove a thin membrane from the inner concave surface of that leaf. A portion of this membrane as it appears under the microscope is shown in Figure 3–10.

In the onion skin cells shown in the diagram, chloroplasts are absent because this portion of the plant grows underground and is not green.

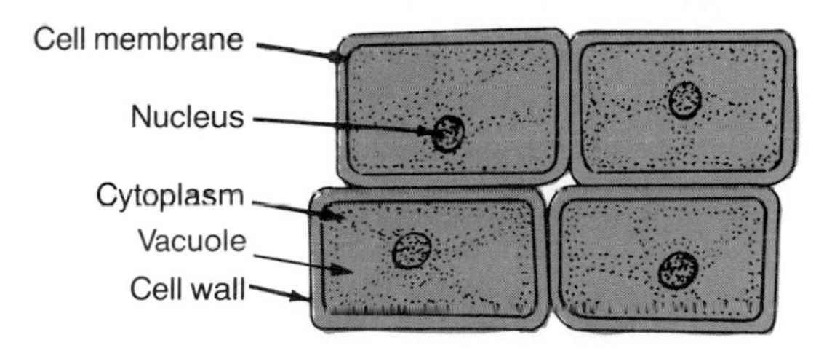

Fig. 3–10. Onion skin cells

The vacuoles can be seen as clear areas, and are distinguished from the granular appearance of the cytoplasm. As plant cells grow larger, the vacuoles increase in size and decrease in number. The rigid cell wall maintains the cell's shape.

Animal cells can also be viewed under the microscope. Cells can be gently scraped from the inside of your cheek mounted on a slide, and stained with methylene blue (see Appendix). The cell organelles found in human cheek cells are identified in Figure 3–11.

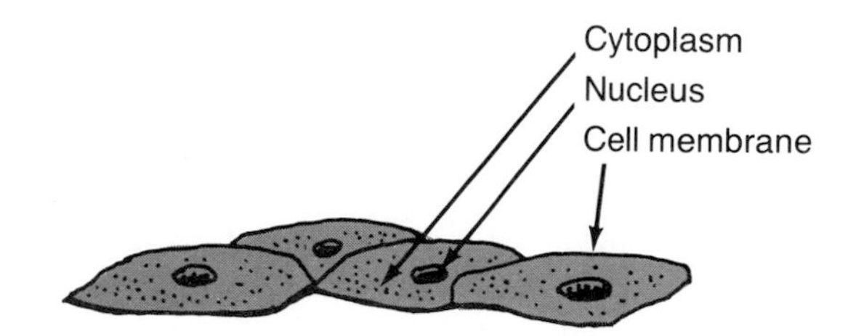

Fig. 3–11. Cheek cells (epithelial cells) in the human

Using Dissection Equipment Safely

The following safety guidelines should be used when working with dissection of laboratory specimens.

1. Carefully read the instructions for the activity and be familiar with the safety guidelines for handling dissecting instruments (see Appendix).
2. Listen carefully to any additional instructions and cautions from your teacher.
3. Find out where the first-aid kit is located in your classroom/laboratory.
4. Be careful in handling sharp-pointed instruments and instruments that have sharp knives or blades.
5. Report any cuts or wounds to your teacher.

Using Staining Techniques

Elodea is a green plant that grows submerged in ponds and streams. A thin, delicate leaf removed from the tip of a stem has only two thin layers of cells. If you stain a piece of the leaf with iodine (Lugol's solution), you can see green plant cells under the microscope. (See Figure 3–12.)

If the plant has been growing in warm water exposed to sunlight, you can see the chloroplasts being moved in a circular pattern by the streaming motion of the cytoplasm (cyclosis).

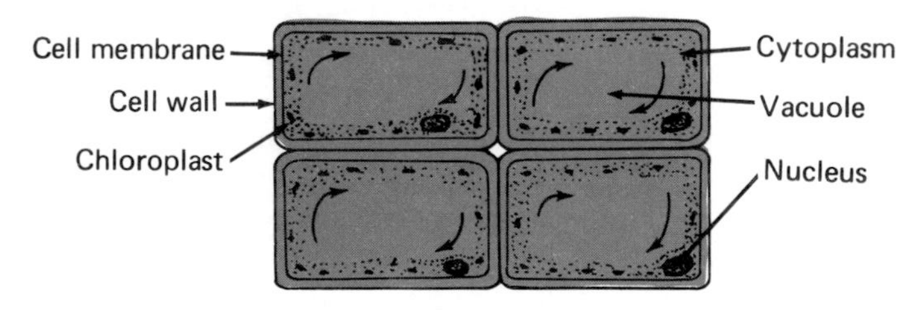

Fig. 3–12. Cells of *Elodea* leaf

Both onion skin and *Elodea* can best be seen by preparing wet mounts. (See Appendix A.) Wet mounts are used with specimens that should not be allowed to dry out. In *Elodea*, cyclosis can only be seen when the leaf is maintained in a watery environment.

Many organelles cannot be seen without the aid of a stain. A stain unites with the organelle in such a way that the color provides contrast with other objects. Most stains become "fixed" to organelles and kill the cells. *Vital stains* do not kill the cell but allow it to continue their life functions. Methylene blue, used to stain cheek cells, is a vital stain.

Handling Chemicals Safely

Stains used in preparing microscope slides are chemicals. The following safety guidelines should be used when working with chemicals:

1. Carefully read the instructions for the activity and be familiar with the safety guidelines for handling chemicals in the laboratory (see Appendix).
2. Listen carefully to any additional instructions and precautions from your teacher.

3. Read the label. Do not use chemicals from containers that are not clearly labeled.
4. Use chemicals only in the way that has been prescribed in the text and by your teacher.
5. Wear protective clothing and keep chemical stains off counters and other materials. Do not touch stains—use the medicine droppers that have been provided to transfer the stains from container to slide.
6. Carefully clean counters after use and wash hands.
7. Never taste chemicals or inhale the vapors from a chemical as they can be toxic.

D

Exceptions to the Cell Theory

A *theory* is a general statement that unifies many isolated facts into a broad explanation. Two requirements for a scientific theory are: (1) It must be based upon *natural* law. (2) It must be *verifiable*. This means that you cannot propose a theory if there is no way to check or verify it. Science is not a system of unchanging beliefs. As new facts are discovered, scientists are ready to modify theories or even to discard them.

So is it with the respected cell theory of the 19th century. Biologists are developing a new concept of the cell as new techniques reveal exceptions. Some of these exceptions are:

1. The cell is considered as the basic unit of life. However, the electron microscope reveals structures within the cell that can reproduce themselves. These are the mitochondria and the chloroplasts. They could be considered more fundamental for metabolism than the cell as a whole. There is even evidence that mitochondria and chloroplasts are descendants of primitive bacteria that began to live long ago inside other cells.

2. Not all parts of living things are composed of bits of cytoplasm and a nucleus surrounded by a cell membrane. For example, skeletal muscle tissue contains many nuclei that are not separated by cell membranes. Also, the slime mold, at one stage of its life cycle, contains thousands of nuclei that are not partitioned off (Figure 3–13).

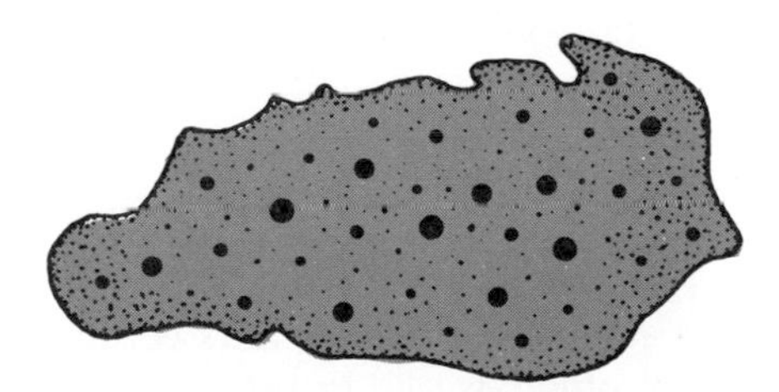

Fig. 3–13. One stage of a slime mold showing multinucleate structure

3. Because virus particles can reproduce, they are sometimes thought to be living cells. However, they are made up on only two kinds of chemicals (protein and nucleic acid), they do not consist of protoplasm, and they do not have any of the structures usually associated with cells.

Reasoning Exercises

1. Lysosomes are often called "suicide sacs." What reason can you give for this?
2. Could a cell live without a nucleus? Explain.
3. Of what materials are chromosomes composed? What is the function of chromosomes?
4. Distinguish between a typical plant cell and a typical animal cell.
5. Distinguish between the cell membrane and the cell wall.

Completion Questions

A

1. The first simple microscope was built by . . . . . .
2. The first person to see bacteria was . . . . . .
3. The concept that cells arise from previously existing cells originated with . . . . . .
4. The concept that all plants and animals are composed of cells was stated by . . . . . .

B

• 5. If the total magnification of a microscope is 430x and that of the eyepiece is 10x, the magnification of the high-power objective is . . . . . .

• 6. The amount of light reaching the objective lens of a compound microscope is regulated by the . . . . . .

• 7. At magnifications of 970x, an oil immersion lens may be used to prevent the loss of . . . . . .

• 8. For a specimen to be in focus under high power, the objective lens must be (closer to, farther from) . . . . . . the specimen than under low power.

9. The microscope that enables the viewer to distinguish easily between structures in a living cell is the . . . . . .
10. The ability of a microscope to distinguish between objects lying very close to each other is known as its . . . . . .
11. The instrument that separates cell components by their density is the . . . . . .
12. In the electron microscope, the beam of electrons is focused by . . . . . .

• 13. 340 micrometers is equivalent to . . . . . . millimeters.

C

14. The network of tubes in the region of the cytoplasm is called the . . . . . .
15. A membrane that permits certain substances to pass through but not others is said to be . . . . . .
16. The synthesis of proteins in the cell occurs at the . . . . . .
17. The organelles that are known as the "powerhouses of the cells" are the . . . . . .
18. Golgi bodies function in the process of . . . . . .
19. The destruction of old worn out cells is accomplished by the . . . . . .
20. Green pigmented plastids that function in photosynthesis are the . . . . . .

21. A tiny spherical body lying near the nucleus of animal cells and functioning in cell division is the......
22. The cell wall is composed mainly of......
23. The movement of chloroplasts in a green plant cell is called......

D

24. A microorganism that consists of only protein and nucleic acid is a......
25. An example of a cell that contains many nuclei is......

Multiple-Choice Questions

A

1. The botanist who stated that all plants are composed of cells was (1) Schwann, (2) Schleiden, (3) Dujardin, (4) Brown.
2. The contribution of Virchow to the development of the cell theory was that he (1) stated that all cells come from cells, (2) named cells, (3) said cells contain nuclei, (4) defined cells on the basis of the presence of living protoplasm.
3. One of the first scientists to observe living microorganisms was (1) Leeuwenhoek, (2) Virchow, (3) Hooke, (4) Von Mohl.
4. A contribution of Hooke to the development of the cell theory was that he (1) stated that all cells come from cells, (2) defined cells on the basis of the presence of living protoplasm, (3) named cells, (4) defined cells on the basis of the presence of nuclei.
5. The cell theory states all of the following *except* (1) cells have definite boundaries, (2) cells are units of structure, (3) cells arise from living cells, (4) cells are units of function.

B

6. Which instrument has played a major role in permitting scientists to discover the chemical makeup of a mitochondrion? (1) electron microscope, (2) centrifuge, (3) compound microscope, (4) oil immersion objective
- 7. We can control the light entering the objective of the microscope by means of (1) mirror and ocular, (2) ocular and coarse adjustment knob, (3) mirror and coarse adjustment knob, (4) mirror and diaphragm.
- 8. The circle (below) indicates the position of the letter X as seen in the field of your microscope. To get the letter X in the *center* of the field, you would move the slide (1) to the left and up, (2) to the left and down, (3) to the right and up, (4) to the right and down.

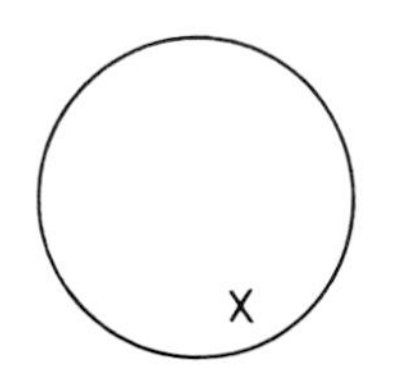

- 9. If the length of a *Paramecium* measures about ¼ the distance across the microscope field and the diameter of the field measures 1600μm, the length of the *Paramecium* is about (1) 400μm, (2) 0.4μm, (3) 0.016μm, (4) 4000μm.

• 10. An object measures 16 mm in length. Its length can be expressed as (1) 16 micrometers, (2) 160 micrometers, (3) 1600 micrometers, (4) 16,000 micrometers.

C *Base your answers to questions 11 through 15 on the diagrammatic sketch of a cell below.*

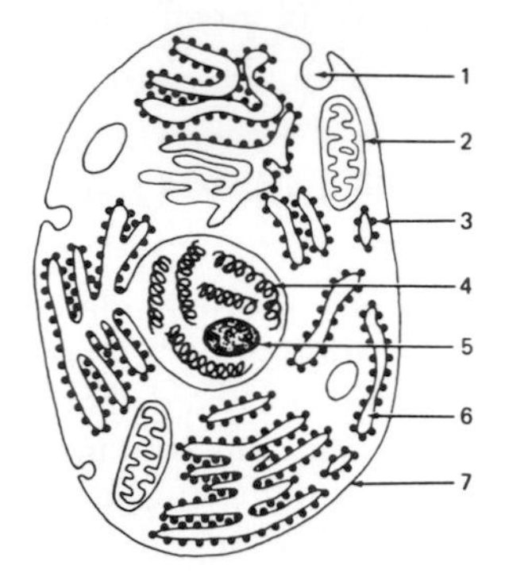

11. Which structure is probably a major pathway in intracellular transport? (1) 5, (2) 6, (3) 3, (4) 7
12. Which structure is composed primarily of lipids and protein? (1) 1, (2) 6, (3) 7, (4) 4
13. Which structure is primarily concerned with the release of energy from nutrients (respiration)? (1) 5, (2) 2, (3) 3, (4) 4
14. Which structure serves as the major site of protein synthesis? (1) 1, (2) 2, (3) 3, (4) 7
15. Which cell structure is composed of DNA and protein? (1) 1, (2) 6, (3) 7, (4) 4

• 16. Wet mounts are often used for microscopic observation of living organisms because water (1) magnifies, (2) prevents drying, (3) holds organisms in place, (4) mixes well with stains.

• 17. Which of the following structures is *not* found in animal cells? (1) nucleus, (2) cytoplasm, (3) cell membrane, (4) cell wall

• 18. The usual purpose of staining a microscopic specimen is to (1) prevent the organism from moving, (2) make viewing more colorful, (3) distinguish details, (4) test the effect of chemicals on organisms.

D 19. A scientific theory must be (1) unverifiable, (2) unchanging, (3) based on natural law, (4) unmodifiable.

20. Virus particles (1) are universally considered to be nonliving, (2) do not consist of protoplasm, (3) cannot reproduce, (4) have many nuclei.

Chapter Test

• 1. The cellular component that *cannot* be seen with a compound microscope is (1) DNA, (2) vacuole, (3) nucleus, (4) cytoplasm.

• 2. A student observed a cell under the microscope. She identified it as a green plant cell and not a human cheek cell because she noted the presence of a (1) nucleus, (2) cell wall, (3) mitochondrion, (4) ribosome.

3. Viruses do not coincide with our concept of the cell because they (1) lack cytoplasm, (2) cannot multiply, (3) contain DNA, (4) are so small.
4. The DNA of a cell is found mainly in its (1) membrane, (2) cytoplasm, (3) chromosomes, (4) vacuoles.
5. • If the ocular (eyepiece) is marked 10x and the high-power objective is marked 43x, the magnification of the microscope is (1) 215, (2) 100, (3) 430, (4) 1000.
6. • A transparent plastic ruler is placed on the stage of a microscope and observed under low power. Two divisions of the ruler can be seen across the width of the field. Each division of the ruler equals 1 millimeter. The diameter of the field is (1) 1 μm, (2) 2 μm, (3) 1000 μm, (4) 2000 μm.
7. The unit of structure and function in living things is the (1) mitochondrion, (2) organelle, (3) tissue, (4) cell.
8. Which structure regulates the entry and exit of dissolved materials in an animal cell? (1) cell wall, (2) nucleus, (3) cell membrane, (4) cytoplasm
9. A structure present in most animal cells but absent from most plant cells is the (1) lysosome, (2) chromosome, (3) ribosome, (4) centrosome.
10. The phase-contrast microscope has aided in understanding the nature of the cell by permitting (1) magnification of cells up to 500,000 times their normal size, (2) detailed observation of unstained living cells, (3) observation of objects an inch or more in thickness, (4) chemical analysis of the parts of the cell.
11. A limitation of the electron microscope is that it (1) cannot be used to study living specimens, (2) cannot magnify above 1000x, (3) uses short wave electrons, (4) suffers loss of resolving power above 1000x magnification.
12. Which statement concerning ribosomes is true? (1) They are the sites of protein synthesis. (2) They function in cell division. (3) They contain DNA. (4) They permit cells to contract.

Chapter 4 The Chemistry of Living Things

With new instruments for research, biologists probed ever deeper into the structure of living things. But even the electron microscope has its limits of magnification. The newest frontier in biology is at the level of the molecule and the atom. Now, biologists are applying the techniques developed by chemists and physicists to study cells. Research in this field of science is called *molecular biology*. Of special interest to the biologist are the organism's ability to manufacture specific chemical compounds and effects on life functions.

To understand the structure and physiology of cells, and how an organism functions, you need a clear understanding of chemistry. This chapter introduces the basic concepts of chemistry as it applies to modern biology.

A Principles of Chemistry

Matter is anything that has mass and occupies space. The air we breathe and the food we consume consist of matter. The basic form of matter is the *element*. When two or more elements combine, they form a *compound*. The smallest part of an element is an *atom* of that element. The atoms of elements are made up of *protons*, *neutrons*, and *electrons*. The atoms of an element have different numbers of protons, electrons, and neutrons that distinguish them from atoms of other elements.

The Atom

Most particles in atoms have two important properties: *charge* and *mass*. Protons have a unit positive charge (+1) and electrons have a unit negative charge (−1). A neutron has a zero charge and is an electrically neutral particle. The mass of a proton is considered to be the same as that of the neutron. Both a proton and a neutron have a mass of 1. An electron (1/1836 of the mass of a proton) has virtually no mass. By studying the chemical behavior of elements, we can determine their chemical properties. The following table summarizes the charge and mass of subatomic particles.

Charge and Mass of Subatomic Particles

Particle	Charge	Mass, atomic mass units
Proton	+1	1
Electron	−1	1/1836
Neutron	0	1

The central portion of the atom is called the *nucleus*. The nucleus is positively charged and contains almost all of the mass of the atom. The nucleus consists of protons and neutrons that are closely bunched together. The electrons are found outside the region of the nucleus.

Model of the Atom

Atoms differ from one another in the number of protons and neutrons in the nucleus. They also differ in the number of electrons found outside the nucleus. The chemical behavior of an atom is determined by the number of protons in the nucleus. This number distinguishes a particular element and is referred to as the *atomic number*. Isolated atoms are electrically neutral. This means that the number of electrons outside the nucleus must be equal to the number of protons inside the nucleus. The atomic number therefore represents the number of electrons as well as the number of protons in the atom. The total number of protons and neutrons in the nucleus is known as the *mass number*. Protons and neutrons each have a relative mass equal to 1.

Elements are assigned symbols. The symbols are a kind of scientific shorthand. The symbol refers to an atom of an element. The symbol for the element carbon is written as C. The atomic number and the mass number are often given with the symbol of the element. The atomic number appears as a subscript before the symbol, and the mass number is written as a superscript after the symbol. For example, an atom of the element carbon is represented as ${}_6C^{12}$.

To show the structure of the carbon atom, we first draw a box representing the nucleus of the atom, as shown in Figure 4–1. Since the atomic number of carbon is 6, we write 6+ to represent 6 protons, as shown in the diagram. The mass number of carbon is 12. The protons which we have already represented have a mass of 6. How many neutrons are needed to make up a total mass number of 12? We write in 6N to indicate the 6 neutrons which are needed to make up the total of 12 units of mass. Figure 4–2 shows the protons and neutrons in the nucleus of an atom of carbon.

Fig. 4–1. The atomic number is 6; 6+ represents the six protons in the nucleus of the atom.

Fig. 4–2. The mass number is 12; 6N represents the number of neutrons in the nucleus of the atom.

Since the neutron has no charge, it is evident that the nucleus has a total of 6 positive charges. Therefore, six electrons with negative charges must also exist in the atom. They are located in *electron shells* ("rings," "orbits," or "energy levels") surrounding the nucleus. None of these shells ever has more than a specific number of electrons.

First shell—maximum of 2 electrons
Second shell—maximum of 8 electrons
Third shell (if an outer shell)—maximum of 8 electrons

In constructing a model of the electron shells for a particular atom, you must first determine the number of electrons in the atom. Beginning with the first shell and moving outward from the nucleus, fill each shell to its maximum until you have accounted for all of the electrons present in the atom. In a carbon atom, fill the first shell with 2 electrons (its maximum) and the remaining 4 electrons in the second shell. (See Fig. 4–3.)

Fig. 4–3. Carbon ($_6C^{12}$). Six electrons in two shells balance the charge of the protons in the nucleus. Some elements have as many as seven shells of electrons

The atomic structure of oxygen, $_8O^{16}$, is shown in Figure 4–4. The atomic structure of ordinary hydrogen, $_1H^1$, is shown in Figure 4–5.

Fig. 4–4. $_8O^{16}$

Fig. 4–5. $_1H^1$

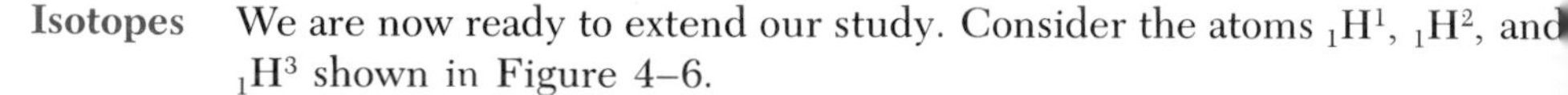

Isotopes We are now ready to extend our study. Consider the atoms $_1H^1$, $_1H^2$, and $_1H^3$ shown in Figure 4–6.

Fig. 4–6. The three isotopes of hydrogen are *protium, deuterium,* and *tritium.*

Each of these atoms has one proton in the nucleus and one electron in the shell. Since the *electrons in the outermost shell determine the chemical properties of an element,* all these atoms act alike chemically. Each is the element hydrogen. Each will combine with oxygen to form water. However, because of the varying number of *neutrons* in the nucleus, each has a different mass number.

Isotopes are atoms that have the same atomic numbers but different atomic masses (weights). This means that isotopes have the same number of protons but differ in the number of neutrons they contain. The three isotopes of hydrogen are called protium ($_1H^1$), deuterium ($_1H^2$), and tritium ($_1H^3$). Heavy water is water whose molecules contain the heavy hydrogen isotopes combined with oxygen.

The atomic number is often omitted in designating isotopes; for example, two of the isotopes of carbon are referred to as carbon-12 and carbon-14. Since all atoms of carbon have an atomic number of 6, the atomic number 6 is understood although not written. Similarly, $_{92}U^{238}$ is referred to as uranium-238.

Radioactivity

Forces within some atoms make their nuclei unstable, and they disintegrate or break apart. As they disintegrate, they emit radiation consisting of particles or electromagnetic waves. Atoms that emit radiation are called *radioactive isotopes.* For example, radium, discovered by Marie and Pierre Curie, is a radioactive element. Because a radioactive element emits particles or waves, it may change to a different element. An isotope that does not emit radiation is called a *stable isotope.* For example, two of the stable isotopes of oxygen are oxygen-16 and oxygen-18.

The presence of radioactivity can be determined by instruments such as the Geiger counter, Wilson cloud chamber, and photographic plate. In order to trace the path of an element through living organisms, scientists introduce a radioactive isotope to replace a stable atom. The atom is then called a *tracer* or *tagged atom.* It behaves like the normal atom in all chemical processes within the organism, but its presence can be traced. For example, biologists have long known that plants use CO_2 (carbon dioxide) to produce sugar in the process of photosynthesis, but they wished to determine some of the steps in this process of sugar production. To do this, they prepared CO_2 with a tagged carbon atom called radioactive carbon-14. The new compounds that plants produced from this radioactive CO_2 containing C-14 were also radioactive. Stable isotopes can be traced by use of the mass spectrometer, an instrument that identifies an isotope by its mass rather than by its radioactivity.

Elements, Compounds, and Mixtures

Atoms may join together to form molecules. If a molecule contains two or more kinds of atoms, the molecule is a *compound.* For example, a small amount of the compound glucose ($C_6H_{12}O_6$) contains billions of molecules, each composed of three kinds of atoms. Each molecule contains 6 carbon atoms, 12 hydrogen atoms, and 6 oxygen atoms. A small quantity of the element oxygen (O_2) may have billions of molecules, each of which is composed of 2 oxygen atoms. Many elements exist as molecules; some of them may also exist as single atoms.

The atoms of molecules are in chemical combination. When several kinds of molecules are present together but are not chemically combined, this arrangement is called a *mixture.* For example, particles of sand (SiO_2) and particles of salt (NaCl) may be put together to form a mixture of sand and salt, but these are not chemically combined. Salt dissolved in water is another example of a mixture of two compounds, NaCl and H_2O. Air is a mixture of elements and compounds such as N_2, O_2, CO_2, H_2O, and others. Protoplasm, the material of the living cell, is a changing mixture of many compounds.

B Chemical Bonding

When atoms are joined to form molecules, they are united by a chemical bond. The *chemical bond* is the means by which two or more atoms are linked together to form a molecule. Two methods of chemical bonding are by (1) *transfer* of electrons and (2) *sharing* of electrons. First we shall investigate chemical bonding by the transfer of electrons.

The outermost electron shell of most elements can contain a maximum of 8 electrons. Note that in Figure 4–7 neither the sodium atom nor the chlorine atom has a complete outer electron shell. The concept of an incomplete outer shell is important to our understanding of chemical bonding. Atoms that have a complete outer shell rarely enter into a chemical transfer of electrons. They are called *inert* atoms. Some examples are the noble gases: helium, neon, and argon.

Atoms with incomplete outer shells tend to complete these shells. One way atoms do this is by transferring electrons. Neither the sodium atom nor the chlorine atom in Figure 4–7 has a complete outer shell. If the single electron of the outer shell of the sodium atom is transferred to the outer shell of the chlorine atom, which is missing one electron, then both atoms have a complete outer shell, as shown in Figure 4–8.

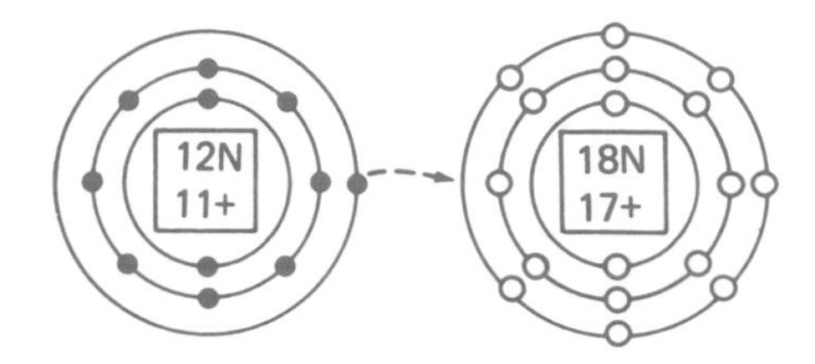

Fig. 4–7. Sodium atom and chlorine atom before the transfer of an electron from sodium to chlorine

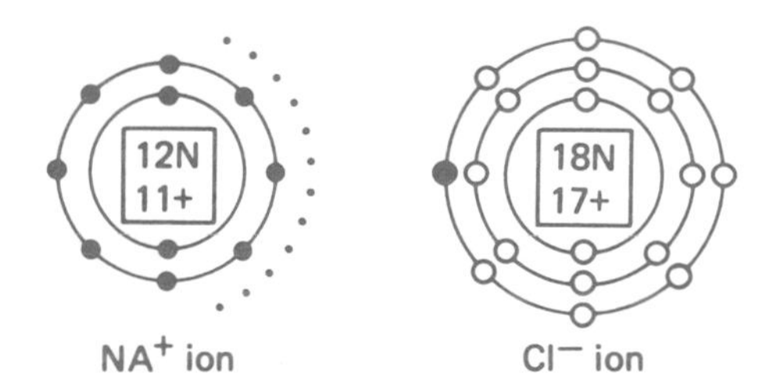

Fig. 4–8. Sodium *ions* and chloride *ions* resulting from the transfer of an electron. Each now has a complete outer shell.

The sodium atom, which lost one electron, now has fewer electrons than protons. It now has a *positive charge* and is called a sodium *ion*. Similarly, the chlorine atom, with one electron more in its shells than protons in its nucleus, has a negative charge and is called a chloride *ion*.

Ionic and Covalent Bonds

An *ion* is an atom, or group of atoms, that has gained or lost one or more electrons. *Ionic bonds* result from the transfer of electrons. The resulting compound, called an *ionic compound*, is held together by the force of the electrical attraction between the oppositely charged ions. Remember that positive ions (Na^+) were formed by a loss of electrons, while negative ions (Cl^-) were formed by a gain of electrons. The force of attraction between these oppositely charged ions is quite strong. This force holding the atoms together in a compound produces *chemical bond energy*. Since this energy is stored in a compound, it is a form of potential energy.

Some atoms achieve a complete outer shell by *sharing* rather than transferring electrons. The shared electrons move in a common pathway that includes the outer shells of both atoms. The force of attraction involved in sharing a pair of electrons constitutes a *covalent bond.* Many compounds are formed by the sharing of electrons. An example is the molecule of the gas methane, CH_4, shown in Figure 4–9.

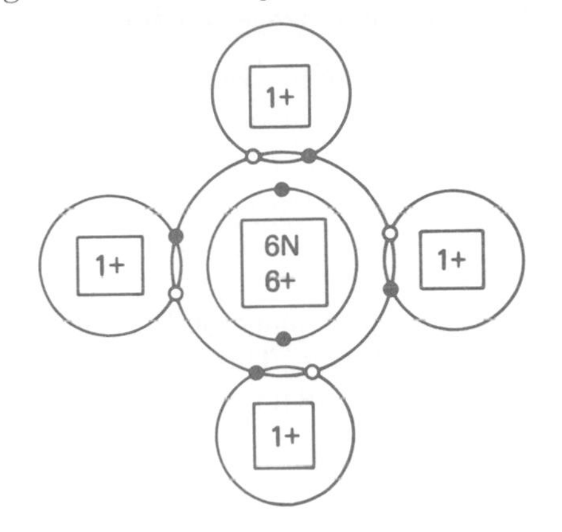

Fig. 4–9. Structure of methane, CH_4

A single molecule of the compound methane has one carbon atom (shown in the center of the diagram) and 4 hydrogen atoms. Remember that carbon has 4 electrons in its *outer* shell and hydrogen has one electron in its outer shell.

In methane, each atom of hydrogen fills its outer shell (2 electrons) by sharing an electron with the carbon atom. At the same time, the carbon atom is able to fill its outer shell (8 electrons) by sharing an electron with each of the four hydrogen atoms.

Since, in chemical reactions, we are concerned only with the electrons in the outer shell, we can simplify Figure 4–9 by using an electron-dot diagram. In Figure 4–10, dots are used to indicate only the electrons in the outer shells of both elements. This diagram can be further simplified by substituting a short dash for each *pair* of shared electrons, as shown in Figure 4–11.

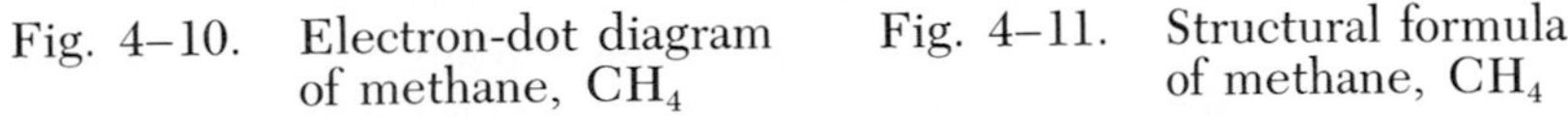

Fig. 4–10. Electron-dot diagram of methane, CH_4

Fig. 4–11. Structural formula of methane, CH_4

A representation using dashes to show the bonds between atoms is called a *structural formula.* Structural formulas are valuable because they show the arrangement as well as the number and kinds of atoms in a molecule. In this sense, they perform a function for the scientist similar to that of our alphabet; for example, the arrangement of the three letters u, s, and e makes the difference between the words "use" and "sue." Review Figure 4–11 to note the number, kind, and arrangement of the atoms in a molecule of methane.

The *molecular formula* indicates the number of various atoms in a single molecule of a compound; for example, H_2O, CH_4, $C_6H_{12}O_6$. Since this formula does not describe the arrangement of the atoms within the molecule, it does not give as much information as does the structural formula.

Ionization

While we may often write a formula for an ionic compound, such as NaCl, these compounds do not exist as molecules of NaCl. A salt crystal consists of equal numbers of two kinds of ions, positive sodium ions (Na^+) and negative chloride ions (Cl^-). If salt is dissolved in water, the ions separate from each other and move around among the water molecules as separate charged particles.

Many covalent compounds, water among them, separate into two ions to a minute degree. This process of separation of a compound into ions is called *ionization.* The ionization of water is represented by the following equation: $H_2O \rightleftharpoons H^+ + OH^-$.

Neutralization

An *acid* is a compound that donates H^+ ions to a solution. For example: *Hydrochloric acid:* $HCl \rightarrow H^+ + Cl^-$.

A *base* is a compound that donates OH^- (hydroxide) ions to a solution. (Or, it removes H^+ ions.) For example: *Sodium hydroxide:* $NaOH \rightarrow Na^+ + OH^-$. Bases are also called *alkalis.*

The typical properties of acids are due to their hydrogen ions, and the typical properties of bases are due to their hydroxide ions. When acids react with bases, the hydrogen ions combine with the hydroxide ions to form water: $H^+ + OH \rightarrow H_2O$.

Neutralization is the removal of hydrogen ions and hydroxide ions from a solution to form water and a salt. Examples of neutralization reactions are shown in the following equations:

Examples of Some Neutralization Reactions

Base	+	Acid	yields	Water	+	A Salt
NaOH	+	HCl	$\rightleftharpoons$	HOH	+	NaCl
KOH	+	HCl	$\rightleftharpoons$	HOH	+	KCl
2KOH	+	H_2SO_4	$\rightleftharpoons$	2HOH	+	K_2SO_4

A *salt* is the compound formed by the union of the positive ion of the base with the negative ion of the acid in a neutralization reaction. Ordinary table salt, NaCl, is just one example of a salt.

Neutralization reactions have many practical applications. For example, suppose a boy accidentally spills lye (NaOH) on his skin. Since lye is a strong base, he should wash his skin with large amounts of water. He should then remove any remaining alkalinity by neutralizing the lye with a mildly acid solution of boric acid. As another example, if a soil is too acid, it is neutralized by adding limestone (calcium carbonate), which forms a base in water.

Reasoning Exercises

1. (a) Which particles in the atom have a mass number of 1?
   (b) Which particle can be considered to have virtually no mass?
   (c) Which particle has a positive charge?
2. Draw the structure of the following atoms: $_2He^4$ (helium); $_3Li^7$ (lithium); $_4Be^{10}$ (beryllium); $_5B^{11}$ (boron); $_7N^{14}$ (nitrogen); $_{12}Mg^{24}$ (magnesium).
3. Name three isotopes of hydrogen. Define isotope. What instrument is used in identifying stable isotopes?
4. Identify each of the following as an element, compound, or mixture: soup, salt, air, uranium, hydrogen, sodium chloride.
5. Name two kinds of chemical bonds. Define each.

C

Chemical Basis of Life

The living cell is a chemical factory which uses the same elements that are found in the nonliving environment. The elements present in greatest percentages in living matter are:

carbon	(C)	oxygen	(O)
hydrogen	(H)	nitrogen	(N)

Elements found in smaller quantities are:

sulfur	(S)	calcium	(Ca)
phosphorus	(P)	sodium	(Na)
magnesium	(Mg)	chlorine	(Cl)
iodine	(I)	potassium	(K)
iron	(Fe)		

Carbon atoms, with four electrons in their outermost shell, have a property that makes them outstanding among the atoms. They can combine to form long chains, which may be thousands of atoms long. It is this special property of carbon that makes possible the giant molecules in living things. An example of a chain of carbon atoms is shown in the structural formula of the molecule of butane, C_4H_{10}, in Figure 4–13. (Note how the hydrogen atoms are arranged around a framework of carbon atoms.)

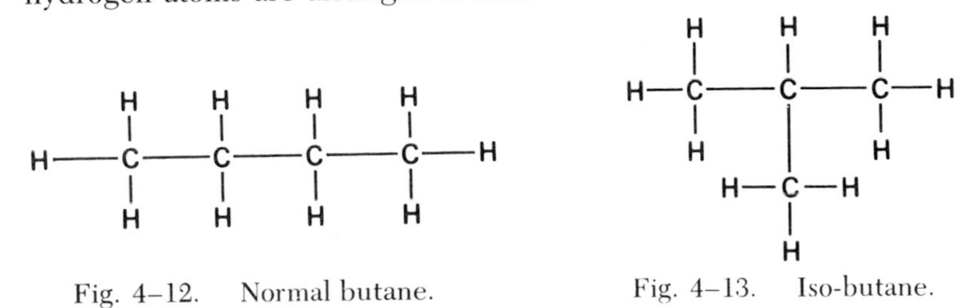

Fig. 4–12. Normal butane. Fig. 4–13. Iso-butane.

The same molecular formula of butane may be arranged in the structural formula shown in Figure 4–14. Compounds with the same molecular formula but different structural formulas are called *isomers*.

Each of these arrangements of C_4H_{10} is a different compound with different properties. With larger molecules, a great many arrangements of the atoms are possible. This ability of carbon to form long chains with many arrangements results in a huge number of different carbon compounds.

The study of carbon compounds is known as *organic chemistry*. The word *organic* means living. The term organic chemistry was originally applied to the chemistry of substances produced in living things. It was formerly thought that such living substances were produced by a vital force and were entirely different from inorganic compounds—those not found in living things. In 1828, however, this distinction between living and nonliving compounds was proved false. Friedrich Wöhler produced the organic compound urea in the laboratory from a nonliving substance. It had previously been found only in living organisms. Organic chemistry includes the study of all carbon compounds in living and nonliving things. The study of the chemistry of living things is called *biochemistry*.

Inorganic Compounds

Organisms consist of inorganic and organic compounds. Compounds that lack carbon are known as *inorganic compounds*. Water, salts, and several acids and bases are important inorganic substances found in living things.

Water. Water is an essential component of every cell. The cells of the body and the fluid surrounding the cells consist of 80 percent water. The chemical reactions in living things depend on the presence of water. The strong bonds between the atoms in water molecules help maintain chemical stability as chemical reactions occur in the body. Water has several unique properties:

Water is the most versatile solvent known. Chemical reactions do not normally occur between large dry masses of matter but between molecules and ions. When a substance is dissolved in water, it may break up into molecules and ions which are continuously in motion. Chemical reactions can occur within the cell because the cell contains a large amount of the solvent water.

Water is a relatively stable compound. Water can be decomposed into hydrogen and oxygen only by the expenditure of a large amount of energy; it does not normally decompose. For this reason, water provides a stable background for other reactions within the cell.

Water ionizes. The H^+ and the OH^- ions formed by the ionization of water are part of many chemical reactions in cells.

Other inorganic compounds. Salts are compounds that ionize when dissolved in water. Ions of potassium, sodium, and chlorine are examples of *mineral elements* that are produced when a salt dissociates in water. Mineral elements are taken into our bodies as components of food substances. It is important that diets contain a sufficient amount of minerals to ensure proper growth of bones and teeth, to regulate nerve responses, and to maintain acid-base balance.

Inorganic acids and *bases* are important in maintaining the proper pH levels in different parts of the body and in regulating certain cellular activities. Acids and bases help to maintain the constant homeostasis of the body.

Organic Compounds

Organic compounds are formed by different combinations of carbon and hydrogen. In addition, they may also contain such elements as nitrogen, oxygen, sulfur and phosphorus. Carbon atoms can join with atoms of other elements and with other carbon atoms. The carbon atoms form organic molecules of great length, variety, and complexity. The major kinds of organic compounds found in living things are proteins, carbohydrates, lipids, and nucleic acids.

Proteins. Proteins contain nitrogen and are the most abundant organic compounds in living things. The main elements present in proteins are carbon, hydrogen, oxygen, nitrogen, and sulfur. Every cell contains large amounts of proteins, which are part of the basic structure of membranes, chromosomes, and other cell parts. Muscle cells are largely protein. It is fibers of protein that produce muscle contraction. In addition, there are noncellular proteins, such as those found in blood plasma, cartilage, hair, and nails. We need proteins in our diet to provide the raw materials for making these structures. Among the foods that are rich in protein are meat, fish, eggs, cheese, legumes (bean-type plants), and grains.

Amino acids. Proteins are composed of smaller building blocks called *amino acids*. There are 20 different amino acids that commonly occur in most organisms. The structure of the different proteins is determined by the kind, arrangement, and number of amino acids.

Amino acids always have two important groups: the amino group (NH_2) and the carboxyl group (COOH). The general structure of an amino acid is shown in Figure 4–15. The letter R represents a variable, or particular molecular chain which is different in each of the 20 amino acids. In addition, a single hydrogen atom forms a bond with the central carbon atom.

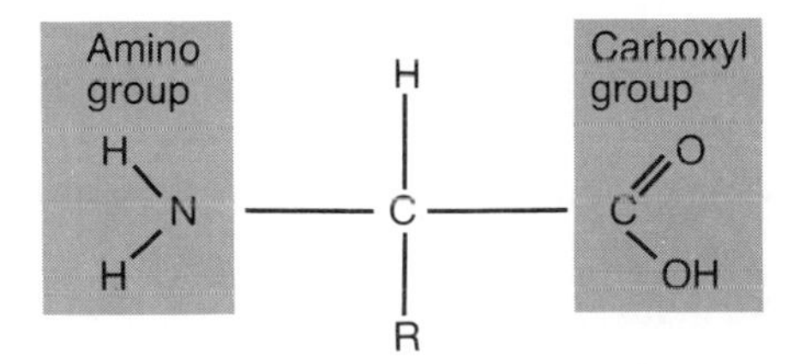

Fig. 4–14. General structure of an amino acid.

Glycine and alanine are two examples of amino acids. In glycine, the R position is filled by an H atom, shown in Figure 4–16; in alanine, the R position is occupied by the CH_3 or methyl group, shown in Figure 4–17.

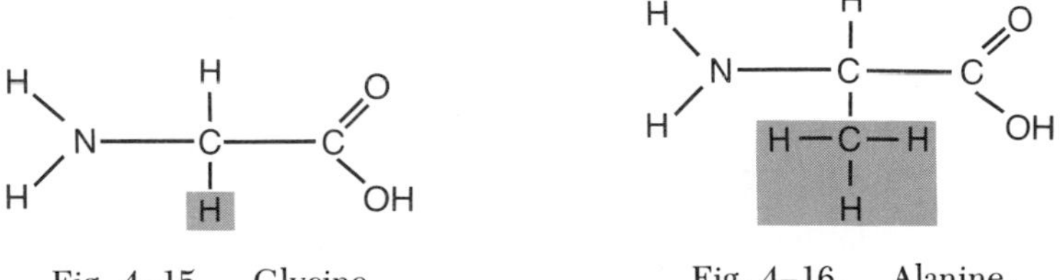

Fig. 4–15. Glycine.

Fig. 4–16. Alanine.

Dehydration Synthesis of Proteins

When two amino acids join together, the amino group of one combines with the carboxyl group of the other. A larger molecule is formed by the synthesis (putting together) of the two amino acids. Because a water molecule is released, or given off in this reaction, it is called *dehydration synthesis*. The remainder of the two amino acid molecules are bonded together to form a larger molecule. Figure 4–18 shows the molecular configuration of the molecule formed by combining the two amino acids, glycine and alanine. The linkage between the amino acids is called a *peptide bond* (CO—NH). When two amino acids combine, they form a *dipeptide;* when three amino acids combine, they form a *tripeptide;* and when more than three amino acids combine, they form a *polypeptide.*

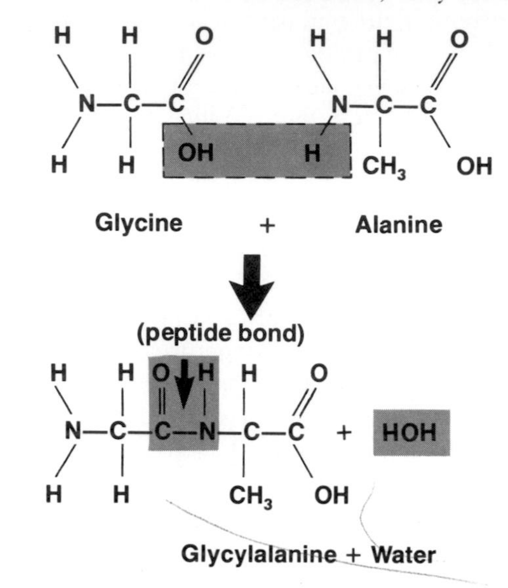

Fig. 4–17. An example of dehydration synthesis: glycine and alanine combine to form the dipeptide glycylalanine and water. The region of linkage of the two amino acids is indicated by the boxed areas.

Structure of proteins. Long-chain polypeptides, containing from 50 to 50,000 amino acid units, make up the huge protein molecules. The straight chains may be linked together, arranged as a helix, arranged as a globule, or folded. The thousands of different proteins found in cells result from an immense number of possible combinations of the amino acid building blocks. In cells, proteins are formed at the ribosomes.

One of the great achievements of molecular biology was the discovery of the complete structure of a protein molecule. Frederick Sanger of Cambridge University was awarded the Nobel prize in 1957 for his discovery of the structure of the insulin molecule. Insulin, one of the smaller proteins, is a hormone secreted by the pancreas. Other proteins, in addition to insulin, are used for many purposes in the body. They function in the form of enzymes, hormones, and antibodies.

Hydrolysis

We have noted that amino acids form polypeptides by dehydration synthesis. The opposite reaction occurs when water combines with a polypeptide: the peptide bond is broken and amino acids are formed. *Hydrolysis* is the decomposition of large molecules into smaller units by combining them with water. Figure 4–19 is an illustration of the hydrolysis of the dipeptide glycylglycine to form two molecules of the amino acid glycine.

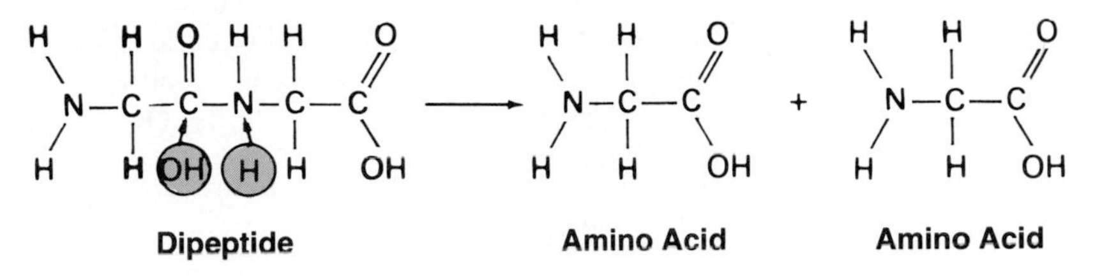

Fig. 4–18. An example of hydrolysis: glycylglycine and H_2O (colored circles) form two smaller molecules, each one the amino acid glycine.

Certain conditions must be present for the dehydration synthesis and hydrolysis reactions to occur. These include proper temperature, pH, and the presence of enzymes.

Carbohydrates. Carbohydrates are organic compounds containing the elements carbon, hydrogen, and oxygen. Carbohydrate molecules have twice as many hydrogen atoms as oxygen atoms. A chemical abbreviation, but not a molecular formula, that expresses this relationship is (CH_2O). Examples of carbohydrates are sugars and starches, which provide energy to the body when taken as food. Cellulose, another carbohydrate, is found in the cell walls of plants. Glycogen is a carbohydrate that is commonly called animal starch.

The sugar *glucose* is a building block of carbohydrates. Its molecular formula is $C_6H_{12}O_6$. Its atoms often form a ring structure. If the same atoms are arranged in a slightly different way, the sugar *fructose* or the sugar *galactose* is formed. Glucose is always present in the fluid surrounding the cells in multicellular organisms, and serves as a ready source of energy. Each of these sugars has different chemical properties.

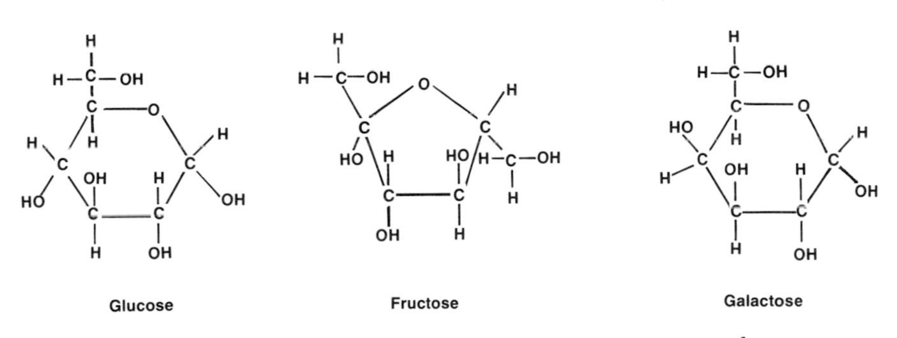

Fig. 4–19. The structural formulas for three monosaccharides—note the different arrangement of the atoms of these sugars.

Dehydration Synthesis of Carbohydrates

The basic unit of carbohydrates is the *monosaccharide*. Monosaccharides can combine by dehydration synthesis to form units called *disaccharides*. The sugars glucose (dextrose), fructose, and galactose are monosaccharides. When two simple sugars combine, a water molecule is released and a disaccharide is formed. The chemical equation for the dehydration synthesis of glucose to form the disaccharide maltose is:

$$C_6H_{12}O_6 + C_6H_{12}O_6 \rightarrow C_{12}H_{22}O_{11} + H_2O$$
(glucose) (glucose) (maltose) (water)

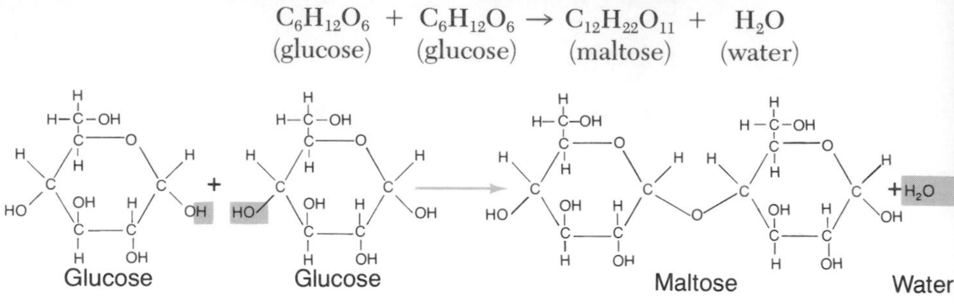

Fig. 4–20. Dehydration synthesis to form the disaccharide, maltose.

Longer chains of more than two molecules of glucose or other monosaccharides are called *polysaccharides*. These large molecules are also formed by dehydration synthesis.

Types of Carbohydrates	
Carbohydrates	**Examples**
$C_6H_{12}O_6$–Monosaccharides	glucose, fructose, galactose
$C_{12}H_{22}O_{11}$–Disaccharides	sucrose, maltose, lactose
$(C_6H_{10}O_5)_n$–Polysaccharides	starch, glycogen, cellulose

Lipids. The lipids are the fats, oils, and waxes. Like carbohydrates, fats contain carbon, hydrogen, and oxygen, but the proportion of hydrogen to oxygen is not the same as in carbohydrates. In carbohydrates the proportion of hydrogen to oxygen is always 2 to 1. The proportion of hydrogen to oxygen varies among lipids, but it is always greater than 2 to 1. Lipids consist of large molecules with many C—C and C—H bonds and release much energy when oxidized. Long-time storage of extra food in organisms is frequently in the form of lipids such as the fats under the skin of animals, and the oils in seeds. In addition, lipids have structural functions: they are an essential part of cell membranes. Food sources rich in fats are milk, butter, fatty meats, olives, and peanuts.

To understand the structure of fats, you must first understand the structures of alcohols and fatty acids. First we shall consider alcohols. *Alcohols* are organic compounds that have the hydroxide (—OH) radical. Two examples of common alcohols are shown in Figure 4–22.

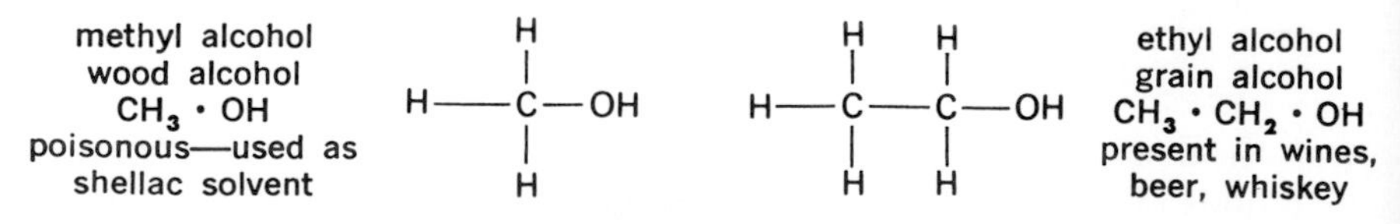

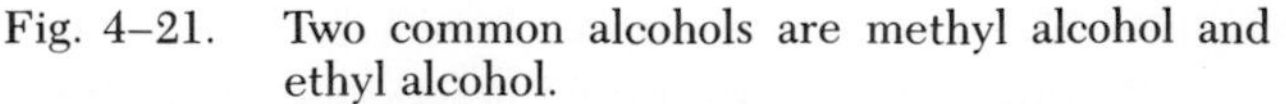

Fig. 4–21. Two common alcohols are methyl alcohol and ethyl alcohol.

Glycerol is an alcohol with *three* hydroxide groups, as shown in Figure 4–23.

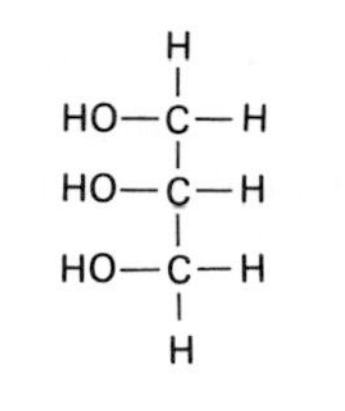

Fig. 4–22. Glycerol.

Organic acids contain the carboxyl group (COOH). A general formula for organic acids is R-COOH. In fatty acids, the R group is a long hydrocarbon chain. An example of a fatty acid is stearic acid, $C_{17}H_{35}COOH$.

Most fats result from the combination of three fatty acids and one glycerol, united by dehydration synthesis, as shown in Figure 4–23: 3 fatty acids + glycerol → fat + $3H_2O$.

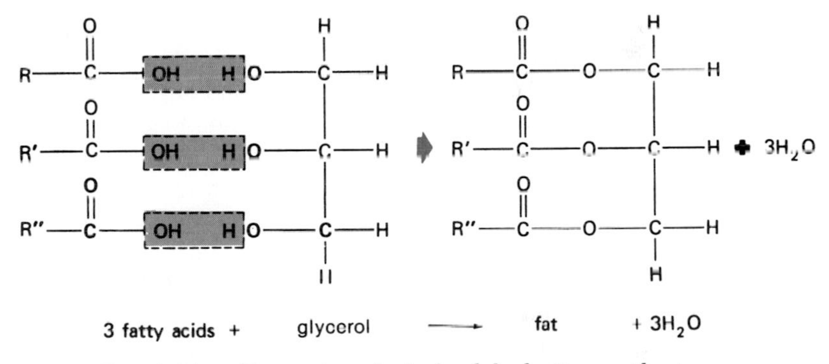

Fig. 4–23. Formation of a fat by dehydration synthesis.

Unsaturated fats. The presence of large amounts of *saturated fats* in the diet is thought to be a cause of the formation of deposits in arteries, leading to heart attack. Although there is controversy among medical groups over this matter, the substitution of unsaturated fats is generally believed to reduce this risk. A portion of an unsaturated fat is shown in Figure 4–24.

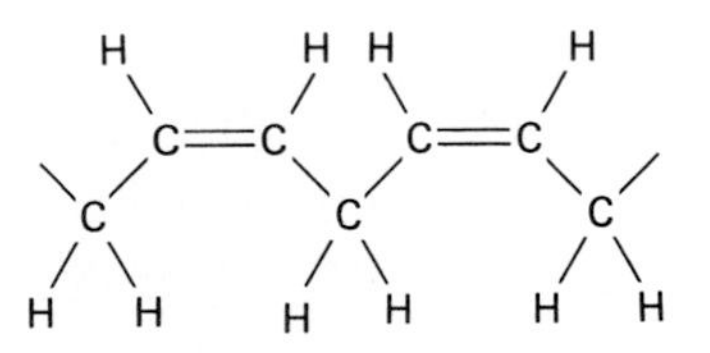

Fig. 4–24. A portion of the R group of an unsaturated fat.

The molecule of a fat is unsaturated when its R portion has double bonds between carbon atoms, where additional hydrogen atoms could be taken on. A saturated fat, however, has all the H atoms that it could take on. Saturated fats have no double bonds between the carbon atoms. A *polyunsaturated fat* has numerous double bonds.

According to the theory accepted by the Department of Health and Human Services in 1980, saturated fats in the diet are converted to cholesterol. Although this fatty substance is essential in the blood, excess amounts may be deposited on the inner linings of arteries and may lead to heart disease.

The role of *lipoproteins*, present in blood, has recently provided new information on the cholesterol story. Lipoproteins are blood proteins whose molecules have a high lipid (fat) content.

There are two kinds of lipoprotein: (1) *HDLs* (High Density Lipoproteins) and (2) *LDLs* (Low Density Lipoproteins). HDLs are believed to remove cholesterol from the blood and to help in excreting it from the body. LDLs are believed to deposit cholesterol on artery linings.

Milk and milk products, as well as meat, contain saturated fats. The oils of fish, vegetables, and margarine are unsaturated.

Nucleic Acids

Nucleic acids are giant molecules of great molecular weight. They are composed of sugars, phosphate groups, and nitrogen groups. They are found in every living cell and carry out the essential functions of storing hereditary information, directing protein synthesis, and transmitting the hereditary information from generation to generation.

Two types of nucleic acid are deoxyribonucleic acid (DNA) and ribonucleic acid (RNA). In eukaryotic organisms, most DNA is found in the cell nucleus, as part of the chromosomes. Cell organelles such as the mitochondria and the chloroplasts also contain some DNA. RNA is not only in the nucleus, but also in the cytoplasm and the ribosomes.

Structure of nucleic acids. Both RNA and DNA are made up of fundamental units called nucleotides. A *nucleotide* is made of three parts: a 5-carbon sugar arranged in a ring, a phosphate group, and a nitrogen base.

Sugar. The 5-carbon sugar is ribose in RNA and deoxyribose in DNA. Deoxyribose has one less atom of oxygen than does ribose.

Phosphate group. This contains one atom of phosphorus linked to several atoms of oxygen and hydrogen.

Nitrogen base. There are five kinds of nitrogen bases in nucleic acid. They are divided into two groups, the purines and pyrimidines:

Purines	Pyrimidines
adenine (A)	thymine (T)
guanine (G)	cytosine (C)
	uracil (U)

These nitrogen bases contain atoms of carbon, hydrogen, and oxygen (only adenine has no oxygen). The purines are larger; their atoms are arranged in two rings. Pyrimidine atoms are arranged in one ring. Uracil is found only in RNA, thymine only in DNA. The other three bases, A, G, and C, occur in both RNA and DNA.

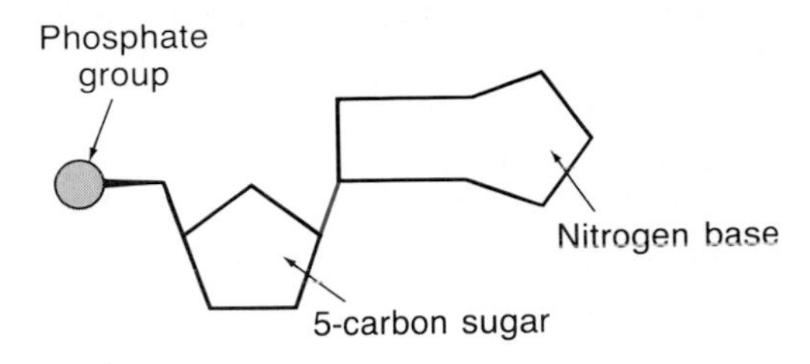

Fig. 4–25. General structure of a nucleotide.

Thousands of nucleotides unite to form a molecule of nucleic acid, which is a long chain, or polymer. The phosphate group of one nucleotide forms a covalent bond with the 5-carbon sugar of the next nucleotide. The phosphates and sugars alternate to form the long backbone of the nucleic acid chain. The nitrogen bases are side branches of the polymer, not part of its long backbone. Many years of research finally showed that nucleic acid chains are coiled in the shape of a helix. A helix is the shape taken by a string that is wound around a cylinder from end to end.

The double helix of DNA. DNA actually consists of two chains, coiled in a double helix. Its actual atomic structure was first proposed by James Watson and Francis Crick in 1953. They built a physical model of DNA to help visualize how the atoms fit together. Much of their reasoning was built upon the earlier work of other scientists on the physics and chemistry of nucleic acid molecules.

DNA structure has been likened to a ladder. Alternating 5-carbon sugars and phosphate groups make the uprights of the ladder. Pairs of nitrogen bases, joined by weak hydrogen bonds, make the rungs between the uprights. Watson and Crick proposed that the rungs always have one

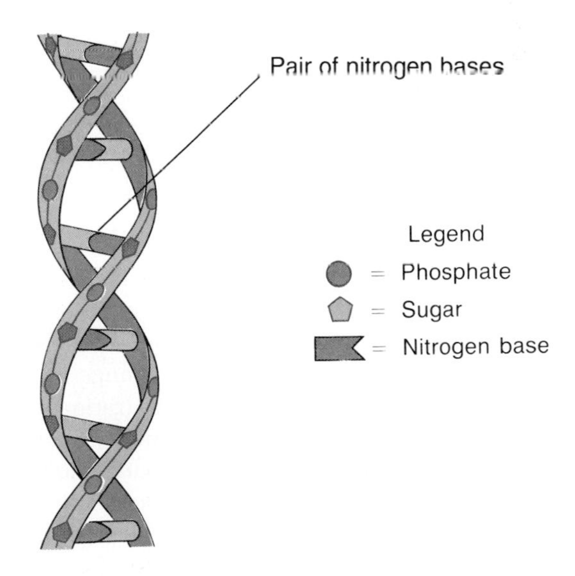

Fig. 4–26. A model of DNA: Each of the uprights of the ladder-like structure is coiled in a helix; each "rung" is a pair of nitrogen bases.

purine and one pyrimidine. In fact, the base pairs in DNA occur only in these combinations: A with T, and C with G. Biologists describe these pairing combinations by saying that adenine (A) is complementary to thymine (T), and guanine (G) is complementary to cytosine (C). The importance of complementary base pairing will be described in detail in Chapter 21.

Ⓓ

Chemical Control

Billions of chemical reactions occur in living things every second. Each reaction is controlled so that it proceeds at the right speed at just the right time. This enables organisms to perform all of their life functions: getting energy, building new molecules, duplicating cells, and so on. Organic compounds called *enzymes* are responsible for this control.

How Enzymes Work

For chemical reactions to occur, the molecules involved need to be activated, or pushed into reacting. The molecules in a living thing face a situation like that of a sled rider at the bottom of a hill. To have a good ride, the sledder must first expend a great deal of energy climbing to the top of the hill. Once at the top, the sledder can enjoy an effortless downhill ride. Similarly, in order to react chemically, molecules must first be provided with some energy to activate them. In a way, they must overcome an energy "hill" known as the "activation energy." With enough activation energy, molecules can reach the top of the hill, and react to form different molecules, called products.

How can molecules acquire enough energy to react? One way is to heat up the molecules. Heat causes molecules to move faster and collide with each other more frequently. The harder and more frequently molecules collide, the more they react. When molecules react, chemical bonds are either broken or formed. By applying an intense heat to a wooden desk, for example, we could cause the wood molecules to speed up, break apart, and combine with the oxygen in the air. In other words, the desk would burn. Such intense heat would have disastrous effects inside the body of a living thing. It would kill the body cells.

Another way to increase the likelihood that molecules will react is to increase the concentrations of the reacting substances. The extra supply of oxygen in rain and wind, for example, causes certain metals to oxidize, or rust. But this is not how living organisms operate.

A third way to facilitate chemical reactions is with *catalysts*. A catalyst is a chemical substance that can speed up the rate of a chemical reaction without itself being significantly changed or consumed. In living things, catalysts, rather than heat or concentration, are used to speed up chemical reactions. Catalysts that function in living things are called *enzymes*. Like all catalysts, enzymes increase the likelihood that molecules will react by lowering the energy hill or amount of activation energy needed to start a reaction. An enzyme cannot bring about a chemical reaction that would be impossible under any circumstances. All an enzyme does is make it easier for a reaction to take place.

Structure of Enzymes

Enzyme molecules are large and complicated. All are composed of protein molecules alone or of proteins attached to other molecules. Recall that proteins are large molecules made up of chains of amino acids. The sequence of the amino acids in the chain determines the type of protein. The largest enzymes are made up of thousands of amino acids. These chemical chains bend and fold into characteristic shapes. An important characteristic of each enzyme is its unique structure, which results from the pattern of these folding chains.

Fig. 4–27. An enzyme is often bent and folded into a highly specific shape.

The non-protein part of some enzymes is called a *coenzyme*. *Vitamins* are usually coenzymes. If a certain vitamin is lacking in a diet, the enzyme that requires this component is incomplete and unable to operate. Under such conditions, certain reactions will cease and the metabolism and health of the organism will be affected. Niacin, one of the B vitamins, for example, is needed to make the coenzyme known as NAD. This coenzyme is involved in controlling the chemical reactions of cellular respiration, which you will read about in Chapter 7. If niacin is absent or not present in sufficient quantities a condition called pellagra may result with symptoms such as disorders of the nervous system, digestive system, skin, numbness, and even mental disorders.

Models of Enzyme Action

The molecules that enzymes act upon are called *substrates*. The unique shapes of enzymes allow them to fit closely with particular kinds of substrate molecules, similar to the way pieces of a jigsaw puzzle fit together. When the substrate(s) and an enzyme combine temporarily, they form an *enzyme-substrate complex*. Substrate molecules will join with an enzyme at a specific place on the enzyme molecule called the *active site*. The shape of this site and the chemical nature of the amino acids at the site determine which substrate molecules are welcome and which are not. This is referred to as *enzyme specificity*. When substrate molecules are joined at the active site of an enzyme, the amount of energy needed to start the chemical reaction is lowered. The reaction leads to the liberating of substances called *products*. After the products are liberated, the enzyme is free to attach itself to other substrate molecules. Enzymes are reusable, and very small quantities are sufficient to increase the rates of chemical reactions.

Because enzymes are essential to the body, they have long been the focus of intensive research. One result of this research is that biologists have revised their views about how enzymes operate. The earlier *lock and key model* of enzyme action indicated that enzymes and substrates fit together perfectly. It was presumed that the surface regions of enzyme molecules have definite shapes which fit the corresponding shapes on the substrate molecules.

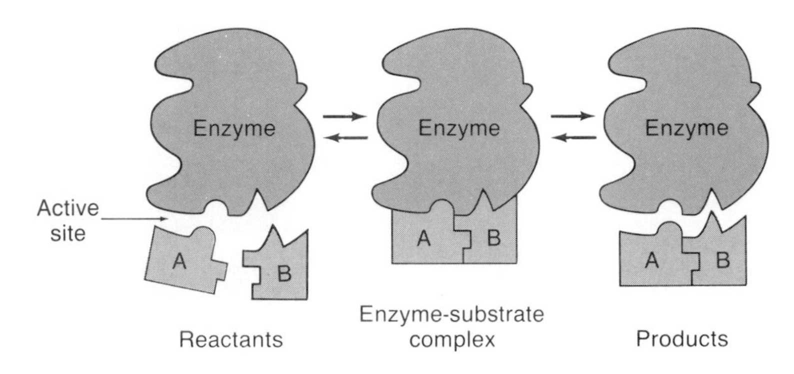

Fig. 4–28. The lock and key model of enzyme and substrate.

Recent research, however, indicates that while enzymes and substrates do fit closely, the lock and key model does not always give the best explanation of how enzymes and substrates form a complex. In some reactions, enzymes and substrates may have shapes that require a bit of molding to fit together. This explanation of how substrates join with enzymes is known as the *induced fit model*. According to this model, an enzyme's active site changes its shape to fit the substrate shape and form the enzyme-substrate complex. Some biologists suggest that the active site may also distort the shape of the substrate. It may be that this strain on the substrate weakens the bonds to be broken, lowering the substrate's resistance to reacting. When its work is done, the enzyme snaps back to its normal shape and is ready for the next substrate. One single enzyme molecule may go through this whole process with thousands of substrate molecules in one second.

Understanding the speed of enzyme action is particularly important in appreciating how enzymes work. For example, one of the human body's fastest acting enzymes, *catalase*, is found in a variety of human cells, including those of the liver. This enzyme catalyzes the breakdown of hydrogen peroxide to water and oxygen. Hydrogen peroxide is a by-product of many natural chemical reactions in the human body. There is one problem however: hydrogen peroxide is poisonous to cells. But catalase prevents hydrogen peroxide from lingering in the cells. In one minute, a single catalase molecule can split five million hydrogen peroxide molecules to form oxygen and water. This is about a trillion times faster than the rate at which the reaction would occur without an enzyme.

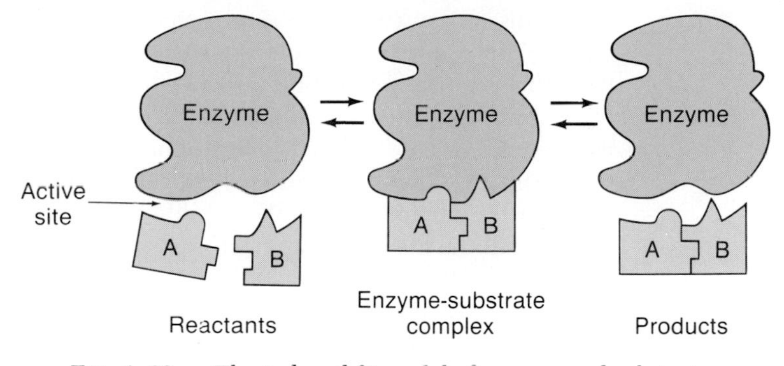

Fig. 4–29. The induced fit model of enzyme and substrate. Compare this enzyme shape to that of Fig. 4–28.

Enzyme Variety. There are over a thousand kinds of enzymes at work in the human body. There's probably one kind for each different chemical reaction that takes place in the body. Some enzymes catalyze reactions only at a specific site in the body. For example, enzymes that assist nerve impulses work only within nerve cells. Enzymes that catalyze reactions that enable muscles to contract are found in muscle cells. Some enzymes, like those that give cells life-supporting energy, are found in all of the body's cells. There are also enzymes—such as those that help digest or break down food—that do not operate within cells, but are in the fluids secreted by the body's digestive system. In digestion, large insoluble molecules, such as proteins, carbohydrates, and lipids, are broken down by enzymes into smaller, more soluble ones so that they may diffuse into the cells and small blood vessels.

Naming Enzymes and Examples of Enzyme Action

Enzymes are usually named for the chemical substrates they act upon. The name of an enzyme is formed by replacing the usual ending of a substrate's name with the ending "ase." For example, the carbohydrate maltose is acted upon by the enzyme maltase.

As you have learned, three major categories of organic compounds found in living things are carbohydrates, lipids, and proteins. The molecules of the carbohydrate group are often referred to as the amyloses. The class of enzymes that catalyze the reactions of the carbohydrates are the *amylases*. Ptyalin, the enzyme found in saliva that begins the chemical breakdown of starch, is an example of an amylase. It also goes by the name of salivary amylase. *Proteases* are enzymes that act on protein substrates. Pepsin (in the stomach) and trypsin (a secretion of the pancreas) are specific examples of proteases. A group of enzymes called *lipases* act on lipid molecules. Steapsin is a lipase that operates on specific fat molecules. The digestive process involves dozens of enzymes. Each one of these enzymes performs a specific task.

The ability of enzymes to break down compounds in food has been put to a number of commercial uses. For example, the enzyme papain in the papaya fruit can split proteins, so it is used as the active ingredient in commercial meat tenderizers. Some laundry detergents contain enzymes that help remove stains by breaking up proteins.

The process of cell respiration—the breaking down of the monosaccharide glucose to provide energy—consists of a series of chemical reactions that requires many different enzymes. These reactions occur first in the cytoplasm, then in the mitochondria of cells. Without enzymes such as lactase and ATPase (named for the energy-rich molecule of adenosine triphosphate) among others, the chemical reactions for energy production would occur far too slowly. We wouldn't have nearly enough energy to perform all the life processes necessary for survival.

Factors That Influence the Rate of Enzyme Action

The catalytic action of an enzyme is influenced by its environment, which may be the cytoplasm, a cell organelle, or even the space outside cells. The rate of enzyme action varies with pH, temperature, and relative amounts (concentrations) of enzyme and substrate molecules.

pH. Most enzymes in the human body work best in a neutral environment—one that is neither acidic nor alkaline (pH = 7). There are, however, major exceptions to this rule. The intestine happens to be alkaline (pH greater than 7), and the digestive enzyme trypsin, among others, works well here. The stomach, on the other hand, is acidic (pH less than 7). This environment suits the enzyme pepsin. The pH at which specific enzymes react best with their substrates is called the *optimum pH*. Enzymes rapidly lose their effectiveness when the pH goes even a little above or below the optimum. If the pH in the intestine falls below 7 (the optimum pH is about 8), the chemical breakdown of food stops or slows down. The same would occur in the stomach if the pH were to rise too much.

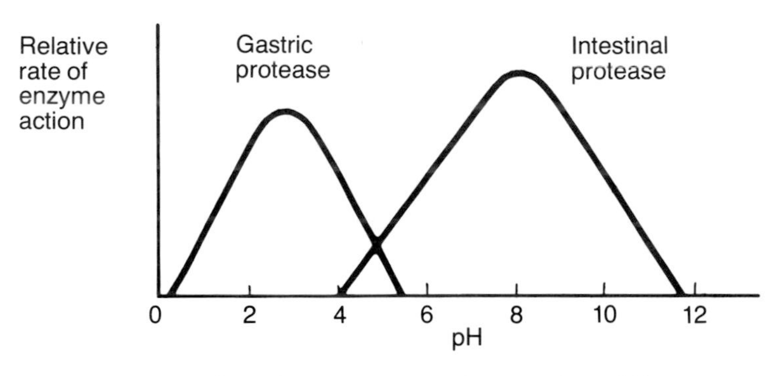

Fig. 4–30. Effect of pH on the rate of action of two different proteases.

Temperature. Temperature is another environmental condition that affects enzymes. The *optimum temperatures* for enzyme action vary with the type of organism. Human enzymes function best at 37 degrees Celsius (98°F), and plant enzymes function best at about 25 degrees Celsius (77°F). However, some enzymes function efficiently in a very cold environment. For example, the enzymes that regulate the chemical activity in cold-water fish such as salmon become ineffective if the temperature rises too much. On the other hand, microorganisms that live in hot springs need enzymes that operate effectively in hot temperatures.

The rate of enzyme action will vary within a narrow range of temperatures. Enzyme-controlled chemical reactions can speed up or slow down with an increase or decrease in temperature. There have been many reports of drowning victims who have been resuscitated without severe biological damage after a long time submerged in cold water. Due to the decreased rate of enzyme action, their metabolism slowed and their energy, oxygen, and nutritional requirements were greatly lessened, allowing them to survive.

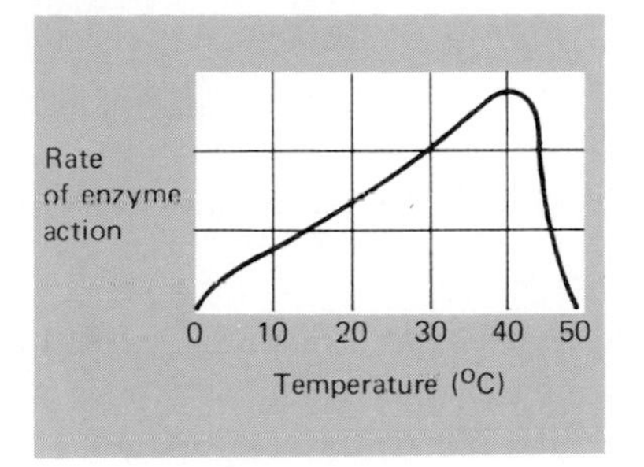

Fig. 4–31. Effect of temperature on enzyme activity.

When enzymes in the human body are subjected to extremely hot temperatures they lose their characteristic shape. This is one example of a process called *denaturation*. The active sites of the enzymes are altered and the enzymes are unable to perform their function of attracting and binding to specific substrate molecules. When many enzymes are denatured, life is threatened. This is why it is so important to control a high fever. A body temperature of 42 degrees Celsius, or 108 degrees Fahrenheit, almost always results in death if prolonged. Once an enzyme has become denatured, it is impossible to restore it to its normal condition.

Concentrations of Enzymes and Substrates. The rate of a chemical reaction that is controlled by an enzyme depends upon the concentrations of both the enzyme molecules and substrate molecules present. When there is a fixed amount of enzyme and an excess of substrate molecules, the

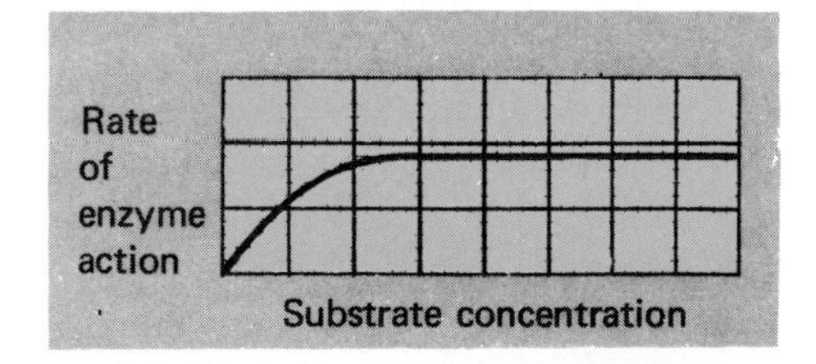

Fig. 4–32. Effect of substrate concentration on rate of enzyme action.

rate of reaction increases up to a point and then levels off. At the point where the reaction rate levels off, all of the active sites on the available enzyme molecules are in use and no sites are available for the additional substrate molecules present. If the situation is reversed—that is, if there is an excess of enzyme molecules and a fixed number of substrate molecules—the rate of the reaction also increases up to a certain point and

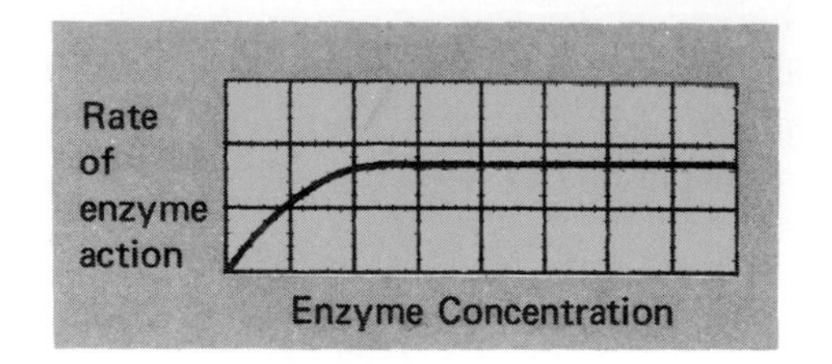

Fig. 4–33. Effect of enzyme concentration on rate of enzyme action.

then levels off. At this point, all of the substrate molecules are binding to enzyme molecules. The active sites on the excess enzyme molecules are available, but no more substrate is available to use them.

Enzymes and Health

You have read how coenzymes such as vitamins contribute to the health of an organism by helping enzymes do their work. There is another class of substances that prevent enzymes from doing what they are supposed to do. These substances are referred to as *inhibitors*. Some inhibitors are competitive, so-called because they compete with the substrates. A *competitive inhibitor* has a shape like that of an enzyme's substrate and can disable the enzyme by binding with it. This prevents the enzyme from attaching to its usual substrates. An enzyme is capable of catalyzing a reaction only with its true substrate. It cannot catalyze a reaction when bound to a competitive inhibitor.

Biologists have learned how to put inhibitors to constructive uses. One major use is destroying harmful bacteria. In 1928, biologist Alexander Fleming accidentally left the lid off the dish containing bacteria he was experimenting with. An airborne mold spore landed in the dish, reproduced, and killed the bacteria. Fleming studied the mold and its deadly effect on the bacteria. After many years of investigation, he showed that the substance in the mold, *penicillin*, acted as an inhibitor. By attaching itself to the bacteria's enzymes, the penicillin prevented them from combining with their true substrates and the bacteria died. The discovery of penicillin was a major breakthrough in the field of medicine. Since the 1940's, penicillin and other bacteria-killing substances, called *antibiotics*, have been used to treat and cure infectious diseases.

Some inhibitors are non-competitive in nature. They bear no resemblance to an enzyme's substrate. Instead of fitting an enzyme's active site, a *non-competitive inhibitor* attaches itself to another part of the enzyme. By doing so, it changes the enzyme's structure so that it cannot interact normally with its substrate. In some cases it may widen or narrow the enzyme's active site so the substrate does not fit properly. Cyanide, mercury, and lead are non-competitive inhibitors of biological enzymes.

Reasoning Exercises

1. Why is water essential to life?
2. Write the general formula for an amino acid. In the formula, what is the meaning of R?
3. Write the word equation for the dehydration synthesis of two amino acids.
4. Use structural formulas to show the formation of (a) a dipeptide, (b) maltose.
5. Why does the synthesis of a double sugar from two glucose molecules result in the formula $C_{12}H_{22}O_{11}$ instead of $C_{12}H_{24}O_{12}$?
6. Write the word equation for the synthesis of a fat. What is the difference between a saturated and an unsaturated fat?

Completion Questions

A

1. Elements with the same atomic number but different mass numbers are called . . . . . .
2. The atomic particle with a mass number of 1 and no charge is the . . . . . .
3. A radioactive isotope used to trace a series of chemical reactions is called a(n) . . . . . .
4. Protoplasm, the material of the living cell, is a mixture containing many . . . . . .

B

5. A chemical bond formed by the sharing of electrons is a(n) . . . . . . bond.
6. An atom which has gained or lost electrons is a(n) . . . . . .
7. A formula for a molecule that shows the arrangement of the atoms is called a(n) . . . . . . formula.

C

8. Organic chemistry is the study of . . . . . . compounds.
9. The building blocks of proteins are . . . . . .
10. A molecule with two amino acid units is a(n) . . . . . .
11. The formation of a larger molecule from two smaller molecules, accompanied by the giving off of water, is known as . . . . . .
12. An example of a common disaccharide is . . . . . .
13. Fats may be hydrolyzed to form fatty acids and . . . . . .
14. The fundamental unit of structure in DNA is the . . . . . .
15. DNA and RNA are two kinds of . . . . . .
16. The sugar present in DNA is . . . . . .
17. The "uprights" of the DNA "ladder" consist of sugar and . . . . . .
18. Adenine and thymine are . . . . . . nitrogen bases.

D

19. The material acted upon by an enzyme is the . . . . . .
20. Because an enzyme operates in only one kind of chemical reaction, enzymes are said to be . . . . . .
21. The specificity of enzyme action is explained by the . . . . . . concept.
22. One model of how enzymes operate is called the . . . . . . model.
23. Chemical substances that prevent enzymes from operating are called . . . . . .

Multiple Choice Questions

A B

1. As the number of neutrons in the nucleus of an atom increases, the atomic number of the atom (1) decreases, (2) increases, (3) remains the same.
2. A helium nucleus contains two protons and two neutrons. The number of positive charges in the nucleus is (1) 0, (2) 2, (3) 8, (4) 4.
3. In a structural formula, a dash represents a (1) transferred electron, (2) pair of transferred electrons, (3) shared electron, (4) pair of shared electrons.
4. The components of NaCl exist as (1) stable isotopes, (2) positive and negative ions, (3) separate molecules, (4) covalent bonds.

C

5. Which process is indicated by the equation below? (1) hydrolysis, (2) osmosis, (3) decomposition, (4) dehydration synthesis.

$$C_6H_{12}O_6 + C_6H_{12}O_6 \xrightarrow{\text{enzymes}} C_{12}H_{22}O_{11} + H_2O$$

6. An amino acid may be recognized if it has an amino group at one end and at the other end a(n) (1) sulfur group, (2) hydroxyl group, (3) carboxyl group, (4) saturated group.
7. Which element is characteristic of all organic compounds? (1) iron, (2) nitrogen, (3) calcium, (4) carbon.
8. Which is the sugar component of a DNA nucleotide? (1) adenine, (2) deoxyribose, (3) glucose, (4) phosphate.
9. In a DNA molecule, a base pair normally could be composed of (1) adenine and guanine, (2) adenine and cytosine, (3) thymine and guanine, (4) guanine and cytosine.

D

10. The "lock and key" hypothesis attempts to explain the mechanism of (1) vacuole formation, (2) enzyme specificity, (3) sharing of electrons, (4) pinocytosis.
11. Which is a function of enzymes? (1) They provide energy for carrying on a chemical reaction. (2) They can speed up the rate of chemical reactions. (3) They become hydrolyzed during chemical reactions. (4) They serve as inorganic catalysts.
12. Of the following chemicals, the one that is classified as an enzyme is (1) galactose, (2) lipids, (3) protease, (4) hydrogen peroxide.

Questions 13 to 16 are based on the following graphs which show the influence of temperature and pH on the rate of action of a certain enzyme.

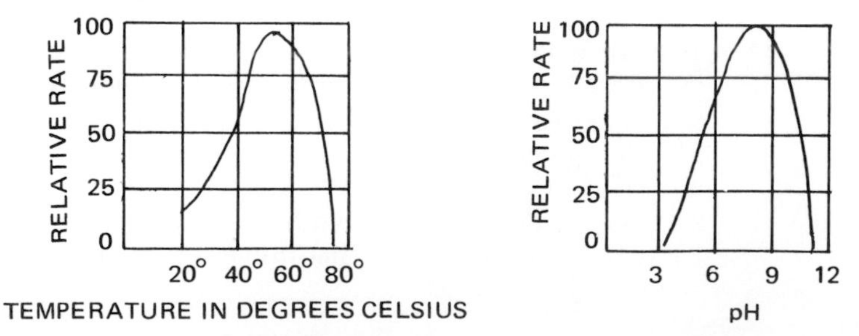

13. The temperature at which maximum enzyme action occurs is (1) 38°C, (2) 50°C, (3) 60°C, (4) 65°C.
14. Enzyme action ceases at a temperature of (1) 20°C, (2) 30°C, (3) 60°C, (4) 75°C.
15. The enzyme functions most effectively at a pH of (1) 6, (2) 7, (3) 8, (4) 9.
16. The rate of enzyme action will be decreased by increasing (1) the concentration of the enzyme, (2) temperature from 50°C to 70°C, (3) concentration of the substrate, (4) ph from 3 to 6.
17. Which group of organic compounds includes the enzymes? (1) carbohydrates, (2) lipids, (3) proteins, (4) starches.

Chapter Test

1. When a salt is dissolved in water, it produces charged particles called (1) alkalis, (2) ions, (3) acids, (4) neutrons.
2. Atoms with the same atomic number but different atomic masses are known as (1) isotopes, (2) isomers, (3) radicals, (4) ions.
3. Which is an example of an organic compound? (1) $C_{17}H_{35}COOH$, (2) $(NH_4)_3PO_4$, (3) H_2O, (4) NaCl.
4. Which of the following compounds has a bond formed by transfer of electrons? (1) NaCl, (2) CH_4, (3) $C_6H_{12}O_6$, (4) H_2
5. Because urea is a nitrogen compound, it cannot be derived from metabolism of (1) amino acids, (2) proteins, (3) glucose, (4) polypeptides.
6. The process by which amino acid molecules are joined together is (1) oxidation, (2) hydrolysis, (3) dehydration synthesis, (4) photosynthesis.
7. The number of bonds for each carbon atom in a structural formula is (1) 1, (2) 2, (3) 4, (4) 3.
8. Which substance plays a major role in most of the chemical reactions occurring in a living cell? (1) water, (2) amino acid, (3) glucose, (4) fatty acid.

Choose the letter A, B, C, D, or E of the correct formula to answer questions 9 through 13. A formula may be used several times or not at all.

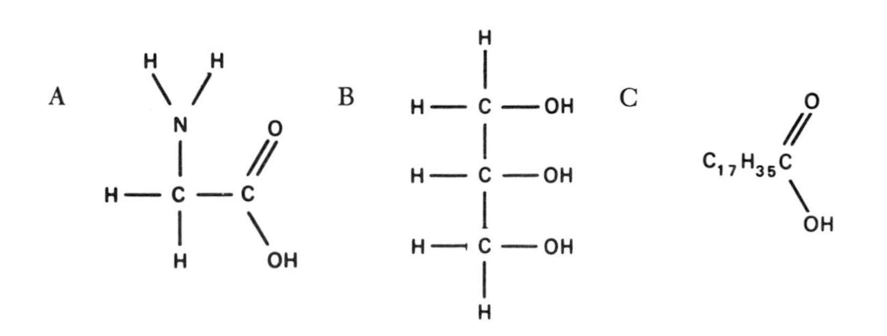

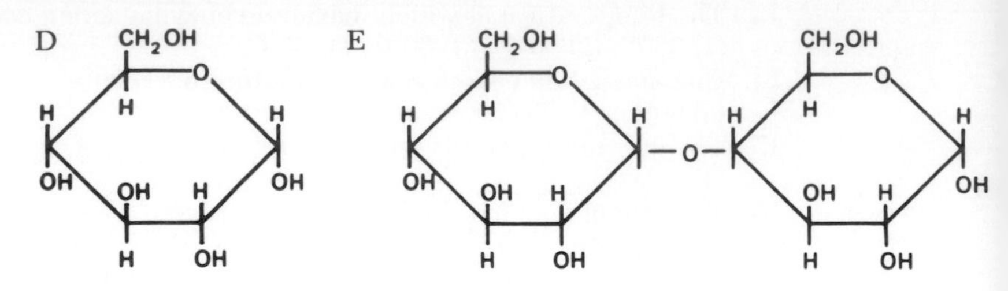

9. This substance is an example of a fatty acid.
10. This substance is hydrolyzed by the enzyme maltase.
11. This substance is a building block used in the synthesis of proteins.
12. This substance combines with fatty acids in fat synthesis.
13. The metabolism of this substance is responsible for the formation of nitrogenous wastes.
14. In living substance, sulfur and nitrogen are elements chemically combined in (1) carbohydrates, (2) oils, (3) glycogen, (4) proteins.
15. To tag glucose in a series of metabolic reactions, it would be reasonable to use radioactive (1) calcium, (2) cobalt, (3) carbon, (4) iron.
16. One difference between a DNA nucleotide and an RNA nucleotide is that the RNA nucleotide (1) is found only in the nucleus, (2) is chemically less complex than a DNA nucleotide, (3) has more oxygen than a DNA nucleotide, (4) is much more acidic.
17. When an enzyme and substrate bind together, the chemical unit formed is called the (1) peptide linkage complex, (2) enzyme-substrate complex, (3) active site complex, (4) activation energy complex.

Unit 1 Unity and Diversity Among Living Things

Portfolio Project

Make a comparison of the parts of a typical animal cell and a typical pla cell. Compare the two cell diagrams shown in Fig. 3-7 on page 49 and Fi 3-9 on page 52. Design a chart or diagram in which you can show how th two types of cells are similar, and how they differ.

UNIT TWO MAINTENANCE IN LIVING THINGS

Plants, animals, and representatives of the other three kingdoms carry on the same life functions. Although greatly diverse, they all meet the challenge of maintaining the life functions such as nutrition, transport, respiration, and excretion. Carrying on the life functions is called *maintenance*. This unit compares the adaptations for maintenance that have evolved in the five kingdoms.

In considering the maintenance of animals, we study five organisms as representatives of ways that animals have been able to maintain life. These are:

Protozoa (Protista)
Hydra (Coelenterata)
Earthworm (Annelida)
Grasshopper (Arthropoda)
Human (Chordata)

In view of the immense diversity of life, the study of only five representative animal types has admitted limitations. However, this approach does help suggest how animals have evolved in diverse ways that enabled them to adapt to their environment.

This unit develops the following concepts of modern biology:

- organisms are adapted to their environment
- structure and function complement each other
- living things maintain a constant internal environment
- living things process energy from the environment

Chapter 5 Nutrition

Food is the primary source for energy and growth. *Nutrition* consists of those activities by which organisms obtain and use food in carrying out their life functions.

The usable portions of foods are known as *nutrients*. These are used mainly as (1) energy sources, (2) the basis for building or repairing cell structures, (3) regulators of metabolic processes.

The portion of a food that does not serve as a nutrient is *waste* material. Thus, food consists of nutrients and wastes. Nutrition refers to more than the food that is taken in. This term includes all the processes concerned with food, including ingestion, digestion, and egestion.

A The Concept of Nutrition

All cells require certain usable materials. They must have:

- Raw materials to build their structures (particularly amino acids, fatty acids, and glycerol).
- Energy sources (simple sugars, as well as fatty acids and amino acids).

- Water as a solvent and as a medium for transporting materials.
- Dozens of different minerals in tiny amounts, chiefly for the control of chemical processes.
- Certain organic compounds (vitamins) to keep their chemical machinery going.

Autotrophic and Heterotrophic Nutrition

Some organisms make their own high-energy foods from simple chemicals such as carbon dioxide and water. This is known as *autotrophic nutrition* (*autotrophic* means "self-feeder"). Of course, these organisms need a source of energy to do this. If the energy source is light, the synthesis of foods is known as *photosynthesis*, the food-production process of green plants. Certain bacteria obtain the energy for autotrophic nutrition from the oxidation of sulfur, iron, or several other simple materials. This process is known as *chemosynthesis*.

Unlike green plants, animals cannot make their own food from simple inorganic substances such as carbon dioxide and water. Animals depend upon the food they take in. This food consists largely of energy-rich organic compounds—carbohydrates, proteins, and fats. *Heterotrophic nutrition* (*heterotrophic* means "other feeder") is the taking in and utilization of preformed high-energy compounds such as starch, proteins, and fats. Many of these must be broken down into smaller molecules, which can pass through membranes. All animals, including humans, are heterotrophs. Heterotrophs use other animals or plants as food. They may even use the decaying products of dead organisms. Mushrooms and yeasts are heterotrophs. So are tapeworms and other parasites. Most bacteria are heterotrophs that live on other things; but a few bacteria are autotrophs.

Autotrophic and Heterotrophic Nutrition
Autotrophic nutrition
photosynthesis—green plants, algae, and some bacteria
chemosynthesis—some bacteria
Heterotrophic nutrition—animals, nongreen plants, parasites, saprophytes, most bacteria

Autrotrophic Bacteria

The bacteria that cause disease and decay obtain preformed, high-energy organic food molecules from living or dead things. They are heterotrophs. Some bacteria, however, are autotrophs that make their own food from simple inorganic substances. Some of these autotrophs carry on photosynthesis, others chemosynthesis. The bacteria that carry on chemosynthesis use inorganic substances such as iron, sulfur, nitrogen, and hydrogen to make their own food.

Marine scientists have recently found clams, mussels, and giant tube worms clustered around hot-water vents in deep regions of the ocean floor. Because no light penetrates these depths, this community of invertebrates depends for organic food on chemosynthetic bacteria. These derive energy to make organic molecules by chemical reactions with hydrogen sulfide which is present in high concentrations. Tube worms contain closely packed bacteria in the form of a tissue within their body.

B

Photosynthesis

Green plants obtain their food by synthesizing low-energy molecules such as carbon dioxide and water into high-energy molecules such as glucose. This method of food-getting is autotrophic nutrition. The energy for powering this synthesis reaction may be supplied in two ways. (1) If light is the source of the added energy, this autotrophic process is *photosynthesis* (synthesis by use of light). (2) If inorganic chemical reactions yield the needed energy, the process is *chemosynthesis*. Most (90%) of the photosynthesis occurring on this planet is carried on by algae living in the sea and in lakes.

What Is Photosynthesis?

The capture of light energy and its conversion to chemical energy in organic molecules is called photosynthesis. Photosynthesis occurs in cells that contain the green pigment chlorophyll. A simplified expression that summarizes this process is:

$$\text{carbon dioxide} + \text{water} \xrightarrow[\text{chlorophyll, enzymes}]{\text{light energy}} \text{glucose} + \text{oxygen} + \text{water}$$

- The raw materials are carbon dioxide and water.
- The energy is supplied by light.
- Chlorophyll acts to trap the light energy.
- Enzymes catalyze reactions that produce a three-carbon compound as the first product.
- More enzymes control reactions that lead to formation of glucose, a six-carbon compound.
- Another product is oxygen.

Biologists used to call the oxygen that is released a by-product. But all the oxygen that is present in the atmosphere comes from photosynthesis—either from photosynthesis occurring today or from far back in the early history of life on earth. You could hardly degrade this important substance by calling it a by-product. Oxygen produced during photosynthesis is responsible for the release of energy through the process of respiration in most animals and plants that are alive today.

The chemical energy that is at first stored in glucose may be transferred to other plant substances. These include starches, proteins, oils, and the cellulose of wood. Animals that eat plants (or other animals) receive a storehouse of energy that originally came from the sun. When we burn wood, coal, and petroleum products, we are releasing the sun's energy that was trapped long ago by photosynthesis.

Laboratory Skills

Formulate a Question and Devise an Experiment

Several questions about the process of photosynthesis can be investigated using controlled experiments. (See Appendix A.)

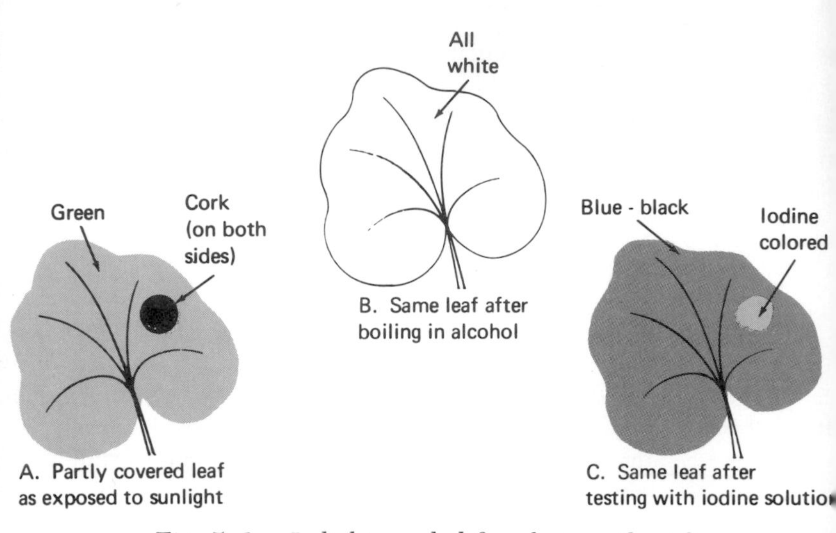

Fig. 5–1. Is light needed for photosynthesis?

Is light needed for photosynthesis? Pin disks of cork on opposite sides of a geranium leaf. Keep the plant in the sunlight for several hours. Remove the leaf from the plant and unpin the corks. Boil the leaf in alcohol to remove its chlorophyll. (*Caution:* Do not use an open flame. Use an electric hot plate instead.) Then cover the leaf with Lugol's iodine solution. (Iodine is used as the *test* for starch. Iodine turns blue-black in the presence of starch.) *Observation:* The uncovered part of the leaf turned blue-black; the covered part remained the color of iodine. *Conclusion:* Light is necessary for a geranium plant to produce starch.

This seems to be a well-controlled experiment: The experimental portion of the leaf received light and the control portion received no light. All other conditions were the same. There was a single variable in the procedure. Only the part of the leaf that received light produced starch. But wait a minute—*what about the cork?* The presence or absence of the *corks* introduces an additional variable. But could the corks be of any significance? Whether you think so or not, the corks' presence or absence introduces a *second variable* in the procedure. This experiment has two variables: (1) the presence or absence of *light* and (2) the presence or absence of *corks.* The experiment proves nothing because it does not have a single variable. It is not a controlled experiment.

Actually, the tightly pinned corks are very important. They prevent the cells below from receiving needed carbon dioxide for photosynthesis. One of the most difficult problems for scientists is to design experiments that avoid hidden variables. Can you design and perform a better experiment to determine if light is needed for photosynthesis?

Is chlorophyll needed for photosynthesis? The leaves of some plants are partly green and partly white. Such a leaf is called *variegated*. Do such plants give you any ideas for an experiment?

Does a green plant use CO_2 during photosynthesis? If you exhale through a straw into a dilute blue solution of bromthymol blue (BTB), your CO_2 turns this indicator yellow. In the absence of CO_2 it turns blue again. *Elodea* is a green plant that grows underwater. Using this information, can you design a controlled experiment to answer the above question? How many test tubes will you need?

Do green plants in the sunlight give off a gas? Use sprigs of *Elodea* in test tubes of water. What gas is probably present in the bubbles that arise from the plant?

Light

Light is a form of energy that travels as electromagnetic waves. It differs in wavelength from other electromagnetic waves such as cosmic rays, X rays, and radio waves. Visible light is that portion of the electromagnetic spectrum with wavelengths ranging from about 400 μm (micrometers) to about 700 μm.

The color of light is the sensation produced in the brain when light of a certain wavelength falls upon the retina of the eye. Humans do not receive a visual sensation from infrared or ultraviolet rays. Many insects are not receptive to light of the wavelength that we call "yellow." Therefore, on summer evenings we use yellow bug lights that provide light for us but do not attract insects.

White light is a mixture of many wavelengths. When white light is passed through a glass prism, its wavelengths are separated into the *visible spectrum*, as shown in Figure 5–2.

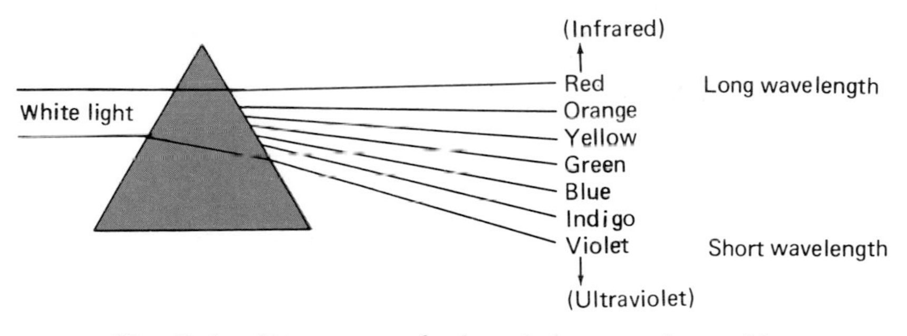

Fig. 5–2. Dispersion of white light into the visible spectrum

Red light has the longest wavelength and the least energy. Violet light has the shortest wavelength and the most energy.

Reflection and absorption. An opaque object appears green to us because it *reflects* the wavelengths of green to our eyes. Its surface has the property of *absorbing all other wavelengths*. If blue light falls on the same green object, it absorbs these blue wavelengths. Since *no* wavelengths are reflected, a green object in a blue light appears black. What is the color of a green object in a green light? Why does red lipstick appear darker under bluish fluorescent lighting?

Chlorophyll appears green to us because it absorbs all the other wavelengths of white light except green. It absorbs red, orange, yellow, blue and violet; it reflects green to our eyes. If chlorophyll does not take in green, can it use the energy of green light for photosynthesis?

The absorption of light by a substance is measured by a *spectrophotometer*. Figure 5–3 shows the *absorption spectrum* of chlorophyll. As you can see from the graph, chlorophyll absorbs mainly from both ends of the spectrum. It takes up much of the radiant energy of the violet-blues and the orange-reds. It helps transform these wavelengths into chemical energy during photosynthesis. Chlorophyll absorbs little of the wavelength for green. These wavelengths are not used much in photosynthesis.

The light from Grolite bulbs that are used for growing plants indoors is reddish-blue. Why are they designed that way?

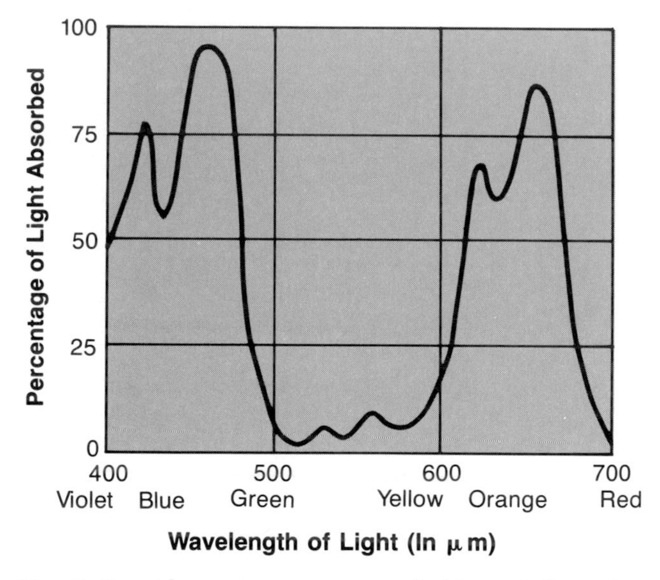

Fig. 5–3. Absorption spectrum of chlorophyll in alcohol

Chloroplasts Chloroplasts are oval-shaped green bodies found within the cytoplasm of green plant cells and algae. A leaf cell has about 40 to 50 chloroplasts; a square millimeter of leaf surface may have 500,000 chloroplasts. Chloroplasts contain chlorophyll and enzymes. All the chemical reactions of photosynthesis occur within these organelles. These are the factories that make most of the world's food.

Throughout the chloroplast (Fig. 5–4) are thin double membranes composed of protein and lipid. The chlorophyll molecules are arranged in an orderly fashion within these double membranes. Double membranes also occur as disks that are arranged in stacks called *grana*. The grana were given this name because, under the light microscope, they appeared like grains. The rest of the chloroplast is filled with a dense protein liquid called the *stroma*. The chloroplast itself is enclosed by a double membrane.

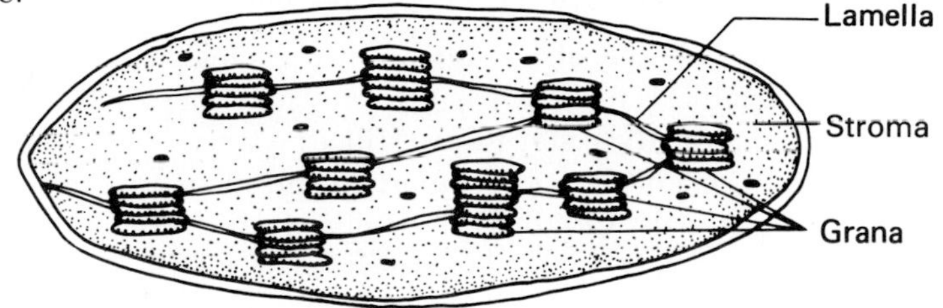

Fig. 5–4. A chloroplast. The chlorophyll is located within double membranes, some of which form stacks of discs called grana.

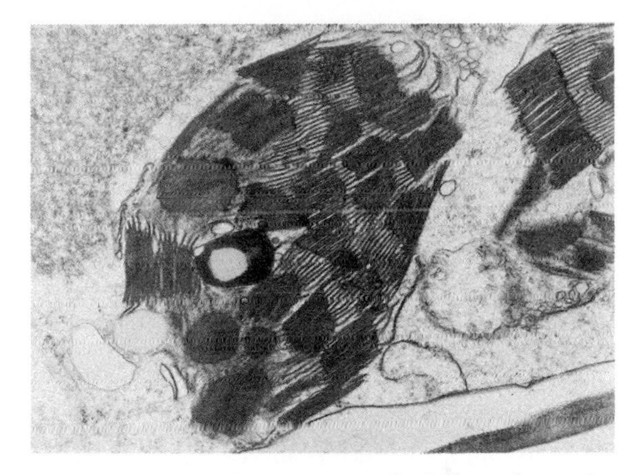

Fig. 5–5. A chloroplast photographed through an electron microscope.

Chlorophyll *Chlorophyll*, the green pigment of plants, is a complex molecule having more than 100 atoms. Its structure is very similar to a part of the molecule of *hemoglobin*, the red oxygen-carrying pigment found in the blood of many animals. This resemblance between chlorophyll and hemoglobin has evolutionary significance because it indicates a chemical relationship. One difference is that each chlorophyll molecule contains an atom of *magnesium*, while hemoglobin contains an atom of *iron*. The arrangement of the atoms in the chlorophyll molecule permits it to trap certain wavelengths of light energy and pass this energy to the chemical reactions involved in the process of photosynthesis.

There are at least six different kinds of chlorophyll in plants. Two of these are shown below:

Chlorophyll *a* $C_{55}H_{72}O_5N_4Mg$
Chlorophyll *b* $C_{55}H_{70}O_6N_4Mg$

Plants may contain additional pigments, such as carotenoids (yellow) and anthocyans (red, blue). Sometimes these pigments mask the green color of chlorophyll. In autumn, when chlorophyll production ceases, the carotenoids and anthocyans become apparent in the rich red, yellow, and brown foliage of that season. The various pigments found in a leaf may be separated by a technique called chromatography.

What Is the Source of the Oxygen That Is Liberated?

By the end of the 19th century, biologists knew enough about photosynthesis to know what the raw materials and the products were, but the intermediate steps were still a mystery.

One of the most important questions was this: Which of the two raw materials, CO_2 or H_2O—both of which contain oxygen—is the source of the oxygen that is liberated? To find out, scientists used tagged atoms of O^{18} as a tracer. Oxygen-18 can be detected because it is a heavier isotope than the more common oxygen-16.

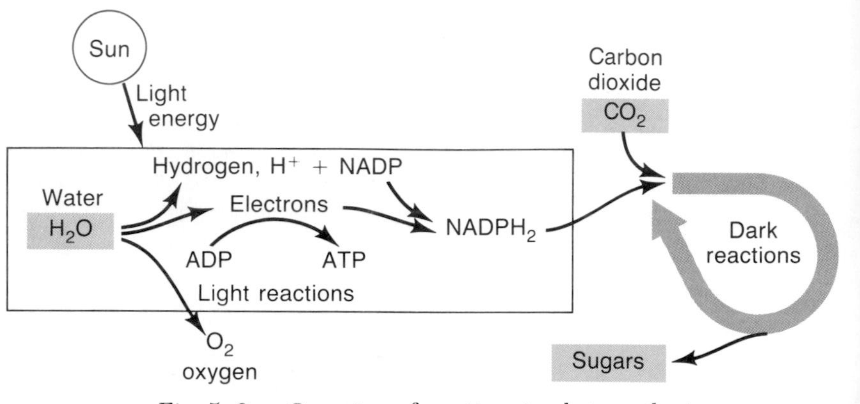

Fig. 5–6. Overview of reactions in photosynthesis.

Using CO_2 and H_2O containing the oxygen tracer, the researchers discovered that *the liberated oxygen comes from the water* (H_2O). The oxygen is not liberated from the carbon dioxide.

Why is this discovery important? It shows that one of the chemical steps in photosynthesis is the *splitting of water* into hydrogen and oxygen:

$$H_2O \rightarrow 2H + O$$

The oxygen is released as a product, but what happens to the hydrogen atoms? It was found that the hydrogen atoms later *reduce* the carbon dioxide to carbohydrate (CH_2O):

$$CO_2 + H \rightarrow (CH_2O) \text{ (not a balanced equation)}$$

Using an asterisk to indicate the tagged atom of oxygen, the overall equation for photosynthesis can now be written in this way:

$$6CO_2 + 12H_2O^* \rightarrow C_6H_{12}O_6 + 6O_2^* + 6H_2O$$

Verify that the equation is balanced with respect to the tagged and untagged oxygen atoms.

Light and Dark Reactions

The chemical reactions of photosynthesis may be divided into two phases: (1) the light reactions and (2) the dark reactions. Both sets of reactions take place while the cell is in the light.

The *light reactions* are those that make direct use of the incoming light energy, which is used to split water into hydrogen and oxygen. The oxygen produced is released as a product. This is the *photo* part of photosynthesis. Some of the light energy is also stored in molecules of a compound called adenosine triphosphate, or ATP. The molecule of ATP is similar to the nucleotides you read about in Chapter 4. It consists of the nitrogen base adenine, a five-carbon sugar, and three phosphate groups. ATP transfers energy from one set of biochemical reactions to another.

The dark reactions have this name because they do not make direct use of light. Instead they use for energy the ATP that was formed in the light reactions. The dark reactions also employ the hydrogen that was formed in the light reactions. From that hydrogen and with the raw material carbon dioxide, the dark reactions synthesize glucose. This is the *synthesis* part of photosynthesis. The light and dark reactions together transfer light energy to the chemical energy located in the C—C and C—H bonds of glucose.

From the glucose produced by photosynthesis, plant cells make other products such as starch, cellulose, proteins, and lipids. These serve ultimately as the food foundation for all plants and animals on earth. Photosynthesis also supplies the oxygen needed by plants and animals for aerobic cellular respiration, which releases the energy in food.

Reasoning Exercises

1. What is the difference between autotrophic and heterotrophic nutrition?
2. Compare photosynthesis and chemosynthesis.
3. Explain two ways in which all life on Earth depends on photosynthesis.
4. Why is a variegated-leafed plant useful for demonstrating that chlorophyll is needed for photosynthesis? (Use *control* and *single variable* in your answer.)
5. Why does a blue object in a red light appear black?
6. Why does foliage turn red and yellow in the autumn?
7. Describe briefly the light and dark reactions.

Ⓒ

The Chemistry of Photosynthesis

In this section, as we probe a bit deeper into the chemical reactions of photosynthesis, we shall be particularly concerned with energy transformations. Refer to the summary diagram in Figure 5–7 as you study the steps.

The Light Reactions

We have already seen that in light reactions the sun's radiant energy splits water. As you probably know, water can be decomposed into hydrogen and oxygen by electrical energy. The splitting of water by light energy is called *photolysis*. But how can sunlight *split* water molecules? In your experience, sunlight falling on water merely evaporates it. The answer lies in the complex organization of the chlorophyll molecule. This special molecule traps light energy to start chemical changes involving *electrons*, instead of causing only a physical change. The following events occur during the light reactions:

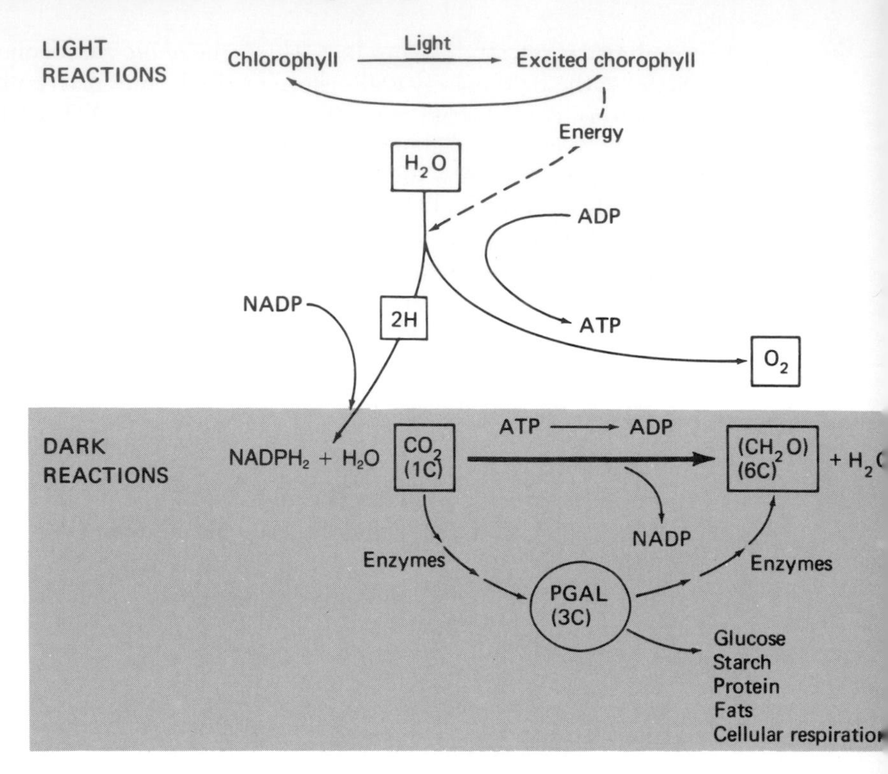

Fig. 5–7. Flow diagram of reactions in photosynthesis

• *Chlorophyll is excited.* The first step is for chlorophyll molecules to trap light energy by becoming excited. In this condition, electrons travel in orbits that are farther away from the nucleus of atoms than usual. These electrons have been raised to *higher energy levels.* In this way, kinetic light energy has been transferred into potential chemical energy.

High-energy electrons of the excited chlorophyll are then passed along to a series of coenzymes in which they gradually lose their energy, step by step. After the chlorophyll discharges its high-energy electrons, it reverts to its former nonexcited state. What happens to the energy of the high-energy electrons? It is utilized in two ways: (1) to split water and (2) to make ATP.

• *Water is split.* With the aid of high-energy electrons, the bonds of water molecules are split, forming hydrogen (H^+) ions and hydroxide (OH^-) ions. Oxygen (O_2) from the hydroxide ions is then released as a product of photosynthesis.

• *Hydrogen is taken up by NADP.* The hydrogen resulting from the splitting of water is picked up by a coenzyme called *NADP* (nicotinamide adenine dinucleotide phosphate). A coenzyme is a nonprotein molecule that works with an enzyme to control the direction of a reversible reaction. NADP is a *hydrogen acceptor.* It combines with hydrogen to form $NADPH_2$ ($NADP + 2H \rightarrow NADPH_2$). In this way, the hydrogen that is produced does not escape or combine again with oxygen. The $NADPH_2$ carries hydrogen and some energy to the dark reactions.

• *Energy is stored in ATP.* The energy of the high-energy electrons does not serve only to split water. Some of this energy is also used to change ADP (present in the chloroplast) to ATP. The high-energy ATP is then used to power dark reactions.

The results of the light reactions are: (1) the energy of light has been transferred to chemical energy in ATP and $NADPH_2$, (2) hydrogen from the splitting of water has been taken up by NADP to form $NADPH_2$, and (3) oxygen from the splitting of water has been released as one of the products of photosynthesis.

The Dark Reactions Overall, the dark reactions consist of the reduction of carbon dioxide by hydrogen to form carbohydrate:

$$CO_2 + H \rightarrow (CH_2O) \quad \text{(not a balanced equation)}$$

The energy for this synthesis is supplied by the ATP and $NADPH_2$ that were produced in the light reactions. The hydrogen used in the dark reaction is furnished by the breaking down of $NADPH_2$: $NADPH_2 \rightarrow NADPH + 2H$. Scientists now have a good understanding of the numerous steps in the dark reactions. These involve many enzymes and coenzymes. We now know that the enzymes that participate in the light reactions are arranged on the grana of the chloroplast; enzymes for the dark reactions are located in the liquid stroma. The joining of one-carbon CO_2 molecules, so they are attached or fixed into the six-carbon glucose, is called *carbon fixation*. The dark reactions are sometimes called carbon fixation.

PGAL. What are the steps by which the one-carbon molecules of CO_2 are joined to form the 6-carbon glucose? To find out, Melvin Calvin and his associates at the University of California used a "lollipop" apparatus (see Fig. 5–8). They supplied CO_2 containing radioactive carbon-14 to algae growing in a lollipop-shaped flask which was kept in the dark.

The light was turned on for a few seconds to permit photosynthesis to take place. Then the algae was released into a container of hot alcohol that killed the algae and stopped their biochemical reactions. Any tagged carbon compounds now present in the alcohol must have been produced from the CO_2 during the algae's brief exposure to light. The compounds produced were then identified by the technique of chromatography. When the exposure to light was as brief as two seconds, a 3-carbon tagged compound was formed. This was *PGAL* (phosphoglyceraldehyde).

PGAL is the first chemically stable compound formed during carbon fixation. Most biologists now consider 3-carbon PGAL, rather than 6-carbon glucose, to be the product of photosynthesis. PGAL can be used by cells as the starting point for synthesis of glucose, starch, proteins, and oils. It can also serve as an energy-rich basis for cellular respiration.

Calvin showed that the formation of 6-carbon sugar does not happen in a single step. Many intermediate enzyme-controlled reactions are involved.

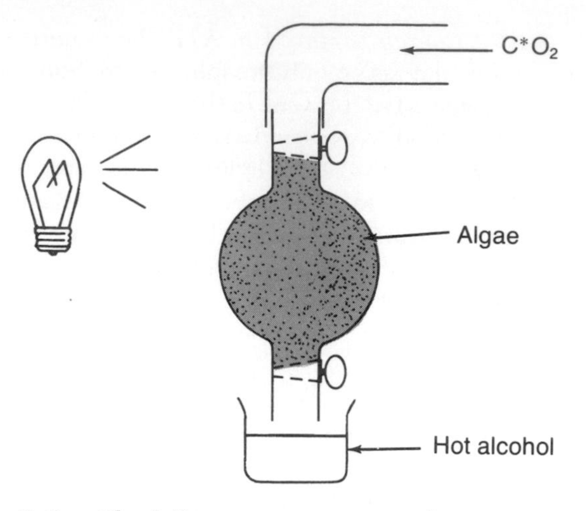

Fig. 5–8. The lollipop experiment to determine intermediate compounds formed during carbon fixation

The rate of photosynthesis is affected by a number of factors including temperature, carbon dioxide concentration, wavelength of light, chlorophyll concentration, and availability of certain minerals. Do you think that doubling the concentration of carbon dioxide in a greenhouse increases or decreases the rate of plant growth?

Increasing the temperature up to 40°C increases the rate of photosynthesis. But a further increase in temperature results in a rapid decrease in this rate. From what you know about enzymes, can you explain why this is so?

Review Facts About Photosynthesis

1. Chlorophyll appears green because it reflects the wavelengths of green light and absorbs the other wavelengths of the visible spectrum.
2. Chlorophyll is present within the chloroplasts in structures called grana.
3. Chlorophyll traps light energy and makes it available for photolysis.
4. Photolysis is the breaking down of water, with the aid of energy from light, into hydrogen and oxygen.
5. The source of the oxygen liberated by photosynthesis is water, not carbon dioxide.
6. ATP carries energy from the light reactions to the dark reactions.
7. $NADPH_2$ carries hydrogen from the light reactions to the dark reactions.
8. In the dark reactions, hydrogen is fixed to carbon dioxide to form PGAL and then glucose. The dark phase is also called carbon fixation.
9. PGAL is a 3-carbon product of photosynthesis.
10. Photosynthesis stores the energy of light as chemical energy in the form of carbon-carbon (C—C) and carbon-hydrogen (C—H) bonds.

D

Adaptations for Photosynthesis

A large land plant, such as an oak tree, has a way of life that differs greatly from the animal way of life. As plants became many-celled and moved to the land, they adapted to new problems. Because multicellular plants are larger than protists, they required special means for transporting materials to all parts. Without a watery environment to supply buoyancy, they needed a new method for support. The anatomy and physiology of plants had to adapt to the relatively dry conditions for life on land.

A many-celled land plant must be able to:

- Use its limited surface area efficiently to provide for the needs of cells deep in the interior.
- Transport materials (such as water and minerals) between the exterior cells and the interior cells and transport food to all parts.
- Obtain, transport, and conserve water.
- Coordinate the activities of a many-celled organism.
- Support leaves high in the air to obtain sufficient light and carbon dioxide. Carbon dioxide and carbonates are plentiful in the ocean, but only 0.04 percent of the air is carbon dioxide. Green plants also must hold their leaves aloft in such a way that they do not shield one another from the sunlight.
- Transfer reproductive cells on land.
- Adapt to extreme variations in the environment. By contrast, the physical environment of the sea is relatively constant.

Simple algae, as single cells or aggregates of cells, form much of the *phytoplankton* that floats on or near the ocean's surface. Phytoplankton (*phyto* = plant, *plankton* = wanderer) contributes more than half of all the oxygen produced by autotrophic organisms.

Structure of the Leaf

The specialized structure for photosynthesis in most plants is the leaf. The main regions of the leaf of a land plant are shown in Figure 5–9.

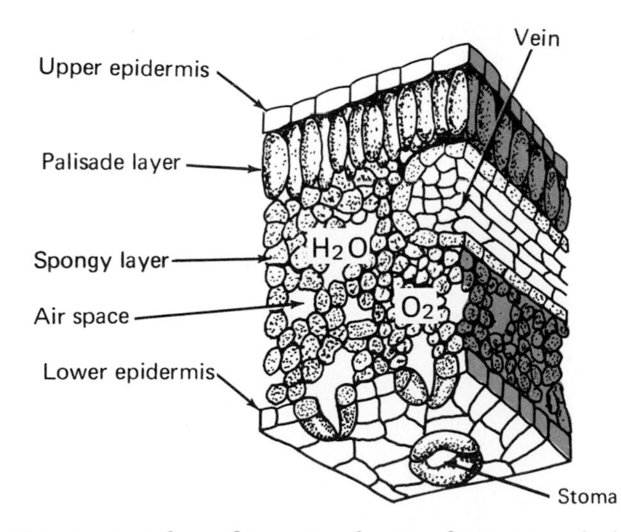

Fig. 5–9. Three dimensional view of a section of a leaf

Upper epidermis. The upper surface of the leaf is a single layer of colorless cells which forms a tough waterproof covering. This is the *upper epidermis*. It protects the underlying cells and helps to prevent the loss of water. In many plants, the upper epidermis is further covered by a waxy *cuticle*, a layer that is practically impervious to water.

Palisade layer. Below the upper epidermis is a layer of long, closely packed cells. This is the *palisade layer*.

These cells are arranged to receive light readily. When receiving light energy, their numerous chloroplasts travel in a circular path while carried by cyclosis of the cytoplasm.

Spongy layer. Below the palisade layer is the *spongy layer*. This is a region of loosely packed cells with many *air spaces* between them. Like the palisade layer the cells of the spongy layer contain chloroplasts.

The spongy layer and the palisade layer carry on most of the photosynthesis of the leaf. The air spaces in the spongy layer increase enormously the moist surface area available to gases diffusing into and out of the photosynthetic cells. The air spaces open through pores in the lower surface of the leaf. The spongy layer also contains *veins*. These are tubelike bundles of vascular (conducting) cells. They branch off from tubes in the stem that carry water up from the root.

Lower epidermis. The lower epidermis consists of a layer of colorless cells, arranged tightly together. Numerous pores in this layer are called stomata. These pores permit gases to enter or leave the air spaces in the spongy layer. Though some stomata occur in the upper epidermis, most plants have more stomata in the lower epidermis.

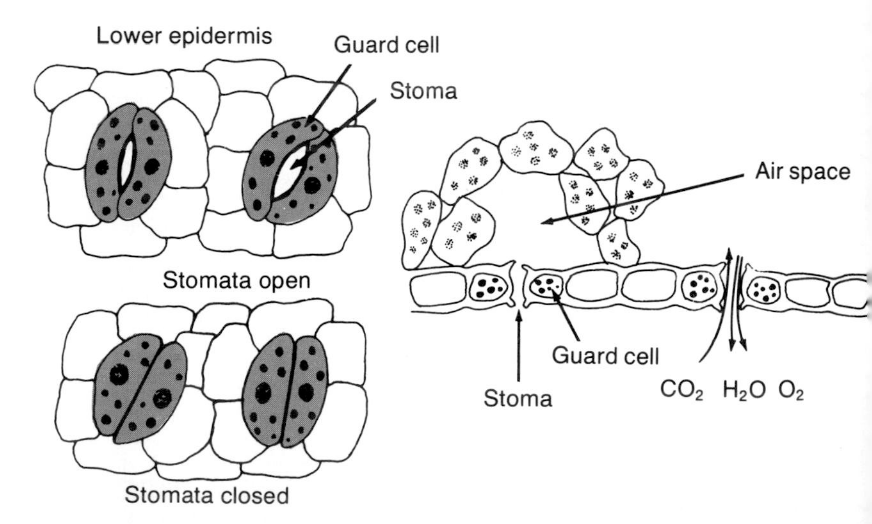

Fig. 5–10. Stomata. At the left are views of the lower epidermis, as seen from below. The top drawing shows the guard cells in a turgid state so that the stomata are open; the bottom drawing shows the stomata closed. At the right is a view of an open stoma as seen in a cross section of the leaf.

The broad, thin shape of most leaves provides a large surface area for the absorption of light energy. Exceptions include the spine of cactus and the needle-shaped leaf of the pine tree. These shapes are adaptations to prevent water loss.

Exchange of Gases in the Leaf

Water, as you recall, is one of the raw materials of photosynthesis. Water is transported throughout the leaf by the veins (Fig. 5–9) and passes into the air spaces. From the air spaces, water vapor readily diffuses into the moist chlorophyll-bearing cells of the spongy layer and palisade layer.

Carbon dioxide, another raw material of photosynthesis, reaches the air spaces through the stomata in the under surface of the leaf. (Some leaves also have stomata in the upper surface.) The moist cell membranes of the photosynthetic cells permit carbon dioxide to diffuse into them. Oxygen, a by-product of photosynthesis, likewise diffuses out of the moist cell membranes into the air spaces. Oxygen then passes out of the leaf through the stomata. Water vapor also passes out of the stomata (Fig. 5–11).

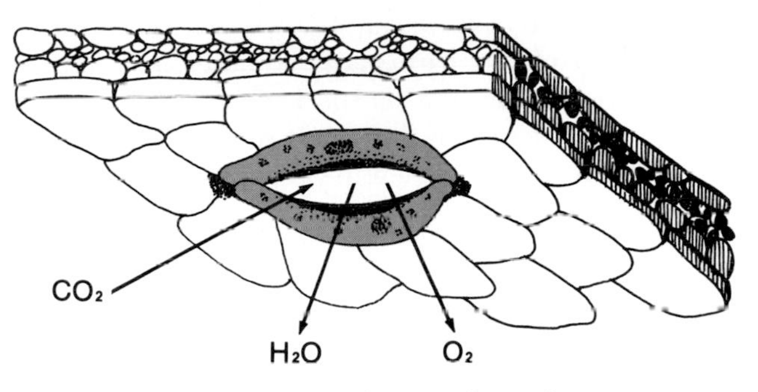

Fig. 5–11. Passage of gases through a stoma

Transpiration. The process by which the leaf gives off water vapor is called *transpiration*. Considerable water is given off by a plant during a day. For example, in a single day a maple tree may lose 50 gallons of water. Transpiration results in the loss of a substance that is precious to land plants. This loss, however, is unavoidable because the stomata are open during the day. As we shall see later, however, transpiration also serves a most important function for the plant.

Opening and closing of stomata. Stomata generally open during the day to admit the carbon dioxide needed for photosynthesis. Stomata generally close at night. The opening and closing of the stomata is controlled by a pair of guard cells that surround each pore. When guard cells swell with water, a condition known as *turgor*, they bend away from each other. This opens the pore. Water loss from each guard cell closes the pore.

Why do swollen guard cells bend away from each other? The inner walls of the guard cells are much thicker than the outer walls. When the guard cells are swollen with water, the outer wall bends much more than the inner wall. This difference causes the cells to take on a curved shape. The change in shape opens the space between the guard cells. Guard cell swelling may be caused by an uptake of potassium ions. This uptake is followed by movement of water into the guard cells.

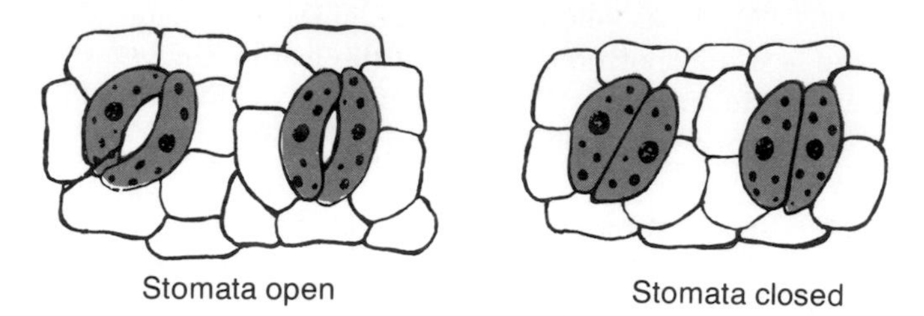

Fig. 5–12. Open and closed stomata

At night, when photosynthesis ceases, the guard cells lose their turgor and become limp. The space between them is lost, and the stomata are closed. Closed stomata prevent water loss by transpiration at night. Stomata also close during the day when a plant is wilting for lack of water. Many plants, particularly aquatic ones, have stomata on the upper leaf surface as well as on the lower.

The closing of stomata at night is an adaptation of land plants for conserving water. As a way of maintaining the plant's internal moist environment, this mechanism is also an example of homeostasis.

Complementarity of Structure and Function

In geometry, two angles that together form a right angle of 90° are called complementary angles. In the same way, we use the word complementary for any objects or ideas that fit together to create a unity. In your study of biology, you have seen many examples of *structure* being specially suited to serve a particular *function*. This relationship is one of the broad concepts of biology known as *the complementarity of structure and function*.

Even such an ordinary organ as the leaf of a plant exhibits examples of such complementarity:

- The cuticle and the thick walls of the epidermal cells prevent the loss of water.
- Cells that carry on photosynthesis are held aloft in the air, so they obtain light and air. The air spaces of the spongy layer provide a moist environment for cells that are far above the moist earth.
- The air spaces provide a large internal surface area for the exchange of gases between the atmosphere and the cells of the spongy layer. Yet, the external openings for these large air spaces are the small stomata. (A similar adaptation occurs in the human lungs where the extensive surface of millions of alveoli is serviced by two small external openings, the nostrils.)
- The guard cells are specialized cells of the epidermis containing chloroplasts and a thick inner wall. These adaptations permit the guard cells to swell in a manner that opens the stoma for the entrance of carbon dioxide when light is present.

Reasoning Exercises

1. What problems did plants face as they moved from water to land?
2. How is excessive loss of water by transpiration prevented?
3. Explain how the stomata open in the morning.
4. What is meant by "the complementarity of structure and function?" Give an example of complementarity in the leaf.

E

Heterotrophic Nutrition

All animals, most protozoans and bacteria, and some fungi are heterotrophs. Because these organisms lack chlorophyll and therefore cannot make their own food by the process of photosynthesis, they utilize organic matter for their nutritional needs. This organic matter is in the form of preformed organic molecules from other living or dead organisms. For example, an animal that eats plants derives its nutrition from the organic molecules formed by the process of photosynthesis in plants.

A *saprophyte* is a heterotrophic plant that obtains food from *dead* organisms. Bread mold, for example, is a saprophyte because the bread that serves as its food originated from a dead wheat plant.

A *parasite* is an organism (plant or animal) that obtains its food from *living* organisms. Some relatives of the bread mold are classed as parasites because they obtain their food from *living* plants. Examples are wheat rust, which causes great economic loss, and bracket fungi, which can often be seen growing on trees in the woods.

Dodder is a nongreen plant that is parasitic on other plants. Indian pipe is a colorless saprophytic plant that lives on decaying matter in the soil. Some so-called parasitic plants retain a degree of autotrophic ability. They depend upon the host only for water and dissolved materials.

Processes for Heterotrophic Nutrition

Heterotrophs take in organic molecules and break them down into simpler molecules so that the molecules can pass through the cell membranes. What is not used must pass out of the organism.

Ingestion. *Ingestion* is the process by which organisms take in food. In animals, ingestion is followed by *digestion*, the breaking down of organic molecules. Many microoganisms, such as bacteria, break down food outside their cells and then ingest the digested food by absorption.

Digestion. By the process of *digestion*, large food molecules are hydrolyzed into small usable molecules. This breaking down by hydrolysis is accomplished by special digestive enzymes. In protozoa, digestion is *intracellular;* that is, the food particle is taken into the cell and there is acted on chemically by digestive enzymes.

In most multicellular animals, digestion is *extracellular*. The food is retained within a digestive cavity of some kind (stomach, intestines), and juices are secreted into this cavity. In the broad category of plants and plantlike protists known as *saprophytes* (molds, mushrooms, many bacteria), the dead organic matter they feed on is digested completely outside the body. The organism secretes juices externally into the food and then absorbs the digested material.

Chemical digestion is mainly limited to the outer surface of the food mass, for the digestive juices cannot penetrate very far. Animals, therefore, must have some way of breaking up the large food particles to allow the juices to penetrate. This is done by the physical actions of grinding, tearing, and cutting. This physical breakdown of food particles is called *mechanical digestion*. A snake does little mechanical digestion; it swallows its victim whole and chemically digests it slowly, over many days.

There are many digestive enzymes, each with a special function, but they may be classified into three groups as indicated in the table that follows.

Some Groups of Digestive Enzymes

Substrate	Enzyme	End Products of Digestion
proteins	proteases	amino acids
carbohydrates	amylases	glucose
fats	lipases	fatty acids and glycerol

Egestion. *Egestion*, or elimination, is the removal of unused organic matter. This unused organic matter has been ingested but not digested. In simple organisms such as protozoans, undigested matter remaining in a food vacuole is evacuated through the cell membrane. More complex organisms have special organs to eliminate undigested matter.

There are various reasons why organic molecules are not digested by the organism. In some cases, the body of an organism cannot make use of certain ingested materials. For example, the human body does not have enzymes that can digest the cell walls of plants. This undigested material passes out of the body without becoming a part of the body's protoplasm. In other cases, an organism may have an appropriate enzyme, but the food material is not exposed to the enzyme long enough for complete digestion to take place.

Adaptations for Heterotrophic Nutrition: Monerans, Fungi, and Plants

Bacteria. Although we have seen that a few bacteria are autotrophs, most are heterotrophs. They secrete digestive enzymes that pass out of the cell where *extracellular digestion* occurs. The products of digestion then enter the cell where their high-energy molecules are used as a source of energy or for growth and repair.

Yeasts. Yeasts are one-celled protists lacking chlorophyll. A package of dried yeast grains purchased in a grocery store is composed of millions of inactive yeast cells. They renew their activity when placed in a sugar solution or in warm dough. Yeasts obtain energy by anaerobic respiration (fermentation) of the sugar that they take in. They release carbon dioxide and alcohol as products of this process.

Molds. It is easy to grow bread mold for examination under the microscope. Place a small piece of bread on a dish and moisten it. (Do not use bread that contains a mold inhibitor.) Keep the moist bread in the open for a very short time so that mold spores in the air may fall on it.

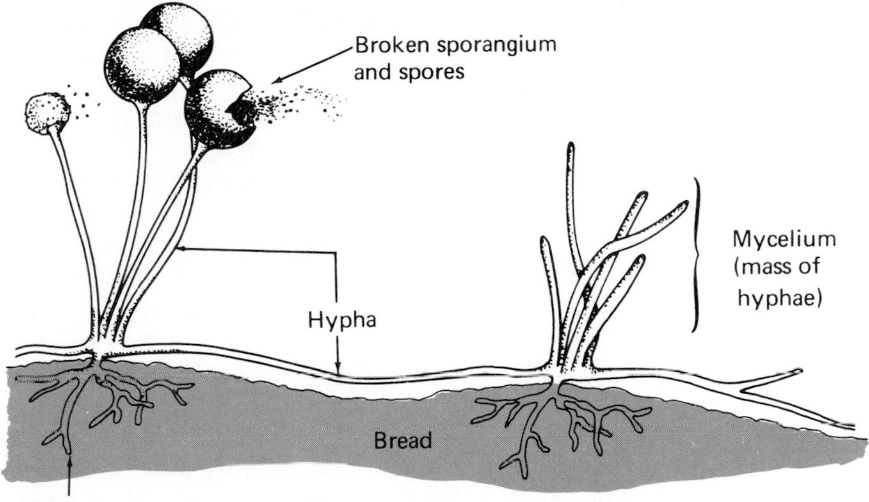

Fig. 5–13. Bread mold

Cover the dish with a glass tumbler to prevent it from drying out and keep it in a warm, dark place for a few days. Soon a mass of white threads becomes visible, and then a mass of tiny dark spheres. The mass of threads is called the *mycelium*. Each individual thread is called a *hypha*.

Using a needle, transfer a tiny portion of the mycelium to a drop of water on a microscope slide. Tease the threads apart. Cover the slide with a cover slip and examine the specimen under the microscope. Since the organization of the mold will be disturbed by the manipulation, examine several areas of the preparation. This procedure should reveal the structure of the mold as shown in Figure 5–13.

Special hyphae which penetrate the bread are called *rhizoids*. These have two functions: (1) attachment of the mycelium to the bread and (2) extracellular digestion.

Some activities of molds are useful to humans. Molds give flavor to cheese, decay dead organisms, and produce antibiotics such as penicillin. Other molds, however, are harmful to humans. Molds cause human diseases such as athlete's foot and ringworm. Plant diseases such as rusts and smuts take a great toll on the wheat, rice, and corn crops. The potato blight, which wiped out the Irish potato in 1845, was caused by a mold. Wet towels left in a laundry hamper develop mildew, a form of mold. Leather shoes left in a damp cellar may develop a luxuriant mold growth in the form of a fuzz.

Digestion in plants. If you test a geranium leaf during the daytime, it will show the presence of starch. On the following morning, however, the starch is all gone. What has happened to it? The starch has been digested to glucose. This soluble substance can pass from cell to cell. The sugar has been *translocated* to other parts of the plant.

Although plants do not have specialized digestive systems, like those found in animals, they do carry on digestion. Chemically, digestion in plants consists of hydrolysis (as in animals) and is controlled by enzymes. Starches, lipids, and proteins are stored in plant cells. These large molecules are converted to simpler usable forms by enzymes that function within the cells. Because this digestion occurs within the cells, it is called *intracellular digestion.*

The principal carbohydrate reserve in plants is starch. It may be found in large amounts in the roots, stems, and fruits of different plants. *Diastase* is a plant enzyme that hydrolyzes starch to the disaccharide maltose. The end products of digestion may be used within the cell or translocated to other parts of the plant for use or storage.

The white potato is an underground *stem* that stores large amounts of starch. When the shoot of a new plant begins to grow from the potato, the starch is first changed to sugar. This can then be transported to all cells of the developing shoot.

The two halves of a lima bean seed are its *cotyledons*. These are joined to a tiny embryo that lies between them. Cotyledons store food which is then supplied to the young embryo when it starts to grow. Which carbohydrate would you expect to find stored in the cotyledons—sugar or starch? What reagents (chemicals) would you need in order to find out? What change in carbohydrates would you expect to find in the cotyledons when the embryo starts to grow? Can you design an experiment to test your hypothesis?

In bacteria, yeasts, and molds, digestion is *extracellular*—outside the cell. The general pattern of extracellular digestion is as follows:

Enzymes secreted by the cell diffuse outward through the cell membrane into the external environment. Here they digest the food, producing such simple, soluble end products as amino acids, glucose, fatty acids, and glycerol. These then diffuse back into the cell where they are used for energy and growth.

Insectivorous plants use extracellular digestion. The Venus's-flytrap closes its leaves when an insect touches trigger hairs inside. When digestion is complete, the leaves open (see Fig. 5-14).

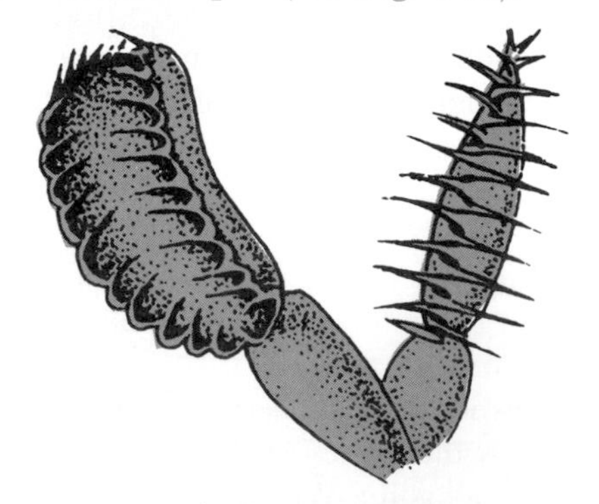

Fig. 5–14. Venus's-flytrap, an insectivorous plant

Heterotrophic Nutrition in Animals

Protozoa. An ameba ingests smaller protists by surrounding them with protoplasmic projections called *pseudopods*. The food particle is then enclosed in a small globule (food vacuole) which is released into the cytoplasm. Enzymes from the lysosomes digest the food as the vacuole circulates with the streaming cytoplasm.

A paramecium feeds on microorganisms drawn into the oral groove by the beating of cilia lining the groove. The food is forced to the end of the gullet, where food vacuoles form. These detach and circulate in a definite pattern. Intracellular digestion occurs within a food vacuole after it merges with a lysosome. The end products of digestion are then absorbed into the cytoplasm. Eventually, the food vacuole merges with the cell membrane, forms an opening to the outside, and expels undigested material.

In most animals, food-getting requires motion for search, pursuit, or capture of food. *Ameba* and *Paramecium* seem to be attracted to food by chemical stimuli. When cultured (grown) in dishes in the laboratory, these protozoans congregate in large numbers around decaying food particles.

Hydra. *Hydra* may be found on submerged vegetation in ponds and lakes. To the naked eye, it appears as a tiny thread, about 0.6 cm (¼ inch) long, that has become unraveled at one end. The microscope reveals that it consists of two layers of cells arranged like a hollow cylinder (see Figure 5–15). The outer layer of cells is the *ectoderm;* the inner layer of cells is the *endoderm.* The foot at one end of the body is used for attachment or locomotion. *Hydra* moves by a slow gliding motion of the foot (which contains ameboid cells), by a slow somersaulting movement, or by an "inching" process. The mouth, at the other end of the body, is surrounded by a circular arrangement of usually six *tentacles* bearing stinging cells called *nematocysts.*

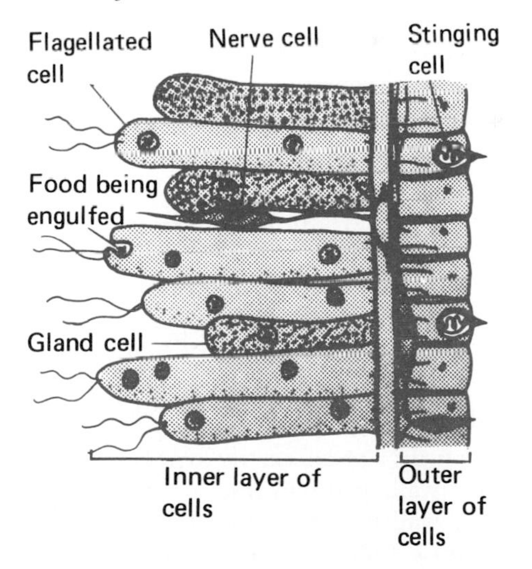

Fig. 5–15. Cells in the body wall of *Hydra*

Hydra ingests only living food, such as minute crustacea and worms which accidentally contact its tentacles. Threads expelled by stinging cells on the tentacles penetrate the prey and paralyze it. The chemical *glutathione,* released from the prey, initiates the feeding reflex in *Hydra.* The tentacles contract, drawing the food into the mouth, which surrounds and engulfs it. The food enters the digestive cavity and is digested. Shortly thereafter, the body wall contracts and egests undigested food particles through the mouth.

Digestion in *Hydra* is both extracellular and intracellular. Let us see why this is true. First, visualize the undigested food in the digestive cavity surrounded by the endoderm cells lining the digestive sac. These endoderm cells secrete enzymes into the digestive cavity where they hydrolyze proteins and fats. Since this digestion occurs *outside* the cells, it is extracellular.

Another type of digestion also occurs. Cells of the endoderm can form outpushings of protoplasm (similar to the pseudopods of an ameba) and thereby engulf fairly large particles of food. The food particles are then hydrolyzed *inside* the cells of the endoderm thus an example of intracellular digestion.

The end products of digestion then pass by diffusion from the endodermal cells to the other cells of the body. Here the food is oxidized for the release of energy.

You can easily culture hydras in the laboratory or at home in a small bowl of pond water. Feed them daily on live *Daphnia* (water fleas). If daphnia are not available, use washed brine shrimp larvae. With a medicine dropper, place a *Hydra* in a drop of water on a depression microscope slide and add a few daphnia or brine shrimp larvae. Observe feeding with a hand lens or low-power stereomicroscope.

Earthworm. The earthworm (*Lumbricus terrestris*) is an annelid with more than 100 segments, indicated by grooves around its cylindrical body. Behind the first segment is the *mouth;* the last has the *anus.* Every segment but the first and last has four pairs of *setae* (bristles) used in locomotion. The earthworm's food consists of fragments of decaying vegetation and animal matter present in the soil. As the earthworm burrows through the ground, it takes in soil and food particles. The soil particles and undigested food pass from the mouth, through the food tube, and out of the anus.

Earthworms are helpful to farmers. As they eat their way through the soil, earthworms make the soil porous so that air can reach plant roots. Earthworms were making the soil porous long before the plow was invented.

Laboratory Skills

Earthworm Dissection

If you dissect an earthworm by making a slit along the *dorsal* (upper) body wall, you will find a tube that is the alimentary canal. Since the body wall is also a tube, the body plan of the earthworm is *a tube within a tube* (Fig. 5–16). The cavity between these tubes is divided at each segment by thin partitions. Many of the internal organs—for example, those for excretion—are *repeated* in almost every segment.

The digestive system of animals is composed of two main parts: (1) the *alimentary canal,* the tube through which the foods pass, and (2) the *digestive glands,* such as the liver and pancreas in humans. In the earthworm, the digestive juices pass from the digestive glands into the alimentary canal. Figure 5–17 shows the specialized regions of the earthworm's alimentary canal.

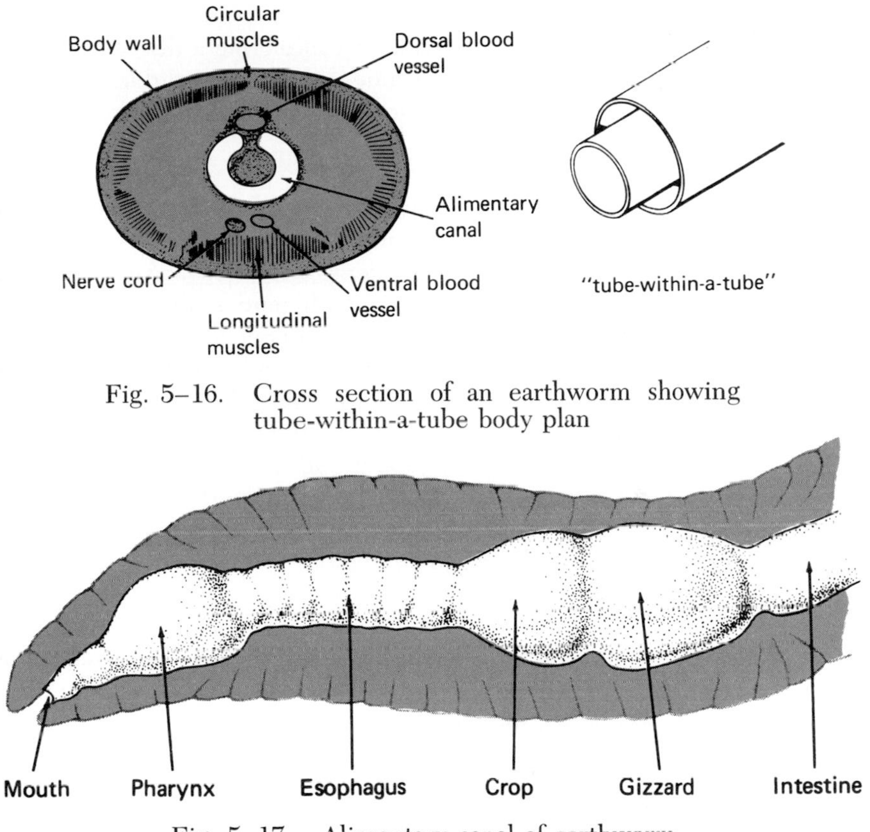

Fig. 5–16. Cross section of an earthworm showing tube-within-a-tube body plan

Fig. 5–17. Alimentary canal of earthworm

Food particles are sucked into the mouth cavity (ingested) when the pharynx is enlarged by muscular activity. The food is forced along the alimentary canal by waves of muscular contractions called *peristalsis.* The muscular walls of the esophagus push the food along to the thin-walled *crop,* where it is stored before being moved to the *gizzard.* The gizzard has thick muscular walls. With the aid of coarse particles of sand, the gizzard grinds the food mass into small particles that are then pushed to the intestine. Here enzymes secreted by the intestinal lining digest the food chemically. Most of the chemical digestion takes place in the small intestine, and it is here that end products are absorbed into the circulatory system. Undigested food is eliminated at the *anus* as feces.

Safety in Dissection

The following safety guidelines should be used when dissecting specimens in the laboratory.

1. Be sure you have read the instructions for handling dissecting instruments. Be careful in using sharp and pointed instruments.
2. Wear goggles and gloves when working with preserved specimens so the formaldehyde does not get in your eyes or irritate your skin.

3. In most cases, it is important to pin your specimen securely to the dissection pan before beginning your dissection.
4. Avoid crowds while performing dissections in the laboratory.
5. Clean and dry your dissection equipment before storing it.
6. Wash your hands after completing a dissection exercise.
7. If your are to continue your dissection during another laboratory period, carefully store your specimen according to directions given by your teacher.

Comparison of earthworm and Hydra. Digestion in *Hydra* and the earthworm may be compared as follows:

• *Hydra* has a *two-way digestive system.* Substances pass in both directions: food enters the mouth, and undigested food passes out of the mouth. The earthworm has a *one-way digestive system:* food and wastes pass in one direction through the alimentary canal, from mouth to anus. A one-way digestive system permits *division of labor.* Various regions are specially adapted to perform their special functions.

• In *Hydra,* digestion is both extracellular and intracellular whereas in the earthworm it is mainly extracellular (carried on in the digestive tube).

• In *Hydra,* digested food passes from cell to cell by diffusion. In the earthworm, a *blood circulatory system* carries digested food to all parts of the body.

Grasshopper. We study the grasshopper as a representative of the insects. Like all arthropods, insects have an exoskeleton (external skeleton) of *chitin.* The body of an insect is divided into three major regions: the *head,* the *thorax,* and the *abdomen.*

The head bears one pair of antennae, three pairs of mouth parts, a pair of simple eyes, and a pair of compound eyes composed of hundreds of lenses. These compound eyes permit an insect to see in many directions and to detect moving objects readily.

On the thorax are *six legs* (three pairs) and two pairs of wings. The abdomen of the grasshopper is divided into numerous segments, none of which has legs.

The grasshopper moves from plant to plant by walking, hopping, or flying and is very destructive to crops. Its complicated mouth parts include appendages for sensing and grasping food and strong mandibles for chewing.

The digestive system of the grasshopper is shown in Figure 5–18. Food, mechanically broken down in the mouth, is sucked through the esophagus into the *crop,* a large thin-walled sac, where it is temporarily stored before entering the muscular *gizzard.* Here it is further broken down by the action of toothlike chitinous plates. From the gizzard, the food passes to the *stomach.* Large branching digestive glands, called *gastric caecae,* on the outside of the stomach pour their juices into this organ where digestion is completed. Digested food is absorbed from the stomach into the blood. Undigested food passes through the intestine and rectum to be eliminated through the *anus.* Like the earthworm, the grasshopper has a tube-within-a-tube body plan, a one-way digestive tract, and extracellular chemical digestion.

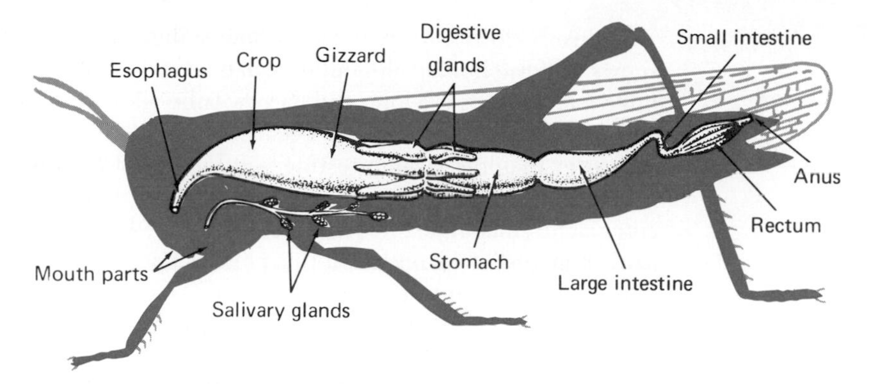

Fig. 5–18. Digestive system of the grasshopper

Digestion in humans. Although the human digestive system appears complicated, it is essentially a tube-within-a-tube. It is similar in this respect to that of the earthworm and grasshopper. The inner tube (alimentary canal) is greatly lengthened so portions are much coiled. Specialization here has increased beyond what we have seen before. Humans have specialized organs for mechanical and chemical digestion.

The upper portion of the human digestive system is shown in Figure 5–19. Three pairs of salivary glands lead into the *mouth* (oral cavity). The *pharynx* (throat) is a region where the respiratory system and the digestive system cross. From the pharynx, food passes down a tube called the *esophagus*.

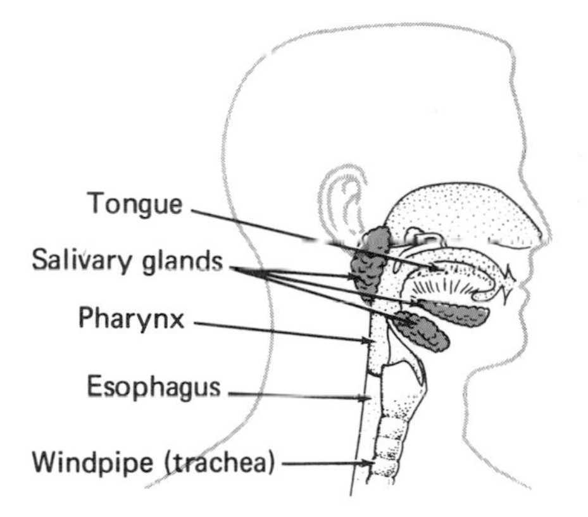

Fig. 5–19. Upper portion of the human digestive system

Comparing Evolutionary Trends		
Protozoa	**Hydra**	**Earthworm, Grasshopper, Human**
No digestive tract (food vacuoles)	Two-way digestive tract	One-way digestive tract (specialized food tube)
Mostly intracellular digestion	Extracellular and intracellular digestion	Mostly extracellular digestion

Figure 5–20 is a diagram of the lower digestive system. This diagram shows that the human alimentary canal is one continuous tube. The *small intestine* in adults is a long and narrow tube about 7 meters (23 feet) long. The *large intestine* is so called because it is wide in diameter. However, it is shorter than the small intestine—only about 1.5 meters (5 feet) long. It is divided into an *ascending colon, transverse colon,* and *descending colon.* The small intestine joins a pouch of the large intestine. The *appendix* is a fingerlike extension of this pouch. The *rectum* and *anus* are at the end of the large intestine.

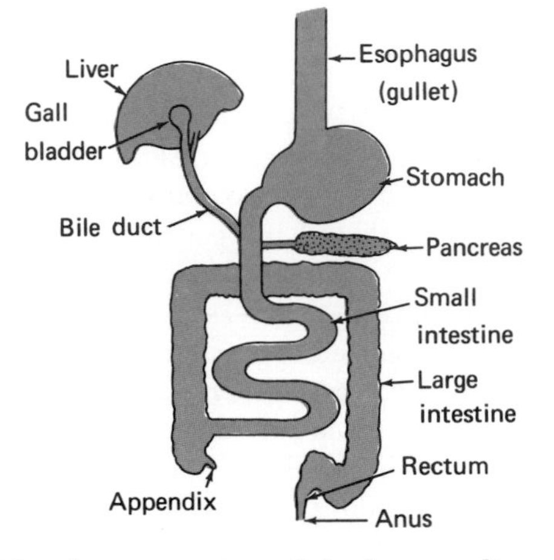

Fig. 5–20. Lower portion of the human digestive system

Glands that pass digestive juices and enzymes into the alimentary canal are:

- *Salivary glands*—secrete saliva into the mouth.
- *Gastric glands*—secrete gastric juices into the stomach. These minute glands are present in the wall of the stomach.
- *Pancreas*—secretes pancreatic juice into the small intestine.
- *Liver*—secretes bile into the upper portion of the small intestine. The gall bladder stores bile.
- *Intestinal glands*—secrete intestinal juice into the small intestine. These microscopic glands are present in the walls of the small intestine.

The human digestive system consists of a continuous tube, the alimentary canal, and the accessory glands and organs that function in conjunction with the alimentary canal.

Reasoning Exercises

1. Why are saprophytes and parasites considered heterotrophs?
2. Why is digestion necessary?
3. Distinguish between intracellular and extracellular digestion.
4. Compare digestion in an ameba and *Hydra*.
5. Explain how digestion in the earthworm is more specialized than in *Hydra*.

6. What are the advantages of a one-way digestive system?
7. Show how the biological theme unity within diversity applies to the digestive systems of the earthworm and grasshopper.
8. Trace the tube-within-a-tube body plan from the earthworm to humans.

Completion Questions

A

1. The usable portions of foods are known as . . . . . .
2. The type of nutrition used by the green plant is . . . . . . nutrition.
3. Some bacteria use . . . . . . instead of H_2O in the process of photosynthesis.
4. Autotrophic bacteria that oxidize iron, sulfur, and hydrogen obtain the energy for food making by the process of . . . . . .
5. The primary source for energy and growth is . . . . . .

B

6. A substance that acts as a catalyst during photosynthesis is . . . . . .
7. During photosynthesis, light energy is converted into . . . . . . energy.
8. Most of the oxygen in the atmosphere results from the process of . . . . . .
- • 9. Chlorophyll may be removed from a leaf by boiling it in . . . . . .
- • 10. The portion of an experiment that serves as a basis for comparison is the . . . . . .
- • 11. A controlled experiment should have only one . . . . . .

12. When white light falls on an object that appears green, the wavelengths for green are . . . . . .
13. The principal colors of light used in photosynthesis are . . . . . . and . . . . . .
14. A metallic element present in the chlorophyll molecule is . . . . . .
15. Stacks of disks within the chloroplasts are . . . . . .
16. The raw material that supplies the oxygen liberated during photosynthesis is . . . . . .

C

17. The coenzyme that carries hydrogen from the light reactions to the dark reactions is . . . . . .
18. A radioactive isotope of carbon that has been used to trace the steps of carbon fixation is . . . . . .
19. Carbon dioxide is used during the . . . . . . reactions of photosynthesis.
20. Oxygen is released during the . . . . . . reactions of photosynthesis.
21. The energy for carbon fixation is directly supplied by . . . . . . and . . . . . .
22. Within the chloroplast, the enzymes for the light reactions are located on the . . . . . . and those for dark reactions are located in the . . . . . .

D

23. Loss of water from the upper epidermis of the leaf is prevented by the presence of a waxy . . . . . .
24. Most of the photosynthesis in the leaf occurs in the . . . . . . and the . . . . . . layers.

25. An adaptation of the leaf that increases the surface area for diffusion of gases to the cells is the presence of......
26. A stoma opens when the guard cells become......
27. The process by which the leaves give off water vapor is known as......
28. Cells in the epidermis that contain chloroplasts are the......

E

29. The type of nutrition in which organisms take in preformed organic molecules is called......
30. A paramecium ingests food by the beating action of......
31. *Hydra* egests food through the......
32. The grasshopper stores food in the thin-walled......
33. Digestion of organic matter outside of cells is known as...... digestion.
34. The structure in an ameba that corresponds in function to the stomach in higher animals is the......
35. • When dissecting specimens, be sure to wear......

Multiple-Choice Questions

A

1. Which organism is a heterotroph? (1) Chlorella (2) grasshopper (3) moss (4) bean plant
2. Which type of organism synthesizes organic molecules from inorganic raw materials? (1) autotroph (2) heterotroph (3) saprophye (4) parasite
3. A process by which some autotrophs meet their nutritional needs is (1) chemosynthesis, (2) parasitism, (3) respiration, (4) metamorphosis.
4. Chemosynthetic bacteria obtain energy for making their own food from (1) radioactive isotopes, (2) chemical oxidations, (3) heat, (4) light.

B

5. • The raw materials for photosynthesis are (1) water and carbon dioxide, (2) oxygen and water, (3) sugar and carbon dioxide, (4) water and oxygen.
6. Organisms that carry on photosynthesis are (1) anaerobic, (2) saprophytic, (3) autotrophic, (4) heterotrophic.
7. • Which energy conversion occurs during the process of photosynthesis? (1) chemical bond energy to mechanical energy, (2) light energy to chemical energy, (3) light energy to nuclear energy, (4) mechanical energy to radiant energy
8. • If a sprig of *Elodea* is placed in a test tube of water containing yellow-colored bromthymol blue and kept in the sunlight, after several hours the solution will be (1) magenta, (2) yellow, (3) blue, (4) colorless.
9. The source of the oxygen produced by photosynthesis is (1) water, (2) carbon dioxide, (3) sugar, (4) starch.
10. Which occurs during the light reactions of photosynthesis? (1) carbon dioxide molecules are split, releasing oxygen; (2) water molecules are split, releasing oxygen; (3) carbon dioxide combines with hydrogen, forming carbohydrates; (4) carbon combines with water, forming carbohydrates

11. Water prepared with O^{18} (heavy oxygen) is supplied to a plant in a well lighted, controlled environment. When analyzed a short time later, the O^{18} would probably be found in (1) glucose only, (2) starch only, (3) carbohydrates, proteins, and fats, (4) the air surrounding the plant.
12. Which of the following is the best equation to represent the overall process of photosynthesis?
    (1) energy + CO_2 + $H_2O \rightarrow C_6H_{12}O_2$ + O_2
    (2) energy + $6CO_2$ + $6H_2O \rightarrow C_6H_{12}O_6$ + $6O_2$
    (3) energy + $6CO_2$ + $12H_2O \rightarrow C_6H_{12}O_6$ + $6O_2$ + $6H_2O$
    (4) energy + $12CO_2$ + $6H_2O \rightarrow C_6H_{12}O_6$ + $6O_2$ + $6H_2O$

(C)

13. Which occurs during the light reactions of photosynthesis? (1) water molecules are split; (2) carbon dioxide reacts with hydrogen; (3) PGAL molecules are changed to sugar; (4) oxygen is combined with carbon dioxide.
14. Energy is carried from the light reactions to the dark reactions by (1) ADP, (2) ATP, (3) CO_2, (4) activated chlorophyll.
15. A coenzyme that carries hydrogen atoms from the light reactions to the dark reactions is (1) $NADPH_2$, (2) ATP, (3) chlorophyll, (4) PGAL.
16. Which occurs during the dark reaction of photosynthesis? (1) carbon dioxide is united with hydrogen; (2) photolysis; (3) water is split into hydrogen and oxygen; (4) ATP is produced.
17. The dark reactions of photosynthesis cannot occur in the absence of (1) light, (2) chlorophyll, (3) CO_2, (4) O_2.
18. The dark reactions of photosynthesis (1) consist of a series of enzyme-controlled steps, (2) consist of a single enzyme-controlled step, (3) use energy directly supplied by excited chlorophyll, (4) use energy supplied by ADP.
19. During photosynthesis, the breakdown of water requires (1) starch, (2) light, (3) PGAL, (4) carbon-14.

D

20. The size of the stomata in a leaf is controlled by the (1) xylem cells, (2) phloem cells, (3) guard cells, (4) heterotrophic cells.
21. When do green plants carry on transpiration? (1) in the daylight only, (2) at night only, (3) during photosynthesis only, (4) both at night and in the daylight
22. The air spaces in the spongy layer of a leaf aid in the (1) movement of starch, (2) absorption of gases, (3) transport of sap, (4) diffusion of chlorophyll.
23. Which process in plants is most closely associated with the activity of guard cells? (1) digestion, (2) reproduction, (3) transpiration, (4) locomotion

E

24. The tube-within-a-tube body plan is characteristic of (1) grasshopper and earthworm, (2) flatworm and frog, (3) tapeworm and sponge, (4) *Hydra* and sea anemone.
25. In the *Hydra,* the digestion of food is (1) extracellular, (2) intracellular, (3) intracellular and extracellular, (4) not necessary.

Chapter Test

1. The chemical process that occurs during the digestion of food is (1) hydrolysis, (2) dehydration synthesis, (3) hydration, (4) dehydration.
2. In an experiment, what should be the relationship between the control group and the experimental group? (1) They should be different in size. (2) They should resemble each other in at least two respects. (3) They should not be similar in any respect. (4) They should be identical in all respects except one.
3. Thick muscular walls for grinding food are present in the earthworm's (1) crop, (2) esophagus, (3) mouth, (4) gizzard.

In questions 4 through 11, select the letter of the item, chosen from the list below, that best matches the statement.

A. *Protozoa* C. Earthworm, grasshopper, human
B. *Hydra* D. All of the above

4. Cilia are used for the capture of food.
5. Digestion is mainly intracellular.
6. It has two-way digestive tract.
7. Tentacles are used in the capture of food.
8. Digestion occurs in food vacuoles.
9. Digestion is *only* intracellular.
10. It has one-way digestive tract.
11. It eliminates undigested food.
12. The basic aspect of the photosynthetic process is considered to be the (1) production of CO_2, (2) production of H_2O, (3) production of chlorophyll, (4) conversion of light energy to chemical energy.
13. Which occurs during the light reactions of photosynthesis? (1) carbon atoms are combined with water molecules; (2) water molecules are separated into hydrogen and oxygen; (3) hydrogen ions are attached to carbon dioxide molecules; (4) PGAL is converted into glucose and oxygen
14. Which of these organisms has a type of nutrition most similar to that of animals? (1) alga, (2) fungus, (3) pine tree, (4) bean plant
15. Which occurs during the process of photosynthesis? (1) light energy is produced, (2) light energy is changed into chemical energy, (3) carbon dioxide and water are produced, (4) chlorophyll is changed into glucose
16. Most molecular oxygen (O_2) in the atmosphere is the result of the (1) fermentation of sugar, (2) breakdown of water molecules, (3) oxidation of surface minerals, (4) decomposition of carbon monoxide.

Base your answers to questions 17 through 21 on the graph on the next page which shows wavelengths of light passing through a chlorophyll solution. Light that is not transmitted by the solution is absorbed.

17. The percentage of light absorbed at a wavelength of 600 μm is approximately (1) 15%, (2) 45%, (3) 90%, (4) 600%.
18. The color of light absorbed most by this solution is (1) blue, (2) green, (3) orange, (4) red.

19. The color of light transmitted most by this solution is (1) blue, (2) green, (3) orange, (4) red.
20. The visible light with the longest wavelength is (1) violet, (2) blue, (3) green, (4) red.
21. The wavelength of light that is *least* effective during the process of photosynthesis is (1) 400 μm, (2) 475 μm, (3) 550 μm, (4) 625 μm.

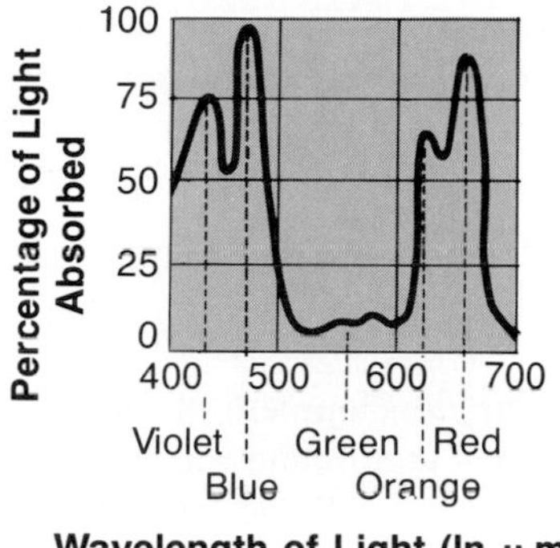

Base your answers to questions 22 through 25 on the equations below and your knowledge of biology.

(1) $12H_2O + 6CO_2 \xrightarrow[\text{light}]{\text{chlorophyll}} C_6H_{12}O_6 + 6O_2 + 6H_2O$

(2) $C_6H_{12}O_6 + 6O_2 \rightarrow 6H_2O + 6CO_2$

22. Equation 1 takes place in all (1) plants, (2) animals, (3) plants and animals, (4) green plants.
23. The name of the compound $C_6H_{12}O_6$ formed in equation 1 is (1) glucose, (2) protein, (3) glycerol, (4) amino acid.
24. Equation 2 represents a process by which energy is (1) stored, (2) released, (3) created, (4) increased.
25. Equation 2 takes place in (1) plants only, (2) animals only, (3) green plants only, (4) plants and animals.
26. A plant that carries on very little transpiration in its natural environment would most likely have a (1) thick leaf cuticle and few stomata, (2) thick leaf cuticle and many stomata, (3) thin leaf cuticle and many stomata.
27. Bread mold absorbs nutrients through (1) hyphae, (2) roots, (3) specialized root hairs, (4) xylem.
28. Which substances enter a green plant chiefly through its leaves? (1) oxygen and minerals (2) water and minerals (3) carbon dioxide and oxygen (4) carbon dioxide and water
29. The fact that, under certain conditions, stomatal openings become smaller enables the plant to avoid excessive loss of (1) carbon dioxide, (2) essential plant hormones, (3) water, (4) glucose.
30. A plant that lacks chloroplasts does *not* (1) give off O_2, (2) give off CO_2, (3) take in water, (4) take in food.

Chapter 6 Transport

Transport is the intake and distribution of materials throughout an organism. Transport occurs across membranes of cells, within the cell itself, and between parts of multicellular organisms. Most multicellular animals have systems of tubes called *vessels* that transport materials. They also have a pumping mechanism in the form of a *heart* or hearts. Among the materials carried by this system are water, oxygen, digested foods, the wastes of metabolism, and hormones. Plants move water and food without the benefit of a pumping mechanism. The stem, the root, and the leaf have adaptations for this important function.

A Structure of the Cell Membrane

Before the development of the electron microscope, scientists could see that the cell membrane was a very thin, flexible layer that surrounded the contents of the cell and kept it from mixing with its surroundings. They knew that food and other materials are able to go through the cell membrane. But how?

Since scientists could not actually observe this process, *models* were constructed to explain the structure and function of the cell membrane. A model is a picture or explanation of all the combined knowledge about a process or structure. A scientific model represents a structure or idea.

In the late 1930s, a model of the structure of the cell membrane was devised that helped scientists explain how it might function. However, it was not until the development of the electron microscope and scanning electron microscope techniques that new information about the structure of the cell membrane became available. This new information led to the *fluid-mosaic model* proposed by S. J. Singer in 1972.

The Fluid-Mosaic Model

Electron micrographs (photographs from an electron microscope) show the cell membrane as a double line. Biologists have found that the membrane consists of two layers of lipid molecules. Protein molecules are embedded in this lipid bilayer. Each lipid molecule, called a *phospholipid*, has a group of atoms including phosphorus and oxygen at one end. This end is called the head, shown as a rounded end in Figure 6–1. The heads form the innermost and outermost surfaces of the membrane. The rest of the phospholipid molecule, called the tail, contains carbon and hydrogen. The tails fill the space between the two surfaces. The chemical structure of the phospholipid molecules varies with the function of the membrane. The protein molecules may be on the inner membrane surface, on the outer membrane surface, or may extend entirely through both membrane surfaces.

The model of the cell membrane is called the fluid-mosaic model because the lipid layer is considered to have a fluid quality. This fluidity allows both the lipid and the protein molecules to move about. Thus, the proteins can change their positions depending on the cell's specific requirements. For example, some proteins may serve as carriers to transport molecules across the cell membrane.

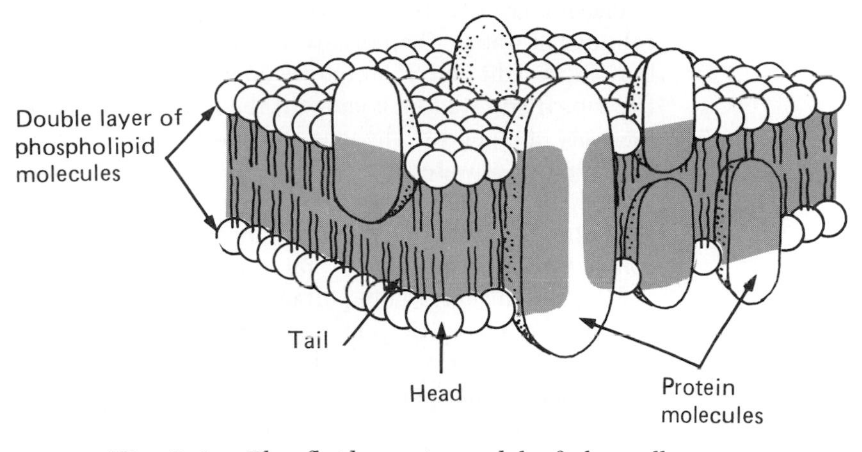

Fig. 6–1. The fluid-mosaic model of the cell membrane; note the arrangement of the lipid and protein molecules

B

Function of the Cell Membrane

The primary function of the cell membrane is to regulate the movement of substances that enter and exit the cell. The membrane prevents certain substances from either entering or leaving the cell. Because the cell membrane prevents the passage of some substances, and permits the passage of others, it is said to be *semipermeable* or *selectively permeable*. The ability of a substance to pass through the membrane depends on the size of the substance molecules and the electrical charge (positive or negative) of the substance molecules. It also depends on the chemical structure of the membrane itself.

There are two basic types of transport across cell membranes. In *passive transport*, the cell does not need to supply energy to move materials through the membrane, while in *active transport*, the cell must supply energy.

Diffusion

An important first step in the transport of substances within living things is to dissolve them. When a lump of sugar dissolves in water, its moving molecules are spread among the moving molecules of water. When a crystal of copper sulfate dissolves in water, its moving ions are spread among the moving molecules of water.

Gases can also dissolve in liquids. For example, when oxygen from the air dissolves in water, the oxygen is in the form of molecules interspersed among the water molecules. This is the oxygen that a fish takes in. The fish does not break down water molecules to obtain oxygen.

Open a bottle of perfume at the front of a room without drafts, and soon people at the back of the room can detect odorant molecules. This is because molecules of the odorant gas gradually spread apart. This random spreading apart of molecules or ions is called *diffusion*. (In the following discussion, we will usually speak of molecules, but this applies to ions as well.)

Place a layer of blue copper sulfate crystals at the bottom of a tall cylinder of water. The crystals dissolve to form a deep blue layer at the bottom. A light blue color moves upward and, after a few weeks, reaches the top. If you wait long enough, the entire cylinder will have the same intensity of blueness. The ions of copper sulfate have diffused throughout the cylinder of water.

At the start, there was a greater concentration of copper sulfate ions at the bottom. As diffusion occurred, the ions spread *from a region of higher concentration to a region of lower concentration of these ions.*

Simple diffusion is an important means for transport within cells. But it would take a long time for molecules of glucose to diffuse from your mouth to your toe. Multicellular organisms have more effective means for long distance transport.

Diffusion through a membrane. Moving molecules may also diffuse through a membrane. Such diffusion of ammonia gas through a moist membrane is shown in Figure 6–2.

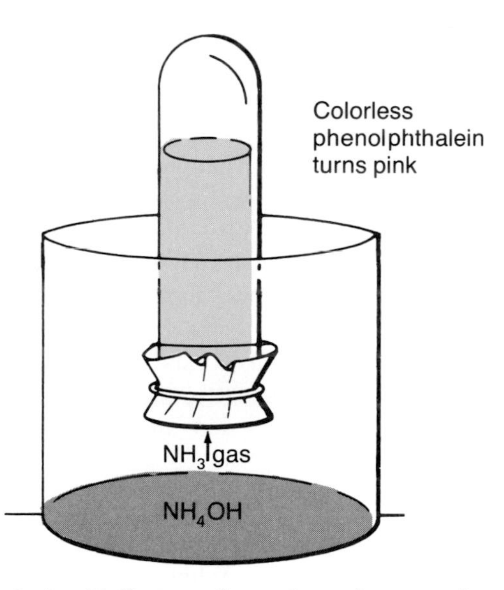

Fig. 6–2. Diffusion of gas through a membrane

At the beginning of the demonstration, the test tube contains a solution of colorless phenolphthalein. Phenolphthalein is an indicator that is colorless in a neutral or acid solution and pink in a base. The ammonium hydroxide in the beaker liberates ammonia gas:

$$\underset{\text{ammonium hydroxide}}{NH_4OH} \longrightarrow \underset{\text{ammonia gas}}{NH_3} + \underset{\text{water}}{H_2O}$$

Molecules of NH_3 (ammonia) *diffuse through the membrane* and combine with water in the test tube to form the base NH_4OH, which turns the phenolphthalein pink.

The diffusion of *liquids* through a membrane is illustrated in Figure 6–3. Note that in setups A and B the positions of the starch suspension and iodine solution are reversed. When iodine and starch unite, a blue-black color is produced. In setup A, the bottom liquid (in the jar) turns blue-black. In setup B, however, the top portion (in the test tube) turns blue-black. This indicates that the molecules of iodine pass through the membrane, regardless of whether they must travel downward or upward. The starch, composed of undissolved particles and large molecules, does not pass through the membrane.

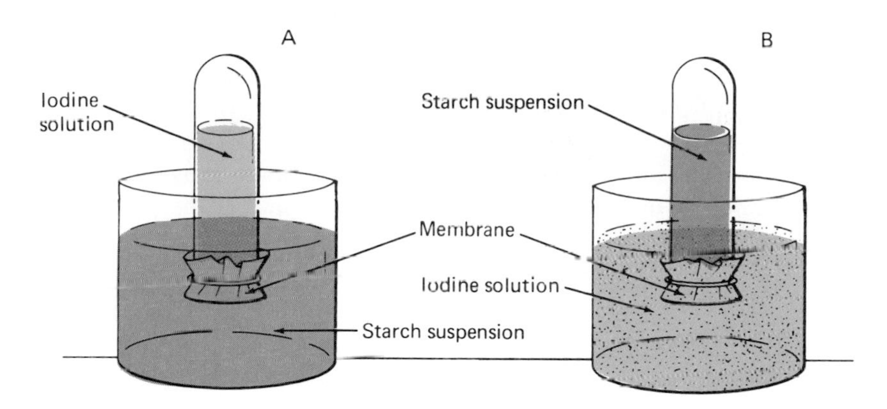

Fig. 6–3. Diffusion of a liquid through a membrane. In each case, it is the iodine that diffuses through the membrane.

A theoretical explanation of diffusion is diagrammatically shown in Figure 6–4. The circles represent molecules of water and the X's represent molecules of glucose. The membrane that separates the two compartments of the container permits passage of both the water molecules and the glucose molecules.

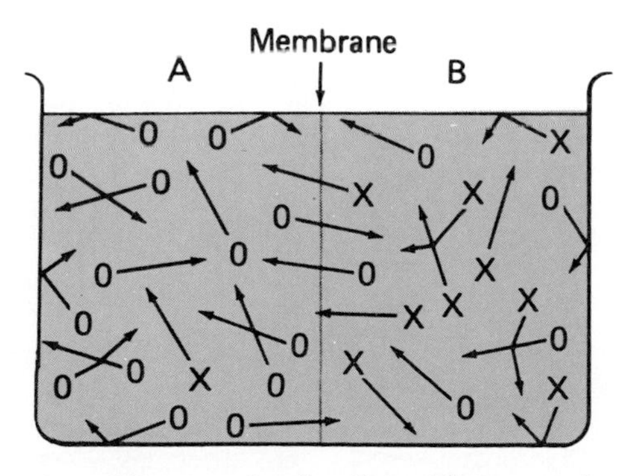

Key: O = Water molecules, X = Glucose molecules

Fig. 6–4. Theoretical explanation of diffusion

Side A is a *dilute solution of glucose.* This means that on this side there is a relatively *high concentration of water molecules.* Side B has a more concentrated solution of glucose; here there is a *low concentration of water molecules.* Let us consider the movement of the water molecules. As they bounce about at random, water molecules pass through the membrane in both directions. However, there are more water molecules in A than in B; therefore, more water molecules will pass from A to B than the other way. This continues until the concentration is the same on both sides. At this time there will be equal numbers of molecules moving in both directions—a condition known as *dynamic equilibrium.*

Now consider the movement of glucose molecules. At the start, more glucose molecules pass through the membrane to side A than to side B. Finally, the concentration of glucose molecules on each side of the membrane is equal. In diffusion, there is a net movement of a substance from a region of higher concentration of its molecules to a region of lower concentration of its molecules.

Diffusion is more complex than shown in the model above. Recent information about the cell membrane shows that more is involved than merely the size of the openings and of the glucose molecules.

Osmosis Diffusion is a general term for migration of materials as a result of random molecular motion. *Osmosis,* however, is a special kind of diffusion that involves the passage of *water molecules* through a membrane.

Elodea is a plant commonly used in home aquariums. If *Elodea* is placed in distilled water (which lacks any salts), water passes from a high concentration of water molecules (outside the cell) to a low concentration of water molecules (in the protoplasm). This causes the cell to swell and then burst. On the other hand, if a leaf is placed into a concentrated salt solution, its cells lose water and shrink.

Plasmolysis is the shrinking of cell contents caused by outward osmosis. Figure 6–5 illustrates plasmolysis of a cell in an *Elodea* leaf that has been placed in salt water. The cell contents shrink as water passes out by osmo

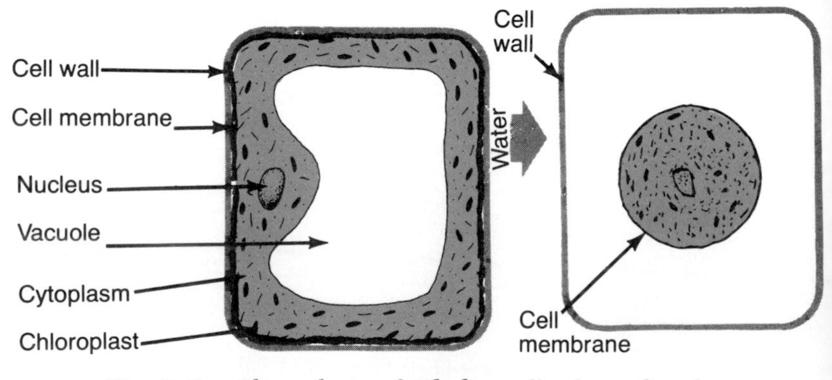

Fig. 6–5. Plasmolysis of *Elodea* cell when placed in strong salt solution.

sis, but the rigid cell wall maintains its shape. The cell membrane, which is normally pressed against the cell wall, can now be seen.

The bursting of cells because of the *inward osmosis* of water occurs when a drop of blood is placed in distilled water. The water molecules are more concentrated outside the blood cells than inside these cells. By osmosis, water molecules pass into the red blood cells causing them to swell and then burst.

Osmosis can be defined as the movement of water molecules through a semipermeable membrane, from a region of higher concentration to a region of lower concentration. A membrane's property of selective permeability is lost when the cell dies. For example, when congo red dye is added to a culture of yeast cells, the dye does not penetrate the cell membranes and the yeast cells appear colorless under the microscope. However, if the mixture is boiled, the living cell membranes lose their selective ability. Then the dye penetrates the cell membrane, and the yeast cells appear red.

Concentration gradient. Diffusion and osmosis are means of passive transport across a membrane. The cell does not supply energy to move molecules from a region of high concentration to a region of low concentration. The difference in concentration of molecules on each side of the membrane is called the *concentration gradient*. This gradient may be compared to the slope of a hill. Diffusion may be compared to a ball rolling down a hill, as shown in Figure 6–6. The ball rolls down without the input of extra energy. Rolling the ball up the hill, however, requires energy in going against the gradient.

Diffusion pathways. Small substances, such as dissolved ions, gas molecules, water molecules, and even glucose molecules may diffuse through a cell membrane along certain pathways. The pathway for a particular substance may depend upon its molecular size and its electrical charge.

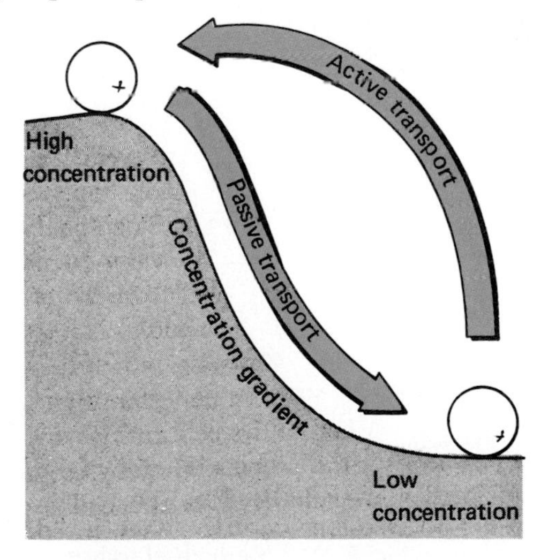

Fig. 6–6. Active and passive transport. It requires no added energy to roll a ball down a hill. Raising the ball up the hill, against the gradient, requires the input of energy.

Active Transport There are numerous situations in living cells in which molecules pass through a membrane in the direction opposite from what we would expect on the basis of the principle of diffusion: the molecules pass from a region of *low* concentration of their molecules to a region of *high* concentration. This process is *active transport.* Active transport is the process by which molecules or ions move against the concentration gradient. Active transport requires the contribution of energy by the cell. Consequently, it is not surprising to find large accumulations of mitochondria, the powerhouses of the cell, in cells which carry on much active transport. For example, many mitochondria are present in human kidney cells where materials move against the concentration gradient.

Protein molecules embedded in the cell membrane have an important role in active transport. They function as transport molecules, moving substances across the membrane against the concentration gradient.

Pinocytosis Large molecules, such as proteins, often enter cells by *pinocytosis*. This is shown in Figure 6–7B. The cell membrane forms a pocket called a pinocytic vesicle. This pocket, containing large molecules from outside the cell, pinches off from the membrane. The result is a cell vacuole containing the large molecules.

Phagocytosis Portions of a cell may engulf chunks of matter or prey by flowing around them and enclosing them in a vacuole. This process is called *phagocytosis*. This is the method by which an ameba, as well as some endoderm cells in

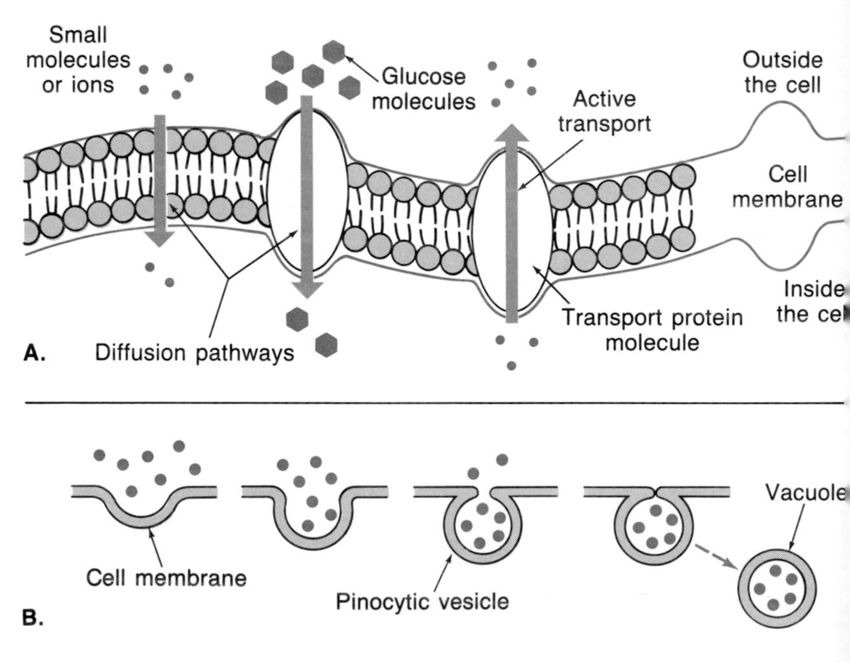

Fig. 6–7. Methods of transport across a cell membrane: A. Small molecules move by diffusion or active transport. B. Particles or very large molecules enter the cell by pinocytosis.

Hydra, ingest food. Human white blood cells known as *phagocytes* also use this method to engulf bacteria.

Particle size and transport. From the viewpoint of particle size, the processes that transport material across a membrane into a cell may be compared as follows:

- *diffusion*—usually small molecules, such as oxygen, carbon dioxide, mineral salts, glucose, and amino acids.
- *pinocytosis*—large molecules, such as proteins, or very small particles.
- *phagocytosis*—undissolved large particles, chunks of matter, or living microorganisms.

Particles taken in by pinocytosis or phagocytosis are inside the membrane of a vacuole. A *lysosome* fuses with the vacuole and its digestive enzymes hydrolyze the contents. The products of digestion can then diffuse into the cytoplasm.

Circulation

Absorption is a general term for the passage of materials through membranes. Once materials have entered a cell, they are transported throughout. *Circulation* is the transport of materials within cells or between parts of a many-celled organism.

Diffusion by molecular motion accounts for some of the spread of materials within the cell. However, this is a relatively slow process and does not account completely for intracellular circulation. Another type of circulation can be observed in the tip of an *Elodea* leaf that is actively growing in light. The chloroplasts are seen to follow a circular motion around the periphery of the cell. This streaming movement of the cytoplasm is called *cyclosis*.

Other examples of cyclosis are the streaming of protoplasm in *Ameba*, the route taken by the food vacuoles of *Paramecium*, and the movement of cytoplasm in the bread mold and the slime mold. Cyclosis helps to distribute materials throughout the cell.

In addition, the branched network of tubes called the *endoplasmic reticulum* transports materials within the cell. Thus, circulation within the cell is by (1) diffusion, (2) cyclosis, and (3) use of the endoplasmic reticulum.

Reasoning Exercises

1. How does the fluid-mosaic model of the cell membrane explain the function of a selectively permeable membrane?
2. Why is solubility important to transport?
3. Why must a salt solution containing an *Elodea* cell be *concentrated* to produce outward osmosis from the cell?
4. Distinguish between passive transport and active transport. What is the role of the living cell membrane in transport?
5. Distinguish between pinocytosis and phagocytosis.
6. How does circulation differ from absorption?

Adaptations for Transport in Plants

Plants are called herbaceous or woody depending on their stem. *Herba-ceous stems*, as found in the bean plant, tomato, and sunflower, are soft thin, and green. They die down each year. *Woody stems*, as in the for-sythia and maple, are firm and contain much supporting cellulose. They live for a number of years. To a biologist, a stem can mean anything from a cornstalk and the thin twig of a rosebush to the trunk of a giant sequoia.

Structure of the Herbaceous Stem

A cross section of the stem of a herbaceous dicot (Fig. 6–8), such as tomato reveals circles arranged in a ring near the outside circumference. These circles are vascular (conducting) bundles that carry materials up and down the stem.

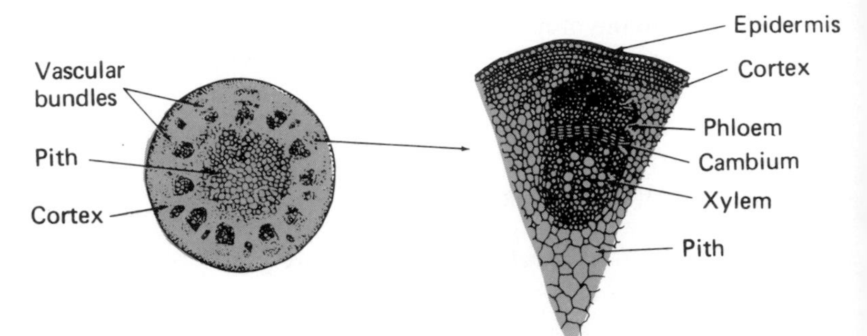

Fig. 6–8. Cross section of a herbaceous dicot stem.
Left: General view. Right: Vascular bundle.

Outside the circle of vascular bundles is the *cortex*. Inside the ring of vascular bundles is the *pith*. The entire stem is enclosed by a layer of epidermal cells. The central area of pith has large, thin-walled storag cells. The turgor of the cortex cells provides support to keep the plan erect. As shown in Figure 6–8, each vascular bundle contains xylem phloem, and cambium.

Xylem cells, toward the center of the stem, have thick walls. Xylem cells provide support, and they form tubes that conduct water and miner-als *upward* through the stem.

The *phloem* consists of thin-walled cells that transport soluble foo *downward*. Phloem cells are located toward the outer edge of the vascula bundle.

Between the xylem and the phloem is the *cambium*. These cells hav the ability to carry on cell division. In dividing, they produce xylem cell toward the inside of the stem or phloem cells toward the outside. Mo plant cells, once differentiated, no longer undergo cell division. Tissue that retain the ability to divide constitute *meristem*. Cambium is an exam-ple of meristematic tissue. As you would expect, meristem is also found a the growing tips of roots and stems.

Structure of the Woody Stem

A striking feature of the woody stem (Fig. 6–9) is the arrangement of i tissues in concentric rings. There are no individual bundles of vascula tissue as in the herbaceous stem. From the center to the outside, there are rings of pith, xylem, cambium, phloem, cortex, and bark.

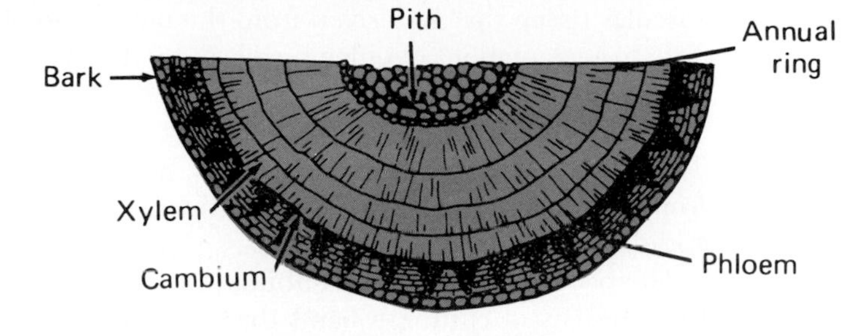

Fig. 6–9. Cross section of a three year old woody stem

Xylem, cambium, and phloem. The largest region of the stem is the woody portion called *xylem.* A woody stem grows wider because of cell division by the thin layer of *cambium* cells that is found near the bark. New cells, derived from cambium, that push toward the center of the stem become xylem. Those that form toward the bark become *phloem.* The phloem, cambium, and xylem together form a large cylinder of conducting tissue, as shown in Figure 6–10.

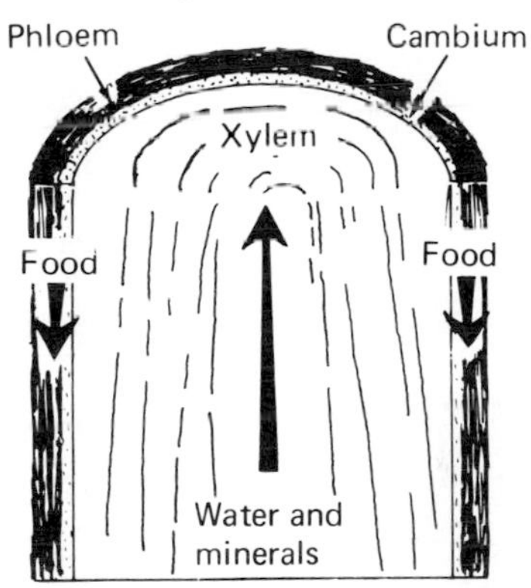

Fig. 6–10. Major directions of transport in vascular tissue of a woody stem

Xylem cells produced in the spring are larger than those that develop in the summer. This variation in size appears to the eye as distinct light and dark *annual rings.* The age of a tree, thus, can be estimated by counting the annual rings in a cross section of its trunk. Some plants, however, have two growth periods in a single year. Biologists can learn much about environmental conditions in the past, such as rainfall of a particular year, by examining tree rings with a microscope.

Older xylem cells that have been pushed toward the center gradually become clogged with deposits. They no longer conduct water, but they provide excellent support to keep the plant upright. Lumbermen call this inner, inactive dark wood *heartwood.* The lighter, active wood nearer the bark is *sapwood.*

Vertical rows of xylem form vascular (conducting) tissue. Thus, the functions of xylem are (1) to transport water and dissolved minerals *upward* to the leaves, and (2) to provide support. Phloem is the thin ring of vascular tissue that is derived from the outer side of the cambium layer. Tubelike adaptations of phloem cells carry dissolved food *downward* from the leaves to the roots.

The xylem, cambium, and phloem act as a cylinder of vascular tissue. This cylinder is shown in Figure 6–10. *Vascular rays* extend horizontally from pith to bark. These help meet the needs of the numerous cells in a wide stem.

The bark consists of the cambium, phloem, and epidermis. *Girdling* a tree consists of cutting a band through the bark, all around the trunk. Because all the phloem tubes are cut, the roots fail to receive food for storage. As a consequence, the tree dies the following spring.

Adaptations of Vascular Tissue

Figure 6–11 shows how xylem and phloem cells establish tubes for up-and-down transport. The cells that form xylem tubes are dead when mature. One kind of xylem tube, a tracheid, develops from long, thin cells that have tapered ends. The tapered ends overlap. Pits in the tapered ends allow water to pass from one cell to the adjoining one. Other xylem tubes, called vessels, develop from long, large cells that have perforations at each end. A long row of these cells acts as a continuous narrow tube.

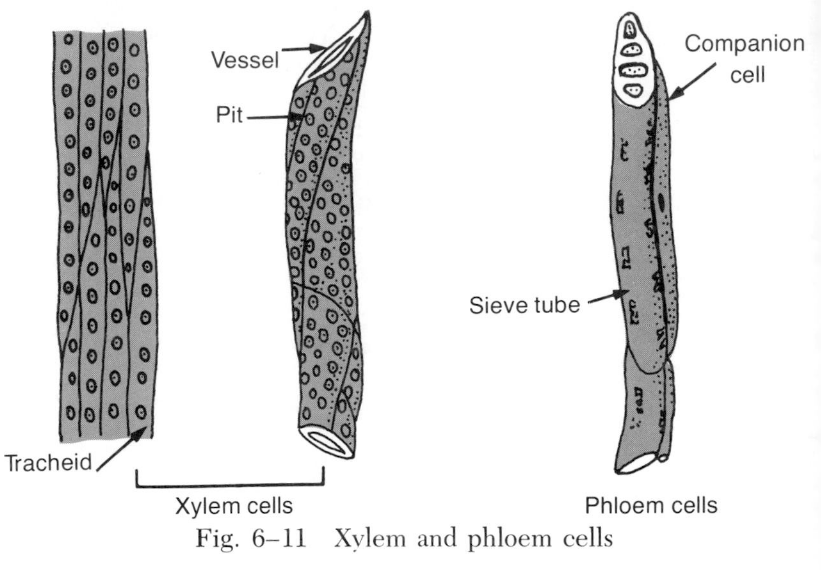

Fig. 6–11 Xylem and phloem cells

Phloem cells remain alive at maturity. At each end of the long conducting cells are narrow perforations. These act as a sieve. Accordingly, a vertical row of these sieve cells serves as a tube of microscopic diameter. The sieve cells contain cytoplasm but no nucleus. Adjacent to them, however, are companion cells. Their nuclei, presumably, provide nuclear control and energy for the sieve cells. The mechanism by which the sieve tubes transport sugars and protein downward appear to help in carrying out the transport process.

The Root

Although roots vary greatly in shape they share these main functions: (1) anchorage in the soil, (2) absorption of water and minerals, and (3) conduction of absorbed materials to the stem. Some roots also store food. Many land plants have as large a system of roots below ground as the system of stems above ground. Often, the ends of the roots extend beyond the circle of branches and leaves above.

The first root that develops from a germinating seed is called the *primary root*. Roots growing out of the primary root are called *secondary roots*. If the primary root remains as the major root of the plant, it is called a *tap root* (Fig. 6–12B). Tap roots grow deep in the ground to reach water. It is difficult to pull a dandelion plant out of the ground because of its long tap root. A tap root that stores much food is called a *storage root*. Carrots, beets, and radishes are storage roots.

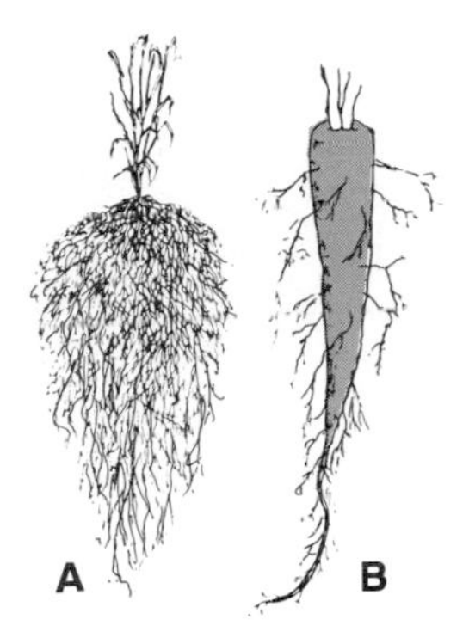

Fig. 6–12. A. Grass—an example of a fibrous root. B. Carrot—an example of a tap root

Some secondary roots form a tangled mass of threadlike roots that spread through a large area. These are called *fibrous roots* (Fig. 6–12). Members of the grass family have fibrous roots that hold the soil and thus prevent erosion by wind or water.

Structure of the Root

As seen in cross section (Fig. 6–13A), the root has three main regions: the *vascular cylinder*, the *cortex*, and *epidermis*.

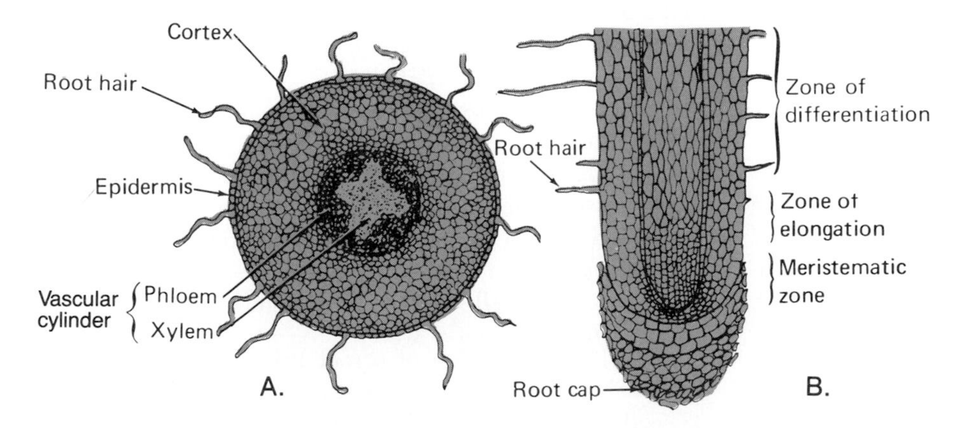

Fig. 6–13. Structure of the root tip; A. Cross section of a root. B. Cross section of root hair

The vascular cylinder in the center contains the conducting tissue consisting of xylem and phloem. Note that the xylem of a dicot root in cross section resembles a wheel with spokes. Phloem occurs between the arms of the xylem. Cambium occurs between xylem and phloem.

The *cortex* is the broad region surrounding the central cylinder. Its thin-walled cells are adapted for food storage.

The *epidermis* is the outer covering. This consists of a single layer of cells that absorb water and minerals from the soil.

Root hairs. Root hairs are located slightly behind the growing region of the root. (See Fig. 6–13B.) Root hairs are specialized cells of the epidermis that have delicate, thin-walled projections (Fig. 6–14).

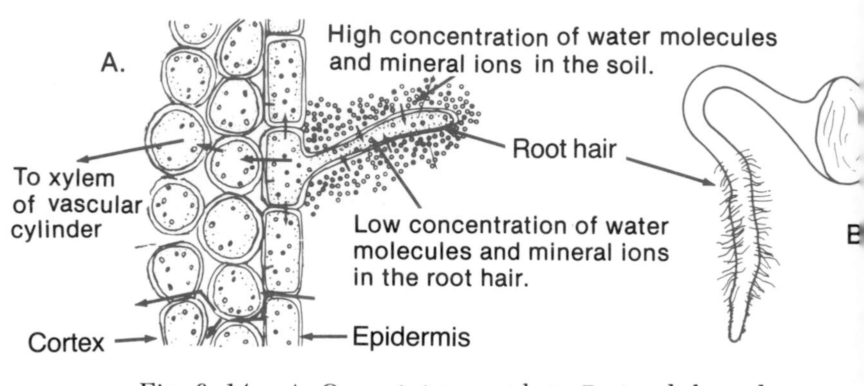

Fig. 6–14. A. Osmosis into root hair. B. A radish seedling. Note the many delicate root hairs that form a fuzz.

Root hairs absorb water and minerals from the soil. Because they protrude from the surface of the root, the *root hairs provide greatly increased surface for absorption.* A single rye plant has 14 billion root hairs with a total area of over 4000 square feet.

When you pull a seedling from the ground, you destroy the delicate root hairs. But germinate radish seeds on moist blotting paper in a covered dish, and you can observe root hairs with the naked eye. They appear like a fine fuzz (Fig. 6–14B).

Figure 6–14 A shows that water and mineral ions enter a root hair by passive transport: osmosis and diffusion. However, energy-using active transport against the concentration gradient also plays an important role. Water passes from the root hairs and other epidermal cells through the cortex and to the vascular cylinder. This transport occurs in two ways: (1) water flows through the cytoplasm from cell to cell by passing through cell membranes and cell walls; (2) water flows just along cell walls, whose cellulose readily absorbs water.

A longitudinal section of a root tip (Fig. 6–13) shows these regions:

- *The root cap.* This thimble-shaped group of cells protects the delicate cells behind as the root penetrates the soil. Carbon dioxide produced during cellular respiration reacts with soil water to form carbonic acid ($CO_2 + H_2O \rightarrow H_2CO_3$). This weak acid dissolves certain minerals, making it easier for the root tip to advance through the soil.

- *The meristematic region.* This is the region where cells are actively dividing into a mass of small, undifferentiated cells.
- *The elongation region.* Here the newly formed cells become longer. Elongation of thousands of cells pushes the root cap farther into the soil.
- *The maturation region.* Here the elongated cells differentiate into cells with specialized functions. The central vascular cylinder and root hairs can be seen in this region. Higher in the root, its vascular cylinder merges with the vascular cylinder of the stem.

Roots absorb not only water and minerals but also oxygen which is present in loose soil. Overwatering of potted plants is harmful because constant flooding deprives the roots of oxygen needed for cellular respiration. Plants need nitrates, phosphates, potassium, calcium, iron, and trace amounts of other mineral ions. Rhododendron and azaleas are examples of shrubs that require soil having a low pH. These plants may do poorly unless provided with an acid fertilizer containing a compound such as iron sulfate.

The Leaf

The veins in a leaf are vascular bundles containing xylem and phloem. These bundles are branched extensions of the vascular tissues in the stem. Conducting tubes extend from roots, through stems and their branches, to all parts of the leaves. Although biologists still do not have a complete explanation of how liquids rise in stems, they do have some theories.

Theories of Plant Transport

Scientific *laws* describe regularities in nature. *Theories*, however, are not descriptive statements. They are attempts to *explain* events. Theories are tested by their ability to predict what will happen under controlled experimental conditions. Such predictions cannot be proved true, only verified or not verified. Thus, the more that scientists successfully test an explanation, the higher the probability that the theory is correct. You have seen many examples (for example, the history of the cell theory) showing that accepted theories have been discarded or modified in the light of new evidence. Theories for the transport of water and food in stems have also changed. Contributions from physics and biochemistry and the development of new apparatus and techniques have modified old ideas.

Upward Transport

Theories for the upward transport of water in stems must be able to explain how water can rise more than 100 meters above the ground, as in giant sequoia trees. Ideas from physics have played an important role in developing our current explanations.

Adhesion and cohesion. *Adhesion* is the force of attraction between *unlike* molecules. For example, water wets glass because it clings to the glass by adhesion. *Cohesion* is the attraction between *like* molecules. Observe, for example, a droplet of water hanging from a faucet. Why don't molecules at the bottom of the droplet fall into the sink? By cohesion they are attracted to water molecules above. Water has great cohesive force.

Capillary action. Stand glass tubing of very narrow internal diameter in a container of water (Fig. 6–15A). The water inside the tube rises above the level of the water in the container. If you use fine tubes of varying diameter, you will find that *the narrower the tube's diameter the higher the rise*. This phenomenon is known as *capillary action*. Why does ink spread on a paper towel? The spaces between the paper's many fine fibers act like capillary tubes.

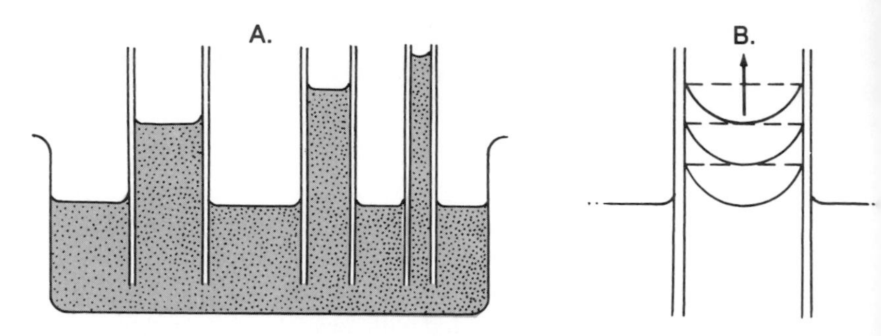

Fig. 6–15. Capillary action. A. Water rises higher in tubes of narrower diameter. B. Solid lines show curved surface produced by adhesion. Dotted lines show subsequent effect of surface tension and cohesion.

The steps in capillary action are illustrated in Fig. 6–15B. Adhesion moves water molecules up the side of the glass tube to produce a *curve* in the water's surface. Cohesive forces, however, produce a surface film at the surface of the water. This film acts like a stretched rubber sheet that tends to contract. (Indeed, water insects walk on this surface film, and it will even support a steel needle.) The surface film contracts and straightens out the curve formed by adhesion. By a continuous series of such steps, the cohesive column of water rises.

In about 1725, Stephen Hales observed that water moves upward in the narrow tubes of xylem tissue. He suggested that the upward transport of water is due to capillary action. This was an attractive explanation for the rise of liquids in stems. Unfortunately, however, experiments have shown that capillary action cannot raise water, even in tubes as narrow as those of xylem, more than a few centimeters.

Root pressure. Biologists found that if they cut the stem of a watered plant close to the ground, water flowed out of the stump. They could measure the pressure of this water. What forces in the root push the water upward? One answer is the pressure of water osmosing into millions of root hairs. The sum of all these individual pressures is the *osmotic pressure* of the root. It was also found that cells located within the root's vascular cylinder engage in active transport. The combination of osmotic pressure and active transport are thought to account for *root pressure*. But measurements of this pressure indicate that it could not be the sole factor in upward transport.

Atmospheric pressure. Is it possible for atmospheric pressure to force water to the tops of tall trees? We live at the bottom of a layer of air that is hundreds of miles deep. Air has weight. Why don't you feel the pressure from the column of air that stands above your outstretched hand? Because pressure is exerted in all directions. The upward pressure on the bottom of your hand is nearly the same as the pressure on top.

Atmospheric pressure, in English units, is about 15 pounds per square inch at sea level. You know of instruments that use atmospheric pressure to raise liquids. The soda straw is one such instrument. When you use a soda straw (Fig 6–16), your mouth tends to create a partial vacuum at the top of the straw. The air pressure on the water at the top of the straw is now less than the atmospheric pressure that is transmitted to the bottom of the straw. Unequal forces within the straw cause the water to rise to your mouth.

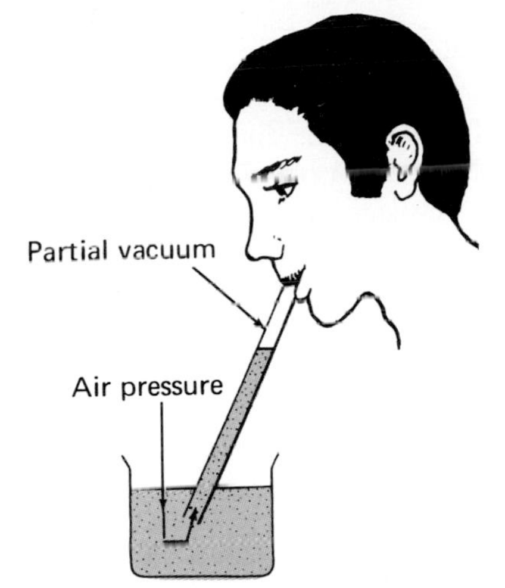

Fig. 6–16. The soda straw. Atmospheric pressure, opposing a partial vacuum, raises liquid in a tube.

If you could produce a total vacuum at the top of a tube, atmospheric pressure could raise water to a height of 10 meters (34 feet). This is the highest that a lift pump can raise water out of a well. Atmospheric pressure has been advanced as a cause for upward transport in plants. But even if, somehow, a vacuum were produced at the top of the xylem tubes, atmospheric pressure could not raise water more than 34 feet.

Transpiration pull–cohesion tension theory. The three explanations described thus far—capillary action, root pressure, and atmospheric pressure—assume that a force from below *pushes* water up the stem. The transpiration–cohesion theory, by contrast, proposes a *pull from above*. According to this theory, a continuous column of water is present in the xylem tubes from the time they are formed in the seedling. Such continuous, fine columns of water have great cohesion. They are like thin steel wires. How are these "wires" pulled up? By transpiration. As water molecules pass out of the leaf's stomata, they exert a pull on the tops of the water columns in the xylem tubes. In this way, a combination of *transpiration* and *cohesion* pulls water from the roots, up the stem, and into the leaves (Fig. 6–17). Thus, although we earlier regarded transpiration as an unfortunate loss of precious water, we see that this process is essential for the life of the plant. Biologists think transpiration–cohesion to be the main reason for the rise of liquids in tall stems.

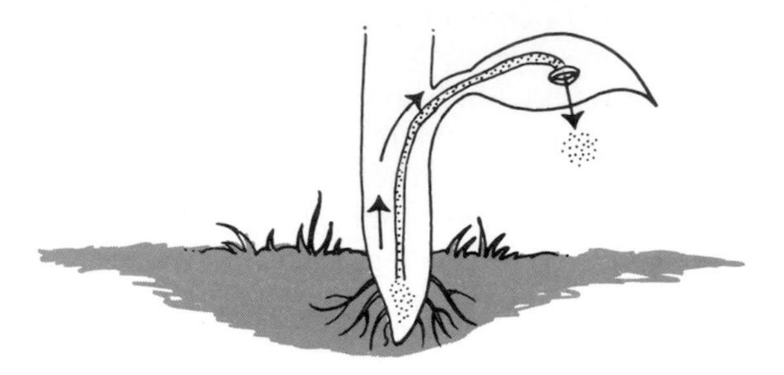

Fig. 6–17. The transpiration–cohesion theory

Downward Transport

Translocation. The transport of food from leaves to other parts of a plant is called *translocation*. Phloem is the tissue that translocates dissolved sugars and proteins to stems, roots, flowers, and fruits. Here these nutrients are used or stored. Although most translocation is downward, in the spring food that has been stored in roots is transported *upward* to stems and leaf buds. The exact mechanism for translocation is not well understood, but current research is disclosing some of the factors involved.

For one thing, experiments have shown that phloem cells engaged in translocation use oxygen. Thus, it is assumed that *active transport* by the living phloem cells plays a role. (Most xylem cells, you recall, are dead.)

Protoplasmic streaming. One of the recent theories that explain transport by phloem tissue is protoplasmic streaming. According to this theory, food is transported from one end of a phloem cell to the other. This is accomplished by the rapid streaming of cytoplasm that, as you recall, is called *cyclosis*. Strands of cytoplasm are known to extend from one phloem cell to the next. This streaming cytoplasm might thus carry food from cell to cell, in a long line. The theory of protoplasmic streaming could account for these puzzling aspects: the speed of translocation, the movement of materials in opposite directions, transport against the concentration gradient, and the use of oxygen and energy.

Reasoning Exercises

1. What is meant by the term *vascular*? What are the two main vascular tissues in an herbaceous stem?
2. How are annual rings formed?
3. Compare xylem and phloem in terms of the direction in which each transports materials. What does each carry?
4. What is an adaptation of root hairs for increasing the amount of absorption?
5. Describe the difference between a scientific law and a scientific theory.
6. Name five theories for the upward transport of liquids in stems.

D Adaptations for Transport in Animals

In single-celled organisms, oxygen enters the cell by diffusion and carbon dioxide leaves in the same way. No part of the cell is so far from its surface that it cannot get enough oxygen and get rid of carbon dioxide by means of ordinary diffusion and cyclosis. Freshwater protists like the ameba and the paramecium are continually taking in water by osmosis, and this must be pumped out by the contractile vacuoles.

Circulation in Hydra

Hydra is built like a hollow sac whose wall is composed of two layers of cells, the ectoderm and the endoderm. Most cells are in contact with water—either with the outside water or with the water within the digestive sac. This simple body plan facilitates the exchange of materials with the external environment. *Hydra* has no special transport system for distributing materials within its body. Materials pass from cell to cell by diffusion.

The single factor that most sharply limits the size of organisms is their transport system. If an ameba were to grow to be a quarter of an inch wide, its center would be so far from the surface that diffusion and cyclosis could not carry sufficient oxygen to the center and remove the wastes. Animals larger than *Hydra* have some sort of circulatory system to carry food and oxygen to the interior and to carry wastes to the external environment.

Circulation in the Earthworm

The earthworm has a special circulatory system containing blood for the transport of materials. It has a *closed circulatory system*. This means that the blood is transported within a closed system of tubes. In an *open circulatory system*, by contrast, the blood leaves the tubes and passes into large open spaces. Grasshoppers have an open circulatory system.

Figure 6–18 shows the main blood vessels in the closed circulatory system of the earthworm. These are the *dorsal* (upper) blood vessel, the *ventral* (lower) blood vessel, and five pairs of *aortic arches*. The dorsal blood vessel carries blood forward (anteriorly). The ventral blood vessel carries blood backward (posteriorly). The aortic arches act as hearts that pump blood from the dorsal to the ventral vessel.

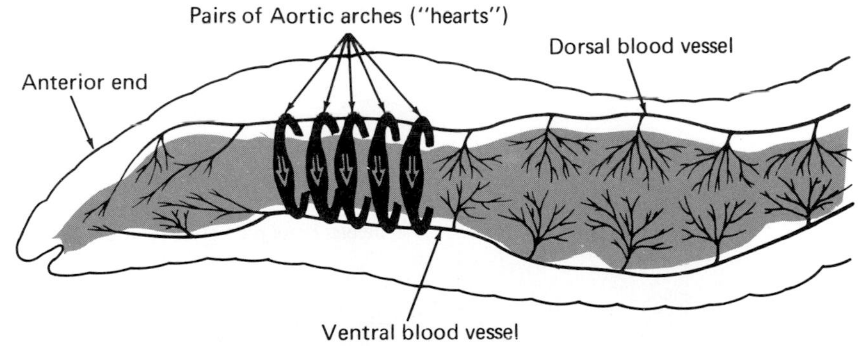

Fig. 6–18. Circulatory system of the earthworm

The smallest branches of the blood vessels are the microscopic thin-walled *capillaries*. Here the exchange of materials between the blood and the cells takes place.

An infolding of the intestine along its length is an adaptation that increases the surface for absorption. Digested foods are picked up by the blood capillaries in the intestine and are then delivered to all the cells of the body. Oxygen is taken into blood capillaries through the moist outer skin. Carbon dioxide is given off at the skin. Nitrogenous wastes are transported by the blood to special excretory structures.

The earthworm's blood carries oxygen and has a hemoglobin-like red pigment to perform this function. Unlike human blood, however, the earthworm's has no red blood cells; the pigment is dissolved in the blood.

As with most multicellular organisms, most of the earthworm's cells are not in direct contact with the external environment. Its circulatory system serves as an intermediary to transport materials between its interior cells and the outside.

Circulation in the Grasshopper

The grasshopper has an *open circulatory system*. Instead of being always enclosed within tubes, the circulating blood at times passes into large open cavities between the tissues called *sinuses*. The *colorless* blood of the grasshopper is pumped by the tubular heart (see Fig. 6–19). A blood vessel carries blood toward the head. The blood then passes through the sinuses between the tissues and returns to the heart. As the blood bathes the tissues, it gives up nutrients and takes up the products of metabolism. The grasshopper's blood is colorless because it does not carry oxygen. Instead, a separate system of air tubes carries oxygen and carbon dioxide.

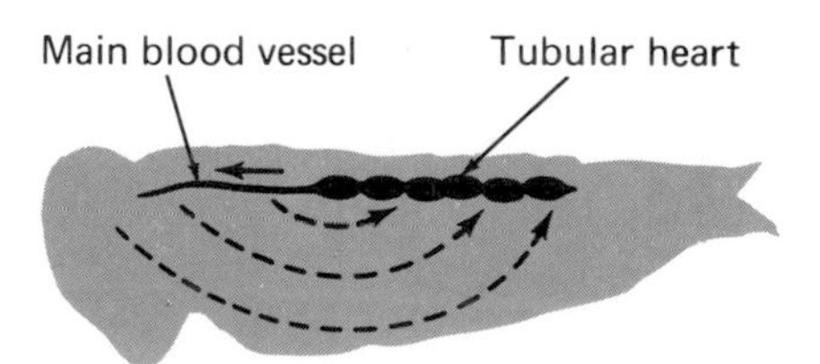

Fig. 6–19. Circulatory system of the grasshopper

Circulation in Humans

In the earthworm and grasshopper, the dorsal blood vessel carries blood forward. In vertebrates, however, the dorsal vessel carries blood to the rear. These two plans of circulation are compared in Figure 6–20.

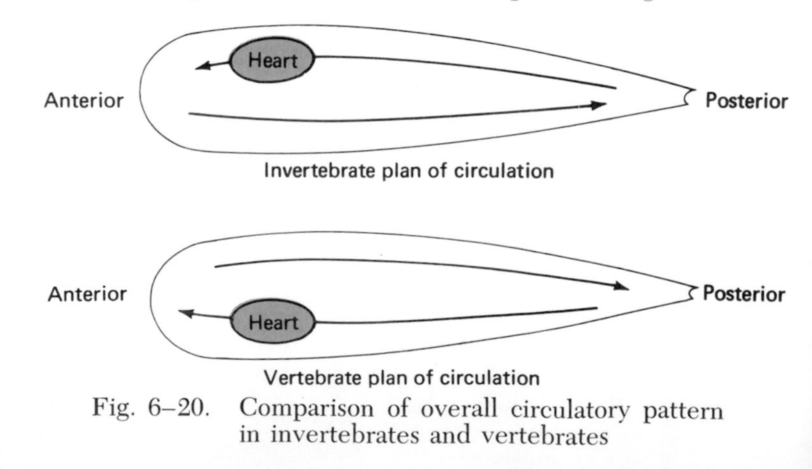

Fig. 6–20. Comparison of overall circulatory pattern in invertebrates and vertebrates

Humans have a closed circulatory system and a blood flow conforming to the overall pattern of circulation in vertebrates. Our blood is pumped by a four-chambered heart through a system of arteries, capillaries, and veins. Hemoglobin, the protein molecule in red blood cells that contains iron, functions to transport oxygen in humans by forming unstable bonds with oxygen molecules.

The transport systems of earthworm, grasshopper, and humans are compared in the following table.

Comparing Transport Systems

	Earthworm	Grasshopper	Human
Open or closed system	Closed	Open	Closed
Pumping organ	5 aortic arches and main vessels	Tubular heart	4 chambered heart
Direction of flow of dorsal vessel	Anterior	Anterior	Posterior
Does circulatory system carry O_2 and CO_2?	Yes	No	Yes

Reasoning Exercises

1. By what type of transport does the paramecium expel excess water? How does it accumulate this excess water? If it did not constantly expel water, what would happen to the organism?
2. Distinguish between the open and closed circulatory systems. Which system circulates blood more rapidly?
3. How do nutrients in the circulatory system of an earthworm enter one of its cells? How is this accomplished in the grasshopper?
4. How do the circulatory systems of the earthworm and grasshopper differ in respect to the transport of oxygen and carbon dioxide?

Completion Questions

A

1. The cell membrane consists of two layers of lipid molecules in which ...... are embedded.
2. When scientists cannot completely describe a process, they often construct a ...... to explain the process.
3. A current model of the cell membrane is called the ......

B

4. If a lump of sugar is placed in a container of water, the sugar molecule and water molecules will become uniformly distributed by the process of ......
5. Membranes which permit only certain substances to pass are said to be ......
6. The shrinking of cell contents caused by outward osmosis is known as ......
7. Active transport is the movement of materials against the......

8. The formation of pockets in the cell membrane for the intake of materials is known as ......

C

9. Food manufactured in the leaves of plants is translocated to the roots chiefly through the ......
10. Epidermal cells called root hairs are specialized for the function of ......
11. Stems of some plants increase in diameter chiefly as a result of cell division in the ......
12. The region of a growing root where elongated cells differentiate into cells with specialized functions is the ......
13. The attraction among water molecules within long xylem tubes is called ......
14. The rise of water in tubes of small diameter is called ......

D

15. Food is passed from cell to cell of *Hydra* by the process of ......
16. In the dorsal blood vessel of the earthworm the blood flows in the ...... direction.
17. The hearts of the earthworm are the ......
18. An example of an organism with colorless blood is the ......
19. The earthworm's blood picks up oxygen through the moist ......
20. Blood circulates slowly in a(n) ...... circulatory system.

Multiple-Choice Questions

A

1. A cell membrane's double layer is composed of (1) protein molecules, (2) phosphorus molecules, (3) phospholipids, (4) hormone molecules.
2. The membrane is considered "fluid" because (1) the molecules can move about, (2) it is composed of water, (3) the proteins have receptor sites, (4) there are spaces in the membrane.
3. Electron micrographs show the cell membrane as (1) two layers of lipid molecules, (2) a head and a tail, (3) phosphorus and oxygen molecules, (4) a double line.

B

4. Diffusion is the process by which (1) molecules or ions move from a region of low concentration to a region of higher concentration, (2) molecules or ions move from a region of high concentration to a region of lower concentration, (3) the same number of molecules or ions move in opposite directions, (4) the molecules or ions do not move.
5. Which of the following can readily pass through the cell membrane? (1) proteins (2) glucose (3) fats (4) starch
6. Molecules pass through a membrane from a low concentration of molecules to a high concentration of those molecules by the process called (1) hydrolysis, (2) active transport, (3) passive transport, (4) diffusion.
7. Which is a characteristic of the cell membrane? (1) It is present only in animals cells. (2) It is nonliving. (3) It is permeable only to water. (4) It selectively regulates the passing of materials.
8. Plasmolysis results from by (1) movement of salt into the cell, (2) active transport, (3) osmosis, (4) cyclosis.

C

9. Which organisms contain vascular tissues? (1) algae (2) bread molds (3) apple trees (4) lichens
10. The major function of xylem tissue in plants is to (1) conduct water upward in a plant, (2) conduct glucose downward in a plant, (3) absorb water and minerals from the soil, (4) absorb oxygen and carbon dioxide from the atmosphere.
11. By counting the annual rings in a branch of a tree you can (1) predict next year's climate, (2) predict how long the tree will live, (3) determine the age of that branch, (4) determine the age of the entire tree.
12. Horizontal transport in stems is accomplished by (1) the cortex, (2) the vascular rays, (3) girdling, (4) photosynthesis.
13. A student placed a stalk of celery in a beaker of water that had been colored with a dye. After a few hours, the student cut the stalk and observed that the dye could be seen scattered in a cross section of the cut stalk. Within which structures in the stem was the dye observed? (1) epidermal cells (2) phloem cells (3) guard cells (4) xylem cells
14. Most of the root hairs of a green plant were destroyed during transplanting, and the plant died after a few days. What is the most likely reason for the death of the plant? (1) The plant's [illegible] was increased. (2) Storage space was destroyed. (3) The absorption surface area was reduced. (4) The hormone concentration was reduced.
15. Phloem tissue in plants is most directly associated with (1) absorption by root hair cells, (2) transpiration pull, (3) conduction of organic materials, (4) capillary action and root pressure.
16. A current theory for downward transport in stems is based upon (1) leaf pressure, (2) root pressure, (3) atmospheric pressure, (4) protoplasmic streaming.

D

17. An organism lacking any special transport system is (1) *Hydra*, (2) earthworm, (3) grasshopper, (4) human.
18. A closed circulatory system is characteristic of (1) *Hydra*, (2) grasshopper, (3) earthworm, (4) *Ameba*.
19. Digested foods enter the transport medium of a closed circulatory system through the (1) heart, (2) arteries, (3) vein, (4) capillaries.
20. A dorsal tubular heart is present in the (1) earthworm, (2) grasshopper, (3) fish, (4) amphibian.

Chapter Test

1. According to the fluid-mosiac model of the cell membrane, the cell's specific requirements of permeability are met by (1) the spaces between the double layer, (2) randomly distributed phospholipids, (3) oxygen and phosphorus molecules embedded in the lipid layers, (4) protein molecules.
2. The cell membrane consists mainly of (1) cellulose and lipid, (2) nucleic acid and glucose, (3) lipid layers containing protein molecules, (4) lipid bearing glucose molecules.

3. Several hours after the apparatus shown in the diagram was set up, the outer water was tested with iodine. The iodine did not change color.

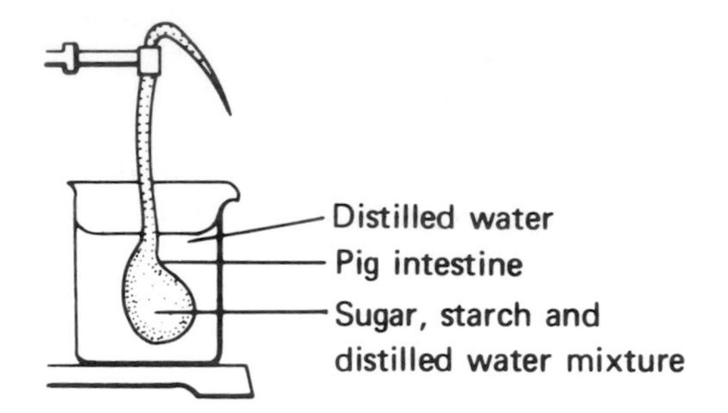

A possible reason for a negative result is that the (1) starch molecules were too large to pass through the membrane, (2) sugar molecules were too large to pass through the membrane, (3) starch was diluted too much by the water, (4) sugar was diluted too much by the water.

4. Which organisms have an open circulatory system? (1) grasshoppers (2) fish (3) earthworms (4) humans
5. The movement of materials against a concentration gradient is known as (1) active transport, (2) fermentation, (3) diffusion, (4) osmosis.
6. A crystal of blue copper sulfate is placed at the bottom of a cylinder of water. In a few days, a blue color has reached partly up the cylinder. This movement is an example of (1) active transport, (2) diffusion, (3) osmosis, (4) pinocytosis.
7. Redwood trees over 250 feet tall are able to transport water to their highest branches. The structures most directly responsible for this transport are (1) xylem vessels, (2) phloem tubes, (3) chloroplasts, (4) cell walls.
8. That mosses lack xylem accounts in part for the fact that mosses (1) often grow best in mountainous regions, (2) can survive in a very dry region, (3) seldom grow more than a few inches tall, (4) are unable to absorb and store water.
9. In a woody stem, the xylem and phloem tubes are separated from each other by a layer of cells known as (1) epidermal cells, (2) palisade cells, (3) spongy cells, (4) cambium cells.
10. Pruning some of the branches from a newly transplanted tree may prove to be helpful because this will result in (1) an increase in mutations, (2) a reduction in transpiration, (3) greater absorption of water, (4) more rapid vegetative propagation.
11. The major factors causing the rise of water to the top of tall trees are probably (1) root pressure and cohesion, (2) capillary action and adhesion, (3) cohesion-tension and transpiration pull, (4) atmospheric pressure and root pressure.
12. If the cut end of the stem of a white carnation is placed in red dye, the petals will eventually become red. This is evidence that (1) some plants can grow without roots, (2) the cambium layer is present in the stem, (3) xylem tissue is located throughout the length of the stem, (4) root hairs are adapted for absorption.

13. A root hair cell may continue to absorb minerals even though the cytoplasmic concentration of these minerals is greater inside the cell than in the soil. This absorption is accomplished chiefly as a result of (1) passive transport, (2) active transport, (3) diffusion, (4) osmosis.
14. Minerals in solution enter bean plants chiefly through structures called (1) lenticels, (2) stomates, (3) root hairs, (4) guard cells.
15. As a result of the function of root hairs, the fluid within the xylem tubes shows an increase in the amount of (1) chlorophyll, (2) glucose, (3) nitrates, (4) proteins.

For items 16 through 20, select the letter of the term best described by each statement.

A. upper epidermis
B. root hairs
C. guard cell
D. phloem
E. palisade layer
F. cambium
G. xylem

16. Increase in diameter of stem.
17. Provides increased surface for absorption.
18. Regulates rate of transpiration.
19. Tissue where photosynthesis occurs.
20. Food travels downward in stems.

For questions 21 through 25 write the letter of the means of transport in living organisms that have the characteristic described by each statement.

Means of Transport

A. An open blood system.
B. A closed blood system.
C. Both an open and a closed blood system.
D. Neither an open nor a closed blood system.

21. Digested nutrients are transported in a liquid medium.
22. A pumping mechanism enables the blood to circulate.
23. Materials are transported very rapidly.
24. *Hydra* is able to transport materials to all its cells.
25. Blood moves out from the heart to the sinuses.

Chapter 7 Respiration

You need the air's supply of oxygen in order to release the chemical energy stored in food. Such activities as muscle contraction, active transport across cell membranes, synthesis of complex compounds from simple ones, and cell division all require energy. The life process of releasing the potential energy of food in a usable form is called *respiration*. Respiration involves more than breathing. Breathing merely moves air in and out of the lungs. The essential part of respiration is oxidation that occurs in an organism's cells. This process is called *cellular respiration*.

A

Energy Changes

The chemical energy present in the organic molecules of food comes from the sun. The sun's radiant energy is transferred to chemical bond energy during the process of *photosynthesis* which occurs in green plants and algae.

The reverse relationship between photosynthesis and respiration is indicated by the double arrows in the equation below:

$$\text{Energy} + \text{carbon dioxide} + \text{water} \underset{\text{respiration}}{\overset{\text{photosynthesis}}{\rightleftarrows}} \text{glucose} + \text{oxygen}$$

As photosynthesis proceeds (from left to right in the equation), energy is stored in the form of glucose. As respiration proceeds (from right to left in the equation), this energy is released for use by cells. The equation shows that photosynthesis stores energy in glucose, whereas respiration releases this energy for use by cells.

An overall equation for respiration, as it occurs in most cells, is:

$$C_6H_{12}O_6 + 6O_2 \rightarrow 6CO_2 + 6H_2O + \text{energy}$$

This equation indicates raw materials and end products of the process, but it gives the impression that respiration occurs as a simple one-step chemical reaction. Actually, respiration within the cell consists of a complex series of reactions controlled by numerous enzymes. Although the above equation shows the oxidation of glucose, the cell may also obtain energy by the oxidation of other energy-rich organic compounds.

Oxidation and Reduction

We generally think of oxidation as the union of a substance with oxygen. Thus, when iron combines with oxygen to form rust, we say that the iron has been oxidized. For the chemist, however, *oxidation is the loss of hydrogen or of electrons*. The opposite process, the gain of hydrogen or of electrons, is called *reduction*. The element oxygen need not be involved in either process. (As a mnemonic device, note that both the words *o*xidation and l*o*ss have the letter *o*.)

The substance that loses hydrogen or electrons is said to be *oxidized;* the substance that gains hydrogen or electrons is said to be *reduced*. If one substance loses hydrogen, another substance gains hydrogen; thus oxidation and reduction reactions proceed at the same time.

Comparison of Burning and Respiration

Both burning and cellular respiration are processes whereby the chemical process of oxidation releases potential energy stored in organic molecules. In both kinds of oxidation, the fuel possesses potential energy in the form of its chemical bonds. These are mainly carbon-carbon and carbon-hydrogen bonds (or C—C and C—H bonds).

Burning releases this stored energy in the form of heat energy and light energy. Cellular respiration, however, releases this energy mainly in the form of high-energy bonds of a special molecule called *adenosine triphosphate*, commonly called *ATP*. ATP later releases its energy for powering chemical reactions within the cell.

The energy required to start a chemical reaction is called its *activation energy*. Different chemical reactions require different amounts of activation energy. The process of burning requires much activation energy in the form of heat. The enzymes that play a part in many biochemical reactions, however, lower the activation energy that is required. Accordingly, the enzyme-controlled chemical reactions of cellular respiration proceed at a low temperature that does not kill the cell.

Burning is a one-step chemical reaction that releases much heat. Cellular respiration, however, consists of a lengthy series of chemical reactions that gradually yields many molecules of energy-rich ATP.

The chemical process of oxidation does not always require oxygen. Burning always requires oxygen and is therefore an *aerobic* oxidation. During cellular respiration, however, some stages of oxidation do not use oxygen and are *anaerobic* oxidations. An organism that uses only anaerobic respiration is called an *anaerobe;* one that uses molecular oxygen at some stage is an *aerobe*. Humans, of course, are aerobes. The bacterium that causes tetanus (lockjaw) is an anaerobe, which explains why it can live in a deep puncture wound without air.

Comparison of Burning and Cellular Respiration

Burning	Cellular Respiration
Uncontrolled, rapid release of energy with accompanying high temperatures	Slower release of energy in measured amounts at temperatures that do not injure the cell
Not controlled by enzymes	Controlled by enzymes
Most of the energy released in the form of heat and light	Most of the energy used to create new chemical bonds of ATP; only a small amount of heat energy liberated
Single chemical reaction	Series of interrelated chemical reactions
Uses oxygen (aerobic)	One form of cellular respiration occurs **with** the use of oxygen (aerobic); another form of cellular respiration occurs **without** the use of oxygen (anaerobic).

The Role of ATP

ATP transfers energy from one set of biochemical reactions to another. It is present in relatively low concentrations in the cell and therefore is not primarily a means of energy storage. Carbohydrates and fats serve that function. ATP makes energy immediately available for chemical reactions. For this reason, ATP has been called the "energy currency" of the cell. For example, ATP can serve as a medium of exchange to carry energy from the mitochondria to the cilia.

The structural formula for ATP (Fig. 7–1) seems complex, but we can break it down into three main units. At the left is a double-ringed unit, containing nitrogen, that is called *adenine.* This is linked to the five-carbon sugar called *ribose.* Adenine and ribose together are known as *adenosine.* We can use the symbol A to represent adenosine. Then come three groups of atoms containing phosphorus. These are called *phosphate groups* and are given the symbol *P.* Notice the wavy lines (∽) connecting the last two phosphate groups. These represent *high-energy* bonds. Accordingly, we can represent the ATP molecule as:

A	—	P∽P∽P	or	A – P∽P∽P
adenosine		triphosphate		

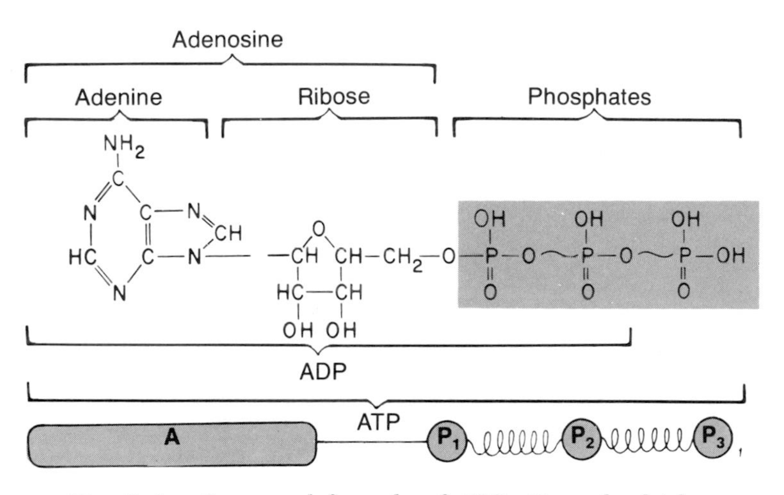

Fig. 7–1. Structural formula of ATP. Note the high-energy bonds (represented as ∽) between the last two phosphate groups.

If one phosphate is removed from ATP, the remaining molecule is called *adenosine diphosphate,* or *ADP.* This molecule has only two phosphate groups and can be represented as A-P∽P. ADP carries less chemical bond energy than ATP.

In chemical reactions, when bonds are broken and new bonds are formed, energy is released. The high-energy bonds of ATP liberate more than twice as much free energy as do the usual phosphate bonds.

Breaking the high-energy bond that holds the third phosphate group has this result:

$$\underset{\text{ATP}}{A - P{\sim}P{\sim}P} \xrightarrow{\text{ATP-ase}} \underset{\text{ADP}}{A - P{\sim}P} + \underset{\text{high-energy phosphate}}{{\sim}P}$$

The hydrolysis and synthesis of ATP can be represented as the equation:

$$H_2O + ATP \overset{\text{ATP-ase}}{\rightleftharpoons} ADP + P + \text{energy}$$

The double arrow shows that the reaction is reversible. During cellular respiration, the reaction proceeds to the left, and ADP takes on energy to form ATP. When the ATP is used in metabolic functions, the reaction proceeds to the right, and ATP releases energy. ATP-ase is the enzyme that regulates these reactions.

ADP and ATP carry energy from those reactions in the cell that release energy to those that use energy. This cycle is shown in Figure 7–2.

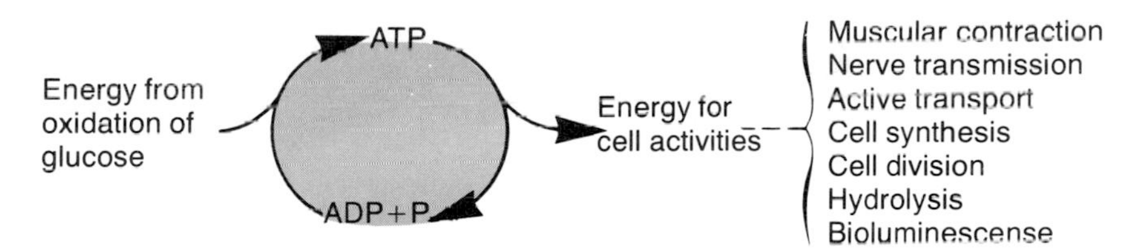

Fig. 7–2. The ADP-ATP cycle makes energy from glucose available for cell activities.

Reasoning Exercises

1. In what ways are photosynthesis and respiration opposite processes from one another?
2. How are cellular respiration and burning similar? How are they different?
3. Describe the structure of ATP.
4. Explain how ATP-ase functions in both the hydrolysis and synthesis of ATP.
5. Describe oxidation. What does it have to do with oxygen?

B

Pattern of Cellular Respiration

With this background about ATP and oxidation, you are now ready to examine the overall pattern of cellular respiration. Figure 7–3 shows that cellular respiration occurs in two phases. At the left is shown the anaerobic phase, which does not use oxygen; and at the right is the *aerobic phase,* which does use oxygen.

The Anaerobic Phase

Oxidation of a molecule of glucose begins with the activation energy provided by two molecules of ATP which are already present in the cell. In a series of enzyme-controlled reactions, one molecule of 6-carbon *glucose*

($C_6H_{12}O_6$) is oxidized to two molecules of the 3-carbon *pyruvic acid* ($C_3H_4O_3$). Counting atoms shows a loss of four hydrogen atoms. This hydrogen loss is an *oxidation*.

The energy released by this oxidation is stored in the high-energy phosphate bonds of ATP. The oxidation of glucose to pyruvic acid is coupled with the synthesis of four molecules of ATP. The enzymes that regulate the anaerobic phase of respiration are located in the cytoplasm of cells.

The pyruvic acid formed in this first series of reactions is the starting point for several other reactions. (See Fig. 7–3.) In anaerobic organisms, pyruvic acid may be converted to (1) *alcohol and carbon dioxide* or (2) *lactic acid*, depending upon the enzymes present. No additional oxidation occurs during these reactions, and no additional ATPs are formed.

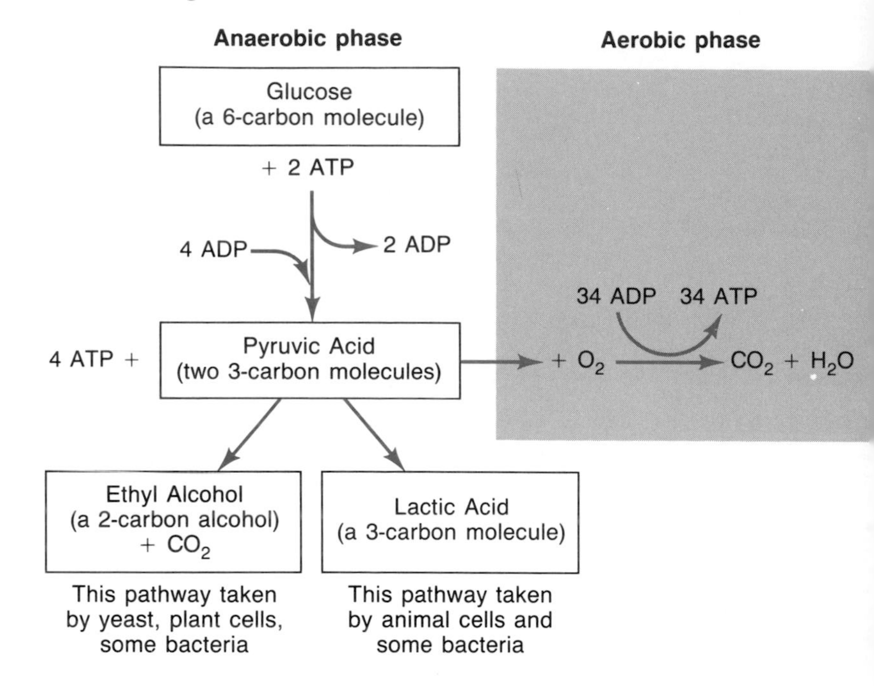

Fig. 7–3. The overall pattern of cellular respiration. One glucose molecule is oxidized to two pyruvic acid molecules, releasing energy for the synthesis of four ATP molecules. Note that two ATP molecules are needed to activate anaerobic oxidation of glucose. Pyruvic acid is then the starting point for three different pathways. In the aerobic pathway, which leads to the products carbon dioxide and water, much more energy is released for the synthesis of ATP molecules. In the fermentation pathways leading to alcohol and lactic acid, no energy for ATP synthesis is released.

Fermentation. All the steps of anaerobic respiration described above, starting from glucose, are also known as *fermentation*. Yeast cells possess the necessary enzymes for the fermentation of sugar to alcohol and carbon dioxide.

Lactic acid bacteria possess enzymes for the series of steps leading to the formation of lactic acid. Fermentation by these bacteria produces yogurt, sauerkraut, and pickles.

The production of gas during the fermentation of sugar by yeast may be demonstrated in the laboratory with a fermentation tube (see Fig. 7–4).

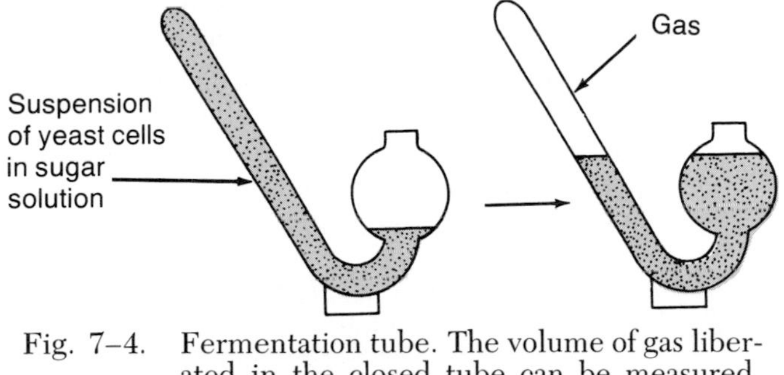

Fig. 7–4. Fermentation tube. The volume of gas liberated in the closed tube can be measured. You can compare the effects of temperature, different kinds of sugar, and different strains of yeast. At the start, what holds up the liquid in the closed tube?

When athletes engage in short bursts of vigorous exercise, such as a sprint, their muscle cells do not receive sufficient oxygen for aerobic respiration. Instead, these cells carry on only anaerobic respiration and produce lactic acid. The accumulated lactic acid reduces the capacity of muscle cells to contract, producing the sensation of *fatigue*. The oxygen debt to these cells is later repaid during sustained moderate exercise when increased intake of air by the lungs and increased blood circulation provide sufficient oxygen to the muscle cells. This is the period of second wind, well known to runners. The lactic acid is carried by the blood to the liver, where it is converted back to glucose or glycogen.

Although four ATPs are formed during the reactions of anaerobic respiration, two ATPs are used to start the reactions. The net gain from one molecule of glucose is two ATPs:

$$\text{Glucose} \xrightarrow{\text{enzymes}} 2 \text{ Lactic acid} + 2 \text{ ATP or}$$

$$\text{Glucose} \xrightarrow{\text{enzymes}} 2 \text{ Alcohol} + 2 \text{ CO}_2 + 2 \text{ ATP}$$

The end products, lactic acid and alcohol, still contain much potential energy.

The Aerobic Phase

In aerobic organisms, the steps of anaerobic oxidation are followed by an aerobic phase that uses molecular oxygen. In Figure 7–3, the aerobic phase is shown by a single horizontal arrow, starting from *pyruvic acid*. This arrow, however, actually represents a complex series of enzyme-controlled chemical reactions that follow in consecutive order. Energy that is released step-by-step gradually helps to form 34 molecules of ATP from two molecules of pyruvic acid.

How are the end products carbon dioxide and water formed? The 3-carbon pyruvic acid is broken down to 1-carbon CO_2. The water is formed in a surprising manner. Hydrogen atoms that have been carried along by a chain of compounds combine with molecular oxygen as the very last step in aerobic respiration. Thus, the oxygen that is so important in aerobic respiration does not participate until the end of the series of chemical reactions.

Why are mitochondria called "the powerhouses of the cell"? Most of the cell's ATP is synthesized at the mitochondria. The enzymes that function in the *aerobic* phase of respiration are located on the shelves of the mitochondria or within their fluid (see Fig. 7–5). The reactions of *anaerobic* respiration, however, occur within the general cytoplasm.

Overall summary equations for aerobic respiration of glucose are:

$$\text{Glucose} + \text{Oxygen} \xrightarrow{\text{enzymes}} \text{Water} + \text{Carbon dioxide} + \text{ATP}$$

$$C_6H_{12}O_6 + 6O_2 \xrightarrow{\text{enzymes}} 6H_2O + 6CO_2 + 36\ \text{ATP}$$

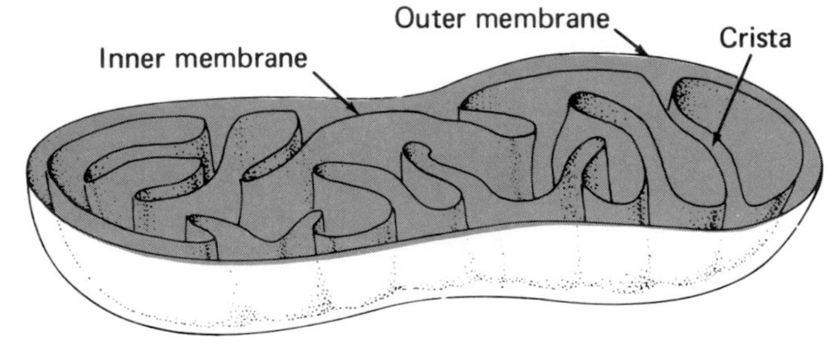

Fig. 7–5. The mitochondrion. This diagram of the internal structure shows shelves of the inner membrane on which are present enzymes that catalyze reactions of the aerobic phase of respiration.

ATP Production

Biologists have recently refined their analysis of the number of molecules of ATP produced during the aerobic respiration of one molecule of glucose. The number differs for prokaryotic and eukaryotic organisms. The prokaryotes are those simple organisms that lack a defined nucleus—the monerans (bacteria and blue-green algae). The eukaryotes have a defined nucleus. The organisms of all the kingdoms except the monerans are eukaryotes. Scientists now believe that the more primitive prokaryotes produce 38 molecules of ATP from a molecule of glucose and eukaryotes produce 36 molecules of ATP.

Ⓒ Chemistry of Cellular Respiration

In anaerobic respiration, glucose is converted to pyruvic acid which is then converted to either lactic acid or alcohol. In aerobic respiration, there are both anaerobic and aerobic phases.

Chemistry of the Anaerobic Phase

As we have seen in Figure 7–3, anaerobic respiration involves two series of reactions. In the first series, one molecule of glucose is converted to two molecules of pyruvic acid. The removal of hydrogen atoms in this series of reactions represents oxidation in which energy is released without the presence of oxygen. The hydrogen atoms that are removed from the glucose are picked up by *coenzymes* and released in subsequent reactions.

The decomposition of the pyruvic acid does not yield additional ATPs. The two series of reactions that constitute the anaerobic respiration phase may be summarized as follows:

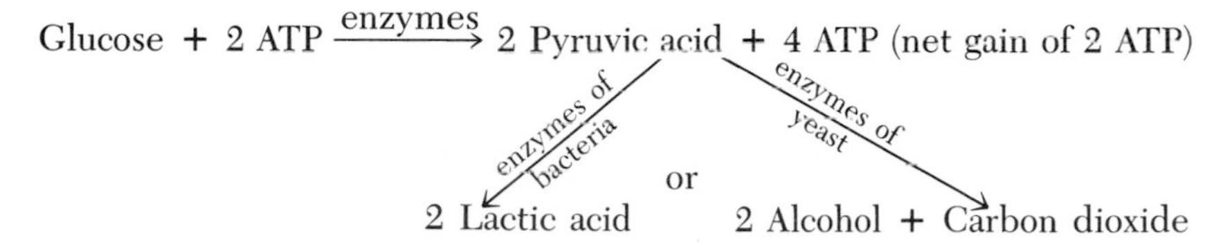

emistry of the Aerobic Phase

The aerobic phase of aerobic respiration begins with the pyruvic acid produced in the anaerobic phase. This phase is called aerobic because free oxygen participates in one of its numerous chemical reactions. A broad overview of the biochemistry of the aerobic phase is given in Figure 7–6. This figure shows that the chemical reactions can be divided into two main groups: the *Krebs cycle* and the *electron transport chain*.

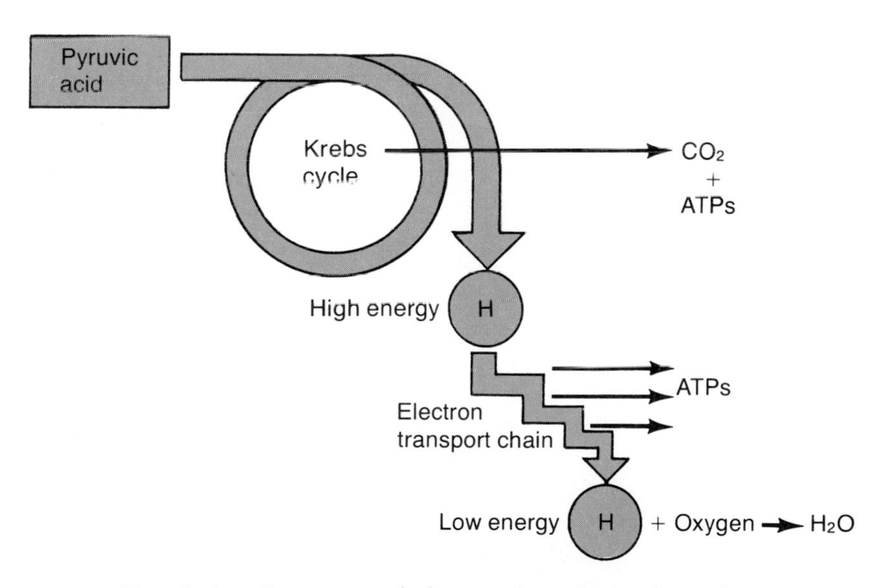

Fig. 7–6. Overview of the aerobic phase of aerobic respiration. The two major sets of reactions are the Krebs cycle and the electron transport chain. Molecular oxygen does not participate until the last step.

The Krebs Cycle

The Krebs cycle is named for Sir Hans Krebs of Oxford University, England, who discovered many of its details and was awarded a Nobel prize in 1953 for his contributions to science. A chemical cycle consists of a series of reactions having products among which is the original substance. As indicated in Figure 7–6, each turn of the wheel of the Krebs cycle produces the following:

1. *Carbon dioxide molecules.* This is one of the final products of aerobic respiration. The 3-carbon pyruvic acid is broken down to 1-carbon molecules of carbon dioxide.

2. *ATP molecules.* Some of the reactions are oxidations that release energy to form ATP, another final product of aerobic respiration.

3. *Hydrogen.* This is *high-energy* hydrogen, which means that the electron of the atom travels in an orbit that is distant from its nucleus. The hydrogen atoms that are released are picked up by coenzymes. (For example, the coenzyme known as NAD is reduced to form $NADH_2$.)

Additional details of the Krebs cycle are shown in Figure 7–7. Note the steps that release CO_2, ATP, and H. As they are released, the hydrogen atoms are picked up by coenzymes and carried to the electron transport chain. The Krebs cycle is also known as the *citric acid cycle.*

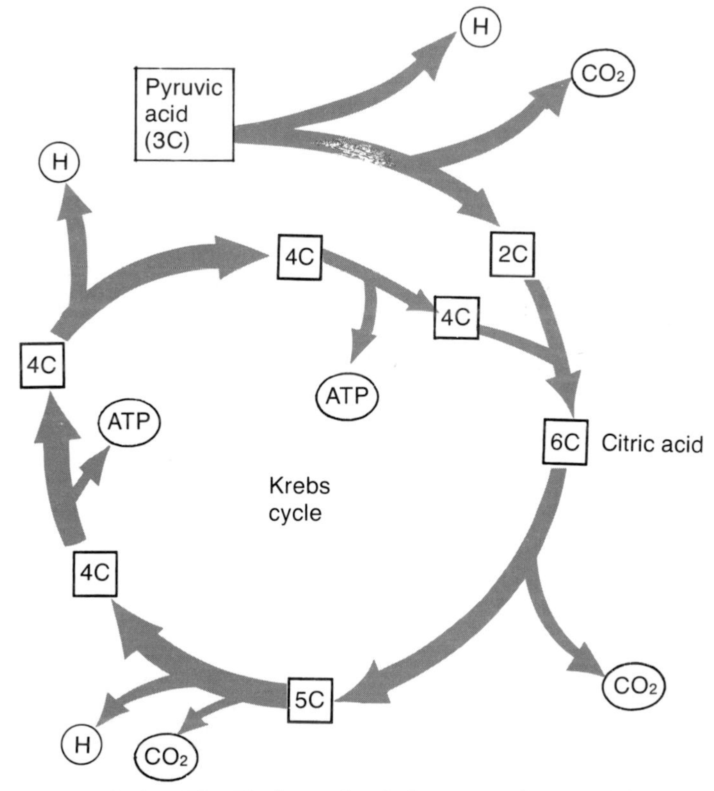

Fig. 7–7. The Krebs cycle. Substances that participate in this series of chemical reactions are indicated by the number of carbon atoms in their molecule. For example, 6C = citric acid.

The Electron Transport Chain. The electron transport chain (see Fig. 7–6) consists of a series of oxidation-reduction reactions that gradually liberate energy for the formation of many ATP molecules. This series of reactions is depicted in the figure as a series of steps in which high-energy hydrogen becomes low-energy hydrogen.

Until now there has been no mention of the *free oxygen* that is such an important raw material in aerobic respiration. The free oxygen does not participate until the final step. At this point it acts as a *hydrogen acceptor*. The oxygen combines with hydrogen to form water, a by-product of respiration.

During the aerobic phase, most organisms produce 34 ATPs for a total of 36 ATPs for the entire process of aerobic respiration from one molecule of glucose. The raw materials and products of aerobic respiration can be summarized as follows:

Aerobic Respiration	
Raw Materials	**Products**
glucose—anaerobically oxidized to pyruvic acid	carbon dioxide—liberated during the Krebs cycle
oxygen—serves as a hydrogen acceptor in the final step	water—produced in the final step by the oxidation of low-energy hydrogen
	ATP—produced at various stages as energy is released during oxidation

The relationship between the anaerobic and aerobic phases of aerobic cellular respiration can be summarized as follows:

Anaerobic phase:

$$\text{Glucose} + 2\text{ ATP} \xrightarrow{\text{enzymes}} 2\text{ Pyruvic acid} + 4\text{ ATP (net gain} = 2\text{ ATP)}$$

Aerobic phase:

$$2\text{ Pyruvic acid} + \text{Oxygen} \xrightarrow{\text{enzymes}} \text{Carbon dioxide} + \text{Water} + 34\text{ ATP}$$

$$\text{Total} = 36\text{ ATP}$$

D Gas Exchange

The oxygen taken into a cell for respiration and the carbon dioxide that is given off, pass through the cell membrane by *diffusion*. Plants and multicellular animals, however, generally have a thick outer covering such as bark or skin that bars the passage of these respiratory gases. Multicellular animals solve this problem in a variety of ways, usually by the presence of a special *respiratory surface*. Consider, for example, the earthworm which has a thin, moist skin adjacent to its circulatory system, as shown in Figure 7–8.

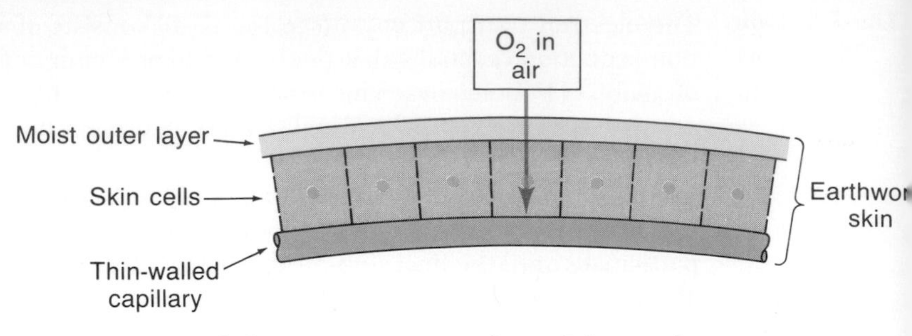

Fig. 7–8. Respiratory surface of the earthworm

Although there are numerous variations of this pattern, the diagram above illustrates the characteristics of an ideal respiratory surface. It is: (1) thin; (2) moist; (3) close to a source of oxygen; (4) close to a gas transport system.

The gills of a fish also show the general pattern indicated above. Blood capillaries close to the surface of the gill absorb dissolved oxygen from the water. The blood then transports the oxygen to all the cells. When a fish is taken from a lake to open air, the fish dies for lack of oxygen. Why should this be so when the atmosphere is so rich in oxygen? The fish dies because its gill membranes become dry. Then these membranes no longer permit the diffusion of oxygen into the blood.

E

Adaptations for Respiration

We have seen that the chemical steps in cellular respiration are similar in most organisms. Living organisms, however, have various structural adaptations for the exchange of respiratory gases. Complex organisms utilizing aerobic respiration must carry oxygen from the external environment to every cell in the interior. Accordingly, respiration in these organisms includes not only the oxidation that occurs in the individual cells, but also mechanisms for the transport of oxygen to the cells and for the removal of carbon dioxide. The respiratory system, therefore, is intimately linked to the transport system. The multicellular organism faces the problem of using its limited body surface in such a manner as to meet the respiratory needs of its millions of internal body cells.

Monera, Protista, and Fungi

Bacteria, blue-green algae, protozoa, algae, and molds are mostly single-celled or colonial organisms. The gas exchange takes place by diffusion through the thin, moist cell membrane that surrounds the cells. Cell walls, where present, constitute no barrier to the diffusion of oxygen and carbon dioxide.

Adaptations in Plants

The multicellular green plant carries on both aerobic respiration and photosynthesis. Carbon dioxide produced in the leaf during respiration may be used immediately for photosynthesis. Oxygen produced during photosynthesis may be used for respiration. Photosynthesis, however, occurs only when light energy is available.

Although green plants carry on both respiration and photosynthesis, their energy needs are slight as compared with animals. The net result of plant respiration and photosynthesis is that plants add more oxygen to the atmosphere than they take in and they remove more carbon dioxide than they liberate.

The leaf of a plant is covered by a dry, impermeable *cuticle* that prevents the admission of oxygen to cells deep in the interior. Within the leaf, however, are large moist spaces between the cells (see Fig. 5–9). These *air spaces* open to the outside by means of the stomata, openings in the leaf surface. Because the cells lining the air spaces are moist, diffusion of oxygen and carbon dioxide occurs through their cell membranes. The exchange of gases in the leaf, thus, occurs across the membranes of internal cells.

The stems of woody plants have small openings called *lenticels*. These permit the exchange of respiratory gases with the external environment. Roots obtain oxygen from air that is present in loose soil. Dissolved in water, the oxygen diffuses through the moist cell membranes of *root hairs* and other cells of the root's epidermis.

Adaptations in Animals

Hydra. The thin, two-cell layered structure of *Hydra* permits almost all of its cells to be in contact with the oxygen-bearing water. As with unicellular organisms, oxygen diffuses into the cells and carbon dioxide diffuses out through the cell membranes. No special system for the transport of respiratory gases is present in *Hydra*.

Earthworm. The skin of the earthworm has a rich supply of blood capillaries. Oxygen diffuses readily into the blood through the thin skin, which is kept moist by mucus. The oxygen is carried by the blood to all the cells of the body. The blood transport system also carries carbon dioxide back to the capillaries of the skin where it diffuses out through the moist skin. Earthworms trapped on a sidewalk after a rain die when the moist skin dries.

The blood transport system of many animals serves to link their cells with a thin, moist membrane that is exposed to the external environment. During the course of evolution, transport systems have evolved respiratory pigments that can carry more oxygen and carbon dioxide than ordinary water. Hemoglobin is an iron-containing respiratory pigment that is red in color. In the earthworm, a kind of hemoglobin is dissolved in the liquid part of the blood. In humans, hemoglobin occurs in red blood cells. A comparison of the oxygen-carrying capacity of these fluids is given in the following table.

Note that earthworm blood carries 13 times as much oxygen as does plain water, and human blood carries 50 times as much.

Comparison of Capacity of Fluids to Carry Oxygen

Fluid:	Water	Blood of Earthworms (hemoglobin dissolved in its blood)	Blood of Humans (hemoglobin in red blood cells)
Oxygen carried by 1000 ml of fluid:	5 ml	65 ml	250 ml

Grasshopper. The grasshopper's body surface is dry and impermeable to oxygen and carbon dioxide. It possesses ten openings along the side of the body for taking in air. These openings are called *spiracles*. The spiracles lead to a system of branched tubes, called *tracheae*. These subdivide into smaller and smaller tubes that reach all parts of the body. Pulsating contractions of the body wall draw air into the tubes and force it out. The inner end of the thin, tracheal tubes contains a fluid. Here is the thin, moist membrane for the exchange of gases with the tissues.

Since air is brought directly to the cells by the system of tracheal tubes, the grasshopper's blood does not contain hemoglobin for the transport of oxygen.

Human. The nostrils and mouth of the human are relatively small external openings in the skin, that are impermeable to respiratory gases.

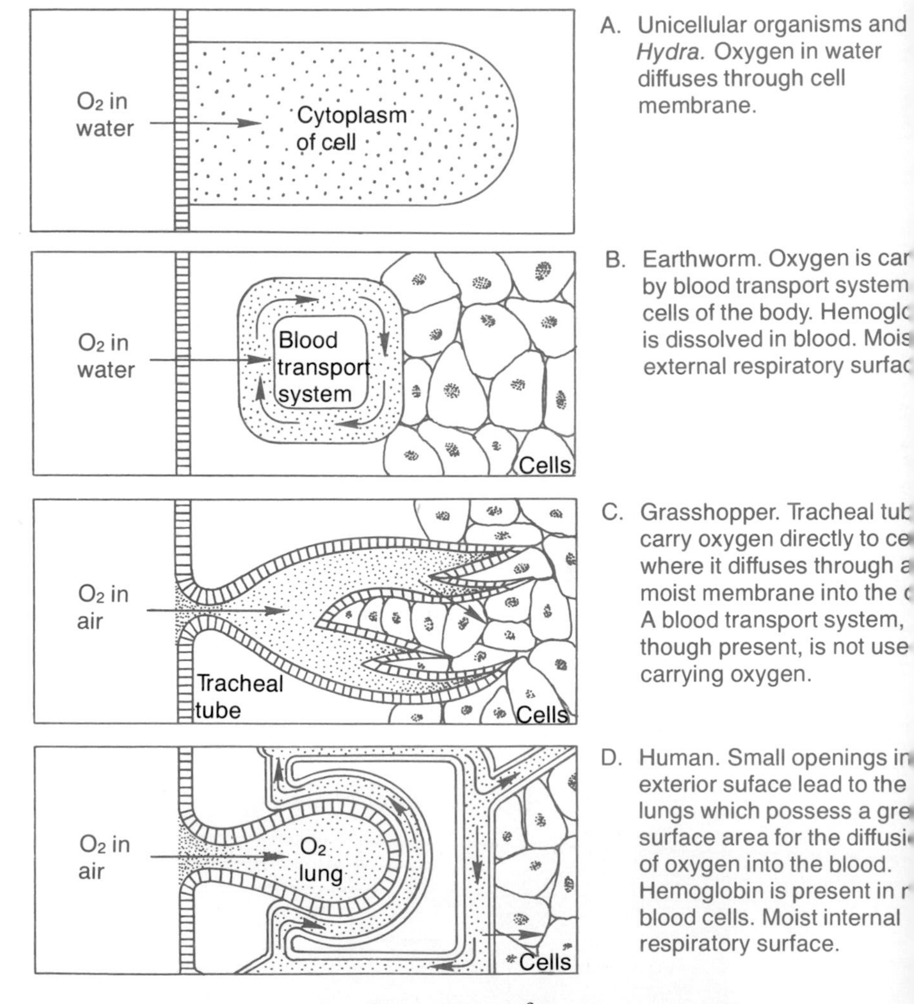

Fig. 7–9. Comparison of respiratory patterns

The trachea (windpipe) and its divisions branch throughout the lungs and end in many small air sacs. Around these air sacs are respiratory membranes separating the air system from capillaries of the circulatory system.

Air sacs in the lungs provide much surface area for the diffusion of oxygen into the blood and for the removal of carbon dioxide. Unlike the earthworm, which has an *external* respiratory surface, the human has an *internal* respiratory surface—thin moist membranes surrounding the air sacs within the lungs. Respiration in humans is more fully described in Chapter 13.

The adaptations for respiration among animals are summarized in Figure 7–9. Only the movement of oxygen is indicated in these diagrams, but the reverse movement of carbon dioxide is implied. In each case, a thin moist membrane is involved.

Reasoning Exercises

1. What characteristics are common to the respiratory surfaces of an earthworm and a human?
2. Distinguish between the respiratory surfaces of an earthworm and a human.
3. Why does a fish die when it is taken from water, even though there is more oxygen in the atmosphere than in the water?
4. Why does the blood of an earthworm carry more oxygen than does an equivalent volume of water?
5. Why might you expect the grasshopper's blood to lack hemoglobin?

Completion questions

A

1. The enzyme that regulates the conversion of ATP to ADP is . . . . . .
2. A gas released by animals during respiration is . . . . . .
3. The name of a compound that transports energy in biochemical reactions is . . . . . .
4. When ATP gives up energy and a phosphate group, it becomes . . . . . .
5. Oxidation is the loss of . . . . . . or . . . . . .
6. Reduction is the gain of . . . . . . or . . . . . .
7. Organisms that use molecular oxygen during respiration are . . . . . .

B

8. Many of the enzymes involved in cellular respiration are located in organelles known as . . . . . .
9. When yeast ferments sugar, the end products are . . . . . . and . . . . . .
10. Two products of aerobic respiration are . . . . . . and . . . . . .
11. During strenuous muscular activity, cells may carry on anaerobic respiration and produce the substance . . . . . .

12. In the anaerobic respiration of one molecule of glucose, the net gain of ATP for eukaryotes is . . . . . .
13. In the aerobic respiration of one molecule of glucose, the net gain of ATP by eukaryotes is . . . . . .
14. Aerobic respiration is almost . . . . . . times as efficient as anaerobic respiration.
15. In monerans, one molecule of glucose may aerobically yield as many as . . . . . . molecules of ATP.

C

16. A cyclic series of enzyme reactions that occurs during aerobic respiration is known as the . . . . . .
17. The series of reactions in the aerobic phase that releases CO_2 is known as the . . . . . .
18. High-energy hydrogen becomes low-energy hydrogen in a series of reactions called the . . . . . .
19. The molecular oxygen used in aerobic respiration later appears in the product . . . . . .

D

20. The respiratory gases pass through cell membranes by the process of . . . . . .
21. A fish taken from water dies because its respiratory surface becomes . . . . . .
22. The respiratory surface should be close to a source of . . . . . .
23. An ideal respiratory surface has a structure that is . . . . . . and . . . . . .

E

24. The openings for the passage of gases in the stems of woody plants are called . . . . . .
25. In protozoa, respiratory gases are exchanged between the organism and its environment through the . . . . . .
26. The skin of the earthworm is kept moist by . . . . . .
27. Hemoglobin contains the metallic element . . . . . .
28. Blood can carry a larger supply of . . . . . . than water carries because of the presence of hemoglobin.
29. The thin moist respiratory membrane of the grasshopper is present at the inner ends of the . . . . . .
30. The openings of the grasshopper's respiratory system are called . . . . . .

Multiple Choice

A

1. During the process of respiration, energy from the oxidation of glucose is stored in molecules of (1) ATP, (2) DNA, (3) ADP, (4) RNA.
2. When do green plants carry on cellular respiration? (1) only during the night, (2) only during the day, (3) during both the night and the day, (4) neither during the night nor during the day
3. Oxidation may be considered as (1) loss of oxygen, (2) loss of hydrogen, (3) gain of hydrogen, (4) gain of electrons.

4. ATP releases energy and a phosphate group and is converted to (1) A-P~P~P, (2) adenosine triphosphate, (3) A-P~P, (4) adenosine monophosphate.

B

5. The brewing and baking industries depend on the activity of organisms that obtain energy by (1) aerobic respiration, (2) dehydration synthesis, (3) fermentation, (4) hydrolysis.
6. Muscle cells engaged in vigorous activity build up a relatively high concentration of (1) lactic acid, (2) pyruvic acid, (3) oxygen, (4) alcohol.
7. Which process is represented by the following equation?

$$\text{Glucose} \xrightarrow{\text{enzymes}} \text{Lactic acid} + \text{ATP}$$

(1) hydrolysis, (2) dehydration synthesis, (3) aerobic respiration, (4) anaerobic respiration
8. Aerobic respiration and fermentation are similar in that both (1) liberate energy, (2) utilize light energy, (3) produce carbohydrates, (4) require oxygen.
9. The organism that converts pyruvic acid to ethyl alcohol and carbon dioxide is a(n) (1) yeast, (2) alga, (3) protozoan, (4) virus.

Base your answer to question 10 on the chart on p. 146.

10. How many molecules of ATP would be produced during aerobic respiration from eight molecules of pyruvic acid? (1) 34, (2) 102, (3) 136, (4) 272.
11. Which organelles are most closely associated with the process of aerobic respiration? (1) ribosomes, (2) mitochondria, (3) nucleoli, (4) vacuoles.
12. The greatest amount of energy is released by the (1) oxidation of glucose to lactic acid, (2) oxidation of glucose to carbon dioxide and water, (3) conversion of glucose to pyruvic acid, (4) conversion of carbon dioxide and water to glucose.

C

13. In aerobic respiration, the final hydrogen acceptor is (1) molecular oxygen, (2) chlorophyll, (3) carbon dioxide, (4) water.
14. All of the following are released by the Krebs cycle *except* (1) ATP, (2) oxygen, (3) hydrogen, (4) carbon dioxide.
15. In aerobic respiration the pyruvic acid used in the aerobic phase was produced in (1) fermentation, (2) the Krebs cycle, (3) the anaerobic phase, (4) the electron transport chain.

D

16. In fish, blood capillaries close to the surface of the gills absorb (1) oxygen molecules from the air, (2) oxygen atoms from molecules of water, (3) oxygen dissolved in the water, (4) hydrogen atoms from molecules of water.
17. Carbon dioxide passes out of a cell by (1) pinocytosis, (2) diffusion, (3) osmosis, (4) phagocytosis.

E

18. Spiracles are used in insects to (1) excrete solid wastes, (2) discharge sperm cells, (3) breathe, (4) aid in detecting vibrations.
19. Oxygen enters the cells of *Hydra* by (1) diffusion, (2) osmosis, (3) hydrolysis, (4) cyclosis.
20. Respiration in earthworms is directly dependent upon large surface areas of (1) moist skin, (2) lungs, (3) tracheae, (4) gills.

21. Which statement about the respiratory surface in large animals is *not* true? (1) The respiratory surface must be external. (2) The respiratory surface must be moist. (3) The respiratory surface must be thin. (4) The respiratory surface must be in touch with a proportionately large blood supply.
22. The respiratory gases of the grasshopper are carried by the (1) lungs, (2) tracheae, (3) hemoglobin, (4) blood vessels.
23. A paramecium gets oxygen through the (1) anal spot, (2) cilia, (3) contractile vacuole, (4) cell membrane.
24. In humans, a thin, moist respiratory membrane is present at the (1) trachea, (2) bronchi, (3) diaphragm, (4) air sacs.
25. The stems of woody plants take in air through their (1) lenticels, (2) spiracles, (3) root hairs, (4) air sacs.

Chapter Test

1. The production of lactic acid occurs during (1) photosynthesis, (2) chemosynthesis, (3) anaerobic respiration, (4) aerobic respiration.
2. Which is an enzyme-controlled series of chemical reactions resulting in the net synthesis of 36 ATP molecules from the oxidation of a glucose moleclue? (1) photolysis, (2) carbon fixation, (3) anaerobic respiration, (4) aerobic respiration
3. Which cell organelles are the sites of aerobic cellular respiration in both plant and animal cells? (1) mitochondria, (2) centrosomes, (3) chloroplasts, (4) nuclei
4. In animal cells, the energy to convert ADP to ATP comes most directly from (1) hormones, (2) sunlight, (3) organic molecules, (4) inorganic molecules.
5. Compared to aerobic respiration, anaerobic respiration is considered to be a less efficient process, because in anaerobic respiration (1) less lactic acid is formed, (2) more oxygen is required, (3) fewer ATP molecules are produced, (4) less energy is used.
6. Reduction may be considered as the (1) gain of electrons, (2) gain of oxygen atoms, (3) loss of hydrogen atoms, (4) loss of electrons.
7. Mitochondria are organelles which (1) are necessary for the process of diffusion, (2) are found in the nucleus, (3) initiate cell division, (4) contain respiratory enzymes.
8. The souring of grape juice by bacterial action is an example of (1) aerobic respiration, (2) anaerobic respiration, (3) immunity, (4) susceptibility.

For each process in items 9 through 12 write the numeral preceding the type of respiration, chosen from the list below, to which that process is most closely related.

(1) Anaerobic respiration, (2) Aerobic respiration, (3) Both anaerobic and aerobic respiration, (4) Neither anaerobic nor aerobic respiration

9. Process that utilizes CO_2 as a raw material
10. Process known as fermentation
11. Process that liberates carbon dioxide and alcohol
12. Process by which glucose is utilized by a cell

Chapter 8 Excretion

As an organism carries on its life activities, its cells produce metabolic wastes. For example, we have seen that the life process of cellular respiration produces carbon dioxide and water as wastes in addition to releasing energy that is stored temporarily in ATP. Some metabolic wastes act as poisons by interfering with the action of enzymes. The accumulation of waste products would contradict the principle of homeostasis—that a stable internal environment must be maintained. *Excretion* is the process of removing the waste products of cellular metabolism.

Excretion does not include the removal of undigested food, or feces. That kind of waste removal is called *elimination* or *egestion*. The undigested food does not enter the cells of multicellular organisms, nor does it enter into the life processes of single-celled organisms.

A Products of Excretion

The wastes produced by various metabolic processes are summarized in the following table.

Wastes From Some Metabolic Processes

Metabolic Activity	Wastes Produced
Aerobic respiration	Carbon dioxide and water
Dehydration synthesis	Water
Protein and nucleic acid breakdown	Nitrogenous wastes
Certain metabolic processes	Mineral salts

Nitrogenous Wastes

Excess amino acids resulting from the digestion of proteins in foods are not stored in cells. Instead, they are broken down, as shown in Figure 8–1.

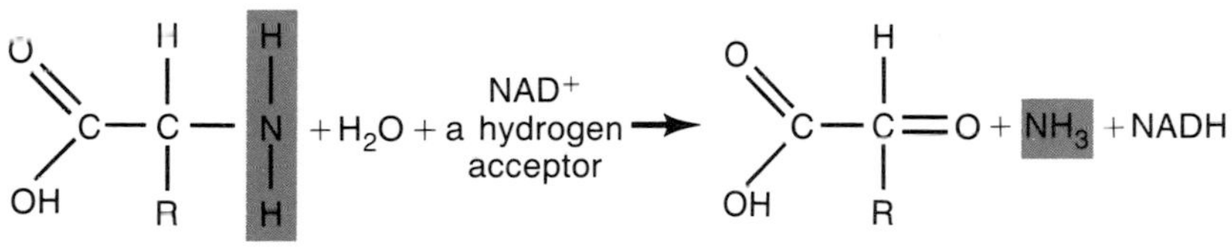

Fig. 8–1. Deamination of an amino acid to form ammonia

The amino group ($-NH_2$) is converted to *ammonia* (NH_3), and the rest of the molecule is oxidized to release chemical energy. This removal of an amino group is called *deamination*.

Although ammonia is highly toxic, it is soluble in water. Thus, its removal is easy for an animal that lives in water. The dissolved ammonia diffuses outward through the cell membrane of protozoans. If a contractile vacuole is present, some dissolved ammonia also is expelled through this organelle.

Multicellular organisms, with a smaller proportion of their cells exposed to water, generally convert ammonia to the less toxic compounds *urea* and *uric acid*. Uric acid is not poisonous because it is insoluble.

A comparison of the forms in which nitrogenous waste is excreted by animals is given in the following table.

Forms of Nitrogenous Wastes

Waste	Toxicity	Water Relationship	Where Found
NH_3	Very toxic	Requires large amounts of water for removal	Microorganisms; many invertebrates living in water; freshwater fish
Urea	Less toxic	Requires large amounts of water for removal	Human; adult stages of amphibia
Uric acid	Comparatively harmless—insoluble	Present in land animals having limited supply of water	Insects; adult stages of reptiles and birds

Inorganic Salts

Inorganic salts of metabolism may include sodium chloride, potassium chloride, and the sulfates and phosphates of ammonia, calcium, and magnesium. These salts are excreted from cells by diffusion through the semipermeable cell membrane. Active transport may play a part in the excretion of salts under certain environmental conditions.

Not all wastes of metabolism are toxic. Water, for example, is a product that is recycled and used again. But the concentration of water must be carefully controlled. A paramecium excretes excess water through contractile vacuoles. If this did not happen, water pressure would burst the cell. The desert rat, which lives in a very dry environment, has as its main source of body water the water produced by cellular respiration.

B

Adaptations in Protists

Freshwater Protozoans

The wastes of metabolism produced by freshwater protozoans include carbon dioxide, water, nitrogenous wastes, and inorganic salts.

Carbon dioxide. This product of cellular respiration passes by diffusion directly into the watery environment.

Water. Water is produced in cellular respiration. In addition, water from the environment enters the cell by osmosis. This osmosis occurs because the concentration of water molecules in the freshwater environment is greater than that within the cell. Cells require water, but an excess can cause swelling and then bursting. Removal of water against the concentration gradient occurs by *active transport* and by the pumping action of the *contractile vacuoles*. Both of these methods use energy supplied by ATP. Saltwater protozoa have no contractile vacuoles because they do not absorb much water.

Small amounts of carbon dioxide, mineral salts, and nitrogenous waste may be present in the water expelled by the contractile vacuoles of the paramecium and the ameba. However, the contractile vacuole is chiefly a homeostatic means of regulating the cell's water balance.

Excretion in Protozoa		
Waste	**How Formed**	**How Excreted**
CO_2	Cellular respiration	Diffusion through cell membrane
H_2O	Cellular respiration; dehydration synthesis	Osmosis; contractile vacuole (if present); active transport
Nitrogenous waste	Removal of $-NH_2$ groups (deamination) from excess amino acids leads to formation of NH_3	Unicellular organisms remove NH_3 dissolved in much water, by diffusion (Contractile vacuole may play a role)
Inorganic salts	General metabolism	Diffusion

Algae As photosynthetic organisms, algae recycle gases between the processes of respiration and photosynthesis. Carbon dioxide and water, which are formed during respiration, are used as raw materials for photosynthesis by the cells. Moreover, some of the oxygen that is a by-product of photosynthesis is used as a raw material for respiration.

C

Adaptations in Plants

Plants do not have specialized organs for excretion. They are able to reuse many of the products of metabolism, giving off only those products no longer useful to them. In other words, they recycle respiratory and photosynthetic gases as in the algae.

If the carbon dioxide and water produced in respiration are not used in photosynthesis, they diffuse into the air spaces and pass out through the *stomata* and *lenticels*. Thus, stomata and small openings in the stem called lenticels, (see Chapter 5), may be considered as excretory structures as well as respiratory structures.

Some of the products of plant metabolism, such as organic acids, might be toxic to the plant. These are *stored in vacuoles* where, in effect, they are sealed off and cause no injury to the plant.

Some of the breakdown processes of plant metabolism yield ammonia and other nitrogen compounds. Ordinarily, these are used by the plant. They are combined with nitrates absorbed by the plant for the synthesis of amino acids and other important compounds.

D

Adaptations in Animals

Excretion in the Hydra

Although it is a multicellular organism, *Hydra* has few problems of excretion because its cells are in contact either with the external water or with the water present in the digestive sac.

Hydra's cells excrete excess water in a manner similar to that found in fresh water protozoa, that is by active transport. *Hydra*'s cells, however, lack contractile vacuoles.

Nitrogenous wastes. *Hydra* excretes nitrogenous waste in the form of ammonia. The ammonia diffuses through the cell membrane of ectodermal and endodermal cells.

Excretion in the Earthworm

The earthworm is much larger than *Hydra,* and most of its cells are not in contact with the external environment. Therefore, special excretory organs are used for the removal of wastes from the cells in its body. This is the case in most multicellular organisms. In the earthworm, these excretory organs are called *nephridia.* The nephridia are pairs of tubes that are found in most of the body segments. They carry wastes from the fluid of the body cavity to pores in the body wall.

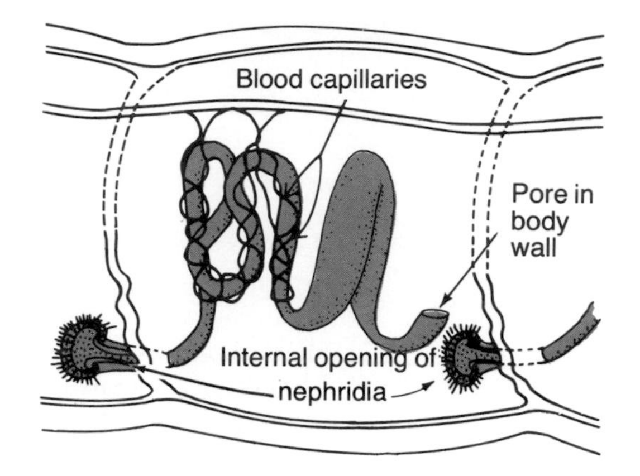

Fig. 8–2. Excretory system of earthworm, showing nephridia and capillaries.

Each nephridium (Fig. 8–2) takes in fluid from the body cavity through a ciliated funnel-shaped opening. Note that each tubule extends through the partition into the succeeding body segment. Here, the tubule is much coiled and surrounded by blood capillaries. As the fluid passes through the coiled section, useful materials are absorbed back into the blood. In this way, only wastes are carried to the outside through the pores in the body wall.

Water serves as a solvent for the nitrogenous wastes (ammonia and urea) and for the mineral salts that are excreted through the nephridia. Carbon dioxide diffuses from the blood stream through the moist skin to the outside terrestrial environment.

Excretion in the Grasshopper

Excretion in the grasshopper is complicated by the fact that this organism lives in a dry environment. The grasshopper cannot "afford" to use water in dissolving and excreting ammonia or urea. Instead, the grasshopper excretes nitrogenous waste in the form of insoluble crystals of *uric acid.* This is a water-conservation adaptation for life in a dry environment.

The specialized structures for excretion in the grasshopper are the *Malpighian tubules* (Fig. 8–3). These are fine tubules that lead from the sinuses of the open circulatory system into the *large intestine.* The Malpighian tubules pick up nitrogenous wastes, mineral salts, and water, but most of the water is reabsorbed back into the blood. The minerals and uric acid are expelled along with digestive waste through the anus.

Most of the carbon dioxide passes by diffusion from the grasshopper's cells into the tracheal tubes which carry it to the atmosphere by way of the spiracles.

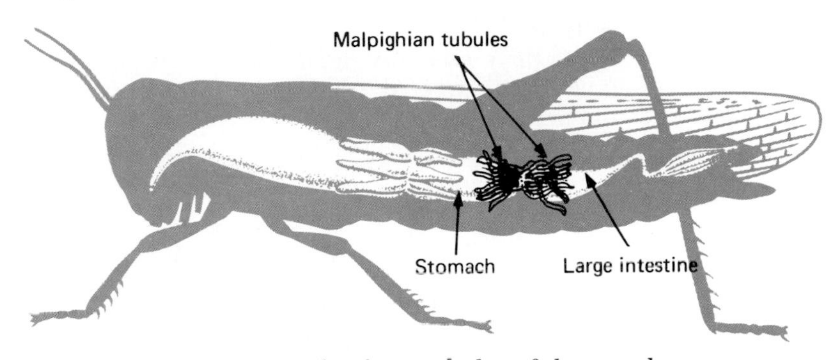

Fig. 8–3. Malpighian tubules of the grasshopper.

Excretion in the Human

Included among the excretory organs of humans are the liver, kidneys, lungs, and skin. Within the kidneys are millions of microscopic tubelike structures called *nephrons*. These resemble the nephridia of earthworms. They remove water, salt, and urea from the blood that passes through the kidneys.

The major excretory wastes in humans are water, urea, carbon dioxide, and mineral salts. *Water* is excreted in air exhaled by the lungs, in sweat given off by sweat glands in the skin, and in urine excreted by the kidneys. *Nitrogenous waste* is given off largely in the form of urea, which is present in urine and in sweat. *Carbon dioxide* is removed from the blood as it passes through the lungs and is expelled into the atmosphere.

Comparison of Nitrogenous Wastes

	Protozoa	Hydra	Earthworm	Grass-hopper	Human
Waste	Ammonia	Ammonia	Urea; ammonia	Uric acid (solid)	Urea, and some uric acid
Structure for removal	Cell membrane; contractile vacuole	Cell membrane	Paired nephridia	Malpighian tubules; intestine	Nephrons of kidney

Reasoning Exercises

1. Distinguish between excretion and elimination. Why is excretion necessary for life?
2. What is deamination? In what forms are nitrogenous wastes excreted?
3. How does the function of the contractile vacuole in protozoa relate to homeostasis?
4. How are plants adapted for the removal of metabolic wastes?

5. Why would it be disadvantageous for humans to excrete nitrogenous waste in the form of ammonia?
6. How is the earthworm adapted for excretion?
7. How do the Malpighian tubules of the grasshopper function in excretion?
8. Name three excretory organs of humans. What liquids carry the urea that is excreted? Which organ of a lower organism resembles the nephron in function?

Completion Questions

A

1. The removal of undigested food through the anus is known as . . . . . .
2. Wastes produced by an organism as it carries on its life processes are called . . . . . . wastes.
3. The removal of the wastes of metabolism is called . . . . . .
4. Nitrogenous wastes are formed from excess . . . . . . acids.
5. Ammonia results from deamination of . . . . . . acids.

B

6. Carbon dioxide is excreted through the cell membrane of protozoa by the process of . . . . . .
7. The gases produced in the respiratory process of algae can also be used in . . . . . .

C

8. Ammonia produced during plant metabolism may be reused by the plant to synthesize . . . . . .
9. Toxic products of plant metabolism are stored in . . . . . .

D

10. The specialized structures for excretion in the grasshopper are called the . . . . . .
11. Uric acid is not poisonous to cells because it is . . . . . .
12. *Hydra* excretes nitrogenous wastes in the form of . . . . . .
13. In the earthworm, nitrogenous wastes are excreted through pairs of tubes called . . . . . .
14. In the grasshopper, nitrogenous wastes are removed from body fluids by structures called . . . . . .
15. Humans excrete urea in the urine and in the . . . . . .

Multiple-Choice Questions

A

1. Which of the following is most likely to excrete most of its nitrogenous waste as ammonia? (1) paramecium (2) grasshopper (3) pig (4) the human
2. If the organism is a protozoan, the substances that might be excreted are (1) carbon dioxide and lactic acid, (2) end products of extracellular digestion, (3) carbon dioxide and ammonia, (4) digestive enzymes and hormones.
3. Which is characteristic of organisms that excrete uric acid as their main nitrogenous waste? (1) They usually live in water. (2) They are usually land dwellers. (3) They can carry on only anaerobic respiration. (4) They cannot metabolize proteins.

4. A certain red dye turns yellow when treated with a mild acid. If a small amount of this red dye is added to 10 cubic centimeters of water and a small aquatic animal is placed in the solution, the reddish solution will turn yellow after about 20 minutes. The most reasonable explanation is that (1) the animal's body is composed of acids, (2) the animal is secreting gastric juice into the solution, (3) products given off by the animal have created acid conditions, (4) a reaction has taken place between the water and the oxygen in the air.

B

5. The major function of the contractile vacuole is (1) removal of nitrogenous wastes, (2) homeostatic regulation of water pressure, (3) digestion of food, (4) removal of excess amino acids.
6. Algae produce CO_2 as a result of the process of (1) aerobic respiration, (2) transpiration, (3) photosynthesis, (4) carbon fixation.

C

7. Plants excrete fewer chemical waste products than animals do. The best explanation for this is that plants (1) do not carry on metabolic activities which produce wastes, (2) can reuse more of their waste products than animals can, (3) have no excretory mechanisms, so they store all their wastes, (4) have shorter lives than animals.
8. Where are the stomata and lenticels located in a tree? (1) The stomata and lenticels are both located in the leaves. (2) The stomata and lenticels are both located in the stems. (3) The stomata are located in the leaves, and the lenticels in the stems. (4) The lenticels are located in the leaves, and the stomata in the stems.

D

9. *Hydra* has few problems with excretion because (1) it excretes nitrogenous waste by contractile vacuoles, (2) its cells are in contact with water, (3) it has few excretory organs, (4) it does not produce toxic waste.
10. Since grasshoppers live in a dry environment, they have a problem with (1) excreting nitrogenous wastes, (2) expelling oxygen, (3) eliminating undigested food, (4) diffusing of carbon dioxide.
11. Humans give off nitrogenous wastes mainly in the form of (1) urea, (2) uric acid, (3) ammonia, (4) nitrogen.
12. Which excretory structures are matched correctly with the organism that possesses them? (1) Malpighian tubules—humans (2) nephridia—earthworm (3) xylem vessels—apple tree (4) nephrons—*Hydra*

Base your answers to questions 13 and 14 on the chart on p. 163.

13. In comparison to its body size, which organism conserves the most water when forming nitrogenous waste? (1) protozoa, (2) hydra, (3) earthworm, (4) grasshopper.
14. Which organism has the simplest structure for removal? (1) protozoa, (2) hydra, (3) earthworm, (4) grasshopper.

Chapter Test

1. A structure used by paramecium for the excretion of liquid wastes is the (1) anal spot, (2) food vacuole, (3) trichocyst, (4) contractile vacuole.
2. Which is the major nitrogenous waste product by water-dwelling organisms such as *Paramecium* and *Hydra*? (1) uric acid (2) ammonia (3) urea (4) nitrates
3. The toxic organic acid waste products of plants usually cause no injury to the plant because they are stored in the plant's (1) nuclei, (2) chloroplasts, (3) mitochondria, (4) vacuoles.
4. Uric acid is not poisonous because it is not (1) toxic, (2) a result of deamination, (3) a nitrogenous waste, (4) soluble.
5. Plants use nitrogenous wastes for the synthesis of (1) ammonia, (2) urea, (3) uric acid, (4) amino acids.

For items 6 through 10, write the letter of the organism, chosen from the list below, that is most closely related to the characteristic given.

(A) *Hydra* (C) grasshopper
(B) earthworm (D) human

6. Has a kidney containing nephrons
7. Intestine is used to eliminate nitrogenous waste
8. Has Malpighian tubules
9. Major nitrogenous waste is uric acid
10. Has paired nephridia
11. The excretory organelles of some unicellular organisms are contractile vacuoles and (1) cell membranes, (2) cell walls, (3) ribosomes, (4) centrioles.
12. Which chemical activity is correctly matched with the waste product it produces? (1) protein metabolism—urea (2) anaerobic respiration—oxygen (3) photosynthesis—carbon dioxide (4) dehydration synthesis—carbon dioxide
13. The grasshopper excretes carbon dioxide mainly through the (1) Malpighian tubules, (2) spiracles, (3) nephrons, (4) nephridia.
14. The earthworm excretes carbon dioxide mainly through its (1) nephridia, (2) contractile vacuoles, (3) skin, (4) tracheae.
15. Which organism produces uric acid as its principal nitrogenous waste? (1) *Paramecium* (2) *Hydra* (3) earthworm (4) grasshopper

Chapter 9 Regulation

The ball is coming through the air toward you. You sense the other players moving around you as the ball gets closer. Should you move into position to get the ball, or should you let someone else get it? Almost without thinking you move into place and with a quick motion the ball is back in the air and into play.

An organism constantly responds to changes in its external and internal environment. The principle of homeostasis requires that the internal environment remain stable in spite of the changes in the external environment. The responses usually involve several of the life processes and systems of the body. These various responses must be *coordinated*, that is they must work together to produce the desired homeostatic effect. Also, these responses must be *controlled* in amount and direction. The coordination and control of life activities is called *regulation*.

Multicellular animals accomplish regulation by means of the *nervous* system and the *endocrine* system. The endocrine system functions by chemical means. Plants, too, have mechanisms for responding to environmental change. They employ chemical controls to bend their stems toward the light and to drop their leaves at the change of seasons.

A Nerve Control

We begin by considering aspects of regulation by nerve cells that are common to both lower animals and to humans.

Stimulus and Response

A *stimulus* is a change in the environment that causes change or activity in an organism. Stimuli may be physical or chemical in nature. Examples of stimuli are changes in temperature, pressure, light, sound, and chemical environment. Stimuli may originate from the external or internal environment of the organism.

The action or movement resulting from a stimulus is a *response*. One-celled organisms may respond directly to a stimulus, as when a paramecium moves away from a crystal of salt. In multicellular animals the impulse carried by nerve fibers causes (1) contraction of muscle cells, (2) secretion by a gland, or (3) stimulation of another nerve fiber.

A *nerve impulse* is an electrical signal that passes along a nerve fiber. Electrical and chemical changes enable an impulse to travel along a nerve fiber, and from one nerve fiber to another. Stimuli such as pressure, light, and sound do not travel along a nerve. A stimulus causes an impulse that leads to sensation in the brain. The electrical and chemical nature of an impulse is the same, regardless of the stimulus.

Receptors and effectors. A *receptor* is specialized nerve tissue that is sensitive to a specific stimulus. Some receptors are merely the naked endings of nerve cells in the skin which are sensitive to changes in temperature. Other receptors are complicated organs such as the eye or ear. Each receptor is specialized to be sensitive to a specific stimulus. For example receptors can be stimulated by chemicals (taste and smell), mechanical stimuli (touch and pressure), light (sight), etc. Some receptors provide information about the degree of contraction of muscles or about the position of parts of the body.

Effectors are the parts of the body that respond. These are the *muscles* that contract or the *glands* that secrete.

The neuron. The *neuron* or nerve cell is the basic unit of the nervous system. Although visible only with the microscope, these cells may be very long; some extend from a toe to the spinal cord. A typical (motor) neuron is diagrammed in Figure 9-1.

The three main parts of a neuron are the cyton (cell body), the axon, and the terminal branches. The *cyton*, containing the nucleus and much cytoplasm, has numerous branched extensions called *dendrites*. These receive stimuli and send impulses to the cyton. From the cyton, the impulses pass along the lengthy *axon*. In many neurons, the axon is covered by a *myelin* (fatty) *sheath* that insulates it from neighboring axons. During development, the myelin sheath is formed from cells that wrap themselves around the axon. The sheath helps speed the passage of impulses. The axon terminates in many fine filaments called the *terminal branches*.

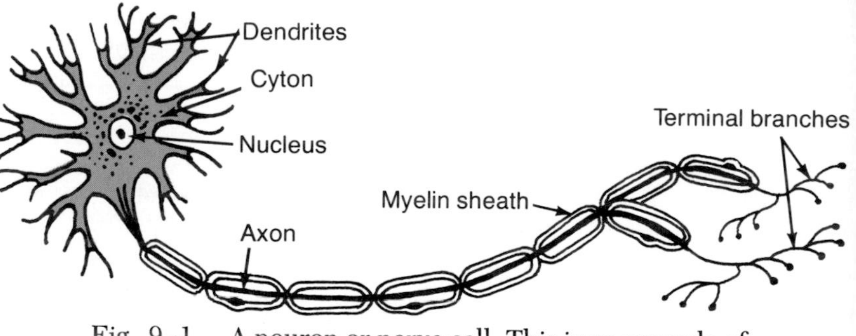

Fig. 9–1. A neuron or nerve cell. This is an example of a *motor* neuron.

The Reflex Arc

The three kinds of neurons and their functions are illustrated in the *reflex arc*. This is the pathway of impulses that occurs in the simple type of behavior known as the *reflex*. Imagine that a tack has just pricked your finger. Pulling your finger away from the point of the tack is a reflex action. For many reflexes, the center of coordination is the spinal cord. Trace the steps of the reflex arc in Figure 9-2.

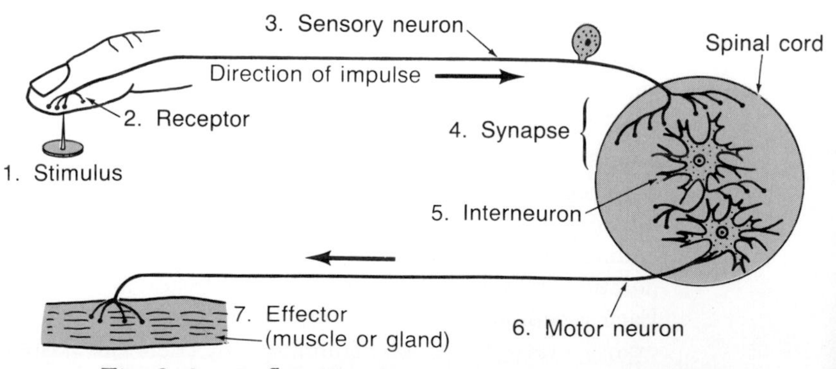

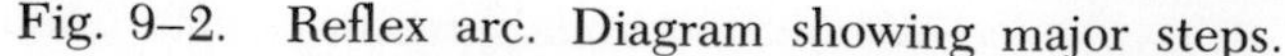

Fig. 9–2. Reflex arc. Diagram showing major steps.

1. *Stimulus.* The pressure of a tack on the skin is the stimulus (the change in the environment).

2. *Receptor.* Bare dendrites in the skin serve as the receptor that detects the stimulus and initiates the impulse.

3. *Sensory neuron.* The sensory neuron carries the impulse *toward* the spinal cord. It is called sensory because its impulses come from a sensory receptor, and lead to sensation in either the brain or spinal cord. Note that the cyton of the sensory neuron is located outside the spinal cord.

4. *Synapse.* The *synapse* is the microscopic gap between the terminal branches of one neuron and the dendrites of the next neuron. Later we will see how the impulse crosses the synapse by means of chemicals released by the terminal branches.

5. *Interneuron.* The interneuron is a small nerve cell that lies between a sensory neuron and a motor neuron within the spinal cord. It has many branches so that incoming impulses may be switched to motor neurons as well as to neurons leading to the brain.

6. *Motor neuron.* Through a synapse with the interneuron, the motor neuron receives the impulse. This neuron carries the impulse *away from* the spinal cord, toward the effector. It is called a motor neuron because its activity leads to action by an effector such as a muscle or gland.

7. *Effector.* At its terminal branches, the motor neuron releases a chemical that causes a muscle to contract, or a gland to secrete. The muscle or gland is called the *effector.*

Nerves. A neuron is microscopic but a *nerve* can be seen as a thin, white string. A nerve is composed of a bundle of axons or dendrites from many neurons, covered with connective tissue. As in the wires of a telephone cable, each axon is insulated from its neighbors by the protective myelin sheath. Nerves containing only sensory neurons are *sensory nerves;* nerves containing only motor neurons are *motor nerves;* nerves containing both sensory and motor neurons are *mixed nerves.*

The Nerve Impulse

The nerve impulse is a series of electrochemical changes that proceed along the membrane of a neuron. The passage of a nerve impulse may be likened to the travel of a burning spark along a fuse cord. In each case, a change at one point causes a change at the next point. However, the fuse cord does not replace itself whereas the nerve fiber does return to its original state and is soon ready to accept the next impulse. The *electrical* aspect of an impulse involves a reversal of positive and negative charges on the outside and inside surfaces of the neuron's cell membrane. The *chemical* aspect involves the diffusion of sodium (Na^+) ions and potassium (K^+) ions through the cell membrane.

Figure 9–3 illustrates a portion of an axon during passage of an impulse from left to right. The top of the illustration shows electrical changes along the axon membrane. The bottom shows chemical changes caused by movement of ions across the membrane. The right-hand piece of the axon shows the resting membrane before the arrival of the impulse. The charge on the outside of the membrane is positive; the inside is negative. Because of this difference in electrical charge, the resting membrane is called a *polarized* membrane.

The impulse has arrived at the middle piece of the axon in the figure. Here the electrical charge on the membrane is reversed: the outside is negative and the inside is positive. This piece of the axon membrane is called a *depolarized* membrane.

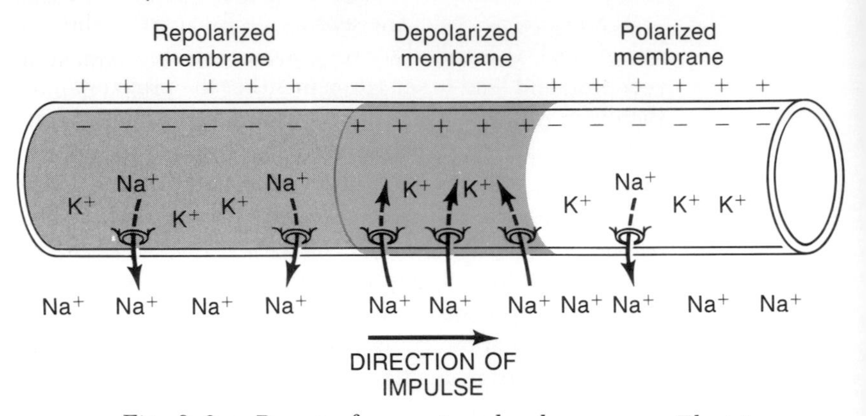

Fig. 9–3. Passage of a nerve impulse along an axon. Electrical changes along the membrane are shown at the top; changes in ion movements are shown at the bottom.

The impulse has passed the left-hand piece of the axon, where the electrical charge has returned to the original condition. This piece of the membrane is called the repolarized membrane. Biologists say that the impulse passes along the neuron as a *wave of depolarization* in the membrane.

Changes in the movements of sodium and potassium ions cause the electrical changes shown in Figure 9–3. Along the polarized membrane, active transport moves Na^+ ions from inside to outside, and K^+ ions from outside to inside. Biologists call this active transport the sodium–potassium pump. It creates a high concentration of sodium outside the membrane, and a high concentration of potassium inside. The bottom part of the figure shows this concentration difference along the polarized membrane. The axon membrane is also much more permeable to K^+ than to Na^+. As a result, some K^+ diffuses from inside to outside. Recall that diffusion is movement from a region of high concentration to a region of low concentration. The outward diffusion of K^+ helps to build an excess of positive charges outside the axon membrane.

A sudden change in the permeability of the membrane allows Na^+ ions to rush from outside to inside. This is shown in the middle piece of the illustration. Enough sodium diffuses into the axon to reverse the balance of electrical charge and depolarize the membrane. Then potassium diffuses from inside to outside in sufficient quantity to restore the positive charge outside the membrane. Then the sodium–potassium pump is restored, and the ion concentrations return to their original levels. The left-hand piece of the illustration shows that the ions along the repolarized membrane return to the resting condition.

Depolarization at a point on the membrane lasts for only *a fraction of a millisecond* (1/1000 second). A brief period of time must pass before another impulse can pass the same point. Yet some neurons can transmit as many as 1000 impulses per second.

Strength of Stimulus

The stimulus must be of sufficient strength to exceed the *threshold*, or initial barrier to its passage. Once this threshold is exceeded, each impulse is of the same strength and speed, regardless of the strength of the stimulus that initiated the impulse. Thus, the impulse has an all or none characteristic. The action in a fuse cord provides an analogy to this all or none response. Initially, a fuse cord is either lighted or not. Once lighted, the spark travels at a constant speed that is not affected by the heat of the match which lighted the fuse.

A stimulus of greater strength initiates a train of more *frequent* impulses. When these impulses result in the production of sufficient chemical to exceed the threshold of the next neuron, the impulse has been carried across the synapse. It is the number of impulses per second, not any variation in their speed or strength, that determines the intensity of a response. This is illustrated in Figure 9–4. Each impulse is represented as a bump in the axon. A strong stimulus causes more impulses to be sent per second. However, each impulse is of the same strength and travels at the same speed in any one neuron.

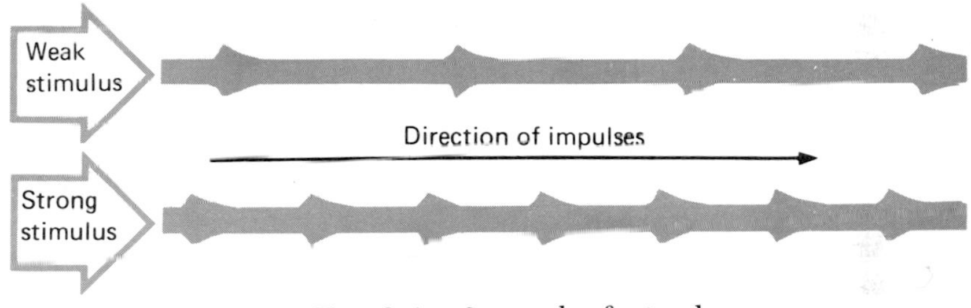

Fig. 9-4. Strength of stimulus.

Neurotransmitters

In about 1920, the American biologist Otto Loewi sought to determine how nerves cause muscles to respond. He knew that a frog's heart, placed in saline solution, continues to beat at its own steady rate. Attached to the heart are two nerves. Stimulating the accelerator nerve increases the heartbeat rate. Stimulating the vagus nerve decreases this rate.

One of Loewi's experiments is illustrated in Figure 9-5. When Loewi stimulated the vagus nerve of the first frog, its rate of heartbeat decreased, as expected. Loewi then transferred fluid from this container to the container with the second heart. The second heart began to beat more slowly. As you might do, Loewi reasoned that a *chemical* intermediary must be involved in the pathway from nerve to muscle.

This chemical was later found to be *acetylcholine*. This was the first *neurotransmitter* discovered. A neurotransmitter is a chemical messenger secreted by a neuron at the terminal branches of the axon. It diffuses across a synapse to affect the next neuron in a pathway. Or, it diffuses from the terminal branches to affect a muscle. Today, sixty years after Loewi's work, a host of neurotransmitters have been discovered that help to explain how the brain functions.

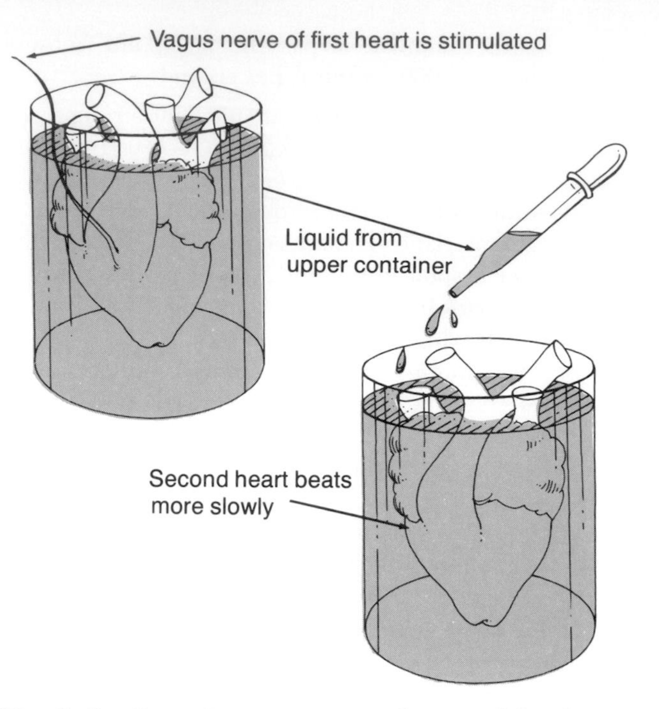

Fig. 9–5. Loewi's experiment with excized frog hearts

The two common neurotransmitters are *acetylcholine* and *noradrenaline.* The latter chemically resembles the hormone adrenaline that is secreted by the adrenal gland. Thus, both a nerve product and the product of an endocrine gland have similar effects in the body. This similarity is an example of the interrelationship between the nervous system and the endocrine system.

Transmission of an Impulse

Figure 9–6 shows a synapse between two neurons. How does an impulse pass from the neuron at the left to the one at the right? The terminal branches of the first neuron have tiny cavities that store a neurotransmitter, such as acetylcholine. When a wave of depolarization reaches these cavities, the cavities release their neurotransmitter. The neurotransmitter molecules diffuse across the synapse and reach the dendrites of the second neuron. Here they combine with receptor molecules on the surface of the dendrite membrane. When sufficient neurotransmitter molecules accumulate here, they initiate a new wave of depolarization in the second neuron. The impulse can cross the synapse in one direction only—from terminal branches to dendrites.

Why can two nerves leading to the same organ have opposite effects? This is because one nerve releases acetylcholine and the other releases noradrenaline. For example, acetylcholine released by the vagus nerve inhibits heart muscle, whereas noradrenaline from the accelerator nerve excites heart muscle. But these neurotransmitters have reverse effects on muscles of the alimentary canal—acetylcholine stimulates and noradrenaline inhibits. It is the target organ, not the neurotransmitter, that determines the response.

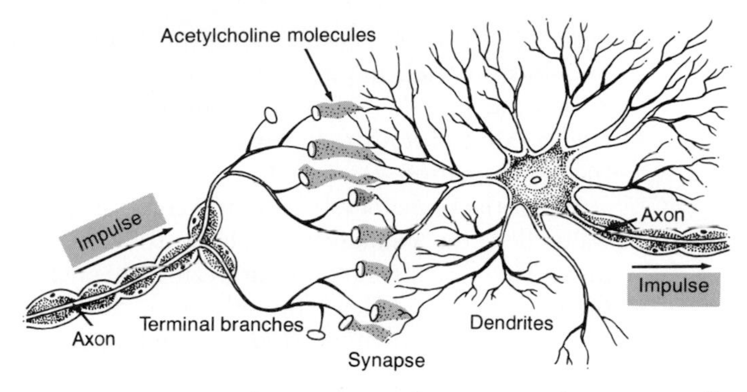

Fig. 9–6. Impulse crossing the synapse by means of neurotransmitter molecules.

If acetylcholine released at synapses were not rapidly destroyed, this chemical would continue its effect on the second neurons, leading possibly to widespread muscle spasms or paralysis. However, acetylcholine is rapidly hydrolyzed by *cholinesterase*, an enzyme that is widely distributed in body tissue.

B

Adaptations in Animals

Protists. Even the simplest one-celled organisms exhibit some form of *irritability*, the capacity to respond to stimuli. Indeed, irritability is often listed as one of the basic properties of protoplasm. Although the ameba lacks specialized structures for sensory reception, it responds to small food particles or certain chemicals with feeding behavior. It responds to other stimuli by withdrawing. The more complex paramecium uses its rows of cilia in coordinated fashion for locomotion. When a paramecium bumps into an object, it backs up by reversing the direction in which its cilia beat. It moves away from intense light and from irritating chemicals but moves toward moderate levels of light and oxygen.

Hydra. The nervous system of *Hydra* (Fig. 9-7) consists of a network of neurons called a *nerve net*. This nerve net lies between the two layers of the body wall. Receptor cells are present in both the ectoderm and endo-

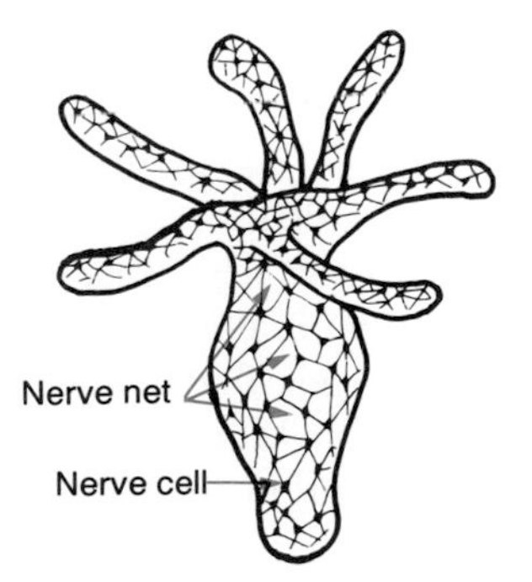

Fig. 9–7. Nerve net in *Hydra*

derm. There is *no specific pathway* or nerve cord for the carrying of impulses; instead, impulses gradually spread throughout the body. Impulses can pass in either direction over the neurons and synapses of *Hydra*. Most of *Hydra's* behavior is limited to feeding and defensive contractile responses.

When the nematocysts (stinging cells) of *Hydra* are struck by a living water flea, the nematocysts release tubelike threads that penetrate its prey. The threads inject a paralyzing chemical. At the same time, the tissues of the prey release the substance *glutathione*. This chemical acts as a stimulus for initiating *Hydra's* feeding reflex. When glutathione is added to water containing a living *Hydra*, the animal periodically shortens its tentacles, opens its mouth, and inserts the tentacles into its mouth. This action illustrates coordinated behavior by a simple organism that lacks a well-developed nerve center.

Earthworm. Unlike *Hydra*, whose nerve net spreads impulses in a diffuse manner, the earthworm possesses a *central nervous system*. This system passes impulses quickly over a definite pathway from receptors to effectors. The earthworm's central nervous system (Fig. 9-8) consists of the simple dorsal *brain* and the solid, ventral *nerve cord*.

The earthworm also possesses a *peripheral nervous system*. This consists of nerves that branch out from the central nervous system to all parts of the body. The peripheral nerves carry impulses from specialized receptors in the skin that are sensitive to vibrations, light, heat, and chemicals. The peripheral nerves also carry motor impulses to muscles and glands.

Tiny swellings visible in each segment of the nerve cord are *ganglia*. Each ganglion consists of the cell bodies of a group of neurons. Thus, ganglia are tiny nerve control centers. The segmentally arranged ganglia receive sensory impulses, as from the skin, and then relay impulses by means of nerves to muscles of that segment. A pair of solid, large ganglia above (dorsal to) the pharynx constitutes the earthworm's primitive brain. This is connected to a large ventral ganglion below the pharynx by a band of nerve tissue that encircles the pharynx.

Although the earthworm's brain seems simple, it coordinates several actions during locomotion. At correct times, it causes contraction and relaxations of muscles that move *setae* (bristles) in the front and rear portions of the body. However, during locomotion, the contraction of muscles in one segment stimulates receptor cells in the next segment, which triggers contraction in that segment. This aspect of locomotion thus seems to proceed along the spinal cord without control by the brain.

Unlike the radially symmetrical *Hydra*, the earthworm is *bilaterally symmetrical*. This means that it has a right and a left side that are copies of each other. Bilaterally symmetrical animals also have a head (cephalic) end that proceeds first. The head end, being the first to explore the environment, has numerous sense receptors that are connected to the anterior, enlarged portion of the central nervous system—the brain. The evolution of more advanced animals was accompanied by additional cephalization—the increased development of the brain as a center for coordination and then for memory and thought.

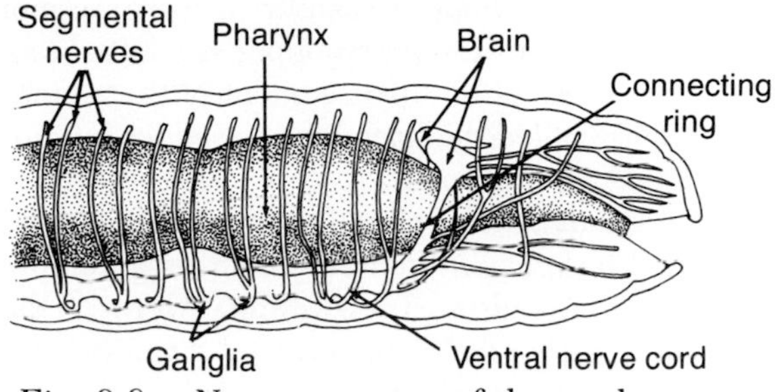

Fig. 9-8. Nervous system of the earthworm

The earthworm can be trained (conditioned) to enter that side of a T-maze which has the most favorable environmental conditions (warmth, darkness and moisture compared to an electric shock). The flatworm, *Planaria*, whose nervous system is even simpler than the earthworm's, is also much used for studying simple forms of behavior. How simple can a nervous system be and still be able to learn something?

Grasshopper. Although the grasshopper is far more active and responsive than the earthworm, its more complex nervous system follows the same general invertebrate pattern (Fig. 9-9). Like the earthworm, the grasshopper has a solid, ventral nerve cord, but its nerve cord is double rather than single. Ganglia in the ventral nerve cord serve as segmental control centers. However, the fusion of segments into large body regions reduces the number of ganglia. As in the earthworm, the ventral nerve cord is joined to the dorsal brain by a ring of nerve tissue that encircles the digestive tube. The solid brain resembles two greatly enlarged, fused ganglia.

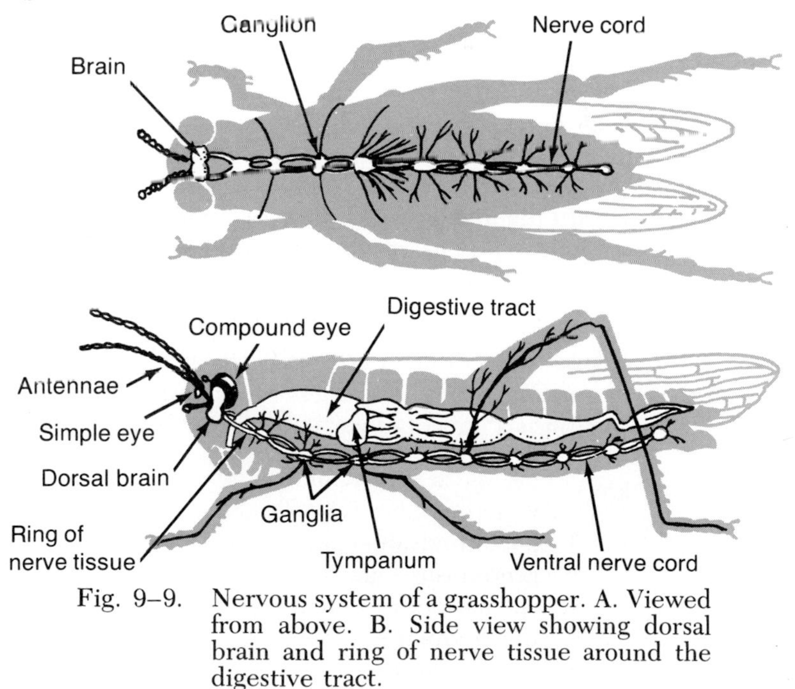

Fig. 9–9. Nervous system of a grasshopper. A. Viewed from above. B. Side view showing dorsal brain and ring of nerve tissue around the digestive tract.

The grasshopper's sensory organs are more complex than those of the earthworm. The grasshopper has both *simple eyes* and *compound eyes*. Each side of the first segment of the abdomen has a membrane-covered cavity called the *tympanum*, used for hearing. The *antennae* are sensitive to touch and smell.

Human. Like all vertebrates, humans have a central nervous system and peripheral nervous system with definite pathways for the passage of nerve impulses. The overall pattern of the vertebrate nervous system differs from that of the invertebrates such as the earthworm and grasshopper. The vertebrate nerve cord is *dorsal* to the food tube, instead of ventral, and *hollow*, instead of solid. The hollow nerve cord is expanded at the anterior end into the brain. Humans have highly developed receptors, such as the eyes, ears, and nose. The characteristics of the human nervous system will be discussed in Chapter 15.

Reasoning Exercises

1. Distinguish between receptors and effectors.
2. Distinguish between a neuron and a nerve.
3. How does *Paramecium* respond to stimuli? How does it coordinate its behavior?
4. How is the feeding reflex initiated in *Hydra*?
5. Why do we say that the nervous system of the earthworm is more complex than that of *Hydra*?
6. How does the nervous system of the grasshopper resemble that of the earthworm? How does it differ from it?
7. Describe how an impulse crosses the synapse.
8. Compare the nerve cord of invertebrates and vertebrates with respect to location and structure.
9. Describe the electrical changes that occur during the passage of the nerve impulse.

C Chemical Control in Plants

What causes a geranium plant to bend toward the light? *Phototropism* is the usual answer. What is phototropism? It is the bending of a plant toward the light. Such circular reasoning gets us nowhere. Fortunately, within the past half-century, plant physiologists have made much progress in explaining *how* tropisms and other plant responses occur.

Tropisms

A *tropism* is a growth of part of a plant toward or away from a stimulus. A tropism differs from a taxis. A *taxis*, as observed in *Paramecium*, is the movement of an *entire organism* in response to a stimulus. A *positive* tropism is a growth of part of a plant toward a stimulus, and a *negative* tropism is a growth away from a stimulus. Some tropisms and their stimuli are:

- phototropism—light
- geotropism—gravity
- chemotropism—chemicals
- thigmotropism—touch
- hydrotropism—water

Many of these tropisms have been explained by the discovery of *auxins*. Auxins are *plant regulators*, chemicals that influence cell division, elongation, and differentiation. *Cell differentiation* is the development of special tissue characteristics by cells that are unspecialized when first formed. There is evidence that many plant regulators are made in certain parts of the plant, then distributed to other parts where they have their effect on growth and development. *Gibberellins* (see page 180) are another type of plant regulator.

Discovery of Auxins

In 1881, Charles Darwin reported his experiments on the phototropism of grass seedlings. Darwin exposed seedlings to light from one side and covered various parts of the seedlings. For bending to occur, he found that the *tip* of the seedling must receive light. Thus, he reasoned, the stem tip plays an important role in phototropism.

Another botanist found oat seedlings to be a good subject for the study of phototropism. The leafy tip of the oat seedling is the *coleoptile*. Bending occurs in the zone of elongation below the coleoptile.

Some of the experiments performed on oat coleoptiles are shown in Figure 9–10. Section A shows that when the coleoptile is covered, or when its tip is removed, no bending occurs.

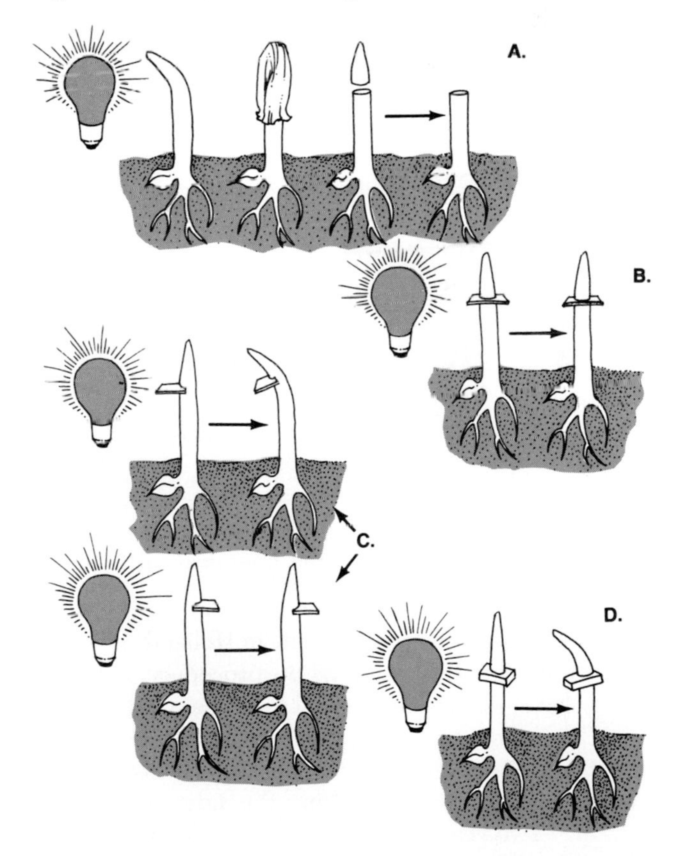

Fig. 9–10. Experiments on phototropism in oat coleoptiles

In section B, a strip of mica is placed between the tip and the rest of the stem. No bending occurs.

In section C, a strip of mica is inserted only part of the way through the stem. When the mica is inserted on the side facing the light, the stem bends toward the light. But when the mica is placed opposite to the light, no bending occurred. The scientist reasoned that the bending must be caused by something passing down the stem on the unlighted side. Could it be a chemical? To find out, he used a strip of agar (a gelatinlike substance) instead of mica. Agar permits chemicals to diffuse through. Section D shows his setup and results. The researcher reached this conclusion: The tip produces a *chemical* that diffuses down the unlighted side of the stem to cause bending.

However, many questions remained. What was the unknown chemical? Could its strength be measured? Could it be isolated? How does it cause bending?

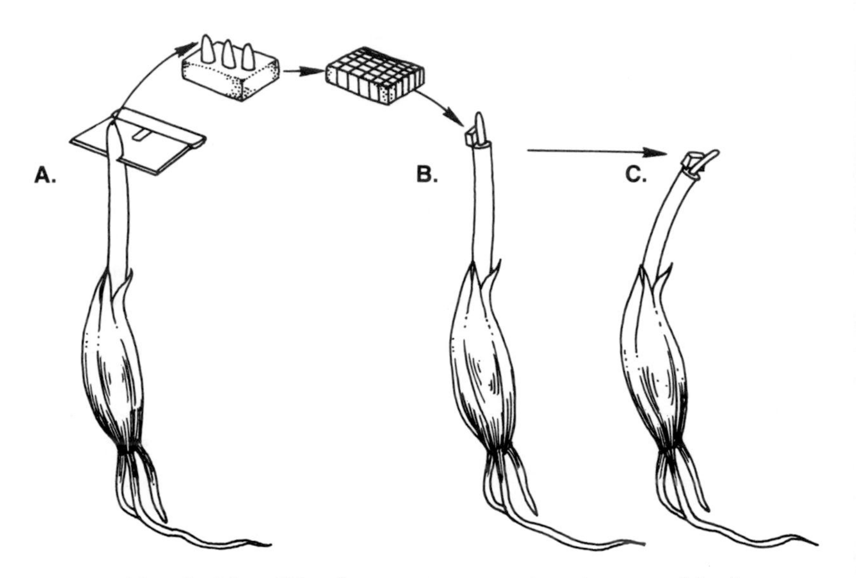

Fig. 9–11. Went's experiment using tiny agar blocks. Note that the seedlings are uniformly lighted from all sides. Any change is due to the chemical in the agar.

In 1926, Frits W. Went, in Holland, succeeded in capturing the chemical. Figure 9–11 shows his procedure. (A) He cut the coleoptile tips from oat seedlings and placed them on a slice of agar. After about an hour, he cut the agar in tiny blocks. Each block contained some of the chemical. (B) He placed a block on the side of a decapitated seedling. (C) The seedling bent away from the side on which the block was placed.

Two years later, Went succeeded in isolating the chemical responsible for this action. It is called *IAA (indole acetic acid)*. IAA is one of a group of plant hormones called auxins.

Explanation of Phototropism This is how plant physiologists now explain the bending of a stem toward the light. Auxin causes growth of cells in the stem. As shown in Figure 9–12 the tip produces auxin. This chemical diffuses down to the region of elongation. Here light causes an *uneven distribution* of auxin—more on the unlighted side than on the lighted side. Biologists hypothesize that the light destroys the auxin on the lighted side, or that light causes the auxin to move to the other side. Increased growth of cells on the unlighted side causes bending toward the lighted side.

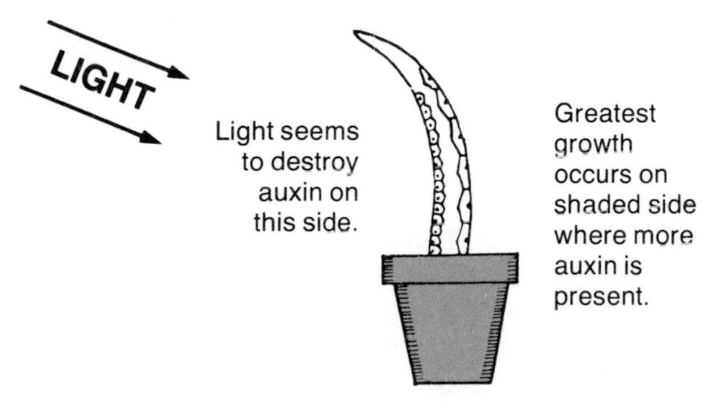

Fig. 9–12. Positive tropism of stem

Is the increased growth due to more rapid cell division or to increased elongation of cells? This seems to differ with various auxins and with various parts of the plant. IAA causes cell elongation in stems. It softens the cell walls permiting the cell to absorb more water and swell.

Geotropism Place a young potted plant in a horizontal position as shown in Figure 9–13. Keep it in a dark place for a few days. The stem with its leaves bends upward. On removing the soil, you can see that the roots bend downward. These responses to gravity are examples of *geotropism*. The stem is negatively geotropic and the roots are positively geotropic. How can we explain the downward bending of the roots?

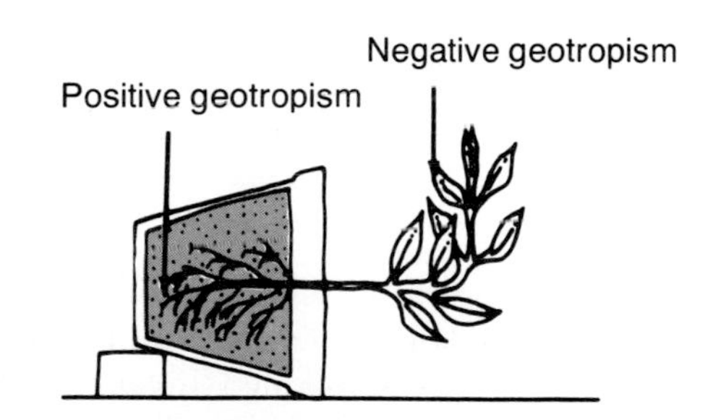

Fig. 9–13. Geotropism. Gravity has opposite effects on root and stem.

Positive Geotropism in Roots Figure 9–14 shows the tip of a root that is growing parallel to the surface. It may have emerged from the seed in this direction, or it may have been diverted by an obstruction.

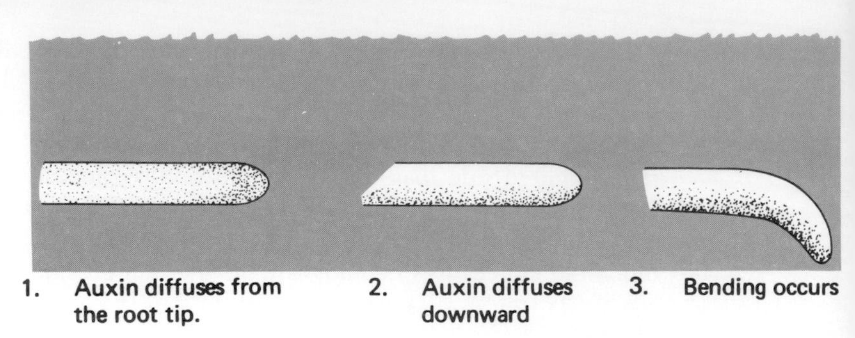

Fig. 9–14. Positive geotropism. A root grows downward toward the pull of gravity.

Three stages are shown. (1) The tip of the root produces auxin that diffuses toward the region of elongation. (2) Gravity pulls the auxin toward the lower portion of the root. (3) We observe that the tip bends downward. This is a puzzling situation. You would expect the auxin in the lower part of the root to cause the root to bend *upward*. Since the bending is toward the region containing auxin, the auxin must have *inhibited* the growth of the root cells. Thus, auxins can inhibit as well as stimulate growth.

Experiments have shown that whereas one concentration of an auxin may cause growth of a plant tissue, another concentration may retard growth of that tissue. Thus, plant hormone responses depend upon (1) the hormones involved, (2) their concentrations, and (3) the tissues affected. A concentration that inhibits root growth may stimulate stem growth.

Gibberellins

Some rice seedlings in Japan grew very fast and tall but were unhealthy and usually failed to produce rice grains. This "foolish seedling disease" was found to result from infection by the fungus called *Gibberella*. Scientists then discovered that the fungus' effect on growth was caused by a chemical that it produces. This chemical was called *gibberellin* or *gibberellic acid*. More than 50 gibberellins have now been found in plants and algae as well as in fungi.

Gibberellins are not responsible for the bending of tropisms. They stimulate stems to *grow longer*. They also affect flowering, root growth, and leaf growth. Artificially applied gibberellins cause some plants to grow to giant size. They are also used to produce large seedless grapes and to speed seed germination.

Uses of Plant Hormones

Synthetically produced plant regulators are used in a number of ways.

- **As weed killers.** The chemical 2,4-D is an artificial auxin that is widely used as a weed killer. It causes broad-leaved plants, such as dandelions, to grow abnormally and then die. This herbicide affects grasses and other monocots much less than it affects the unwanted dicots. Thus, in proper concentration, 2,4-D can rid a lawn of weeds without harming the grass. However, it must be kept from ornamental shrubs and garden vegetables. Since corn is a monocot, 2,4-D is used to rid cornfields of weeds.

- **To stimulate root formation for cuttings.** Many kinds of woody plants can be propagated by inserting a cutting of stem into the ground. The stem develops roots and becomes a new complete plant. Auxins stimulate the formation of new roots. By use of synthetic auxins, growers have achieved success with plants that formerly could not be propagated in this way. Rooting powders, sold in garden supply stores, contain synthetic auxin.
- **To produce seedless fruit.** Auxin applied to the ovaries of some flowers causes them to develop into fruits without pollination having occurred.
- **To prevent fruit from falling before maturity.** Auxin prevents the falling of fruits before they are fully matured. Spraying plants with certain auxins can strengthen the abscission layer, a group of cells formed where the petiole is attached to the stem. This delays the falling of fruit from a tree.

Regulation in Plants

The tendril of a pea plant revolves in a broad sweep until it strikes a support. Within half an hour, the tendril has wound a tight coil around the support. (Fig. 9–15A). This *thigmotropism* (response to touch) depends upon auxin activity and changes in cell turgor. Touch the compound leaf of the sensitive plant *Mimosa pudica* (Fig. 9–15B). Within five seconds the stimulated leaflets bend upward. These changes, too, result from a loss of cell turgor. Morning glories open in the morning, but the flowers of the night-blooming cereus open in the evening. The daisy was originally called the "day's eye" because its flower turns to follow the sun.

Fig. 9–15. Plant responses. A. Tendril of a pea plant coils around a support. B. Leaflets of the sensitive plant, *Mimosa pudica*, respond quickly to a touch stimulus by folding together.

Reasoning Exercises

1. What is the difference between a tropism and a taxis?
2. Explain why stems bend toward the light.
3. Explain why roots grow in the direction of the pull of gravity.
4. Give four uses of plant hormones in agriculture.
5. Roots generally grow toward water. What name would you give to this response? How is this response adaptive for survival?

D

Chemical Control in Animals

Chemical control in animals differs from that in plants. Animals have special cells for the production of hormones. In lower invertebrates, hormones are formed in scattered groups of cells. But higher invertebrates, such as mollusks, crustaceans, and insects, possess definite *glands* that produce chemical hormones for the function of control.

Hormones

The chemical secretions of endocrine glands are called *hormones.* A hormone is a chemical that is secreted in one place and has its effect at a distance. Hormones are often called chemical messengers. Each kind of hormone has its own effects. Because they are carried throughout the body in the blood, some hormones have widespread effects. An organ that is influenced by a hormone is called the *target organ* for that hormone.

The word *endocrine* means "internally secreting." Endocrine glands pass their secretions into their blood capillaries rather than into ducts. Glands having ducts are called *exocrine* (externally secreting) glands. Endocrine glands are called *ductless glands.*

Comparison of Exocrine and Endocrine Glands

Exocrine (Duct) Glands	Endocrine (Ductless) Glands
Secretions are liberated externally through a duct.	Secretions are liberated into the capillaries of the bloodstream.
Secretions are juices such as gastric juice, saliva, sweat, bile, and tears.	Secretions are hormones, such as thyroxin, adrenaline, and insulin.
Effects of secretions are produced in the region where the duct empties.	Effects of hormones may be produced throughout the body or in special target organs.

Role of Animal Hormones

Although hormones are known mainly for their role in humans (for example, insulin and adrenaline), current research indicates that hormones are also found in a wide variety of animals. The role of hormones in the metamorphosis and mating of insects is well known.

The series of changes in an insect's life history from egg to larva, to pupa, to adult is called *complete metamorphosis.* Three hormones are known to play a role in these changes. One of them, for example, promotes the growth of the larva but plays no role in causing the larva to metamorphose to the pupa stage. The *juvenile hormone* actively prevents the metamorphosis of the larva to the pupa stage. In the presence of large amounts of juvenile hormone, the larva can increase in size, but it does not proceed to the next stage. As the concentration of juvenile hormone decreases, the larva changes to the pupa. In the complete absence of this hormone, the pupa becomes an adult. Juvenile hormone thus acts as a brake on the process of metamorphosis, tending to keep the insect in a juvenile stage. Agriculturalists are now considering using a chemical such as juvenile hormone to control the spread of harmful insects.

Completion Questions

A

1. The activities of an animal are regulated by its nervous system and its . . . . . .
2. A series of chemical and electrical changes that pass along a nerve fiber is a (n) . . . . . .
3. Effectors may be muscles or . . . . . .
4. Three major portions of a neuron are the cyton, terminal branches, and . . . . . .
5. The gap between the two neurons is the . . . . . .
6. Two chemicals that can carry impulses across the synapses are . . . . . . and . . . . . .
7. The enzyme that destroys acetylcholine is . . . . . .
8. When the inside of the membrane of an axon is negative, the membrane is said to be . . . . . .
9. A wave of depolarization is another name for a(n) . . . . . .
10. The stronger the stimulus the more . . . . . . are the impulses that pass along the neurons.
11. Neurons that carry impulses away from the spinal cord are . . . . . . neurons.
12. Neurons present between sensory and motor neurons are called . . . . . .

B

13. The type of nervous system present in *Hydra* is known as a (an) . . . . . .
14. The earthworm's solid nerve cord is on the . . . . . . (dorsal, ventral) side of its body.
15. The capacity of protoplasm to respond to stimuli is called . . . . . .
16. An animal whose neuron system carries impulses in all directions is . . . . . .
17. In *Hydra,* the substance glutathione initiates the . . . . . . reflex.
18. *Paramecium* moves toward food by coordinated movement of its . . . . . .
19. The earthworm's brain consists of a pair of large, solid . . . . . .
20. The development of a head end is associated with animals that are . . . . . . symmetrical.
21. The grasshopper has a ventral nerve cord and a . . . . . . brain.
22. In vertebrates such as the human, the nerve cord is . . . . . . (dorsal, ventral) to the food tube.
23. In vertebrates, the nerve cord is . . . . . . (solid, hollow).

C

24. An example of an artificial plant hormone used as a weed killer is . . . . . .
25. An auxin can stimulate or . . . . . . growth, depending on its concentration.
26. The sheath surrounding the young leaves of oat seedlings is called the . . . . . .
27. The bending of a plant toward or away from a stimulus is known as a(n) . . . . . .
28. A movement of an animal toward or away from a stimulus is known as a(n) . . . . . .

29. The formation of different kinds of cells for specific functions is called . . . . . .
30. Light coming from the right side of a plant stem decreases the concentration of auxin on the . . . . . . side of the stem.
31. The bending of a plant toward the light is described as positive . . . . . .

D

32. The chemical messengers of the body are the . . . . . .
33. Coordination of body functions is accomplished by the endocrine system and the . . . . . . system.
34. The organ that is affected by a specific hormone is called the . . . . . . organ.
35. Another name for a ductless gland is a(n) . . . . . .
36. Hormones are carried to the various parts of the body by the . . . . . .
37. Hormones are secreted by . . . . . . glands.
38. Gastric juice and saliva are both secreted by . . . . . . glands.
39. Compared with nerve responses, most endocrine-controlled responses last a . . . . . . time.
40. The insect hormone that delays metamorphosis is called . . . . . .

Multiple-Choice Questions

A

1. Changes in the environment that bring about responses are called (1) reflexes, (2) auxins, (3) synapses, (4) stimuli.
2. Impulses are transmitted from neuron to neuron by means of (1) receptors, (2) auxins, (3) neurotransmitters, (4) effectors.
3. A dog runs in front of a car. In which order would impulses travel through the neural pathways in the driver's body? (1) sensory, motor, interneuron (2) motor, sensory, interneuron (3) sensory, interneuron, motor (4) interneuron, sensory, motor
4. Which of the following is a neurotransmitter? (1) secretin (2) catalase (3) insulin (4) noradrenaline
5. Loewi's experiment on frog hearts led to the discovery of (1) blood types, (2) pacemaker, (3) accelerator nerve, (4) acetylcholine.
6. At the synapse (1) there is contact between two neurons, (2) an electric current jumps a gap, (3) static electricity jumps a gap, (4) chemicals are released.
7. The axon of a neuron is protected by (1) dendrites, (2) acetylcholine, (3) a myelin sheath, (4) terminal branches.
8. Which type of neuron is responsible for transmitting impulses to a gland? (1) sensory (2) motor (3) interneuron (4) ganglionic
9. The nerve impulse may best be considered as (1) a wave of depolarization, (2) movement of the stimulus toward the spinal chord, (3) an electric current, (4) a response to a stimulus.
10. The stimulation of one neuron by an adjacent neuron is most closely associated with the (1) production of electrical discharges, (2) secretion of ATP, (3) secretion of neurotransmitters, (4) rapid oxidation of glucose.

B

11. Nerve impulses do not follow a definite pathway in the *Hydra* because the *Hydra* does *not* have (1) muscle cells, (2) receptors, (3) a nerve net, (4) a nerve cord.
12. Impulses are *not* transmitted over a definite pathway from receptors to effectors in the (1) *Hydra*, (2) human, (3) grasshopper, (4) earthworm.
13. A definite pathway from receptors to effectors is characteristic of a (1) nerve net, (2) central nervous system, (3) hormone, (4) neurotransmitter.
14. The nervous system of an earthworm *differs* from that of a *Hydra* in that the earthworm (1) possesses a ventral nerve cord with connecting nerves, (2) transmits impulses in either direction along a modified neuron, (3) possesses fused ganglia and a nerve net, (4) uses its nervous system to respond to external stimuli only.

C

15. A naturally occurring auxin is (1) ATP, (2) DNA, (3) IAA, (4) 2,4-D
16. To speed up the formation of roots on stem cuttings, gardeners may use (1) ADP, (2) auxins, (3) ribonucleic acid, (4) acetylcholine.
17. Phototropism and geotropism are plant growth responses. These are the result of the fact that the stimuli light and gravity (1) cause equal auxin distribution in roots and stems, (2) are toxic to roots and stems, (3) slow down the lengthwise growth of individual cells, (4) result in unequal auxin distribution in roots and stems.
18. Which chemicals in animals are most similar in function to that of auxins in plants? (1) poisons (2) nutrients (3) hormones (4) substrates
19. The bending of plants toward the light is the result of (1) an unequal concentration of sugar in the stem, (2) a decrease in the amount of water in the cells of the plant, (3) an unequal distribution of auxins in the stem, (4) an increase in the rate of photosynthesis.

D

20. The nervous system and the endocrine system are similar in that both (1) have rapid responses, (2) secrete chemicals, (3) use circulatory fluid for transport, (4) have responses that last for long periods of time.
21. Which is true of both the nervous system and the endocrine system? (1) They bring about rapid responses to stimuli. (2) They send messages by impulses. (3) They assist in the maintenance of homeostasis. (4) They are under the direct control of the cerebellum.
22. Hormones are produced by (1) exocrine glands, (2) duct glands, (3) salivary glands, (4) ductless glands.
23. Endocrine responses *differ* from nerve responses in that endocrine responses are (1) more rapid, (2) electrical in nature, (3) carried by neurons, (4) of longer duration.
24. Ductless glands secrete their substances directly into (1) special tubes, (2) digestive juices, (3) the bloodstream, (4) receiving organs.

Chapter Test

1. Nerve control depends mainly on the functioning of (1) muscles, (2) neurons, (3) glands, (4) impulses.
2. A change in the external or internal environment that initiates an impulse is called a (1) response, (2) dendrite, (3) stimulus, (4) axon.
3. A reaction to a stimulus is a (1) response, (2) dendrite, (3) impulse, (4) axon.
4. Organs of response such as muscles or glands are (1) stimuli, (2) axons, (3) dendrites, (4) effectors.
5. In the neuron, the cell body that contains the nucleus is the (1) cyton, (2) axon, (3) impulse, (4) terminal branches.
6. Multicellular animals accomplish regulation by means of the nervous system and the (1) reproductive system, (2) endocrine system, (3) homeostatic system, (4) immune system.
7. The basic unit of the nervous system is the (1) dendrite, (2) neuron, (3) axon, (4) myelin sheath.
8. The coordination and control of life activities is called (1) homeostasis, (2) response, (3) regulation, (4) neurons.
9. The gap between the terminal branches of one neuron and the dendrites of the next neuron is the (1) myelin sheath, (2) axon, (3) stimulus, (4) synapse.
10. The neuron that carries the impulse *away from* the spinal cord toward the effector is the (1) motor neuron, (2) sensory neuron, (3) axon, (4) myelin sheath.
11. A chemical that aids in the transmission of a response across a synapse is the (1) axon, (2) neurotransmitter, (3) cyton, (4) stimulus.
12. The animal that possesses a nerve net composed of modified neurons and has no central nervous system is the (1) paramecium, (2) hydra, (3) earthworm, (4) grasshopper.
13. An organism that has sensory organs that include eyes, tympana, and antennae is the (1) ameba, (2) hydra, (3) earthworm, (4) grasshopper.
14. An organism that has a nervous system consisting of a highly developed brain and a dorsal nerve cord is the (1) earthworm, (2) human, (3) grasshopper, (4) planaria.
15. An organism that has a primitive brain composed of fused ganglia, a ventral nerve cord, and peripheral nerves is the (1) ameba, (2) human, (3) earthworm, (4) hydra.
16. Nerves containing both sensory and motor neurons are (1) effectors, (2) synapses, (3) interneurons, (4) mixed nerves.
17. Plant hormones that influence division, elongation, and differentiation of plant cells are (1) neurotransmitters, (2) tissues, (3) auxins, (4) axons.
18. Chemical control in animals differs from that in plants because animals possess cells specialized for the production of (1) auxins, (2) axons, (3) hormones, (4) tropisms.
19. Glands that synthesize and secrete hormones that control the activities of animals are (1) endocrine, (2) auxins, (3) exocrine, (4) neurotransmitters.

20. The body system that aids in distributing hormones secreted by the endocrine glands is the (1) reproductive, (2) circulatory, (3) excretory, (4) nervous.
21. Ductless glands that secrete internally are (1) exocrine, (2) digestive, (3) endocrine, (4) lymph.
22. Chemicals that promote developmental changes including flowering, fruit formation, and seed development in plants are (1) axons, (2) neurotransmitters, (3) plant hormones, (4) cytons.
23. A hormone that affects the metamorphosis of certain insects is (1) insulin, (2) adrenaline, (3) juvenile, (4) adult.
24. A growth-promoting chemical in plants is (1) axon, (2) gibberellin, (3) juvenile hormone, (4) 2,4-D.
25. The growth of part of a plant toward the light is called (1) geotropism, (2) chemotropism, (3) hydrotropism, (4) phototropism.
26. The bending of roots in a downward direction during growth is an example of (1) geotropism, (2) chemotropism, (3) hydrotropism, (4) phototropism.
27. Which is the best explanation for the growth pattern of the plant represented in the diagram below?

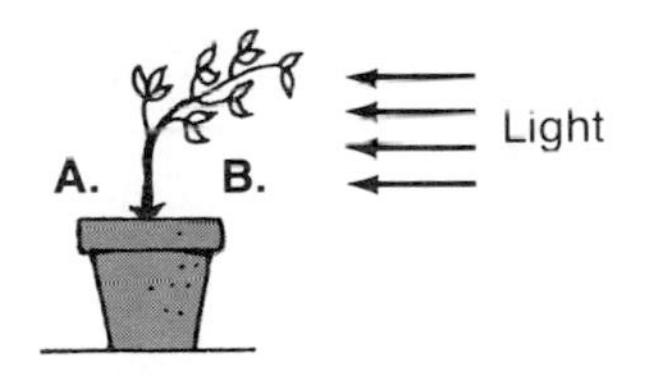

(1) Light affects the distribution of auxins. (2) More photosynthesis takes place on side *B* than on side *A*. (3) Cells on side *B* grow faster than those on side *A*. (4) Light stimulates a geotropic response.

28. A central nervous system is present in (1) *Hydra* and human, (2) *Paramecium* and *Hydra*, (3) earthworm and grasshopper, (4) ameba and human.
29. The two systems that directly control homeostasis in most animals are the (1) nervous and endocrine systems, (2) endocrine and excretory systems, (3) nervous and locomotive systems, (4) excretory and locomotive systems.
30. A green plant bends toward the light as a result of an (1) unequal distribution of auxins, (2) equal distribution of auxins, (3) unequal distribution of neurotransmitters, (4) equal distribution of neurotransmitters.

Chapter 10 Locomotion

Sponges, corals, and barnacles are firmly fastened to one spot, unlike most animals, which can move from place to place. Organisms that do not move are *sessile;* those that do move are *motile. Locomotion*, the ability to move from place to place, has provided animals and many protists with certain advantages in the struggle for survival. Plants are not motile.

A Advantages of Motility

Obtaining food. Motile animals are able to move from one feeding place to another. Plant eaters, such as a deer, and animal eaters, such as a cheetah, can search to find food that they prefer to eat. Sessile animals, such as barnacles and corals, can only live in places where food is in the immediate surroundings.

Ability to disperse and migrate. Some species of animals occupy vast areas of the earth. Locomotion, in part, makes them able to disperse away from where they are born and settle in new territories. Some kinds of animals travel regularly to live where there is a constant food supply or a favorable climate. *Migration*, or regular back and forth travel, helps animals avoid food shortages or severe weather. Whales, ducks, and salmon are examples of animals that migrate.

Fig. 10–1. Left: A cheetah is a motile organism. Right: Goose barnacles are sessile organisms.

Ability to seek shelter. Motile animals move to avoid harsh condtions, such as stormy weather, a hot sun, or extreme dryness.

Escape from predators. Locomotion makes it possible for many individuals to escape from *predators*, the animals that eat them. Though the lobster usually walks slowly, a flip of its powerful tail helps it retreat rapidly from danger. Animals of many sizes, from small fish to large deer, depend on their ability to escape from predators.

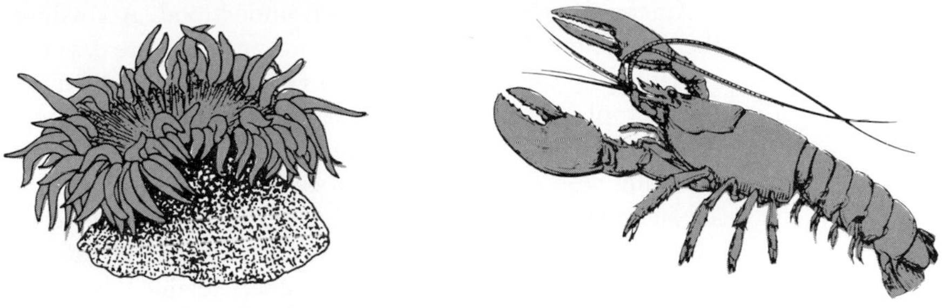

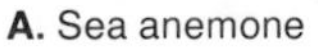

Fig. 10–2. Motility. A. Although the sea anemone may seem to be sessile, it moves slowly in its environment. B. The lobster, however, is capable of both slow and fast movement.

Mating. If the sperm cells of a fish were released at random into a lake, they would have only a slight chance of finding egg cells. Most kinds of fish swim near each other when they release their reproductive cells. Locomotion permits mating individuals to come together.

B

lations for .ocomotion

ocomotion in Protists

Protists and animals have many kinds of adaptations for locomotion. Among protozoa, these include the use of pseudopods, cilia, and flagella.

Use of pseudopods. An ameba moves over surfaces by means of *pseudopods* or false feet. Pseudopods are temporary fingerlike outpushings of the cell surface formed as the advancing front of the flowing cytoplasm seems to push back the cell membrane. An ameba's changing shape during locomotion is shown in Figure 10–3A. This type of locomotion is also found in certain white blood cells and is called *ameboid movement*.

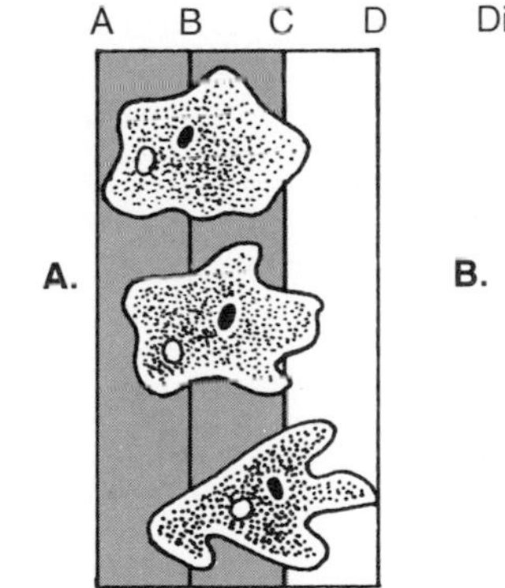

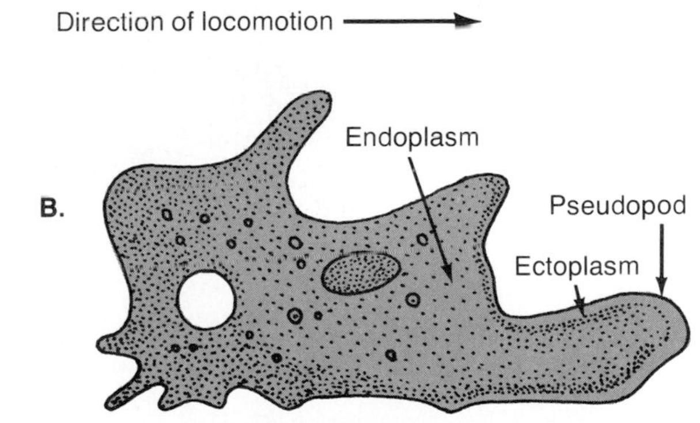

Fig. 10–3. Ameboid movement. A. Changing shape of an ameba as cytoplasm from the rear flows through the cell and pushes ahead in the form of pseudopods at the front. B. The outer layer of the cytoplasm, the ectoplasm, is a firm gel and the inner layer, the endoplasm, is a liquid sol.

Ameboid movement is not well understood. According to one theory, the formation of an ever-advancing new outside layer of the ameba is explained by sol-gel relationships (Figure 10–3B). The interior portion of the protoplasm, or *endoplasm*, is in the rather fluid state called a *sol*. The exterior portion, or *ectoplasm*, is in the more firm state called a *gel*. (For example, when jello hardens, a sol is changed to a gel.) At the tip of the advancing pseudopod, the sol changes to a firmer gel as it encounters the water environment. Near the posterior region of the ameba, the gel is changed to a liquid sol which is added to the flowing stream of protoplasm. The change from liquid sol to firm gel is accompanied by a contraction.

A new theory proposes that cytoplasmic streaming and ameboid movement may be caused by simple forms of microfilaments present in the cytoplasm. Microfilaments are thin protein fibers which are believed to function in various plant and animal contractile fibers, including those of muscle cells.

Use of cilia. The paramecium is an example of a protozoan that swims through water by beating of numerous minute *cilia* (Figure 10–4). Cilia are short, microscopic, hairlike extensions of the protoplasm, covered by cell membrane. (Although they are hairlike in shape, cilia should not be confused with hair. Hair is a nonliving structure, and strands of hair are much larger than the microscopic cilia.) The cilia beat in a coordinated manner with a sweeping motion, acting much like oars on a rowboat.

Cilia line the outer surface of the paramecium and also line the oral groove. As these cilia beat, food is drawn down the oral groove and into the gullet where a food vacuole begins to form. Cilia are the means of locomotion in many protozoa and algae. They are also found on ciliated cells in the human body, such as the cells that line the trachea.

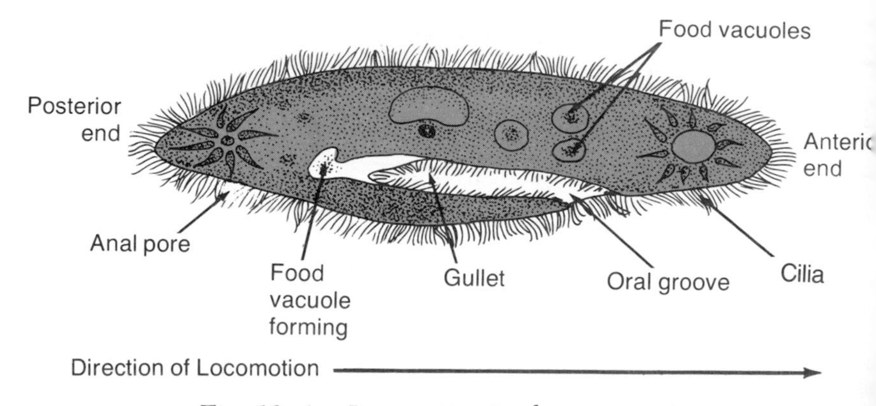

Fig. 10–4. Locomotion in the paramecium

As seen under the electron microscope, the cilia and flagella of eukaryotes have eleven sets of microtubules that run from the base to the tip. Two central fibers are surrounded by nine pairs of fibrils. This 9 plus 2 pattern is shown in Figure 10–5. The flagella of prokaryotes are made of a single fibril.

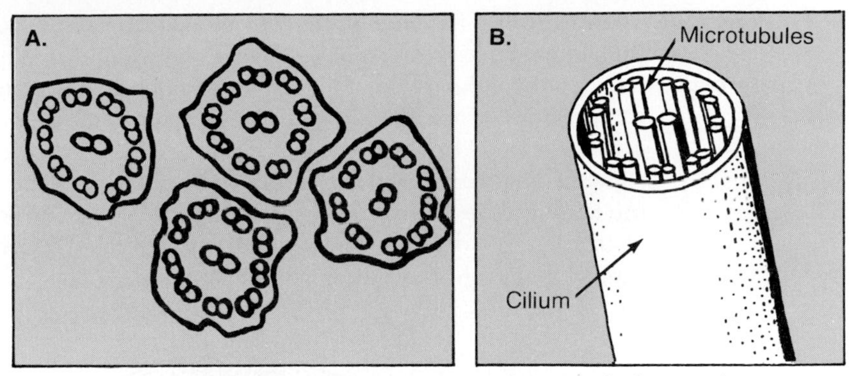

Fig. 10–5. The 9 plus 2 pattern of microtubules in cilia and flagella. A. The cross section of a group of cilia. B. Drawing of a single cilium.

Use of flagella. An example of a protist that moves by means of whiplike motions of a flagellum is *Euglena*. As the flagellum whips backward, the organism is pulled forward (Figure 10–6). Flagella are much larger than cilia; an organism may have one or two flagella.

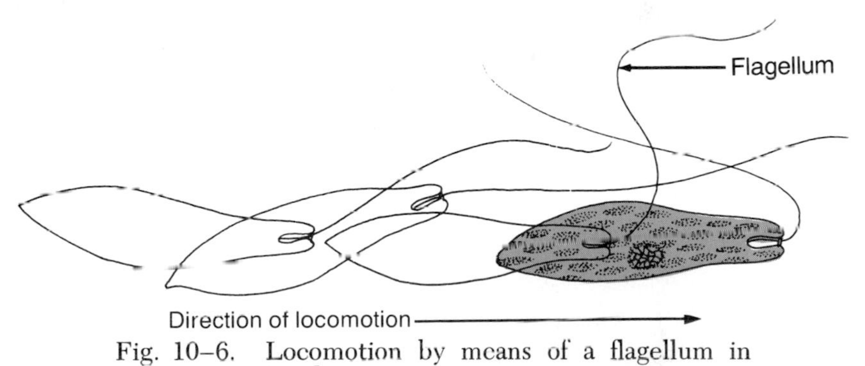

Fig. 10–6. Locomotion by means of a flagellum in *Euglena*

Locomotion in Hydra

Hydra is essentially a sessile organism. Instead of pursuing food, it usually remains attached to a submerged leaf and captures minute organisms that accidentally make contact with its waving tentacles. However, hydra does have primitive muscle cells and can make three types of movement: (1) it can somersault, base over tentacles (Figure 10–7); (2) it can bend over, attach its tentacles to the bottom, and then bring the base closer, in a kind of inching-along fashion; and (3) it can glide along on its base. This motion is accomplished with the aid of ameboid cells at the base.

Fig. 10–7. Locomotion in *Hydra*. Contractions of primitive type muscle cells cause a movement similar to somersaulting.

Locomotion in the Earthworm

The earthworm has *longitudinal muscles* which extend along the length o the animal and *circular muscles* which go around it (Figure 10–8). Th body cavity of the earthworm is filled with a fluid that can be only slightl compressed. When the circular muscles contract, pressure on the flui causes the body to become long and thin. When the longitudinal muscle contract, the worm shortens and becomes broader. The lower portion o the body wall in almost every segment of the worm's body has four pair of bristles called *setae*. These setae are operated by muscles that ca extend them into the soil or withdraw them.

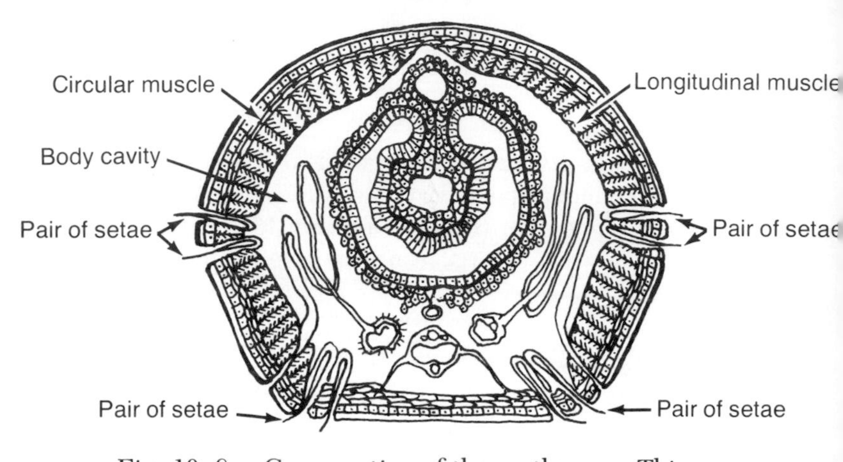

Fig. 10–8. Cross section of the earthworm. This cross section shows the four pairs of setae and the longitudinal and circular muscles.

First the setae in the rear portion of the worm dig into the soil an serve as anchors while the worm becomes long and thin, pushing th head end forward. Then the setae in the front dig into the soil, the rea setae are withdrawn, and the longitudinal muscles contract to bring u the rear portion of the worm. This sequence of events is repeated agai and again. The coordination of this complex series of events shows how much more advanced is the earthworm's central nervous system than th nerve net of hydra. But unlike more advanced organisms, the earthworm does not have a skeleton for attachment of muscles.

Exoskeletons and Endoskeletons

The skeleton of an animal may be on the outside or on the inside of its body. An *exoskeleton* (outside skeleton) is present in such arthropods as crabs, lobsters, spiders, millipedes, and insects. The exoskeleton is composed of *chitin*. This is a nonliving material that may be thick and heavy, as on the lobster's claws, or thin and light as on the grasshopper's wings.

One disadvantage of an exoskeleton is that it is not living. Therefore, it does not increase in size as the young animal grows. The exoskeleton must be periodically shed, a process known as *molting*. After a crab has molted, for example, it is virtually unprotected until its new soft skeleton hardens.

An *endoskeleton* (inside skeleton) is present in chordates such as the fish, frogs, reptiles, birds, and mammals. This skeleton may be composed of cartilage or bone. The vertebrate endoskeleton is composed of live cell material and can grow with the animal.

Locomotion in the Grasshopper

The grasshopper uses its six legs and four wings to move much faster than the earthworm (Figure 10–9). One of the grasshopper's advantages over the earthworm is that the grasshopper has an exoskeleton. Let us see why having a skeleton is an advantage for locomotion.

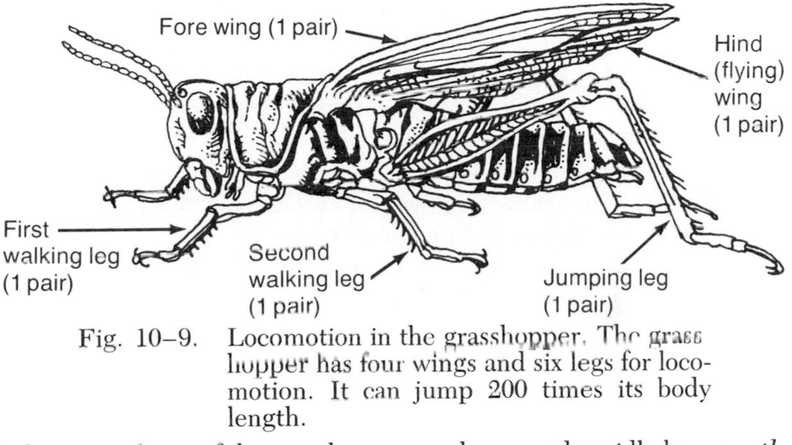

Fig. 10–9. Locomotion in the grasshopper. The grasshopper has four wings and six legs for locomotion. It can jump 200 times its body length.

The appendages of the grasshopper can be moved rapidly because *they act as levers* which are pulled by the grasshopper's muscles. As you may recall, a lever is a simple machine that can multiply either force or distance. A pull exerted through a short distance on one end of a lever can make the other end move a greater *distance* in the same period of *time*. This is a gain in *speed*. The grasshopper's legs and wings, with their stiff skeleton, act as levers that are pulled by muscles in such a manner that the grasshopper can walk, jump, and fly with considerable speed (Figure 10–10). Joints in the exoskeleton provide for flexibility and freedom of motion.

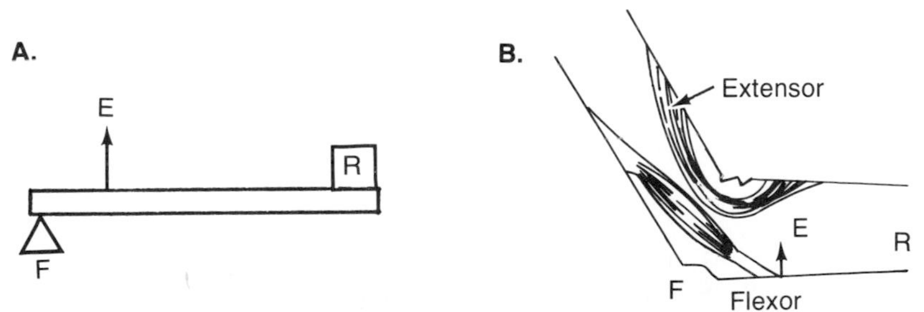

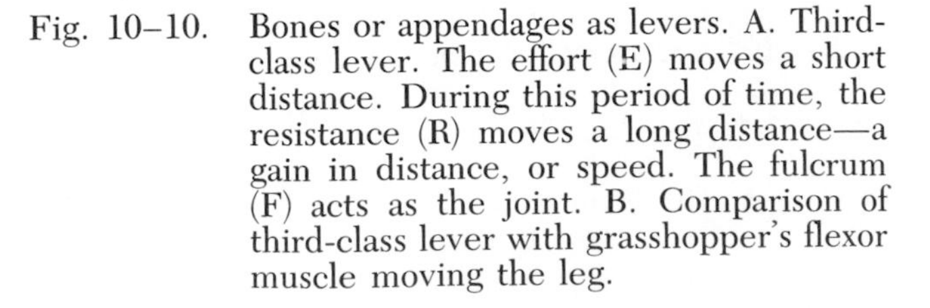

Fig. 10–10. Bones or appendages as levers. A. Third-class lever. The effort (E) moves a short distance. During this period of time, the resistance (R) moves a long distance—a gain in distance, or speed. The fulcrum (F) acts as the joint. B. Comparison of third-class lever with grasshopper's flexor muscle moving the leg.

You have an endoskeleton and the bones of your legs are surrounded by the muscles that move them. But the hollow exoskeleton of the grasshopper's legs has muscles on the inside.

The grasshopper's muscles act in *opposing pairs.* Some muscles are *flexors;* they narrow the angle at a joint. Others are *extensors;* they straighten the angle at a joint (Figure 10-10B). The contraction and relaxation of opposing muscles during walking, jumping, and flying are coordinated by the grasshopper's central nervous system.

Locomotion in Humans Humans have an endoskeleton made of living bone and cartilage, not an exoskeleton like that of insects. Humans, however, resemble grasshoppers in their method of locomotion in that they use muscles in pairs to extend and flex jointed appendages. If humans have jointed appendages, why are we not classified along with the grasshopper and lobster as Arthropoda, the jointed-limbed animals? This is because we do not have other characteristics of the arthropods that are more fundamental, such as chitinous exoskeleton, solid ventral nerve cord, and so on. Locomotion in humans is discussed more fully in Chapter 16.

Reasoning Exercises

1. Compare the advantages and disadvantages of both sessile and motile organisms.
2. Choose four examples of organisms and describe the adaptations for locomotion in each.
3. Give examples of organisms that have exoskeletons and those that have endoskeletons. Explain the advantages and disadvantages of both exoskeletons and endoskeletons.
4. Explain what is meant by the statement that "muscles work in opposing pairs."

Completion Questions

A

1. A life function that enables some animals to escape from predators is . . . . . .
2. An example of a sessile animal is . . . . . .
3. The probability of survival is greater in organisms that are . . . . . . (sessile, motile).

B

4. The structure used for locomotion by *Euglena* is the . . . . . .
5. Bristles used in locomotion by the earthworm are known as . . . . . .
6. The grasshopper's skeleton has flexibility at the . . . . . .
7. The shedding of a young grasshopper's skeleton is known as . . . . . .
8. The type of skeleton that grows as the animal grows is the . . . . . .
9. Muscles interact with each other in . . . . . . pairs.
10. A muscle that bends a bone at a joint is called a(n) . . . . . .

Multiple-Choice Questions

A

1. The term used to describe the ability of an organism to move from place to place is (1) sessile, (2) dormant, (3) molting, (4) motile.

2. An example of an organism that has an advantage in procuring food because of locomotion is (1) a barnacle, (2) a cow, (3) a coral, (4) a sponge.

B

3. Which structures are *not* associated with locomotion in protozoa? (1) flagella, (2) pseudopodia, (3) cilia, (4) setae
4. Which organism normally produces chitin? (1) human, (2) earthworm, (3) hydra, (4) grasshopper
5. Which organism uses setae during locomotion? (1) earthworm, (2) grasshopper, (3) protozoan, (4) hydra
6. Which organism is usually a sessile animal? (1) ameba, (2) grasshopper, (3) earthworm, (4) hydra
7. Which organism moves by the interaction of muscles and chitinous appendages? (1) hydra, (2) paramecium, (3) grasshopper, (4) human
8. A paramecium moves by means of (1) pseudopods, (2) hairs, (3) flagella, (4) cilia.
9. Somersaulting is a method of locomotion in the (1) hydra, (2) paramecium, (3) ameba, (4) earthworm.
10. An exoskeleton is present in (1) hydra, (2) grasshopper, (3) fish, (4) bird.
11. Which moves without the use of skeletal levers? (1) grasshopper, (2) human, (3) earthworm, (4) frog
12. The skeleton of a grasshopper consists of (1) chitin, (2) living tissue, (3) bone, (4) cartilage.
13. An example of an animal that is sessile is the (1) sponge, (2) euglena, (3) hydra, (4) earthworm.
14. Somersaulting is a method of locomotion in (1) earthworms, (2) protists, (3) monerans, (4) hydras.
15. Sol-gel relationships are used to explain locomotion in (1) amebas, (2) paramecia, (3) hydra, (4) earthworms.

Base your answers to questions 16 and 17 on Fig. 10-10 on p. 193.

16. What part of your leg acts as a fulcrum? (1) thigh, (2) knee, (3) calf, (4) foot.
17. Where is the resistance when kicking a ball? (1) thigh, (2) knee, (3) calf, (4) foot.

Chapter Test

1. A coral, a sponge, and a barnacle can be described as (1) motile, (2) fast moving, (3) slow moving, (4) sessile.
2. Organisms that have many kinds of adaptations for locomotion are called (1) motile, (2) sessile, (3) sessile and motile, (4) sponges.
3. The ameba is able to move and get food because of adaptations for locomotion called (1) cilia, (2) pseudopods, (3) flagella, (4) paramecia.
4. The paramecium is able to move at a much faster rate through the water than the ameba because of adaptations of (1) cilia and cell membranes, (2) pseudopods and cilia, (3) pseudopods and cell membranes, (4) cilia and flagella.

5. The adaptation for locomotion that means "false foot" is a (1) cilium, (2) pseudopod, (3) flagellum, (4) cell membrane.
6. Locomotion in the earthworm is accomplished by the interaction of muscles and (1) setae, (2) bones, (3) nephridia, (4) cartilaginous appendages.
7. The protist *Euglena* is able to move through the water by an adaptation called the (1) cilium, (2) flagellum, (3) pseudopod, (4) cell membrane.
8. An organism that has primitive muscle cells as an adaptation to aid in locomotion is the (1) paramecium, (2) earthworm, (3) euglena, (4) hydra.
9. An organism that has two types of muscles and setae as adaptations for locomotion is the (1) euglena, (2) hydra, (3) earthworm, (4) grasshopper.
10. A skeleton that is on the outside of an organism is called (1) a flexor, (2) an endoskeleton, (3) an exoskeleton, (4) chitin.
11. The skeleton of an organism that is made up of nonliving material is called (1) cartilage, (2) exoskeleton, (3) endoskeleton, (4) fulcrum.
12. The kind of skeleton that grows along with the organism is (1) a flagellum, (2) chitin, (3) exoskeleton, (4) endoskeleton.
13. Organisms that have a skeleton have an advantage in the process of locomotion because they have attachment points for (1) chitin, (2) muscles, (3) pseudopods, (4) molting.
14. Muscles and a skeleton help organisms in the process of locomotion by increasing their (1) molting, (2) chitin, (3) time, (4) speed.
15. Muscles in some organisms act in pairs that are (1) flexors, (2) extendors, (3) opposing, (4) molting.
16. Muscles that tend to straighten out bones at a joint are called (1) flexors, (2) extendors, (3) opposing, (4) molting.
17. Muscles that tend to bend bones at a joint are called (1) flexors, (2) extendors, (3) opposing, (4) molting.
18. The type of skeleton that a human has is called (1) chitin, (2) an exoskeleton, (3) an endoskeleton, (4) cartilage.
19. The skeleton of a grasshopper is made from a nonliving substance called (1) extendors, (2) cartilage, (3) chitin, (4) exoskeleton.
20. Locomotion is accomplished by the interaction of muscles and chitinous appendages in (1) hydras, (2) paramecia, (3) grasshoppers, (4) euglenas.

Unit 2 Maintenance in Living Things

Portfolio Project

Choose one of the organisms shown in an illustration in Chapters 5-10. Make your own diagram of the organism showing the structures used for locomotion, transport, and nutrition. Be sure to label each structure you show and identify its function.

UNIT THREE HUMAN PHYSIOLOGY

If you were to compare the functions of the human body with those of other organisms in the five kingdoms, you would find that there is little that is fundamentally different about the way humans engage in nutrition, respiration, transport, and the other life functions. Human cells perform many of the same chemical reactions that occur in organisms of other kingdoms, with molecules that differ only slightly. Like monerans, protists, plants, and lower animals, humans use molecules of DNA and ATP and employ the same chemistry and physics of oxidation and diffusion. At the same time, however, in accordance with the principle of diversity, humans perform many of these life functions in ways that show refinements and advances that distinguish them from other life forms.

Unit II, Maintenance in Living Things, traced the structures and functions that evolved in the five kingdoms to carry out the life processes. Some highlights of human anatomy and physiology were included in the discussions that described the similarities and differences in the various forms of life. Unit III, however, includes more information about the anatomy and physiology of the human body. Chapters on each of the life functions illustrate the interrelationships among the human systems and provide information that can help you make positive decisions for maintaining good health.

hapter 11 Nutrition in Humans

The life function of nutrition includes all of those activities by which an organism obtains the food needed for growth, repair, energy, and regulation. This life function includes more than the mere selection and intake of food. It includes digestion, absorption, utilization, and egestion. For example, a person who eats wisely but cannot absorb digested food properly has poor nutrition. As heterotrophs, humans ingest preformed, high-energy, organic food molecules.

A 'utrition in Humans

The usable portions of foods are known as *nutrients*. These are used mainly as (1) energy sources, (2) the basis for the building or repair of cell structures, and (3) regulators of metabolic processes. Foods also contain substances that cannot be digested and are passed out of the body unused. For example, humans cannot digest the cellulose cell walls of plants. This kind of waste in food is called *roughage*. A *food*, therefore, consists of nutrients plus roughage.

Actually, roughage is valuable. The fibrous matter in vegetables and whole grains provides bulk to be worked on by the muscles of the alimentary canal. This exercise aids in the regular elimination of feces and prevents constipation.

There are six main groups of nutrients: (1) carbohydrates, (2) proteins, (3) fats, (4) vitamins, (5) minerals, and (6) water. The characteristics of these organic and inorganic compounds were discussed in Chapter 4, The Chemistry of Living Things. In this chapter, the chart entitled The Nutrients (page 200) summarizes the nutrients and lists the major food sources of each nutrient.

From your study of the molecular structure of organic compounds, you may recall that carbohydrates, proteins, and fats are large molecules. These large molecules must be broken down, or digested into smaller molecules, before they can pass through cell membranes and be used by the body. From the chemist's viewpoint, digestion consists of hydrolysis (this process was described in Chapter 4). Vitamins, minerals, and water are small molecules that can be absorbed without digestion.

Laboratory Skill

Use and Interpret Indicators in Tests for Nutrients

An *indicator*, in chemistry, is a substance that indicates the presence, and sometimes the concentration, of a substance in a mixture. For example, litmus paper lets you know whether a solution is acid or basic. (Litmus turns red in an acid and blue in a base.) Several indicators are used in the high school laboratory to test for the presence of various nutrients.

Test for Sugar

You will recall that glucose and other simple sugars are monosaccharides. To test a food for the presence of simple sugar, place the food in a test tube and add enough clear blue Benedict's solution to cover it. Heat to boiling. An orange-red cloudiness or precipitate indicates the presence of glucose; a green color indicates the presence of a trace of glucose. In the absence of simple sugar, Benedict's solution retains its clear blue color. This test does not work with a disaccharide.

Test for Starch

To test a food sample for starch, add iodine solution (Lugol's solution) to the sample. The iodine solution turns blue-black if starch is present.

Test for Protein

To test a food for the presence of protein, place a small amount of the food in a test tube and cover it with dilute nitric acid. Heat gently. (*Caution! Hot nitric acid is dangerous.*) Pour off the nitric acid, rinse the contents of the tube with water, and add ammonium hydroxide. If protein is present, the food sample turns yellow after the nitric acid treatment and turns orange after the ammonium hydroxide treatment.

Another test for protein can be demonstrated by placing some raw egg white in a test tube. Add one drop of a 1% solution of copper sulfate and five drops of a 10% solution of sodium hydroxide. A purple color indicates the presence of protein. (This is called the *Biuret test.*)

Test for Fat

For a simple test for fat, rub a food sample on a piece of unglazed paper and hold it to the light. If the paper becomes translucent, fat is present.

Test for Water

To test a food for water, gently heat a sample in a dry test tube. If droplets of water condense at the cooler top of the test tube, water was present in the food sample.

Test for Vitamin C

Although tests for most vitamins are complex, the test for ascorbic acid (vitamin C) is relatively simple. This test utilizes *indophenol* which forms a clear blue solution when dissolved in water. Ascorbic acid causes this solution to become colorless.

To perform the test, first add ten drops of blue indophenol to a test tube. Then add, one drop at a time, a solution of the food sample being tested. Shake the tube each time. Keep an accurate count of the drops needed to turn the indophenol colorless. The greater the number of drops needed, the *lower* the concentration of ascorbic acid present in the food sample.

You can use this test to compare the amounts of vitamin C in fresh, canned, and frozen fruit juices. How could you find out if letting a glass of freshly squeezed orange juice stand around for a day has any effect on its vitamin C content?

Safety in Heating Materials in the Laboratory

1. Wear safety goggles and a laboratory apron whenever heating substances in the laboratory.
2. Always handle hot test tubes, beakers, or other glassware with tongs or an asbestos mitt.
3. When heating materials in a test tube, always point the open end of the test tube away from yourself and others.
4. Keep all inflammable substances, such as alcohol, far away from an open flame.
5. If you are heating something at your work station, do not leave it unattended.
6. Know the location of the fire extinguisher, fire blanket, first aid kit, fire exit from the laboratory, and fire alarm.
7. Discuss safety rules for fires in the laboratory with your teacher. Minor burns should be immersed in cold water. In case of severe burns, notify your teacher immediately. If clothing catches on fire, NEVER RUN, smother the fire with a fire blanket.

Reasoning Exercises

1. What are nutrients? How are they used?
2. Use the chart, The Nutrients, to determine what use humans make of fats, carbohydrates, and proteins.
3. What activities are included in the life function of nutrition?
4. What name is given to waste in food? What is its importance in human nutrition and digestion?
5. Name four minerals present in food and give their use to the body.
6. Which nutrients require digestion? Why is this so?

B

The Nutrients

Carbohydrates

The carbohydrates include monosaccharides, such as glucose, disaccharides, such as sucrose, and polysaccharides such as starch and glycogen. The polysaccharides, are large molecules consisting of numerous branching units of such monosaccharides as glucose and fructose. Starch and

The Nutrients			
Nutrient	**Composition**	**Uses**	**Sources**
Carbohydrates (sugars and starches)	Carbon, hydrogen, and oxygen	Source of energy	Cereals, potatoes, bread, fruit, candy, ice cream
Proteins	Carbon, hydrogen, oxygen, nitrogen. Many proteins also contain sulfur, phosphorus, and iron	Synthesis of compounds needed for growth and repair. Proteins are also oxidized for energy.	Beef, fish, liver, peas, beans, nuts, milk, cheese, eggs
Fats and oils	Carbon, hydrogen, and oxygen	Source of energy	Butter, cream, lard, bacon, fats in meats, vegetable oils, nuts
Water	Hydrogen and oxygen	Transport of materials. The solvent in which chemical reactions take place.	Drinking water, milk and other beverages, fruits and vegetables. Most foods contain water.
Mineral salts	1. Calcium and phosphorus	For strong bones and teeth	Milk, cheese, eggs
	2. Iodine	To manufacture thyroxin, the secretion of the thyroid gland	Sea foods, iodized salt
	3. Iron	To manufacture hemoglobin, the red pigment in the blood that carries oxygen	Liver, meats, eggs, vegetables
	4. Fluorine	Fluorides prevent tooth decay by making the enamel hard	Present naturally in some drinking water. "Fluoridated water" has controlled amounts of fluorides added.
	5. Sodium	Needed for proper functioning of cells	Table salt (sodium chloride)
	6. Chlorine	Part of the hydrochloric acid needed for digestion of food in the stomach	Table salt (sodium chloride)
Vitamins	(see Table, *Some Important Vitamins*, page 203)		

glycogen are insoluble *storage* forms: starch in plants and glycogen in animals. Glycogen is sometimes called animal starch. Glucose absorbed from the human digestive tract is stored as glycogen in the liver and muscles. When needed for energy, the glycogen is hydrolyzed back to glucose. Glucose is soluble, and transported where needed by the blood.

Nutritionists suggest that carbohydrates, which are sources of energy, should constitute 50 percent of the diet in humans. Complex carbohydrates, such as cellulose, are nondigestible by humans and increase the amount of roughage. Complex carbohydrates are found in fruits and vegetables as well as in whole grains. Many breads now on the market are made with whole grain fibers to provide additional roughage.

Proteins The body needs twenty different amino acids to synthesize the many proteins it requires to maintain and repair body tissues. Humans can convert some amino acids to others. Eight amino acids, however, cannot be synthesized and must be consumed as part of the diet. These eight amino acids are called the *essential amino acids*.

One of the essential amino acids is tryptophan. Tryptophan is absent in cornmeal. Populations in Africa that subsist on a diet consisting mainly of cornmeal develop the *protein-deficiency disease* called *Kwashiorkor.* Victims of this disease, particularly growing children who need large amounts of protein for growth, are lethargic and fail to grow normally.

All the amino acids needed to synthesize a particular protein must be present at the same time. If one necessary amino acid is absent, the others will be deaminated and used in cellular respiration to release energy.

A *complete protein* contains all the essential amino acids. An *incomplete protein* lacks one or more of the essential amino acids. A combination of incomplete proteins can, however, provide complete protein. For example, both rice and beans are foods that contain incomplete proteins. If eaten at the same meal, each complements the other to provide a complete protein diet. People who follow a vegetarian diet lacking meats and fish, foods that provide complete protein, should make full use of such complementary foods.

Fats Fats are large molecules containing the stored energy of numerous carbon–carbon and carbon–hydrogen bonds. Fats are synthesized in the human body from fatty acids and glycerol. When stored in adipose (fat) tissues throughout the body, they represent much stored energy. Fats together with proteins are needed to synthesize cell membranes. (See the fluid-mosaic model of the cell membrane discussed in Chapter 6.

Excess consumption of fats is a common problem in the American diet. However, it is important to consider not only the total amount of fat consumed but also the kinds of fat. Fats may be *saturated* or *unsaturated.* A molecule of saturated fat contains all the hydrogen atoms it can hold (see diagrams in Chapter 4). The carbon-to-carbon backbone of its fatty acid component contains only single bonds. An unsaturated fat, however, contains double bonds in the fatty acid portion of the molecule. These are positions where additional hydrogen atoms could be taken on.

There is evidence that excess consumption of saturated fats is one of the factors leading to the formation of deposits of cholesterol in the coronary arteries of the heart. These deposits block the flow of blood to the heart muscle, a condition called *atherosclerosis*. Saturated fats are solid at room temperature. They are found in meat and in milk and milk products.

Unsaturated fats are oils that are liquid at room temperature. They do not seem to be involved in cardiovascular (heart and blood vessel) disease. A molecule that is unsaturated at several points is called *polyunsaturated fat*. Polyunsaturated fats are found in fish, vegetable oils (such as corn oil), and margarine.

Minerals

You are already familiar with the mineral phosphorus as an important component of ATP, RNA, and DNA. Many other minerals are important for the proper functioning of the body. The most abundant mineral, calcium, is deposited in teeth and bones to make them hard. Iron is vital in the formation of hemoglobin.

As minerals are excreted in sweat and through the kidneys, they must be replaced in order to maintain a healthy body. The table, The Nutrients, provides a partial list of minerals that are needed by the body. Many other minerals, such as zinc, are required in trace amounts. Minerals are used by the body in the form of dissociated ions which come from dissolved mineral salts.

Vitamins

Like minerals, vitamins perform various functions. Some vitamins are parts of coenzymes that participate in cellular respiration. They are especially important in the normal growth processes of children. For adults, vitamins are necessary for repair and to maintain the healthy functioning of the body.

Vitamin-deficiency diseases led to a recognition of the need for these hitherto unknown substances present in food. For example, in the 15th, 16th, and 17th centuries, many sailors on lengthy voyages became ill with scurvy. When vessels stopped at islands where citrus fruits could be obtained, the sailors recovered. Later, it was discovered that citrus fruits contain one of the then-unknown substances vital for health, vitamin C. When the composition of vitamin C was learned, it was given the name, ascorbic acid.

About ten vitamins are now recognized. A well-balanced diet should provide all the vitamins needed by an average person. However, they may be taken as daily supplements in pill form or prescribed by physicians in massive doses in unusual circumstances.

Water

A person might live for over a month without food but cannot live more than a few days without water. As an excellent solvent, water is the main

Some Important Vitamins			
Vitamins	**Uses**	**Results of Deficiency**	**Sources**
A (carotene)	Growth and repair; healthy eyes and skin	Poor growth, night blindness, skin and membrane problems	Green and yellow vegetables, butter, eggs, liver
B_1 (thiamine)	Growth, appetite and metabolism, healthy nerve tissue	Loss of appetite and weight, incomplete digestion, nerve disorders, beriberi	Meat, seafood, whole grains, poultry milk, eggs
B_2 (riboflavin)	Oxygen use by cells (cellular respiration); healthy skin and mouth	Skin disorders, fatigue	Milk, meat, eggs, green vegetables
Niacin (part of vitamin B complex)	Healthy skin, digestion, and metabolism; functioning of the nervous system	Digestive and skin disorders, pellagra (digestive and nervous disturbances)	Meat, fish, poultry, whole grains, eggs
B_{12}	Production of red blood cells	Pernicious anemia (lack of an adequate number of red blood cells)	Liver, green vegetables
C (ascorbic acid)	Healthy teeth, gums, and blood vessels; repair	Sore and bleeding gums, weak bones, scurvy	Fruit (especially citrus), tomatoes leafy vegetables
D	Growth and maintenance of bones and teeth, calcium and phosphorus metabolism	Poor bone and teeth development, rickets (poor bone development)	Produced in skin when exposed to sun; fortified milk
K	Blood clotting, liver function	Problems in clotting of blood	Synthesized by bacteria in intestine; green vegetables

component for the transport fluid, the blood, and the medium in which chemical reactions of cells take place. It is a lubricant for the joints and for the digestive system and it cools the body by evaporation as sweat.

Water that is lost from the body by breathing, urination, elimination, and sweating must be speedily recovered. The need for water is signalled through the sensation of thirst which is regulated in an unknown way by the hypothalamus of the brain. We take in water through drinking it plain or in fluids such as milk, cocoa, and soups. Practically all foods contain some water.

Daily Calorie requirements vary according to an individual's gender, age, size, and activities. For example, the average daily Calorie requirement for an active 16-year-old boy who is 6 feet tall and weighs 180 pounds is 3,600 Calories. An active 16-year-old girl who is 5½ feet tall and weighs 125 pounds needs 2,500 Calories a day.

Energy, Vitamin, and Mineral Values of Some Foods

Type of food	Serving (ready-to-eat)	Protein	Calcium	Iron	Vitamin A value	B-vitamins		Vitamin C (ascorbic acid)	Food energy (in Calories)
						Thiamine	Riboflavin		
Milk, whole fluid	1 cup	*	****		*		***		160
Cheese, process Cheddar	1 ounce	*	***		*		*		115
Meat, poultry, fish (lean)	2 ounces	***		**	*	*	*		140
Eggs	1 large	*		*	*		*		80
Dry beans	¾ cup	**	*	****		*	*		160
Peanut butter	2 tbsp.	*		*					190
Bread, whole wheat	2 slices	*	*	**		*			135
Bread, enriched	2 slices	*		*		*	*		135
Cereal, ready-to-eat	1 ounce			***	**	**	**	**	110
Citrus juice	½ cup					*		*****	50
Other fruit, fruit juice	½ cup			*	*			***	80
Tomatoes, tomato juice	½ cup			*	**	*		*****	30
Dark green and deep yellow vegetables	½ cup		*	*	*****		*	****	45
Potatoes	1 medium			*		*		****	75
Other vegetables	½ cup			*	*			**	30
Butter, margarine	1 tbsp.				*				100
Sugar	2 teaspoons								25

Part of daily need from a serving:
*****About 50 percent or more
****About 40 percent
***About 30 percent
**About 20 percent
*About 10 percent

Calories The energy value of foods is measured in Calories. A *Calorie* is the amount of heat required to raise the temperature of one kilogram of water one degree Celsius. The Calorie content of foods is measured by burning a food sample in a calorimeter. A *calorimeter* is a closed chamber surrounded by a known mass of water. The increase in water temperature indicates the Calories of heat energy released by the complete oxidation of the food. There are, for example, 9 Calories in one gram of fat, 5 Calories in one gram of carbohydrate, and 4 Calories in one gram of protein.

Food Additives Chemicals are added to modern processed foods as food additives. These may improve the taste, color, or texture of foods. Many improve the keeping quality of foods that must remain on the shelf or in machines for long periods of time. Some of these additives have been shown to be carcinogenic (cancer-causing) and their use is forbidden. Others are still under investigation. *Saccharin,* the artificial food sweetener, has been retained by Congress on the permissible list while lengthy tests on its safety are performed.

Nitrites, added to hot dogs, bacon, and luncheon meats, protect food against bacterial decay and also provide the desired red color. The use of nitrites is now questioned because, in the stomach, they may release nitrous acid (or nitrosamines). Nitrous acid removes nitrogen atoms from one of the components of DNA, changing it to a different substance and thereby potentially changing the genetic makeup.

Monosodium glutamate (MSG) is a flavor enhancer most commonly used in preparing oriental foods. However, the use of MSG is not restricted to oriental foods. Excess consumption of this substance can cause some people to become ill.

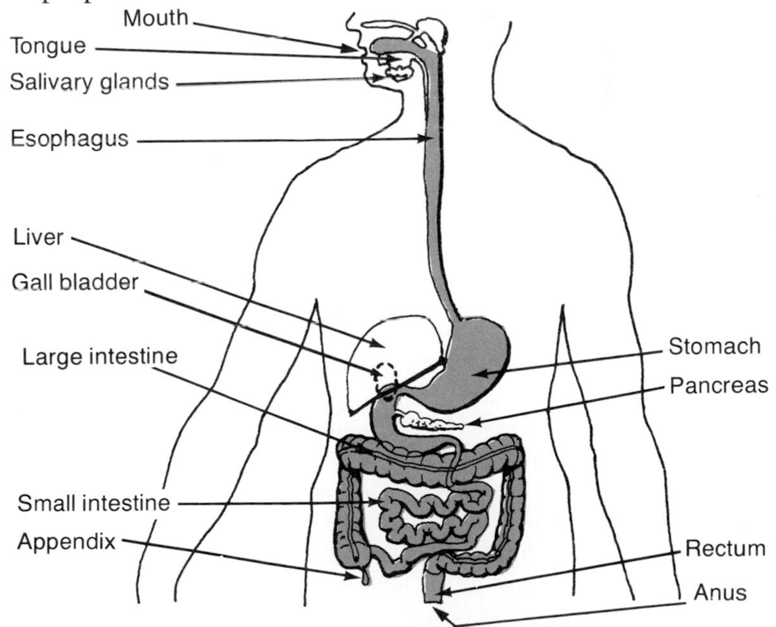

Fig. 11–1. The digestive system showing the alimentary canal and the digestive glands

Do you read labels on food packages? The U.S. Food and Drug Administration (FDA) requires that all food packages list all the ingredients, including any food additives, that are contained in a food product.

C

The Digestive System

As discussed in Chapter 5, the human digestive tract and the body wall can be considered a tube-within-a-tube. The inner tube, or *alimentary canal*, is a coiled tube through which ingested material moves in one direction. The alimentary canal with its digestive glands constitutes the *digestive system*.

Digestion in the Mouth

The mouth and alimentary canal contain many mucous glands in their epithelial linings. *Mucus*, the secretion of these glands, acts as a lubricant for food.

The digestive juices of the mouth are contained in the saliva secreted by the salivary glands. When you chew food (mechanical digestion), you mix it with saliva and break it up into smaller particles to provide more surface for the action of digestive juices. Saliva contains a salivary *amylase* (ptyalin) which hydrolyzes starch to a double sugar (disaccharide) called *maltose*. However, it does not break down starch completely to simple sugars (monosaccharides). When the food and saliva reach the stomach, the acid pH in that organ stops the action of the salivary amylase.

Swallowing is a coordinated reflex action that forces food from the mouth to the esophagus. The esophagus and trachea are two tubes which lead from the pharynx. During swallowing, the top of the trachea rises against a flap called the *epiglottis*. This flap diverts the food mass toward the esophagus so that the food does not block the passage of air into the trachea.

The Esophagus

Food is moved from the esophagus, or gullet, to the stomach by a series of wavelike muscular contractions and relaxations known as *peristalsis*. These peristaltic waves start in the esophagus and continue along the entire alimentary canal.

The walls of the esophagus, stomach, and small intestine contain visceral muscles. Some of these are circular while others are longitudinal. They are thus well adapted to producing the ringlike contractions and relaxations of peristalsis. Some of the lining epithelial tissue is specialized for the production of mucus.

Digestion in the Stomach

The stomach is a muscular organ that churns the food and initiates the digestion of proteins by proteases. Another function of the stomach is food storage. Because it is an expandable sac, the stomach permits humans to eat now and digest later.

Proteins are the only important nutrients acted upon by the stomach's *gastric juice*. This juice is secreted by microscopic *gastric glands* located in the lining of the stomach. In the stomach, proteins are only partially hydrolyzed. They form intermediate products of protein digestion known as *peptones* and *proteoses*.

As produced by the gastric glands, gastric juice contains *pepsinogen* and *hydrochloric acid*. Within the cavity of the stomach, the HCl changes pepsinogen to the activated protease, *pepsin*. The hydrochloric acid provides the optimum pH for the hydrolytic activity of this *gastric protease*. The hydrochloric acid also helps to kill germs taken in with the food.

Why are the gastric glands not themselves digested? This is because the glands contain the inactive pepsinogen. Why aren't the walls of the stomach digested? Indeed, sometimes they are, resulting in the sores called *ulcers*. It is believed, however, that the layer of mucus helps to protect the stomach lining.

Rennin is an enzyme present in the gastric juice of many mammals, including cows and humans. Rennin is *not* a digestive enzyme. It curdles milk proteins; that is, it changes them to a solid state. In this way, the proteins are separated from the water that would dilute the protease. Rennet is a commercial preparation of rennin from calf stomachs that is used to make custards.

In 1883, Dr. William Beaumont, an American Army surgeon, performed studies on the human stomach that are the basis for modern understanding of stomach function. His patient, Alexis St. Martin, had received a shotgun wound that resulted in a permanent opening leading from the outside body wall into his stomach. Through this hole Beaumont inserted pieces of meat tied to a string, and later removed the meat for observation. Beaumont's reports of the digestive action of gastric juice are classics of scientific experimentation.

Saliva and gastric juice add water to the stomach which churns and changes the food to a liquid mass called *chyme*. This is of the proper consistency to enter the small intestine. The lower end of the stomach is separated from the small intestine by a ring-shaped muscle known as the *pyloric sphincter*. The sphincter opens for short periods, allowing the chyme to enter the small intestine a little at a time.

Digestion in the Small Intestine

It is in the small intestine that the hydrolysis of food is completed. The liver, pancreas, and intestinal glands pour their secretions into the small intestine.

- *Liver*. Bile, secreted by the liver and stored in the gallbladder, has no digestive enzymes. However, bile salts aid in the digestion of fats by emulsifying them. *Emulsification* is the breaking up of large globules of fats or oils into tiny globules. This process provides more surface for the action of the enzyme lipase.

Bile is strongly alkaline. It neutralizes the acid of the stomach and provides the alkaline medium required by the digestive enzymes that function in the small intestine.

- *Pancreas*. Pancreatic juice contains *proteases*, *amylases*, and *lipases*. There are several kinds of proteases, each of which is specific in its action. For example, one enzyme acts on the bonds between the amino acids aspartic acid and arginine; another enzyme acts on the bonds between the amino acids valine and tyrosine. Amylase continues the hydrolysis of starch to maltose, and lipase hydrolyzes fats to fatty acids and glycerol.

• *Intestinal glands.* Like the pancreas, these microscopic glands in the lining of the small intestine secrete proteases, amylases, and lipases. These complete the digestion of proteins, carbohydrates, and fats.

Villi are microscopic, fingerlike projections in the lining of the small intestine which also participate in digestion. Their cells contain enzymes needed to complete the digestion of proteins and carbohydrates. Because these digestive activities occur within cells of the villi, digestion in humans is intracellular as well as extracellular. The table below summarizes the chemical digestion of three kinds of nutrients:

Summary of Chemical Digestion

Nutrient	Digestion
Carbohydrates	Digestion begins in the oral cavity and is completed in the small intestine.
Proteins	Digestion begins in the stomach and is completed in the small intestine.
Fats	Most lipid digestion occurs in the small intestine.

Absorption in the Small Intestine

In the small intestine, the end products of digestion diffuse into the blood. An enormous number of tiny projections called *villi* absorb these end products of digestion. Villi covering the lining of the small intestine are so numerous that they look like a fuzz. They greatly increase the surface for absorption.

As shown in Figure 11–2, each villus has an outside lining of epithelial cells through which absorption occurs. Inside the villus are a network of blood capillaries and a projection of the lymph system called a *lacteal.* Amino acids and simple sugars pass into the capillaries. Fatty acids and glycerol enter the lacteals where fats are again formed, but the suspension of fat droplets in the lacteals give them a milky appearance. The lacteals are part of the lymph system. The largest lymph duct empties into a large vein; in this way, fats absorbed in the lacteals of the villi reach the circulating blood.

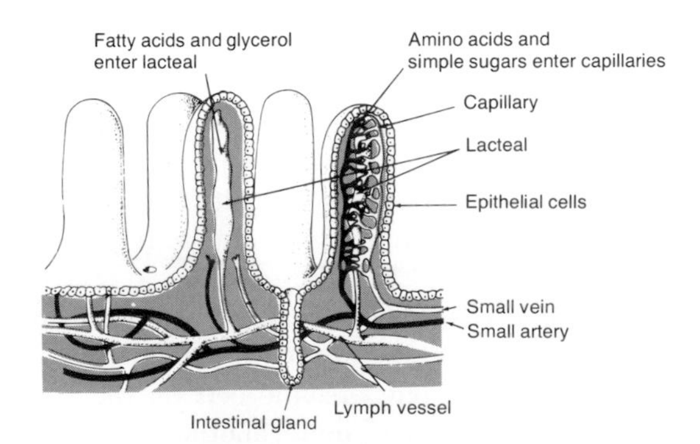

Fig. 11–2. Diagram of villus and portion of lymph system

The small intestine is an excellent example of the adaptation of structure for function:

- Presence of muscles permits contractions that mix the liquids and bring them into intimate contact with the villi.
- Great length provides greater surface for absorption.
- Folds in the wall provide greater surface for absorption.
- Projections in the form of villi provide greater surface for absorption. The human small intestine has a surface area about ten times greater than the skin surface.
- Thin membranes of the epithelial cells, the capillaries, and the lacteal permit absorption of digested food.

The Large Intestine

No digestion of food occurs in the large intestine. During the process of digestion, water has been added to the alimentary canal at each step. The absorption of water from the alimentary canal back into the bloodstream is an important mechanism for the conservation of water by land animals.

Bacteria which normally inhabit the large intestine produce important vitamins for the body. When a patient is given strong doses of antibiotics, valuable bacteria of the large intestine may be destroyed. The patient may then have symptoms of vitamin deficiencies. Consuming yogurt helps restore the normal flora of the large intestine. Bacteria in the large intestine also break down the small quantities of incompletely digested proteins that reach the large intestine. This bacterial action may liberate sulfur-containing gases.

The feces, or wastes, are stored in the lower part of the large intestine, the rectum, and eliminated (defecated) through the anus. This opening is controlled by both involuntary and voluntary muscles. Bacteria constitute from 10 percent to 50 percent of the bulk of the feces. The remainder is largely water and the undigested cellulose of plant cell walls. Minerals, mucus, and epithelial cells are also present.

Reasoning Exercises

1. Describe the difference between mechanical and chemical digestion.
2. How is food moved through the digestive tract? Would this movement occur if you were standing on your head?
3. Which organ churns food and starts the digestion of protein? What acid is located there? How does this acid aid in digestion?
4. Explain the difference in function between the small intestine and the large intestine.
5. What is the function of mucus throughout the digestive system?

D

Some Problems of the Digestive System

Ulcers. Ulcers are sores in the lining of the stomach, esophagus, or upper part of the small intestine. Symptoms may include pain, bleeding, nausea, vomiting, and loss of appetite. An infection of the bacterium *H. pylori* causes most ulcers. These bacteria cause the mucus glands that line the digestive tract to produce mucus of poor quality. This mucus normally protects

Summary of Human Digestion

Organ	Glands	Secretion	Enzymes	Action	Additional Notes
Mouth	Salivary	Saliva	Amylase (ptyalin)	Starch → maltose (a disaccharide)	Mechanical as well as chemical digestion Mucus flow, started here, continues throughout alimentary canal
Esophagus	Mucous	Mucus	None	Lubrication	Peristalsis begins
Stomach	Gastric	Gastric juice	Protease (pepsin)	Proteins → peptones and proteoses	The hormone gastrin stimulates flow of gastric juice HCl provides acidity and kills germs Storage of food
Small Intestine	1. Liver	Bile	None	Emulsifies fats	Provides alkaline medium
	2. Pancreas	Pancreatic juice	Proteases	Proteins → peptones, proteoses, and amino acids	The hormone secretin stimulates flow of pancreatic juice
			Amylase	Starch → maltose	
			Lipase	Fats → fatty acids and glycerol	
	3. Intestinal glands	Intestinal juice	Protease	Peptides → amino acids Peptones and proteoses → amino acids	Absorption of end products occurs in small intestine
			Amylases	Disaccharides → simple sugars	Villi facilitate absorption
			Lipase	Fats → fatty acids and glycerol	
Large Intestine	Mucous	Mucus	None	Lubrication	Reabsorption of water Bacterial action Formation of feces

the lining from the harm that the stomach's own gastric juices can cause. The hydrochloric acid in gastric juice can create a sore, or erosion in the lining. Killing the bacteria with antibiotics leads to healing of ulcers.

Constipation. A function of the large intestine is the reabsorption of water that has been added to the alimentary canal as part of digestive juices. If too much water is removed from the undigested food as it passes through the large intestine, the feces harden. They are eliminated infrequently and with difficulty, a condition called constipation.

Diarrhea. Diarrhea is a condition that is the opposite of constipation. Increased peristaltic action forces the undigested food through the large intestine too rapidly to permit adequate reabsorption of water. The feces are soft and watery, and defecation is frequent. The loss of water may lead to severe dehydration of the body. Diarrhea may be a symptom of gastrointestinal infection or of emotional tension.

Appendicitis. Appendicitis is an inflammation of the appendix which is located where the small intestine joins the large intestine. The symptoms of appendicitis, abdominal pain, nausea, and fever, may lead people to follow the wrong procedure and take a laxative. This can result in a burst appendix and as a consequence infection of the abdominal area. The warning signals of appendicitis should lead to an immediate call to a physician. Surgery may be necessary.

Gallstones. Gallstones are hardened deposits that form in the gallbladder when cholesterol settles out of the bile. The stones may block the passage of bile from the gallbladder and cause considerable pain.

Completion Questions

A

1. A food consists of roughage and . . . . . .
2. Digestion consists of the chemical process of . . . . . .
3. The nutrient which is the richest source of energy is . . . . . .
4. The usable portions of foods are known as . . . . . .

B

5. Chemicals added to processed foods to increase shelf life are called . . . . . .
6. The energy value of foods is measured in units called . . . . . .
7. The polysaccharide used for storage in plants is . . . . . .
8. The polysaccharide used for storage in humans is . . . . . .
9. An amino acid that cannot be synthesized in the human body is called a(n) . . . . . . amino acid.
10. An unsaturated fat can take on more atoms of . . . . . .
11. The fats in meat and milk are . . . . . . (saturated, unsaturated).

C

12. The digestion of starch begins in the . . . . . .
13. The substance that lubricates the alimentary canal of humans is . . . . . .
14. The first organ in the alimentary canal of humans in which proteases react chemically with food is the . . . . . .
15. The series of wavelike contractions of the alimentary canal is called . . . . . .
16. The main functions of the stomach of humans are digestion and . . . . . .
17. The undigested food wastes of humans are called . . . . . .
18. Bile aids in the digestion of fats by the process of . . . . . .
19. The intestinal glands and the . . . . . . secrete proteases, amylases, and lipases.
20. The part of the alimentary canal in which most of the digested food is absorbed is the . . . . . .

D

21. Excess absorption of water from the large intestine may result in the condition known as . . . . . .

22. Inadequate absorption of water from undigested food may result in the condition known as . . . . . .
23. An open sore on the inside lining of the digestive tract is called a(n) . . . . . .
24. Gallstones are hardened deposits of the substance . . . . . .
25. When symptoms of appendicitis appear, the afflicted individual should avoid taking the kind of medicine called a(n) . . . . . .

Multiple-Choice Questions

A

1. Foods consist of nutrients and (1) salts, (2) enzymes, (3) feces, (4) roughage.
2. A kind of a nutrient that requires no digestion is (1) water, (2) proteins, (3) fats, (4) carbohydrates.
3. The usable portions of food are known as (1) roughage, (2) calories, (3) enzymes, (4) nutrients.
4. • When heated with Benedict's solution, glucose forms a precipitate that is (1) blue, (2) orange-red, (3) yellow, (4) white.
5. • The formation of an orange-red color when a substance is boiled with Benedict's solution indicates the presence of (1) monosaccharide, (2) an acid, (3) sucrose, (4) disaccharide.

B

6. Which of the following adds flavor to foods? (1) FDA, (2) MSG, (3) nitrates, (4) amino acids
7. A carbohydrate that cannot be digested by humans is (1) glucose, (2) starch, (3) cellulose, (4) amino acid.

Base your answers to questions 8 through 10 on the chart below and on your knowledge of biology.

Nutrient	Function	Food Source
carbohydrates	energy source	*C*
A	energy reserve	salad oil
proteins	*B*	meat, eggs

8. Which of the following nutrients could most correctly be inserted in space *A*? (1) fats, (2) minerals, (3) sugars, (4) starches
9. Which function could most correctly be inserted in space *B*? (1) provide quick energy in emergencies, (2) act as a solvent for reactions, (3) maintain and repair body tissue, (4) increase mineral concentration
10. Which of the following food sources could most correctly be inserted in space *C*? (1) bread, (2) meat, (3) butter, (4) water
11. Glycogen is a storage form for (1) proteins, (2) carbohydrates, (3) minerals, (4) vitamins
12. Kwashiorkor is a nutritional disease caused by a deficiency of (1) proteins, (2) vitamins, (3) carbohydrates, (3) cellulose.

13. A complete protein contains all the (1) amino acids, (2) essential amino acids, (3) fatty acids, (4) essential fatty acids.
14. Cardiovascular disease seems to be associated with the consumption of (1) polyunsaturated fats, (2) saturated fats, (3) amino acids, (4) complete proteins.

C

15. Enzymes acting on starch are found in (1) pancreatic juice, (2) gastric juice, (3) secretin, (4) bile.
16. Digested fats are absorbed in the small intestine by structures called (1) lacteals, (2) capillaries, (3) root hairs, (4) cilia.
17. The chemical process that occurs during the digestion of food is (1) hydrolysis, (2) dehydration synthesis, (3) hydration, (4) dehydration.
18. An end product of fat digestion is (1) glucose, (2) starch, (3) amino acids, (4) fatty acids.
19. Which process prepares nutrients for transportation through the human body? (1) digestion, (2) excretion, (3) circulation, (4) assimilation.
20. The end product of protein digestion consists of (1) glucose, (2) fatty acids, (3) glycerol, (4) amino acids.
21. Food is moved along the alimentary canal by the process of (1) digestion, (2) osmosis, (3) peristalsis, (4) diffusion.
22. Which secretion does *not* contain digestive enzymes? (1) bile, (2) saliva, (3) gastric juice, (4) pancreatic juice
23. Bile directly helps to (1) hydrolyze fat, (2) emulsify fat, (3) digest glycerol, (4) emulsify glycerol.
24. Which structures in the small intestine of humans serve to increase the area for absorption? (1) intestinal glands, (2) villi, (3) pseudopods, (4) cilia
25. The alkaline medium required for the action of enzymes in the small intestine is provided by (1) pancreatic juice, (2) intestinal juice, (3) ptyalin, (4) bile.

Chapter Test

1. Food includes nutrients and (1) water, (2) roughage, (3) amino acids, (4) vitamins.
2. Small molecules that can be absorbed without digestion are the (1) minerals, (2) complex carbohydrates, (3) proteins, (4) fats.
3. Large molecules that must be digested before they can be absorbed include (1) water, (2) fats, (3) minerals, (4) fructose.
4. Essential amino acids are those which humans cannot (1) digest, (2) synthesize, (3) hydrolyze, (4) emulsify.
5. Food is ingested through the (1) salivary glands, (2) large intestine, (3) mouth, (4) rectum.
6. The secretion stored in the gallbladder is called (1) saliva, (2) gastric juice, (3) intestinal juice, (4) bile.
7. The dispersal of a drop of oil into small globules is called (1) hydrolysis, (2) deamination, (3) unsaturation, (4) emulsification.
8. The lining of the small intestine is adapted for absorption by the presence of (1) root hairs, (2) the epiglottis, (3) cilia, (4) villi.

9. Monosodium glutamate (MSG) is added to food to (1) protect it from bacterial action, (2) make it taste better, (3) give it a red color, (4) make it taste sweeter.
10. Complete proteins contain all the essential (1) fats, (2) carbohydrates, (3) amino acids, (4) additives.
11. The passage of bile may be blocked by (1) gallstones, (2) mucus, (3) villi, (4) an inflamed appendix.
12. Fat molecules that could take on more hydrogen atoms are called (1) supersaturated, (2) saturated, (3) unsaturated, (4) desaturated.
13. The usable portion of food that cannot be digested is (1) roughage, (2) calories, (3) additives, (4) nutrients.
14. • If a food sample is rubbed on a piece of paper and the paper becomes translucent, the sample contains (1) fat, (2) protein, (3) sugar, (4) starch.
15. • An iodine solution turns blue-black when placed on food containing (1) fat, (2) protein, (3) starch, (4) sugar.
16. • The Biuret test is used to test for (1) fat, (2) protein, (3) starch, (4) sugar.
17. The energy value of food is measured in units called (1) grams, (2) calories, (3) International units, (4) degrees Celsius.
18. A food additive which makes food taste sweet is (are) (1) nitrates, (2) saccharin, (3) MSG, (4) vitamins.
19. A decreased reabsorption of water in the large intestine results in (1) gallstone deposits, (2) diarrhea, (3) appendicitis, (4) constipation.
20. A lubricant for food as it passes through the alimentary canal is (1) pepsin, (2) bile, (3) gastric juice, (4) mucus.
21. Gastric juice contains pepsinogen and (1) bile, (2) hydrochloric acid, (3) mucus, (4) saliva.
22. An enzyme that changes part of milk into a solid is (1) bile, (2) hydrochloric acid, (3) saliva, (4) rennin.
23. Bile is secreted by the (1) liver, (2) pancreas, (3) intestinal glands, (4) rectum.
24. The digestion of protein is completed in the (1) small intestine, (2) esophagus, (3) stomach, (4) large intestine.
25. No digestion of food occurs in the (1) mouth, (2) stomach, (3) large intestine, (4) small intestine.

Chapter 12 Transport in Humans

The process of transport consists of the absorption of materials and the circulation of these materials throughout an organism. In humans, the function of transport is performed at the organism level by a closed circulatory system which is different from the open system of the grasshopper. In this chapter on the circulatory system in humans, three major areas will be discussed—the media for transporting materials, the pathway of circulation, and the protective functions of blood.

A

Transport Media

The Blood

The transport media used to carry materials throughout the human body are (1) blood and (2) intercellular fluid (ICF), or lymph. Blood is a tissue. A tissue is defined as a group of similar cells having the same general function. In tissues such as bone and cartilage, the cells are embedded in a solid material called the *matrix*. In bone, the matrix is firm and in cartilage it is softer. In blood, the intercellular matrix is a liquid called *plasma*.

Plasma

Plasma is a clear, straw-colored liquid consisting mainly of water, dissolved proteins, and inorganic ions. The general functions of plasma are:

- to serve as the liquid matrix of blood tissue
- to transport products of digestion such as amino acids, simple sugars, fats, vitamins, salts, and water
- to transport nitrogenous wastes (urea) and carbon dioxide
- to transport hormones and antibodies
- to help regulate body temperature

Red Blood Cells

Three types of solid components are suspended in the plasma: *red blood cells*, *white blood cells*, and *platelets*. The red blood cells of humans are disk-shaped structures that are concave on each side (biconcave disks). After their formation in bone marrow, they lose their nuclei. Because they lack nuclei, red blood cells are often called *corpuscles* instead of cells. Red blood cells contain the red pigment *hemoglobin*, a protein which gives blood its red color. Hemoglobin contains iron and helps to transport oxygen and carbon dioxide.

Red blood cells survive for only about 120 days and are then destroyed and removed by the liver and spleen. The spleen also stores red blood cells. New red blood cells are constantly produced in large numbers in the marrow of the long bones in the human body.

White Blood Cells

The white blood cells are produced in bone marrow, in lymph nodes, and in the spleen. White blood cells increase greatly in number when infection is present in the body. There are several kinds of white blood cells. One kind is the *phagocyte* (*phago* = devouring; *cyte* = cell). Phagocytes leave the capillaries by passing between the cells that form the capillary walls and move by *ameboid motion* (using pseudopods) toward masses of bacteria. They engulf many bacteria and then die. The process of engulfing particles is called *phagocytosis*. A mixture of tissue fluid, living and dead bacteria, and white blood cells is called *pus*.

Lymphocytes are another kind of white blood cell. Lymphocytes help to develop immunity against proteins that are foreign to the human body. These foreign proteins are known as *antigens*. The lymphocytes help develop *antibodies* which act against the antigens to neutralize them.

Comparison of Red and White Blood Cells		
	Red Cells	**White Cells**
Function	Carry oxygen and CO_2	Engulf bacteria, produce antibodies.
Number	5 million/mm^3	7000-8000/mm^3
Where produced	Bone marrow	Bone marrow, lymph nodes, spleen
Nucleus	No nucleus	Nucleus present

Platelets The *platelets* are fragments of the cytoplasm of certain giant bone cells. They are roughly disk-shaped and are about half or one-third the diameter of a red blood cell. Lacking a nucleus, platelets are not really cells. They are about 35,000 times more numerous than white blood cells and last about 10 days in the body. The main function of platelets is to initiate the complex series of biochemical reactions that cause blood to clot.

ICF and Lymph In the exchange of materials between blood capillaries and cells, there is an intermediary. This is *intercellular fluid* or *ICF* (also called *tissue fluid*). ICF consists of water and dissolved materials that are forced by the blood pressure out of capillaries. ICF bathes the cells. It carries food, oxygen, and other materials to the cells and returns carbon dioxide (CO_2) and other materials to the blood capillaries (see Fig. 12–1).

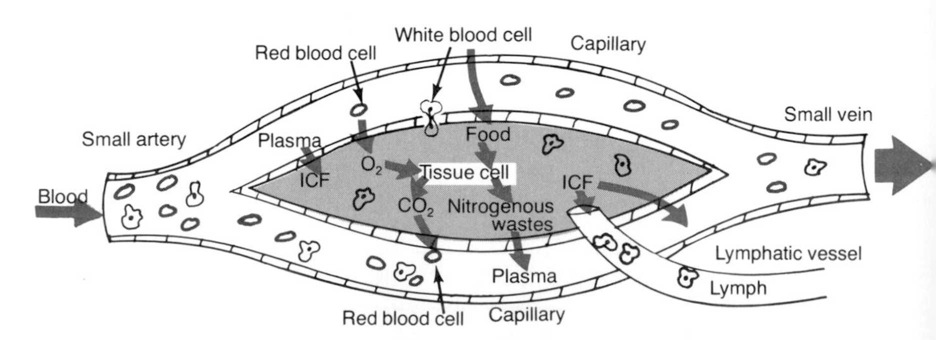

Fig. 12–1. Diagram of tissue cell surrounded by capillaries. Plasma and white blood cells pass out of the capillaries, as ICF forms. ICF passes back into the capillaries or into microscopic lymph vessels. ICF within lymphatic vessels is called lymph.

The high internal pressure at the arterial end of a blood capillary forces out the ICF, but lower pressure at the venous end permits the return of much ICF to the capillaries. However, not all ICF returns to blood capillaries. Some of this fluid enters microscopic openings of the *lymphatic system.* This is a network of tubes that permeate the body. The colorless tissue fluid within this network of vessels is called *lymph.*

The lacteals that absorb fats in the intestinal villi are also part of the lymphatic system. Small lymphatic vessels join to form larger ones. The largest lymphatic vessel is the *thoracic duct.* This vessel empties three-fourths of the lymph into a large vein near the base of the neck. Liquid lost from the capillaries as ICF is thereby returned to the circulating blood.

Lymph flows mainly because it is squeezed by contractions of surrounding muscles during random body movements. Lymphatics have valves to prevent backflow.

The main functions of the lymphatic system are:

1. It maintains the volume of circulating blood by collecting ICF and returning it to a vein.

2. Lacteals in villi pick up fats which are later added to the bloodstream.

3. The lymphatic system is part of the body's *immune system* that protects against germs and other foreign materials. *Lymph nodes* contain masses of phagocytic cells that destroy bacteria. Physicians can detect some infections by finding swollen lymph nodes in the armpit, neck, groin, behind the knee, or other locations.

Reasoning Exercises

1. Differentiate between white blood cells and red blood cells.
2. How do white blood cells protect the body?
3. Explain one way in which the lymphatic system protects the body.

Ⓑ

The Protective Functions of Blood

Blood Clotting

The circulatory system protects the body by (1) blood clotting, (2) phagocytosis, and (3) immunological reactions.

The clotting of blood involves a complex series of enzyme-controlled reactions that forms a plug in injured blood vessels. Clotting normally begins when delicate platelets encounter a rough surface, such as a torn blood vessel. The platelets adhere to the walls and form a loose plug which is then strengthened by the clot.

The platelets and damaged tissue cells release an enzyme called *thromboplastin* (see Fig. 12–2). Thromboplastin converts the enzyme *prothrombin,* a protein that is present in plasma, to its active form, *thrombin.* Thrombin then catalyzes the conversion of the dissolved blood protein *fibrinogen* ("fibrin former") to insoluble strands of *fibrin.* The network of fibrin strands acts as a log jam to trap red blood cells and

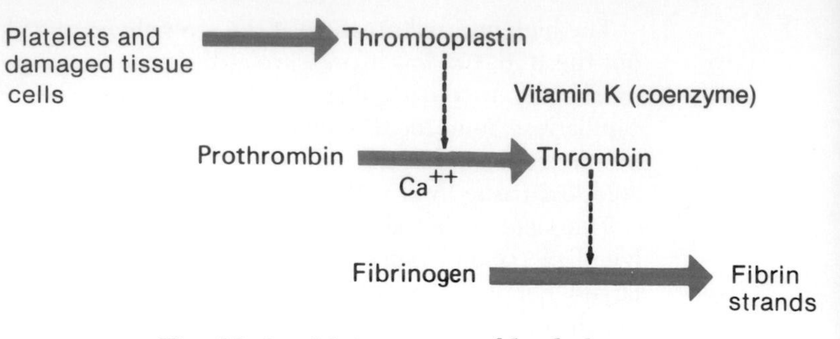

Fig. 12–2. Major steps in blood clotting

platelets. As the plug contracts, it squeezes out a clear liquid called *serum.* In addition to stopping blood flow, the clot also forms a temporary framework into which cells can migrate to heal the wound.

When whole blood is caused to clot in a test tube, the clear fluid above the clot is *serum.* Serum, is not the same as plasma. It is plasma with the proteins involved in blood clotting removed.

Although blood clots have an important protective function, a clot that forms in circulating blood may be dangerous. Such a clot, called a *thrombus,* may block blood flow to heart muscle, causing a heart attack, or to the brain, causing a *stroke.*

Heparin is a natural anticoagulant that inhibits the conversion of prothrombin to thrombin. It is produced by cells of the liver and other tissues. Physicians use heparin to prevent unwanted thrombosis following surgery or after a heart attack or stroke.

Vitamin K helps the liver produce clotting factors. A lack of this vitamin inhibits the normal clotting of blood and may be a cause of internal bleeding.

To prevent whole blood from clotting in the laboratory, technicians add a chemical that removes calcium ions. This is because calcium is needed in the formation of thrombin.

Phagocytosis

The body's *first line of defense* against disease is the intact skin and mucous membranes. The latter are constantly guarded by antibacterial fluids such as mucus, saliva, and tears. The *phagocytes,* described above, constitute the *second line of defense.* Their ability to engulf invading organisms is aided by the immune response described below.

The Immune Response

The *immune response* constitutes the body's *third line of defense.* This action consists of the union of antigens and antibodies. An *antigen* is any foreign chemical that promotes the formation of matching antibodies. Most known antigens are proteins but some are polysaccharides and lipids. A bacterium carrying several kinds of antigen molecules on its surface is commonly also called an antigen. So is a virus and any substance that may cause an allergic reaction, such as pollen, dust, and foods.

An *antibody* is a protein, produced by the body, that combines with an antigen and neutralizes it. Masses of clumped antigens and antibodies are then engulfed and destroyed by phagocytic white blood cells. Antibody and antigen fit like a lock and key. Each antibody, thus, is *specific* for a single kind of antigen.

Antibodies are manufactured in tissues of the lymphatic system, such as lymph nodes, bone marrow, and spleen. Groups of white blood cells known as *lymphocytes*, form in the bone marrow and the spleen and produce large numbers of antibody molecules after being contacted by antigens. Some offspring of these active lymphocytes are "memory cells." Years after an infection has disappeared, they speedily form the identical specific antibody molecules needed against a renewed attack.

Some antibodies make bacteria easier prey for phagocytes. Other antibodies clump bacteria or dissolve them by uniting with antigens on their cell walls and membranes. Toxins (poisons) produced by harmful bacteria also act as antigens. These are neutralized by antibodies called *antitoxins*.

The Immune System and Disease

All the body's structures involved in producing antibodies are known as the *immune system*. Study of the immune system is known as *immunology*. Immunological reactions help to explain (1) immunity to disease, (2) allergy, (3) blood types, and (4) rejection of grafts.

Immunity to Disease

An infectious disease in the body resembles a condition of warfare between attacking and defending forces. The attacking forces are bacteria and other microorganisms. Damage to the body is caused not only by bacteria but also by the toxins they produce. These are poisons given off by bacteria during their metabolism. The body uses combinations of antibodies and phagocytes against both bacteria and toxins.

Immunity is the resistance of an organism to disease, and *susceptibility* is the organism's lack of immunity. Children are often exposed to disease. Each time the immune system responds by making antibodies to destroy the new germs, immunity may be developed to the disease. That is why children's diseases do not usually affect adults. Most adults acquired immunity during childhood. Populations completely free of a given disease develop no immunity to it. When measles was first introduced into Polynesia, it killed adults by the thousands.

Immunity may be classified as active immunity and passive immunity. In *active immunity*, the individual builds his or her own antibodies by having the disease in a strong or mild form. In *passive immunity*, antibodies produced by other organisms are given to the individual. Active and passive immunity are compared in the table on page 220.

Antibodies that the body builds against some killed microorganisms may also be effective against live microorganisms. For example, active immunization against typhoid fever consists of injecting killed typhoid fever bacteria which have the same antigens on their surface. The body then becomes immune to the live typhoid fever bacteria. Similarly, the *Salk vaccine* against polio consists of viruses that have been killed by the addition of formaldehyde. The body then produces antibodies that provide immunity against live polio virus. The *Sabin vaccine* for polio consists of weakened live viruses and is administered orally.

Active and Passive Immunity

Active Immunity	**Passive Immunity**
Acquired by having the disease or a mild form of it. Inject: 1. Weakened or killed bacteria or viruses. 2. Weakened toxin. (**Toxoid** is toxin weakened by a chemical such as formaldehyde; **toxin-antitoxin** is toxin weakened by the addition of antitoxin.)	Given by an inoculation. Inject: 1. Antibodies (for example, a serum containing antitoxin). 2. Gamma globulin from pooled blood.
Takes a relatively long time to acquire but lasts a long time.	Immunity is conferred rapidly but does not last long.
Administered usually before exposure to the disease, as a preventive.	Administered when the person has the disease, to help the body's defense.

Interferon. Another substance used by the body to fight infectious diseases is called *interferon.* Interferon is not an antibody. It is a defensive protein produced by living cells that have been entered by a virus. This substance interferes (hence its name) with reproduction by the virus. Interferon promises to be useful for a wide variety of viral diseases and possibly for cancer as well. Research including clinical trials with interferon has been limited by its scarce supply. Recently, however, biologists have used genetic engineering to develop bacteria that produce large quantities of interferon at little expense.

Preparation of toxin and antitoxin. *Toxin* may be prepared from bacteria grown in the laboratory in eggs containing chick embryos. When the toxin is weakened by adding formaldehyde or by heating, the product is a *toxoid.* If dilute diphtheria toxin is injected into a horse, the horse produces antitoxins. If increasingly strong injections of toxin are given to the horse at set intervals, it develops a high concentration of diphtheria antitoxin in its blood. A sample of blood taken from the horse is allowed to clot. The liquid that remains after the clot has formed is horse serum containing diphtheria antitoxin. This serum may be administered to build passive immunity in a child who is sick with diphtheria. The antitoxin may also be combined with toxin to form toxin-antitoxin for developing active immunity.

Gamma globulin. Pooled blood is blood donated by a large number of healthy persons and mixed together. During their lifetimes, these persons may have recovered from a variety of diseases. Pooled blood, therefore, usually has a wide variety of antibodies. When the proteins are extracted from this blood, the fraction (portion) of these proteins that contains the antibodies is the *gamma globulin.* (Gamma is the third letter of the Greek alphabet.) Administration of gamma globulin by a physician may cure a patient through passive immunization.

DPT shots, routinely given to most children in this country, provide active immunity to diphtheria, pertussis (whooping cough), and tetanus. Public health officers, however, have recently been alarmed at the increasing number of parents who fail to have their children receive the complete series of immunizations and booster shots.

Vaccination. The word *vaccine* originated with Edward Jenner, an English physician of the early 19th century. He used the cow (*vacca* = cow) to prepare the first safe immunization against smallpox. People in farm areas had long known that milkmaids who were exposed to the blisters of cows that had cowpox became slightly ill with the mild disease of cowpox; however, they rarely fell ill with the more dangerous smallpox. When Jenner administered cowpox virus to people, they developed active immunity to smallpox.

Because this discovery was made before viruses were known about, it was not possible for Jenner to understand why he obtained these results. Today, we know that the cowpox virus is an attenuated, or weakened, form of the smallpox virus. The antigens on the surface of the cowpox virus stimulate the human's immune system to produce matching antibodies. These antibodies are also effective against the similar antigens that are on the surface of the smallpox virus.

Molecular biologists have now succeeded in producing *synthetic vaccines* against some viruses. These researchers assemble short chains of amino acids (polypeptides) that mimic a protein site on the surface of a virus. Introduced into living organisms, the artificial antigens give rise to antibodies that provide immunity against the virus.

Allergies

Allergy is an extreme sensitivity (or *hypersensitivity*) in some individuals to antigens that do not affect most people. The cause of the allergic response is an imbalance of certain kinds of antibodies. The effect on the body depends upon the allergen and the route of entry. Pollens cause the runny nose and eyes of hay fever. Food allergens present in shellfish, nuts, and tomatoes may cause vomiting or diarrhea but sometimes result in a skin rash or hives. Dust, insect bites, and drugs can also act as allergens.

In an allergic response, the antigen-induced antibodies bind to certain large cells that then produce an irritating substance called *histamine.* Although the action of histamine is actually protective to the body, this is the substance that initiates the familiar distressing symptoms of hay fever or other allergies. To provide relief for mild conditions, antihistamine drugs are available, but they may also cause drowsiness—a danger for car drivers.

Asthma is an allergic reaction causing constriction of the air passages. Severe attacks are medically controlled by the hormone adrenaline.

Blood Types

When the practice of blood transfusion was first attempted, it was soon found that the mixing of some bloods resulted in death due to the formation of clumps. The mystery was solved in 1900 by Karl Landsteiner, a Viennese physician, who discovered that each human has one of four major blood types called *O*, *A*, *B*, and *AB*. These classifications are basec upon the presence or absence of antigens on the surface of red blood cell and are determined by heredity.

There are two antigens, called *A* and *B*. A person who has type *A* antigen is said to have blood type *A;* a person who has type *B* antigen ha blood type *B;* a person whose red blood cells contain both type *A* antiger and *B* antigen has blood type *AB;* a person who has neither antigen on hi cells has blood type *O*.

Present in the plasma may be *antibodies* that agglutinate (or clump) rec cells containing these antigens. The antibody that agglutinates cells con taining antigen *A* is called anti-*A;* the antibody for antigen *B* is callec anti-*B*. An individual with type *A* antigen could not have anti-*A* anti body—for this person would clump his or her own cells. However, thi type *A* individuals does have anti-*B* antibody.

Blood Types: Antigens and Antibodies

Blood Type	Antigen on Cells	Antibody in Plasma
O	—	anti-A anti-B
A	A	anti-B
B	B	anti-A
AB	A, B	—

Blood Typing

Blood typing is the laboratory procedure used to determine an individu al's blood type. Though blood typing is a simple procedure that can be performed as an exercise in school, only the results from certified labora tories should be used. The materials required for blood typing are two bottles of antibodies. The bottle marked *Anti-A serum* contains anti-*A* antibodies; the other, *Anti-B serum*, contains anti-*B* antibodies. A drop of each serum is placed at opposite ends of a microscope slide (Figure 12–3) and a drop of the diluted blood of the patient is then added to each of these serums.

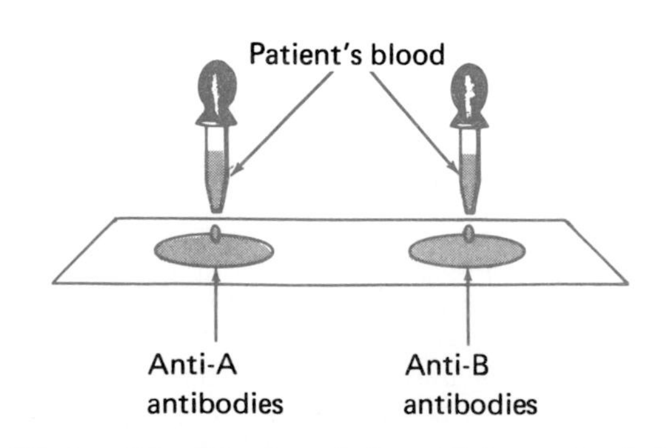

Fig. 12–3. Blood typing. A drop of the patient's blood is added to each kind of antibody.

The contents of each drop are stirred by use of separate toothpicks and the two drops are examined after a few minutes. The examiner looks for evidence of clumping which appears to the naked eye as heavy dots of agglutinated cells. Clumping occurs when cells carrying an antigen are mixed with the corresponding antibody. The four possible kinds of observation are shown in Figure 12–4.

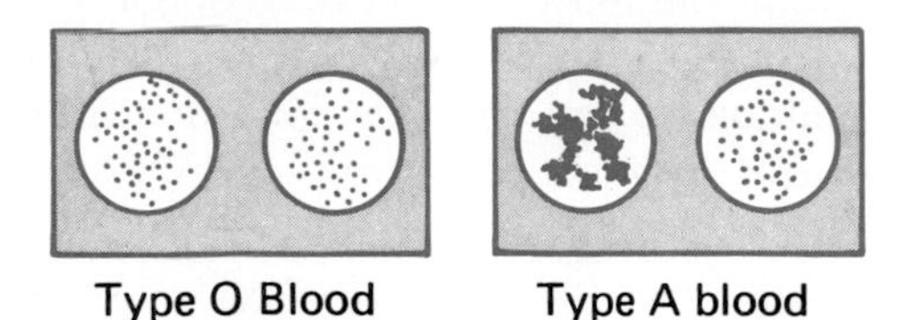

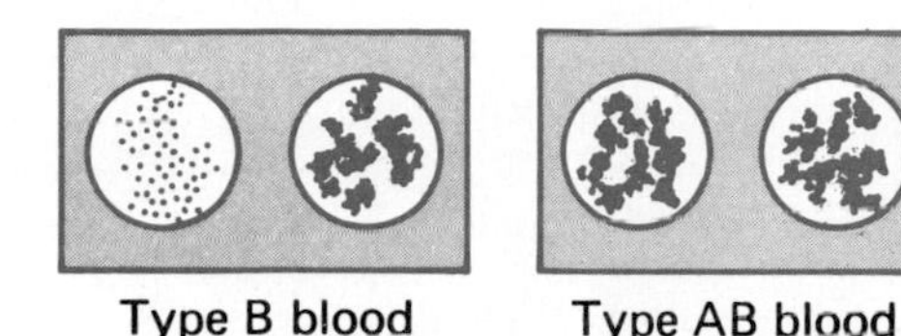

Fig. 12–4. Blood typing. On each slide, the anti-*A* serum was placed on the left side and anti-*B* serum was placed on the right side.

Blood Transfusions

Clumping in the blood vessels may block flow to a vital organ. In any blood transfusion, it is important that the cells of the *donor* not be agglutinated by the plasma of the recipient. The reverse possibility—agglutination of the recipient's cells by plasma of the donor—is not so serious. The small volume of the donor's blood is so rapidly diluted by the larger volume of the recipient's moving bloodstream that there is little chance that the donor's antibodies can clump the recipient's cells.

In practice, however, before a transfusion is made, the bloods of prospective donor and recipient are *cross matched*. This procedure detects the presence of any antigens that might cause trouble.

Consider the situation in which the donor is type A and the recipient is type B. In such a transfusion, the anti-*A* antibodies in the plasma of the recipient would agglutinate the type *A* red cells of the donor. Such clumping in the bloodstream of the recipient could be fatal to that individual. Suppose the donor is type B and the recipient is type A. Again the recipient's plasma agglutinates the donor's cells as they are introduced. The anti-*B* antibodies in the recipient's plasma agglutinate the type *B* cells of the donor.

Now consider the case of a type O donor and a type B recipient. In this case, the donor has *no* antigen on his or her cells, therefore, no matter what antibodies are present in the recipient's plasma, the donor's red cells will not be agglutinated. Type *O* is called the *universal donor* because this type can give blood to any other type, usually with no ill effect. You may ask why the anti-*B* antibodies of the type *O* donor do not clump the red cells of the recipient. Recall, however, that the donor's plasma becomes greatly diluted. We are concerned that the cells of the *donor* not be agglutinated.

Since a type *AB* individual has no antibodies to clump a donor's cells, this person can receive transfusions from any blood type. Type *AB*, thus is the *universal recipient.* (Does any kind of transfusion cause clumping within the bloodstream of the donor?)

Persons of all blood types, of course, can receive from, or donate to their own blood type. The following table summarizes the possible kinds of transfusions.

Possible Kinds of Blood Transfusions

Blood Type	Can Receive	Can Donate To
O (universal donor)	O	All
A	A,O	A, AB
B	B,O	B,AB
AB (universal recipient)	All	AB

Blood plasma. Plasma is used in place of whole blood for some types of emergency situations such as accidents, severe burns, and battle wounds. Plasma restores the volume of circulating fluid and keeps the blood pressure high enough to sustain circulation to vital organs. Plasma has several advantages: It contains no red blood cells that can be clumped; plasma can be dried to a powder, sterilized, and stored indefinitely; it can be shipped wherever needed and restored to its original volume by adding sterile distilled water. However plasma lacks the cells which may be needed.

Rh Factor

The *Rh factor* is an antigen present on the red blood cells of about 85 percent of people in the United States. The *Rh factor* was discovered by experiments on Rhesus monkeys in 1940, and its name comes from the first two letters of Rhesus. *Rh positive* (Rh^+) individuals have this antigen; people who lack this antigen are *Rh negative* (Rh^-).

It is possible for a pregnant woman to be *Rh* negative and have an *Rh* positive fetus (embryo), provided that the father is *Rh* positive. Blood of the mother and the fetus have separate circulations, but some seepage of red blood cells of the *Rh* positive baby may cross the placenta into the blood of the *Rh* negative mother. The mother then produces anti-*Rh* antibodes. These pass back into the fetal circulation where they destroy the fetus's red cells. The baby may be born with a severe anemia known as *erythroblastosis fetalis* ("bursting of the red blood cells of the fetus").

Usually few of the baby's red cells cross the placenta until the time of birth. As a result, the first *Rh* positive baby of an *Rh* negative mother is usually not affected. By the second or third such pregnancy, however, the mother builds a concentration of antibodies sufficient to harm the fetus within her. For this reason, doctors make frequent blood-antibody tests of pregnant women who are *Rh* negative. If the antibody concentration rises, the doctor prepares to give the newborn a transfusion of compatible whole blood, a procedure popularly called washing out the baby's blood.

When a person is to receive a blood transfusion, it is important to know the *Rh* types as well as the *ABO* blood types of the recipient and of the prospective donor. An *Rh* negative male or female who receives a transfusion of *Rh* positive blood builds anti-*Rh* antibodies. If this person requires an additional transfusion in the future, the antibodies that are now present will destroy the transfused red blood cells. Moreover, an *Rh* negative woman will build antibodies that may later harm her first *Rh* positive child.

The *ABO* blood types are distinct from the *Rh* factor. An individual who is blood type A and *Rh* negative is described as A negative (A–). Other blood factors do not ordinarily affect blood transfusions.

AIDS

AIDS *(Acquired Immune Deficiency Syndrome)* is a fatal disease caused by the human immunodeficiency virus (HIV). HIV kills the white blood cells called helper T cells, which are an important part of the immune system. By weakening the body's immune system, HIV infection makes a person susceptible to a variety of infectious diseases, and even cancer. This stage of HIV infection is called AIDS. A person may become infected with the HIV virus by having unprotected sex with an infected person, by sharing needles with an infected person, or being born to an HIV infected mother. Although currently there is no cure, there are some treatments for HIV that can slow the progress of the disease. AIDS is the leading cause of death for Americans between the ages of 25 and 44.

Organ Transplants

The immune system permits the body to distinguish between self and non-self. Skin transplants have long been made, for example, from a person's thigh to his or her face. Transplants of tissues and organs were then successfully accomplished between identical twins, who share the same heredity. But similar attempts between unrelated individuals were unsuccessful. The foreign tissue acted as an antigen that promoted the formation of antibodies, resulting in rejection of the graft.

Recently, however, new understandings of the immune system have permitted great success in transplanting organs such as the kidney, and even the heart, between unrelated persons. Irradiation and chemicals called immuno-suppressors are employed to diminish action of the immune system. Since this procedure leaves the recipient unprotected against infection, large doses of antibiotics are simultaneously administered.

Many states now encourage motorists to complete a donor card. This card specifies the organs that may be removed in the event of death, for transfer to an organ bank.

C Transport Vessels

Three kinds of tubes transport blood in the human body. These are *arteries, capillaries,* and *veins.* In addition, lymph vessels are present for the transport of lymph.

Comparison of Arteries, Veins, and Capillaries Arteries carry blood from the heart, and veins carry blood to the heart After an artery leaves the heart, it branches repeatedly into ever smalle arteries, until the narrowest branches, the *arterioles,* are microscopic From these branch the still narrower capillaries. These fine vessels per mit the passage of a thin stream of red blood cells. Capillary walls, *onl one cell thick,* permit the diffusion of materials between the bloodstrea and tissues of the body. It is at the capillaries that blood takes on an discharges materials for its function of transport.

The capillaries join together to form tiny veins or *venules.* These con nect with larger veins until the very largest veins empty into the heart

Flow of Blood in the Arteries Blood flows in arteries because of the pumping action of the chambers o the heart called *ventricles.* The elasticity of artery walls permits them t accept the increased flow of blood resulting from the contraction of a ventricle. If arterial walls were rigid instead of elastic, the heart would b under greater strain. Hardening of the arteries *(atherosclerosis)* leads t heart strain.

Blood pressure refers to the pressure exerted by blood against the wall of arteries. The pressure resulting from contraction of the left ventricl (systole) is called *systolic pressure.* The pressure resulting from the relaxa tion of the left ventricle (diastole) is called the *diastolic* pressure. Bot readings are significant to an examining physician. The blood pressure o a normal young adult at rest is about 120/80. The first number states th systolic pressure and the second number the diastolic pressure.

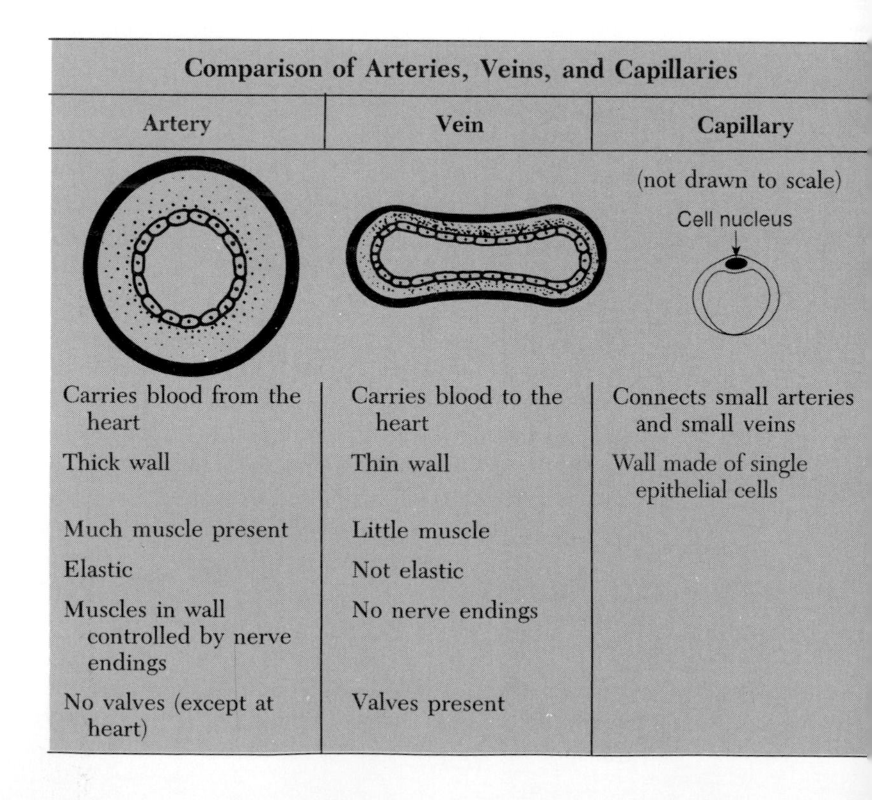

Comparison of Arteries, Veins, and Capillaries

Artery	Vein	Capillary
Carries blood from the heart	Carries blood to the heart	Connects small arteries and small veins
Thick wall	Thin wall	Wall made of single epithelial cells
Much muscle present	Little muscle	
Elastic	Not elastic	
Muscles in wall controlled by nerve endings	No nerve endings	
No valves (except at heart)	Valves present	

The *pulse* is a wave of alternate stretchings and contractions of artery walls that proceeds from the aorta along all arteries and arterioles. The stretching does *not* represent the advancing front of a wall of blood. The frequency of the pulse rate is the same as the heartbeat. Most arteries are deep within the body, but the pulse rate may be detected at a few places, such as the wrist, where an artery is close to the surface. Muscles in the walls of arterioles contract or relax in response to nerve and chemical stimulation. The constriction of an arteriole reduces the supply of blood to the capillaries it feeds. In this way, the supply of blood to a tissue is controlled.

Flow of Blood in the Veins Contractions of the left ventricle are not sufficient to force blood through all the arteries, through the whole bed of capillaries, and back to the heart through the veins. The flow of blood in the veins is helped in two ways:

1. During body movements, skeletal muscles press upon veins and tend to force blood in both directions. However, valves present in veins permit blood to flow only toward the heart; blood is blocked from flowing in the wrong direction. When a person sits motionless for some time, blood may collect in veins of the feet. Moving or stamping the feet starts the blood moving again, accompanied by a tingling feeling.

2. During breathing, air pressure is reduced in the chest cavity. This lowered air pressure helps venous blood to flow toward the heart.

The Heart and Blood Vessels The structure of the human heart is shown in Figure 12–5. A partition separates the right side from the left side. On each side, veins empty blood into thin-walled receiving chambers called *atria*. The atrium of each side contracts, forcing blood through a valve into thick-walled receiving chambers called *ventricles*. Contraction of each ventricle then forces blood through a valve into a large artery which carries blood away from the heart.

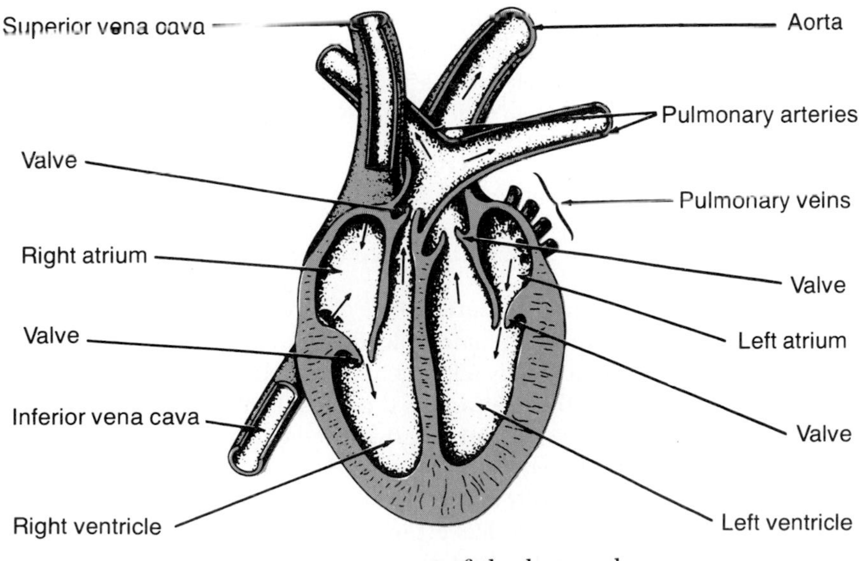

Fig. 12–5. Diagram of the human heart

As shown in the figure, the heart has two sets of valves: one set between the atria and the ventricles below them; the other set between the ventricles and the large arteries into which the ventricles empty. Closing of valves at the proper time prevents the backflow of blood. Such a backflow would cause the heart to work harder. The incomplete closing of heart valves and the narrowing of their openings are two of the causes of heart disease.

The closing of heart valves is heard through a stethoscope as a "lub-dub." Unusual heart sounds may indicate defects in the heart, such as the constriction of the passageway or the improper closing of a valve.

When placed in a saline solution of the proper concentration, heart muscle tissue contracts slowly and rhythmically by itself, without stimulus from the outside. In the heart, the speed and extent of the contraction is regulated by the *pacemaker*. Branches from the pacemaker start contractions of muscle fibers in the two atria to the AV node and then to the two ventricles. The pacemaker is controlled by two nerves originating in the medulla (lower part) of the brain. The *accelerator nerve* stimulates the pacemaker and the *vagus nerve* slows the pacemaker.

Battery-operated artificial pacemakers are now surgically inserted within the chest in cases where the natural pacemaker fails to properly regulate the heartbeat.

Reasoning Exercises

1. How are the walls of the human heart adapted for their functions?
2. How is the structure of arteries adapted for their functions? How is the structure of veins adapted for their functions?
3. What is lymph? Distinguish between lymph and plasma.
4. What is meant by the systolic pressure?
5. Distinguish between red blood cells, white blood cells, and platelets. What are the functions of each?
6. Give three functions of the lymphatic system.

Ⓓ The Path of Circulation

The four-chambered heart of birds and mammals permits complete separation of oxygenated blood from unoxygenated blood. The right side of the heart sends unoxygenated blood to the lungs for oxygen. Blood rich in oxygen then returns to the left side of the heart for pumping to the rest of the body. By contrast, the three-chambered heart of the frogs sends to its body a mixture of oxygenated and deoxygenated blood.

Of the four chambers of the human heart (see Fig. 12–5), the left ventricle has the thickest muscular wall. This chamber has the task of pumping blood to all parts of the body except the lungs.

Figure 12–6 presents an overview of the circulatory pathway by means of a block diagram. Figure 12–7 presents a more detailed diagram of the three main pathways of circulation.

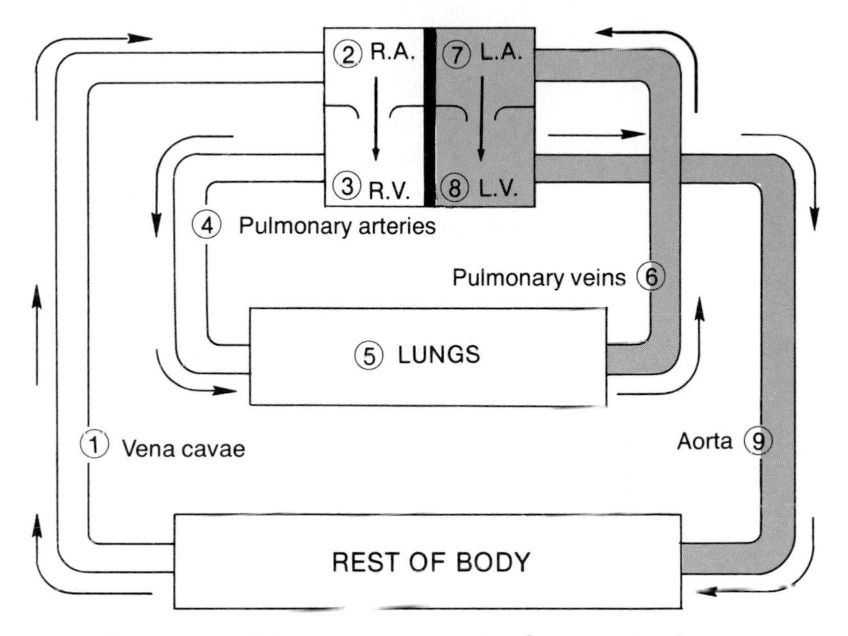

Fig. 12–6. Block diagram of the human circulatory system. Deoxygenated blood is shown clear; oxygenated blood is shown in color. Arteries carry blood from the heart; veins return blood to the heart.

Pulmonary Circulation

Pulmonary refers to the lungs. The pulmonary circulation is the pathway of blood between the lungs and the heart. The large *pulmonary artery* leaves the right ventricle, and then divides into two arteries that carry blood to the lungs. Here the arteries divide to form capillaries. Blood from the right side of the heart has little oxygen and is dark red in color. When the blood acquires oxygen in the capillaries of the lungs, it turns bright red. From the lungs, blood enters the *pulmonary veins*, which return it to the left atrium. Thus, the blood is dark red (deoxygenated) in the right side of the heart and bright red (oxygenated) in the left side.

Systemic Circulation

The systemic circulation is the circulation of blood through the major systems of the body. The left atrium contracts, forcing oxygenated blood through a valve into the left ventricle. The left ventricle then contracts, forcing blood into the *aorta*, the largest artery in the body.

The arteries subdivide to form capillaries in the various organs and tissues. Exchange of materials occurs between the blood capillaries and intercellular fluid at the tissues. The capillaries then unite to form veins, which become progressively larger. The *superior vena cava* from the head region and the *inferior vena cava* from the trunk region empty deoxygenated blood into the right atrium.

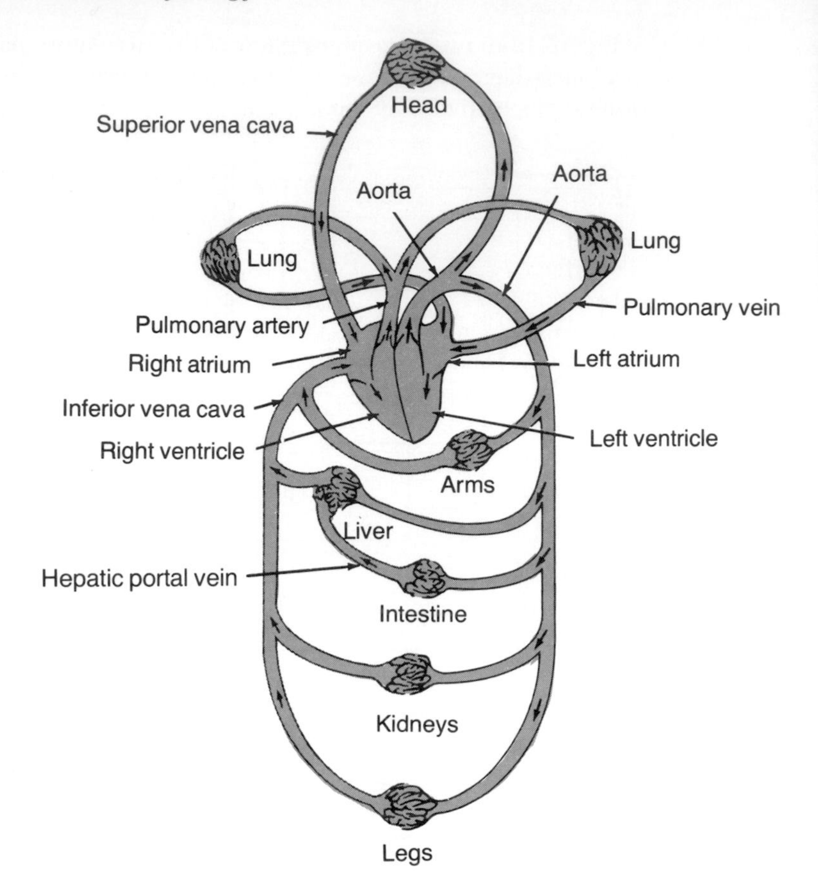

Fig. 12–7. Circulation in the human

Coronary circulation. Although the heart is filled with blood, its thick walls are not supplied by the blood within its chambers. Instead, two small arteries, the *coronary arteries*, branch off from the beginning of the aorta and spread over the heart's surface. They are called "coronary" because they look like a crown on the heart (*corona* = crown). Branches of the coronary arteries supply oxygen and food to specific regions of the heart muscle, and coronary veins return blood to the right atrium. A person with a coronary heart attack has suffered a blockage of a branch of a coronary artery. This results in damage to a region of heart muscle tissue.

Occasionally, a baby is born with an opening in the partition between the two ventricles. Because this opening allows mixing of oxygenated and unoxygenated blood, the infant may die unless the wall is closed surgically. This is one cause for the condition called "blue baby."

Portal Circulation. The portal circulation consists of veins that carry blood from the stomach, the small intestine, and the large intestine to the *liver* and from the liver to the inferior vena cava. The *hepatic portal vein* (see Fig. 12–7) carries blood rich in digested food to the liver where excess carbohydrate is removed for storage. ("Hepatic" refers to the liver.) The *hepatic vein* then continues the pathway to the inferior vena cava. Let us examine this situation in further detail.

The pathway of the portal circulation is shown in Figure 12–8. Blood leaving the small intestine has picked up large quantities of glucose in the capillaries of the villi. If this glucose were to pass into the general circulation, there would be a great increase of blood glucose shortly after meals. This would violate the principle of *homeostasis*. This principle states that the internal environment of the body remains stable. Instead, excess glucose is changed to *glycogen* as the blood passes through the liver. Glycogen is an insoluble polysaccharide which is stored in the liver (and also in muscle). When the chemical energy stored in glycogen is needed by the body, the glycogen of the liver is changed back to soluble glucose and returned to the blood. Hormones called *insulin* and *glucagon* control this homeostatic mechanism. See Chapter 15 for more information on hormones.

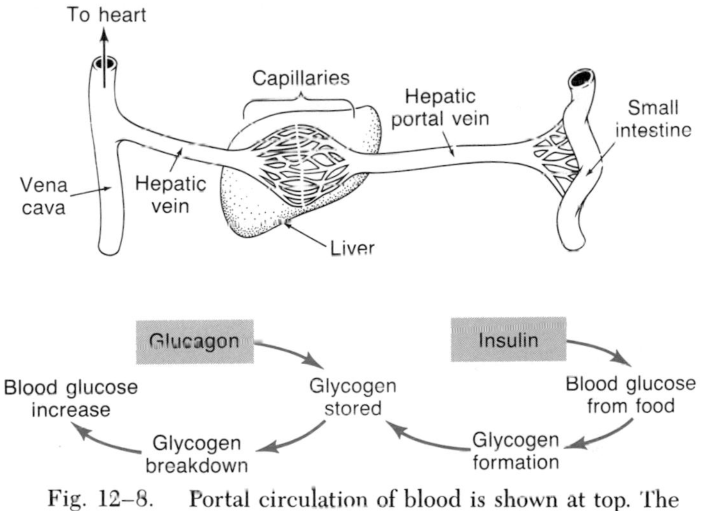

Fig. 12–8. Portal circulation of blood is shown at top. The bottom shows the action of the hormone insulin on glucose in the blood, and the action of the hormone glucagon on glycogen stored in the liver.

Harvey and Circulation

For 15 centuries before the time of Willian Harvey, biology was dominated by the views of Galen. This 2nd-century Greek physician said that blood ebbs back and forth through the heart. Blood supposedly passed between the two sides of the heart by invisible pores in the partition. Throughout the Middle Ages, no one dared to challenge the views of Authority.

William Harvey, an English physician of the 17th century, showed that veins carry blood to the heart and that the heart pumps the blood by arteries to the various organs. Harvey therefore is credited with discovering the general pathway of blood circulation. One major portion of this pathway, the role of capillaries, was beyond Harvey's powers of observation because the micrscope had not yet come into general use. Marcello Malpighi, an Italian microscopist, discovered the capillaries in 1661 (33 years after Harvey's report). An understanding of the basic plan of circulation was complete with this new discovery.

Harvey's reasoning was based on observation acquired through dissection and experiment. He discovered that the arrangement of valves in the veins and within the heart permits blood to flow in one direction only. When he cut an artery, he noticed that blood spurted only from the end that is nearer the heart. Therefore, he reasoned that arteries must carry blood *from* the heart. When he cut a vein, blood flowed only from the end that was farther from the heart. Therefore, he reasoned veins carry blood *to* the heart.

Harvey's work illustrates (1) that reasoning based upon observation and experiment can challenge the views of "Authority"; (2) that some discoveries must await the development of needed instruments.

Ⓔ

Some Malfunctions of the Transport System

High Blood Pressure

High blood pressure, or hypertension, is the most common form of cardiovascular disease. In this condition, the arterial blood pressure remains above normal. High blood pressure may result from a kidney ailment or a narrowing of one or more of the branches of a coronary artery. When arteriosclerosis (hardening of the arteries) reduces the elasticity of major arteries, the heart has to work harder to force the blood through them. Other factors causing high blood pressure include stress, an excess of sodium from salt in the diet, heredity, aging, and cigarette smoking. High blood pressure can lead to damage of artery linings.

Several kinds of medicine can be used to control high blood pressure. Physicians advise overweight patients to reduce. Psychotherapy has been helpful in cases where the high blood pressure is due to emotional stress. Cigarette smoking, which narrows arteries and arterioles, should be discontinued.

Heart Attack

There are two conditions that are commonly called heart attack: (1) coronary thrombosis and (2) angina pectoris.

Coronary thrombosis is a blockage in a coronary artery, or one of its branches, caused by a blood clot that forms in that vessel. If the clot was formed elsewhere in the body and is carried to the heart, it is called an *embolus* rather than a thrombus. The blockage causes a portion of heart muscle to be deprived of oxygen and die. Subsequently, scar tissue forms in that region. Coronary thrombosis is accompanied by a sudden pain in the chest, usually over the heart area. The pain may also radiate to the left arm, throat, or back.

Angina pectoris is a related condition that is caused by a *narrowing of the coronary arteries* or their branches. As in coronary thrombosis, a region of heart muscle receives an insufficient supply of blood. The symptoms are pain in the center of the chest and often in the left arm and shoulder.

Blood Conditions

In the blood condition *anemia*, there is a lowered number of red blood cells. In the blood condition *leukemia*, there is an elevated number of white blood cells. Both conditions may be diagnosed by means of a blood count. This laboratory procedure consists of the examination of smears of stained blood under the microscope. Fatigue, associated with anemia, is caused by the failure of the blood to carry sufficient oxygen to the various tissues of the body. This failure can be due to a reduced amount of hemoglobin or to the lack of sufficient red blood cells. Leukemia is a kind of cancer of the bone marrow that causes the production of large numbers of nonfunctional white blood cells.

Completion Questions

A

1. The liquid portion of the blood is called . . . . . .
2. The red pigment in the blood is called . . . . . .
3. The liquid that bathes the cells of the body is . . . . . .
4. The blood cell fragments that play a role in blood clotting are the . . . . . .

B

5. Proteins in plasma that assist blood clotting are prothrombin and . . . . . .
6. Cells in the blood that aid in blood clotting are the . . . . . .
7. A foreign protein that stimulates the formation of antibodies is called a(n) . . . . . .
8. The injection of toxin-antitoxin results in . . . . . . immunity
9. The defensive protein that interferes with the reproduction of viruses is called . . . . . .
10. The distressing symptoms of allergy are initiated by a substance called . . . . . .
11. In blood typing, if both drops of serum show clumping, the individual is blood type . . . . . .
12. Destruction of a fetus's red cells can result when the mother has Rh . . . . . . blood and the fetus has Rh . . . . . . blood.
13. Blood plasma can be used for transfusions without fear of causing clumping because it contains no . . . . . .
14. The type of immunity in which the body receives antibodies from another organism is . . . . . . immunity.

C

15. The interchange of materials between the circulating blood and the intercellular fluid takes place at the blood vessels called . . . . . .
16. The blood vessels containing valves are the . . . . . .
17. Blood moves in veins because of pressure exerted by . . . . . .

D

18. In humans, the heart chamber that pumps blood to the lungs is the . . . . . .
19. The largest artery in the body is the . . . . . .
20. The liver becomes more active in converting glycogen to glucose when the amount of glucose in the blood (increases, decreases) . . . . . .
21. The circulation of the blood to and from the lungs is called the . . . . . . circulation.
22. The circulation of blood to and from the muscle of the heart is called the . . . . . . circulation.

Ⓔ 23. A sudden sharp pain in the chest and left arm may be the sign of a(n) . . . . . .

24. Reduced amounts of hemoglobin occur in the disease . . . . . .
25. Hardening of the arteries is called . . . . . .

Multiple-Choice Questions

[A] 1. Which function of the human blood includes the other three? (1) transporting nutrients within the body, (2) transporting oxygen, (3) maintaining homeostasis, (4) collecting wastes

2. Food, waste, and hormones are carried by the (1) red blood cells, (2) plasma, (3) white blood cells, (4) platelets.
3. The cells that lack nuclei when they are mature are the (1) red blood cells, (2) white blood cells, (3) cartilage cells, (4) heart muscle cells.

Ⓑ 4. A blood clot consists mainly of (1) serum and corpuscles, (2) plasma and corpuscles, (3) fibrin and corpuscles, (4) plasma and platelets.

5. A chemical substance in the blood that aids in the formation of a clot is (1) fibrinogen, (2) ammonium hydroxide, (3) hemoglobin, (4) heparin.
6. Antibodies are chemicals that are (1) produced by the body in response to an antigen, (2) synthesized from carbohydrates, (3) nonspecific, (4) transported by red blood cells.
7. A drop of anti-*A* serum and a drop of anti-*B* serum are placed side by side on a slide. A drop of blood of unknown type is added to each drop of serum. If blood cells clump in anti-*A* and not in anti-*B*, the unknown blood is probably type (1) *A*, (2) *B*, (3) *AB*, (4) *O*.
8. A blood transfusion that would probably not cause difficulty is (1) *AB* donor with *B* recipient, (2) *A* donor with *AB* recipient, (3) *B* donor with *A* recipient, (4) *B* donor with *O* recipient.
9. An individual with type *A* blood may receive a blood transfusion from types (1) *A* and *O*, (2) *A* and *AB*, (3) *A*, *AB*, and *O*, (4) *O* and *B*.
10. Blood plasma does not have to be typed because it (1) contains antigens, (2) contains antibodies, (3) lacks red blood cells, (4) lacks water.

[C] 11. The backward flow of blood in veins is prevented by (1) muscles, (2) valves, (3) the heartbeat, (4) lymphatics.

12. A blood vessel that has thick walls and much muscle is a(n) (1) artery, (2) lacteal, (3) capillary, (4) vein.
13. The exchange of materials between the cells of the body and the blood occurs principally at (1) the heart, (2) capillaries, (3) veins, (4) arteries.

Ⓓ 14. The circulation of blood between the heart and the lungs is called (1) portal circulation, (2) systemic circulation, (3) pulmonary circulation, (4) coronary circulation.

15. For the blood of a normal person to pass from the right side of the heart to the left side, it must (1) diffuse through the partition between the two sides, (2) pass through the valve that connects the two sides of the heart, (3) enter the lymph vessels, (4) pass through the lungs.
16. Oxygenated blood enters the human heart at the (1) left atrium, (2) right atrium, (3) left ventricle, (4) right ventricle.
17. Carbohydrates are stored in the liver in the form of (1) saturated fats, (2) bile, (3) glucose, (4) glycogen.

Ⓔ 18. An insufficiency of red blood cells occurs in (1) angina pectoris, (2) anemia, (3) coronary thrombosis, (4) leukemia.
19. Coronary thrombosis consists of (1) a narrowing of a coronary artery, (2) a lack of hemoglobin, (3) a lack of red blood cells, (4) a clot in a coronary artery.
20. In angina pectoris there is (1) a narrowing of coronary arteries, (2) an increase in white blood cells, (3) a lowering of blood pressure in the aorta, (4) a decrease in red blood cells.

Chapter Test

1. The transport media in the human body are (1) lymph and ICF, (2) blood and blood cells, (3) lymph and blood, (4) lymph and plasma.
2. Blood is a(n) (1) liquid matrix, (2) plasma, (3) tissue, (4) intercellular fluid.
3. The clear, straw-colored liquid transport medium is (1) white blood cells, (2) plasma, (3) red blood cells, (4) antibodies.
4. Plasma is composed of 90 percent (1) water, (2) salts, (3) proteins, (4) tissue.
5. Blood cells without nuclei are the (1) white blood cells, (2) red blood cells, (3) plasma, (4) ICF.
6. Red blood cells are produced in the (1) hemoglobin, (2) bone marrow, (3) spleen, (4) liver.
7. Red blood cells are often called (1) ICF, (2) platelets, (3) hemoglobin, (4) corpuscles.
8. The color in the red blood cells comes from a red pigment called (1) corpuscles, (2) platelets, (3) hemoglobin, (4) ICF.
9. White blood cells that surround and kill bacteria are called (1) corpuscles, (2) platelets, (3) phagocytes, (4) hemoglobin.
10. White blood cells that help develop immunity against proteins foreign to the human body are called (1) phagocytes, (2) lymphocytes, (3) antibodies, (4) antigens.
11. A mixture of tissue fluid, living and dead bacteria, and white blood cells is called (1) phagocytosis, (2) antigens, (3) pus, (4) platelets.
12. Cells that carry oxygen and carbon dioxide are (1) white blood cells, (2) red blood cells, (3) lymphocytes, (4) platelets.
13. Cells that have the main function of initiating blood clotting are (1) platelets, (2) white blood cells, (3) red blood cells, (4) lymphocytes.

14. The colorless tissue fluid within the network of vessels of the lymphatic system is called (1) blood, (2) lymph, (3) phagocytosis, (4) corpuscles.
15. The three kinds of tubes that transport blood in the human body are the arteries, (1) capillaries, and lymph, (2) veins, and capillaries, (3) lymph, and veins, (4) capillaries, and muscles.
16. Blood is carried *to* the heart by (1) veins, (2) muscles, (3) capillaries, (4) arteries.
17. The smallest of the tubes that transport blood are the (1) veins, (2) lymphatics, (3) capillaries, (4) arteries.
18. The tubes that join together to form tiny veins are the (1) nephridia (2) capillaries, (3) arteries, (4) tracheal tubes.
19. The wave of alternate stretching and contracting of artery walls is called the (1) veins, (2) arterioles, (3) pulse, (4) peristalsis.
20. Blood in veins is kept flowing only toward the heart by (1) the pulse, (2) arteries, (3) valves, (4) lymph.
21. The human heart has four (1) veins, (2) chambers, (3) pacemakers, (4) arteries.
22. Systolic pressure results from contraction of the (1) atria, (2) valves, (3) ventricles, (4) pacemaker.

Base your answers to questions 23 and 24 on the diagram and information below.
A student took a small sample of human blood. A drop of the sample was mixed with Anti-*A* serum and another drop of the blood sample with Anti-*B* serum. The results are shown in the diagram below.

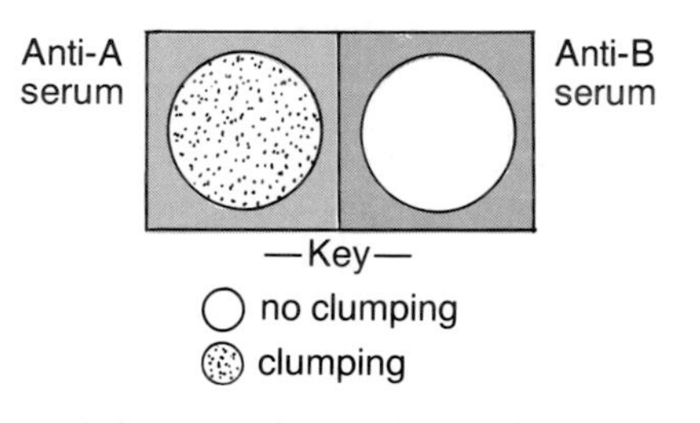

23. The blood type of the sample is (1) *A*, (2) *B*, (3) *AB*, (4) *O*
24. This blood sample contains which antigen(s)? (1) *A*, only, (2) *B*, only, (3) *A* and *B*, (4) neither *A* nor *B*
25. Cigarette smoking and excess salt in the diet are two causes of (1) leukemia, (2) coronary thrombosis, (3) high blood pressure, (4) anemia.

Chapter 13 Respiration in Humans

Humans have an external covering, the skin, which does an excellent job of preventing the loss of precious water from the body. At the same time, this impervious skin prevents the body's cells from obtaining oxygen directly from the atmosphere and discharging carbon dioxide into it, as does the earthworm with its thin, moist skin. Instead, the respiratory surface of humans is internal—deep within the air sacs of the lungs. Two small openings in the skin, the nostrils, serve as entry and exit for the gases used in respiration by the billions of cells in the body's interior. It is the function of the respiratory system to transport the respiratory gases from the external environment through the nostrils, to the gas-exchange surface in the lungs. The circulatory system assists the respiratory system by linking the respiratory surface in the lungs with all the cells of the body. It carries the raw materials for cellular respiration and removes waste products of respiration.

Respiration involves both the exchange of the respiratory gases, oxygen and carbon dioxide, with the environment and also the energy-releasing process of cellular respiration. Since humans are aerobes, the steps in their cellular respiration include both the anaerobic and aerobic phases (see Chapter 7). However, under conditions of oxygen deprivation, such as intensive physical exertion, muscle cells may carry out only the anaerobic phase. The lactic acid that accumulates as a result is responsible for the sensation of fatigue until the oxygen debt is repaid.

A Strucure of the Respiratory System

The structure of the respiratory system is shown in Figure 13–1. Respiratory gases from the environment enter the blood through this system.

The nasal cavity. Air enters the two nostrils and passes into the nasal passages. These cavities within the nose are lined with an epithelial membrane that bears cilia and secretes mucus. Hairs in the nose, and mucus trap dust and bacteria, thus filtering the incoming air. As air passes through the nasal passages, it is also warmed and moistened. People who breathe through the mouth lose these advantages.

The pharynx (throat). This cavity at the back of the oral cavity is a passageway for both air and food. The adenoids and tonsils are located in the pharynx.

From the pharynx, two tubes lead downward: the *trachea* that carries air and the *esophagus* that carries food. How is food kept out of the trachea where it would block the flow of air? This is accomplished by the *epiglottis* (*epi* = on, *glottis* = the opening of the trachea), a cartilaginous flap that prevents food from going the wrong way into the air passage. During the act of swallowing, the top of the trachea rises against the epiglottis, closing the entrance to the trachea. Solid and liquid food are then properly diverted into the esophagus.

At the top of the trachea is the larynx. This is often called the voice box or *Adam's apple.* The larynx is composed mainly of cartilage. The vocal

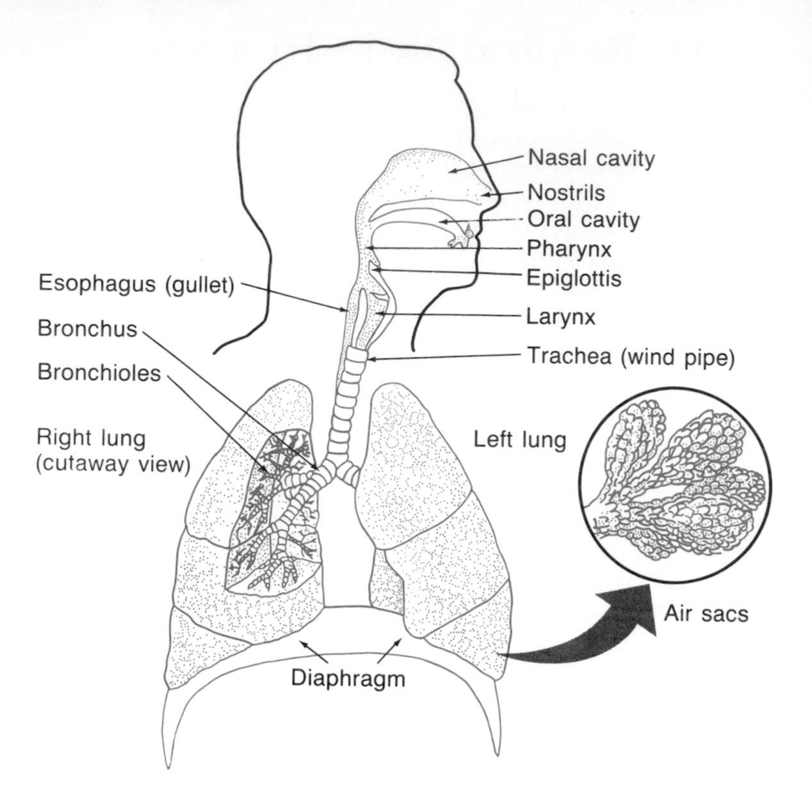

Fig. 13–1. Human respiratory system

cords in the larynx produce sound when vibrated by exhaled air as we speak or sing.

The trachea. This large tube, commonly called the windpipe, is about 11 cm (4½ in.) long and extends from the larynx to the bronchi. The walls of the trachea contain rings of cartilage that keep the tube open for the passage of air.

The trachea and its branches are lined with a ciliated epithelial membrane that sweeps foreign particles back up to the pharynx. Deposits from cigarette smoking slow and may stop the protective beating of the cilia. Particles of matter from air pollution have the same effect.

The bronchi. The trachea divides at its lower end into two smaller cartilage-ringed tubes called the *bronchi*. The bronchi extend into the lungs, where they divide into smaller and smaller tubes called *bronchial tubes* which also have cartilaginous support.

The bronchioles. When the subdivisions of the bronchial tubes reach a diameter of 1 mm or less, the cartilage is lacking and the tubes are now called *bronchioles*. Their walls contain smooth muscle and nerve endings. Contractions of the bronchioles occur during attacks of asthma.

The alveoli. (See Fig. 13–2.) The bronchioles lead to the functional units of the lung, the *alveoli*, or air sacs. Each alveolus resembles a cluster of grapes. The thin, moist walls of the alveoli are composed of a single layer of cells, and the alveoli are surrounded by a network of capillaries.

The exchange of gases between the external air and the blood occurs at the alveoli. Deposits from air pollutants and cigarette smoke can decrease the efficiency of this gas exchange.

The total number of alveoli in both lungs is estimated to be about one billion. The total surface of the alveoli is about 100 square meters! Thus, two small openings in the thick, dry skin surface, the nostrils, lead the external air to a thin, moist membrane within the lungs whose surface area is 50 times that of the body surface.

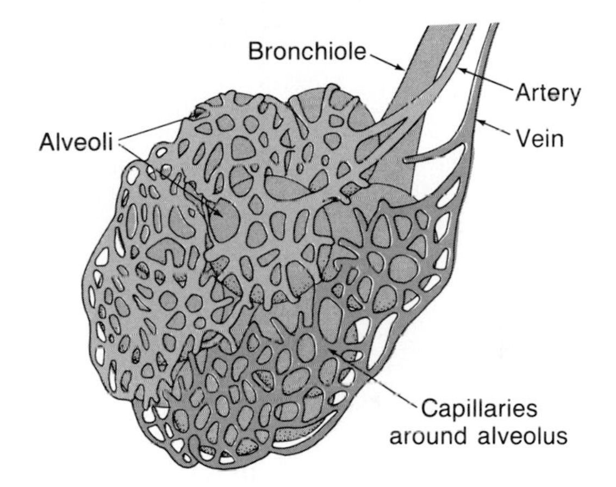

Fig. 13–2. Alveoli and the capillaries that surround them.

The lungs. The lungs are two large, spongy organs enclosed within the rib cage. Each lung contains a bronchus and its bronchioles and alveoli. The lungs are highly elastic but have no muscles for moving air. During breathing they respond passively to the actions of the diaphragm and rib cage.

Diaphragm and rib cage. The *diaphragm* is a sheet of muscle that separates the thoracic (chest) cavity from the abdominal cavity. Twelve pairs of ribs surround the thorax. Nerves from the brain and spinal cord cause contractions and relaxations of the diaphragm and of the muscles that move the ribs. The diaphragm and the ribs cause pressure changes in the chest cavity. These changes in air pressure move air into or out of the lungs.

B

Mechanisms for Gas Exchange

Breathing

Breathing is the process of drawing air into the lungs (inhalation) and expelling it (exhalation). The bell-jar model of the chest (see Fig. 13–3) helps to explain this process. In this model, the glass bell jar represents the wall of the chest cavity, the glass tubing represents the trachea and bronchi, the rubber balloons represent the lungs, and the rubber sheet represents the diaphragm.

Inhalation. Pulling down the diaphragm increases the volume of the chest cavity and decreases its air pressure. Since the pressure of the outside air is now greater than the pressure inside the chest cavity, air moves into the lungs, inflating them.

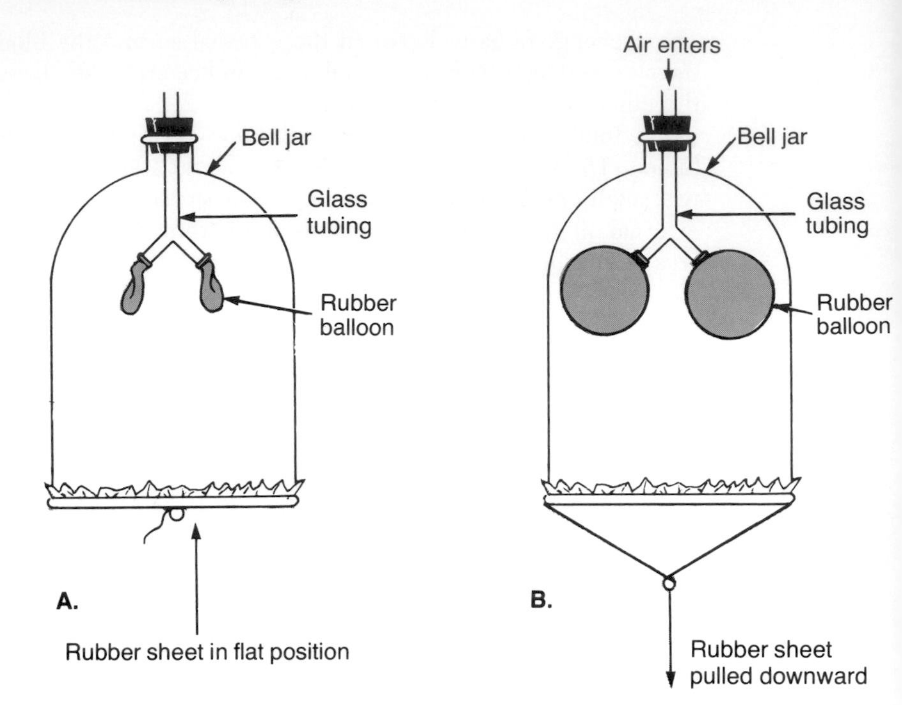

Fig. 13–3. Bell-jar model of the chest showing (A) exhalation and (B) inhalation

Exhalation. When the diaphragm is allowed to return to the flat position, the volume of the chest cavity decreases. The increased air pressure on the lungs forces air from the lungs to the outside.

The bell-jar model is valuable in showing that the flow of air into and out of the lungs is caused by changes of pressure in the chest cavity. The model also shows that the lungs play a passive role in the flow of air; there are no muscles in the lungs that cause the air to move in and out. However, there are a number of inaccuracies in this model: (1) The chest wall is not a rigid container. It contains ribs that move during breathing to change the pressure in the chest cavity. (2) The diaphragm in the relaxed position is arched upward in a dome shape. At inhalation, this sheet of muscle contracts to a more flattened position, thus increasing the volume of the chest cavity. (3) The lungs are closely pressed to the chest wall; there is no big space in the chest cavity as shown in the model.

External and Internal Respiration; Gas Exchange

The process of respiration in humans may be divided into three parts: (1) external respiration, (2) internal respiration, and (3) cellular respiration. Study Figure 13–4 as these three divisions are discussed.

1. External Respiration. External respiration consists of breathing and the exchange of gases between the alveoli and the blood.

- *Breathing.* This merely consists of moving air between the outside environment and the alveoli.
- *The exchange between the alveoli and the blood.* Oxygen diffuses into the capillaries through the single layer of moist cells that make up the

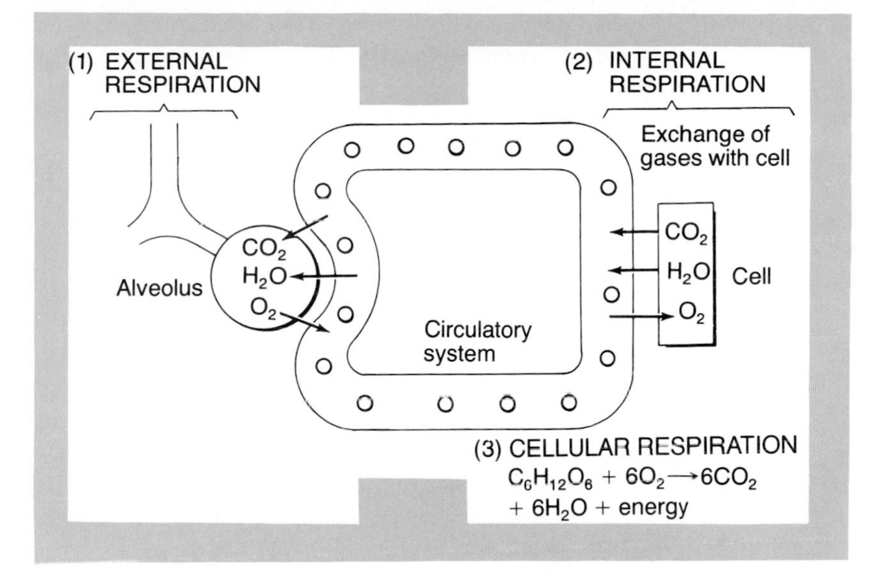

Fig. 13–4. Pathway of the gases in respiration

walls of the alveoli. In the capillaries, the hemoglobin of the red blood cells takes up the oxygen. Carbon dioxide and water diffuse in the opposite direction, from the blood into the alveoli.

2. Internal Respiration. Internal respiration consists of the exchange between the blood and the cells. Oxygen diffuses from the blood capillaries into the cells, where it is used in cellular respiration. Carbon dioxide and water, the products of cellular respiration, diffuse into the blood.

3. Cellular respiration. Aerobic respiration in the tissue cells results in the release of energy, largely in the form of chemical bond energy in ATP molecules, and the formation of carbon dioxide and water.

Transport of Oxygen by the Blood

Oxygen is mainly carried by hemoglobin of the red blood cells. *Hemoglobin* is an iron-containing protein compound. Hemoglobin combines loosely with oxygen to form the compound *oxyhemoglobin*. Hemoglobin may be symbolized as Hb, and oxyhemoglobin as HbO_2 (these are not chemical formulas). The combination of hemoglobin and oxygen is shown by the equation:

$$Hb + O_2 \rightleftharpoons HbO_2$$

This reaction is reversible. In which direction does the reaction proceed at the alveoli? At the tissue cells?

Blood containing oxyhemoglobin is bright red in color; blood containing hemoglobin is dark red in color. When a vein is cut and the dark red blood comes to the surface, the hemoglobin becomes oxygenated when the blood meets the air. Thus, the appearance of venous blood after it meets the air is bright red. You can see dark red blood when a nurse uses a glass syringe to draw blood directly from a vein in your arm.

Transport of CO_2 by the Blood

Carbon dioxide is transported from the tissue cells principally in the form of the *bicarbonate ion* (HCO_3^-). This ion is formed with the aid of enzymes in two steps:

1. $CO_2 + H_2O \rightleftharpoons H_2CO_3$
2. $H_2CO_3 \rightleftharpoons H^+ + HCO_3^-$

These are reversible reactions. At the alveoli, the reactions proceed backward, releasing CO_2 and water.

Regulation of Rate of Breathing

During increased activity, muscle cells add more carbon dioxide to the blood. An increase in the amount of dissolved carbon dioxide in the plasma stimulates the *respiratory center* in the medulla of the brain. The respiratory center sends impulses to the diaphragm and rib muscles to increase the rate and depth of breathing. This increased breathing removes the excess carbon dioxide from the blood and brings more oxygen to all the cells. These steps are an example of *homeostasis* or self-regulating feedback. The respiratory center is also stimulated by lactic acid which is produced anaerobically in muscles during strenuous exertion.

Reasoning Exercises

1. How might someone suffocate if their epiglottis does not function properly?
2. What does cigarette smoke or particulate matter do to decrease respiratory efficiency?
3. Why can you not voluntarily hold your breath for a long time?

Ⓒ Some Malfunctions of the Respiratory System

Bronchitis. Bronchitis is an inflammation of the membrane that lines the bronchial tubes. The membrane becomes swollen and discharges mucus which clogs the air passages. Sharp chest pains, a cough, and difficulty in breathing are symptoms of bronchitis. A dry cough, known as "smoker's cough," is an early stage in the development of chronic bronchitis from cigarette smoking.

Asthma. Asthma is an allergic response marked by contraction of the walls of the bronchi. The contraction causes a constriction of the passageway and prevents the person from getting enough air. The person suffering an asthma attack feels suffocated. In a severe attack, emergency medical personnel may use adrenaline to relax the bronchial muscles.

Emphysema. Emphysema is a serious lung disease that became widespread with the increasing use of cigarettes. This disease causes the walls of the alveoli to enlarge and then degenerate (break down), thus reducing the respiratory surface. The lungs lose their elasticity, and lung capacity decreases. A person suffering from emphysema may experience shortness of breath after performing as simple a task as tying a shoelace. Emphysema is not curable, but many patients may be kept alive with proper medical treatment.

Pneumonia. Pneumonia is a bacterial or viral infection of the lungs that can cause the alveoli to fill with fluid. This prevents proper exchange of gases in the alveoli and makes breathing difficult.

Lung cancer. Lung cancer is characterized by the uncontrollable growth of tumors. There is a proven correlation between the incidence of lung cancer and cigarette smoking.

Completion Questions

A

1. The scientific name for the throat is the......
2. The trachea divides to form two......
3. The functional units of the lungs are the......
4. During swallowing, food is prevented from entering the trachea by the......
5. Dust and germs in the trachea are swept up to the mouth by the action of......
6. The sheet of muscle that aids human breathing is the......
7. The wall of the human trachea is supported by rings of......

B

8. The exchange of gases between the cells and the blood is part of (internal, external)...... respiration.
9. Most of the carbon dioxide is carried by the blood in the form of......
10. Oxygen is carried by red blood cells in the form of......
11. The respiratory center of the brain is indirectly stimulated by ...... in the blood.

C

12. Degeneration of the walls of the alveoli occurs in the disease......
13. An inflammation of the lining of the bronchial tubes is called......
14. An allergic response that constricts the bronchial tubes is......
15. Pneumonia can be due to a bacterial or...... infection.

Multiple-Choice Questions

A

1. When human muscle cells fail to receive enough oxygen from the blood, they produce (1) carbonic acid, (2) lactic acid, (3) hydrochloric acid, (4) boric acid.
2. The respiratory surface of humans is located in the (1) skin, (2) nasal cavity, (3) diaphragm, (4) lungs.
3. The vocal cords are in the (1) epiglottis, (2) pharynx, (3) larynx, (4) bronchioles.
4. In humans, a thin, moist respiratory membrane is present at the (1) trachea, (2) bronchi, (3) diaphragm, (4) alveoli.

B

5. Which is a direct result of the increase of carbon dioxide in the blood? (1) ability to expend more energy, (2) increased rate of breathing, (3) decreased rate of heartbeat, (4) decreased rate of respiration
6. As blood passes through the lungs, gases are exchanged with blood vessels called (1) veins, (2) arteries, (3) arterioles, (4) capillaries.
7. The exchange of gases between the cells and the blood is part of (1) exhalation, (2) internal respiration, (3) external respiration, (4) inhalation.

8. During inhalation, the diaphragm is (1) raised, (2) lowered, (3) stationary, (4) lowered and then raised.

Ⓒ 9. The disease in which the walls of the air sacs enlarge and then degenerate is (1) pneumonia, (2) bronchitis, (3) emphysema, (4) asthma.
10. Chest pains, difficult breathing, and a cough are symptoms of (1) pneumonia, (2) bronchitis, (3) emphysema, (4) asthma.

Chapter Test

1. The exchange of respiratory gases with the blood takes place at the (1) alveoli, (2) larynx, (3) nostrils, (4) epiglottis.
2. Cartilage is *not* present in the (1) trachea, (2) bronchioles, (3) bronchi, (4) epiglottis.
3. Oxygen is carried by human blood mainly (1) in the form of bicarbonate ions, (2) dissolved in plasma, (3) by white blood cells, (4) as oxyhemoglobin.
4. Most of the carbon dioxide is transported by human blood as (1) bicarbonate ions, (2) hemoglobin ions, (3) oxyhemoglobin, (4) carbon dioxide.
5. The exchange of gases in human lungs takes place at the (1) alveoli, (2) trachea, (3) bronchi, (4) diaphragm.
6. Two diseases directly related to cigarette smoking are (1) bronchitis and asthma, (2) pneumonia and lung cancer, (3) pneumonia and emphysema, (4) emphysema and lung cancer.
7. Degeneration of the alveoli occurs in (1) lung cancer, (2) asthma, (3) emphysema, (4) bronchitis.
8. The medulla regulates breathing rate in response to the (1) oxygen concentration in the platelets, (2) oxygen concentration in the red blood cells, (3) carbon dioxide concentration in the plasma, (4) carbon dioxide concentration in the white blood cells.
9. Change in air pressure in the chest cavity is due to the movement of the (1) diaphragm and ribs, (2) diaphragm only, (3) lung muscles, (4) diaphragm and lung muscles.
10. Deposits in the air that are inhaled are most likely to (1) cause constriction of the bronchioles, (2) stop the protective beating of the cilia in the trachea and its branches, (3) cause the moist walls of the alveoli to dry up, (4) decrease anaerobic respiration.

Chapter 14 Excretion in Humans

Although the kidneys are the principal organs of excretion in humans, the lungs, the liver, and the sweat glands in the skin also have important roles in removing the waste products of metabolism. The main metabolic wastes of the human body are *urea*, *carbon dioxide*, *water*, and *salts*. Removing these wastes rids the body of substances that can be harmful and is a significant factor in maintaining homeostasis.

A The Urinary System

The human urinary system consists of the kidneys, ureters, urinary bladder, and urethra. These are shown in Figure 14–1 along with associated blood vessels.

The Kidneys

The human kidneys are two bean-shaped, fist-sized organs that lie along the back wall of the abdomen, about level with the bottom ribs. Blood passing through the body picks up salts and ions from various tissues and urea from the liver. At each circuit, a large portion of the blood enters the two *renal arteries* that lead to the kidneys (see Fig. 14–1). Blood that has delivered wastes to the kidneys returns by the two *renal veins* to the systemic circulation. Wastes removed from the blood are excreted from the kidneys in the form of *urine*. The two *ureters* are tubes that carry urine from the kidneys to the hollow *urinary bladder*. At intervals, a valve opens and the urine passes out of the bladder through a tube called the *urethra* to the outside.

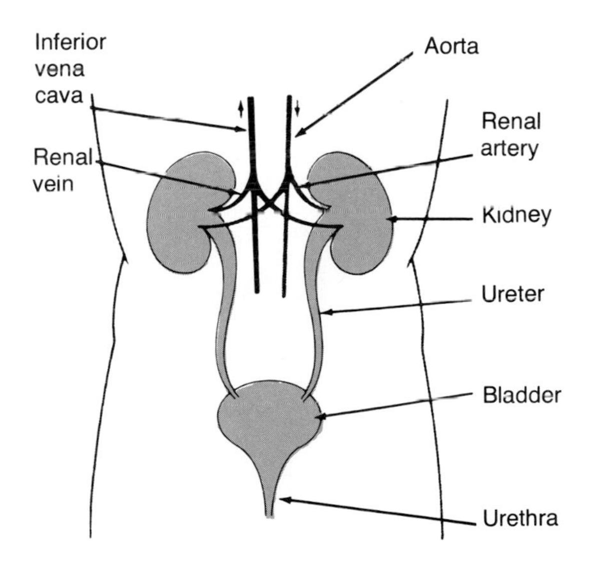

Fig. 14–1. Human urinary system

Microscopic Structure of Kidney: The Nephron

Each kidney has a large central cavity and a solid outer region. (See Fig. 14–2.) Within the solid portion are about a million functional units of the kidney, called *nephrons*. (See Fig. 14–3.) Each nephron is a microscopic, thin-walled tubule about 3 cm (1¼ in.) long. One end of the nephron is expanded into a double-walled cup, the *Bowman's capsule*. From each Bowman's capsule a highly coiled portion descends to form a *loop*, followed by an ascending coiled portion of the tubule.

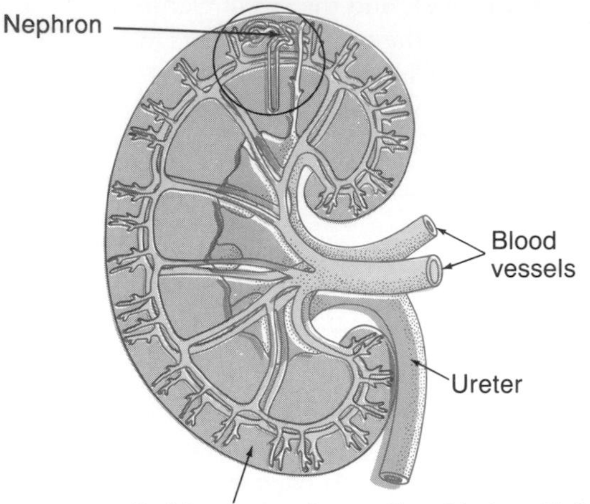

Fig. 14–2. Kidney anatomy.

Nephrons empty into larger *collecting tubules* which carry urine to the cavity of the kidney. Blood is supplied to the nephron by a small branch of the renal artery. This branch forms a knot of capillaries in the cup of Bowman's capsule. The knot of capillaries is called a *glomerulus*. From the glomerulus a small blood vessel leads to a second highly-branched network of capillaries. The second network surrounds the loop. These capillaries lead to small veins which eventually unite to form a renal vein.

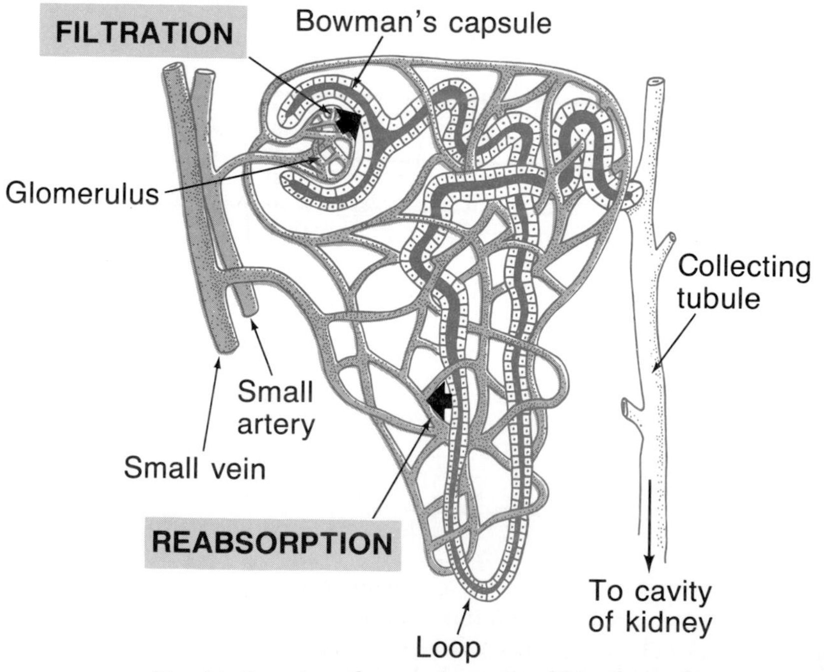

Fig. 14–3. A nephron and associated blood vessels.

The removal of wastes by the nephron involves three processes. The first is filtration at the Bowman's capsule. The second and third are reabsorption, and secretion, which both occur at the coiled portions of the tubule and the loop. The main features of these processes are summarized in Figure 14-4.

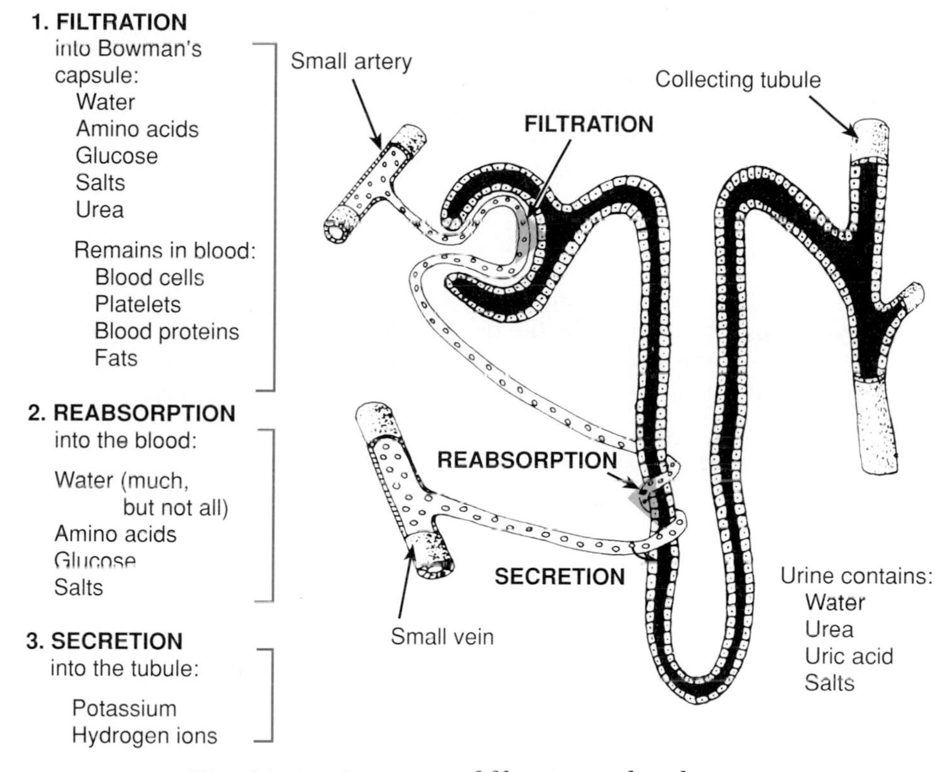

Fig. 14–4. Summary of filtration and reabsorption

ormation of Urine

Filtration. Materials diffuse from the blood capillaries of the glomerulus into Bowman's capsule. This diffusion is caused by the high blood presure in the ateries that supply the capillaries. Diffusing into the capsule are water, glucose, amino acids, salts, and urea. *Not* diffusing but remaining in the blood are the blood cells and most of the blood proteins. The *filtrate* (material that diffuses through) is essentially the same as plasma except for the absence of proteins.

Reabsorption. The filtrate passing into the Bowman's capsule contains digested food materials needed by all the cells of the body. It also contains large amounts of water needed by land animals. The loss of these substances in urine would be a critical matter. However, these materials do not all pass out of the body with the urine. Instead, as the filtrate passes along the coiled tubules and the loop, much of its content is *reabsorbed* into the capillaries that surround this region of the nephron. Water passes back into the blood by osmosis, but glucose and amino acids move from the cells of the tubule by active transport. Energy for this *active transport* is supplied by ATP. Glucose, amino acids, vitamins, and minerals are reabsorbed into the blood to a greater extent than is urea.

Secretion. The cells lining the tubule secrete some substances from the blood into the tubule. This movement is the opposite of reabsorption. For example, secretion into the tubule determines the level of potassium ions and hydrogen ions in the urine.

Urine contains water, urea, uric acid, salts, some hormones, breakdown products of hemoglobin, and other organic materials.

Homeostasis. The kidneys perform two major functions: (1) they excrete nitrogenous waste products of protein metabolism; and (2) they regulate the concentration of salts and other substances present in body fluids. In these ways, the kidneys help maintain a stable internal environment for the body's cells.

B

Other Organs for Excretion

The Lungs

Carbon dioxide and water, produced in the cells by aerobic respiration, are carried by the blood to the lungs. These waste materials diffuse into the alveoli and pass out of the body with the exhaled air. The lungs therefore are organs of excretion as well as respiration.

The Skin

Structure of the skin. Figure 14–5 shows that the skin consists of two layers: (1) the epidermis, which is the thin outer layer; and (2) the dermis, which is the thicker inner layer, or true skin.

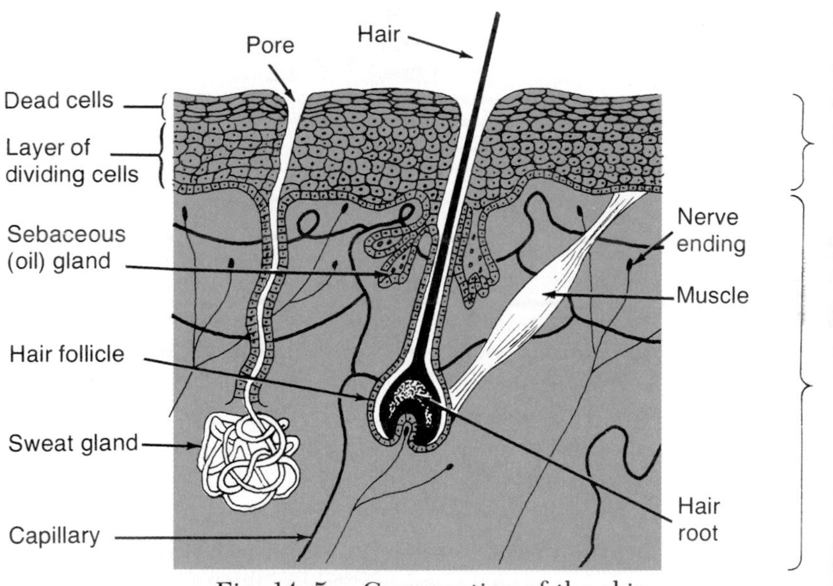

Fig. 14–5. Cross section of the skin

At the bottom of the *epidermis* is a layer of cells that divide to produce the cells above. As the new cells are pushed away from their source of food and oxygen, they become filled with protein and gradually die. At the skin surface, therefore, dead cells are constantly being rubbed off and replaced from below. The epidermis is watertight and covered with a fine oil film. The main function of the epidermis is to protect the active tissues below.

The inner layer, the *dermis,* lies below the epidermis. It is a thick layer consisting mainly of connective tissue. Present are capillaries, lymph vessels, nerve endings, fat, oil and sweat glands, and hair follicles.

The *sweat glands,* found in the dermis, are coiled, tubular structures that open by pores in the surface of the skin. Their excretory product, *sweat* or *perspiration,* consists of water, urea, and salts that are removed from blood capillaries. Sweat is about 98 percent water. The evaporation of water is a physical process that uses heat. Does sweating make you hot? On the contrary, the loss of heat used in evaporation of sweat cools your skin.

Functions of the skin. The functions of the skin are as follows:

1. *The skin is a protective organ.* When unbroken, the skin protects the body from mechanical injury and bacterial infection. In addition, the skin prevents loss of water and the drying of all tissues within.

2. *The skin is an organ of sensation.* The skin has nerve endings that detect changes in temperature, pressure, pain, or touch.

3. *The skin is an organ of excretion.* Its perspiration includes some urea and uric acid.

4. *The skin helps to regulate the temperature of the body.* Although the body loses some heat with urine and exhaled air, more than 80 percent of its heat loss occurs through the skin. The evaporation of sweat accounts for part of this heat loss. The loss of heat from blood in the dermis is also an important factor.

The skin is richly laced with a network of blood vessels that lose heat to the outside. When the body becomes overheated from vigorous exercise or from a warm environment, blood vessels near the skin's surface *dilate* and carry a larger volume of blood. Since more blood is now close to the surface, there is a greater heat loss, and the body becomes cooler.

Conversely, in a cold environment, there is increased flow of blood to vessels and capillaries in the lower layers. The ensuing reduction in heat loss helps to maintain the body's temperature.

These changes in blood flow are noticeable in the flushing of the skin during exercise and in the paling of the skin when cold. How then can you explain why the ears and nose turn red during freezing weather? To protect cells of these exposed regions from dying of cold, the body sends them an additional blood supply at the cost of lowering the general body temperature.

The Liver

Excretory functions of the liver. The excretory functions of the liver are to remove worn-out red blood cells and to produce urea as a nitrogenous waste. Red blood cells survive in the circulatory system for about 120 days, after which they are destroyed and removed by the liver and the spleen.

Deamination and urea formation. When humans eat foods containing too much protein, an excess of amino acids forms in the body. These amino acids are not stored for future use. If not used for such functions as growth and repair, they are changed to a nitrogenous waste and excreted. Physicians warn of the harmful effects on the kidneys of excess consumption of meats, fish, and eggs.

The first step in handling excess amino acids is *deamination* within the liver. Deamination is the removal of amine ($-NH_2$) groups. The amine groups are converted to ammonia (NH_3), which is toxic. In a series of enzyme-controlled reactions, the ammonia is combined with carbon dioxide to form the nitrogenous compound *urea*, which is nontoxic and is soluble in water. Urea passes from the liver to the blood which carries it to the kidneys and skin. Urea is the main form in which nitrogenous wastes are excreted by humans. In Figure 14–6, note the two amine groups. Both NH_3 and CO_2 go into the formation of urea. Urea was the first organic compound of the body to be synthesized by a chemist (Frederich Wöhler, in 1828).

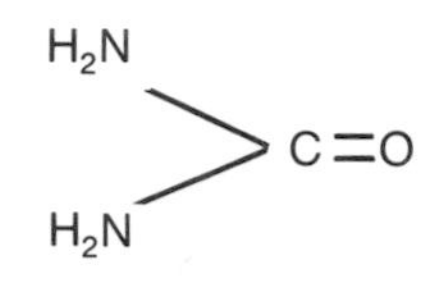

Fig. 14–6. Structural formula for urea

Ⓒ

Some Malfunctions of the Excretory System

Kidney Disease. The kidneys are severely affected by infections, heart disease, and toxic substances. Environmental pollutants such as the heavy metals lead and mercury, damage both blood vessels and tubules of the kidneys. Extremely high protein diets, especially crash reducing diets, may lead to kidney malfunction.

Gout. Gout is an extremely painful condition in which uric acid crystals precipitate out of the bloodstream, especially in joints or in the big toe. Uric acid is an insoluble nitrogenous waste that, like urea, is formed in the liver and transported to the kidneys for elimination. Excessive consumption of protein foods and defective removal by the kidneys are causes of gout.

Reasoning Exercises

1. Why would it be disadvantageous for humans to excrete nitrogenous waste in the form of ammonia?
2. Name three excretory organs of humans. What liquids carry the urea that is excreted?
3. What would the body lose if the kidneys did not function in reabsorption as well as filtration?
4. How does the skin help you maintain a stable body temperature?
5. Why do many people with kidney disease need to have their blood artifically filtered using a dialysis machine?

Completion Questions

A

1. Microscopic structures within the human kidneys that remove urea from the blood are the ......
2. Urine is carried from the kidneys to the bladder by the ......

3. The functional unit of the human kidney is the . . . . . .
4. The tube in humans that discharges urine from the bladder is the . . . . . .
5. Filtration of materials from the blood into the nephrons occurs at the . . . . . .
6. A tiny mass of capillaries in a Bowman's capsule is known as a(n) . . . . . .
7. The removal of wastes at the nephrons involves the processes of . . . . . . and . . . . . .

B

8. Humans excrete urea in the urine and in the . . . . . .
9. The liver acts as an organ of excretion by deaminating excess . . . . . . to form the waste known as . . . . . .
10. Urea formed in the liver is removed from the blood in the . . . . . . and . . . . . .
11. The inner layer of the skin is called the . . . . . .
12. Two wastes excreted through the lungs of humans are . . . . . . and . . . . . .
13. Sweating cools the body because the physical process of . . . . . . uses heat.

C

14. The nitrogenous waste precipitated out of the bloodstream in the condition known as gout is . . . . . .
15. Two heavy metals that can damage the kidneys are . . . . . and . . . . . .

Multiple-Choice Questions

A

1. The bladder of humans empties to the outside through the (1) urethra, (2) uretor, (3) capillary network, (4) kidney tubule.
2. The fact that large numbers of mitochondria are observed in the tubule cells of nephrons suggests that this region of the nephron is involved in the process of (1) active transport, (2) passive transport, (3) osmosis, (4) diffusion.
3. The reabsorption of glucose from the kidney tubules into the bloodstream occurs by (1) diffusion, (2) digestion, (3) active transport, (4) hydrolysis.
4. One of the kidneys' functions is to (1) complete the digestion of urea, (2) destroy old red blood cells, (3) maintain the normal composition of the blood, (4) maintain a supply of glycogen.
5. Filtration of the blood in the kidney occurs at the (1) urethra, (2) Bowman's capsule, (3) bladder, (4) loop of the nephron.
6. Reabsorption in the kidney of water and other needed substances occurs at the (1) Bowman's capsule, (2) glomerulus, (3) urethra, (4) loop of the tubule.

B

7. An insoluble nitrogenous waste is (1) uric acid, (2) urea, (3) ammonia, (4) nitrates.
8. The lungs excrete (1) ammonia, (2) oxygen, (3) carbon dioxide, (4) uric acid.
9. In humans, which organ excretes water and dissolved salts? (1) lungs, (2) skin, (3) thyroid gland, (4) small intestine

10. In humans, which organ excretes carbon dioxide and water? (1) lungs, (2) skin, (3) thyroid gland, (4) small intestine

Ⓒ 11. Common environmental pollutants likely to damage the kidneys are (1) aluminum and zinc, (2) lead and mercury, (3) sodium and potassium, (4) carbon dioxide and water.

12. Gout is caused by deposition in the joints of crystals of (1) boric acid, (2) urea, (3) ammonia, (4) uric acid.

Chapter Test

1. Urine is carried to the bladder by the (1) urethra, (2) renal artery, (3) ureters, (4) collecting tubules.
2. The kidneys remove nitrogenous wastes from the blood primarily in the form of (1) uric acid, (2) ammonia, (3) urea, (4) amino acids.
3. Kidney disease is most likely to result from a dietary excess of (1) carbohydrates, (2) protein, (3) vitamins, (4) fats.

Below is a diagram of the human circulatory system. For items 4 through 10, write the number of the structure that is most closely related to the function explained.

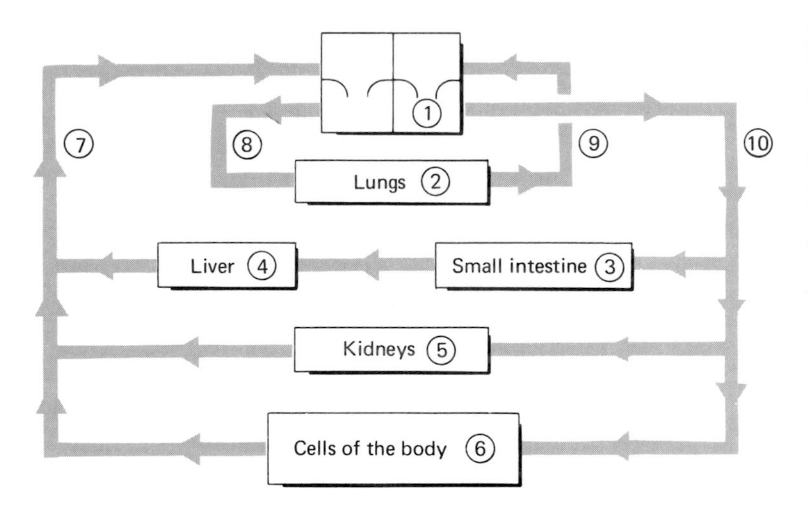

4. Carbon dioxide enters the circulatory system.
5. Urea leaves the circulatory system.
6. Oxygen enters the circulatory system.
7. Amino acids enter the circulatory system.
8. Urea is formed from excess amino acids.
9. A thin, moist membrane is in contact with the external environment.
10. A vein carries oxygenated blood.

ıapter 15 Regulation in Humans

The nervous system and the endocrine system together share the job of controlling the body's activities. The nervous system operates primarily by means of nerve cells and the endocrine system functions by means of chemicals, yet the two systems are similar in several respects.

- Both the nervous system and the endocrine system secrete chemicals. The chemicals of the nervous system include the neurotransmitters which carry impulses across synapses. The chemicals of the endocrine system are the hormones secreted by ductless glands.
- Both systems play a major role in maintaining homeostasis, in keeping the internal environment stable despite changes in the external environment.

The two systems differ mainly in that nerve responses are more rapid than endocrine responses and last for a shorter period of time. The two systems are compared in more detail in the table below.

Comparison: Nervous and Endocrine Systems

Nervous System	Endocrine System
Similarities	
Nerves secrete chemical substances called neurotransmitters.	Endocrine glands secrete chemical substances called hormones.
Some neurons secrete noradrenaline	The adrenal medulla secretes noradrenaline.
The nervous system helps to maintain homeostasis.	The endocrine system helps to maintain homeostasis.
Differences	
Nerve responses are rapid and of short duration.	Endocrine responses are slow but last for a long time.
Nerves transmit impulses via neurons.	Hormones are carried by the plasma of the blood.

A

ıe Nervous System

The nervous system in humans has the same basic components found in the nervous systems of other animals. These components, described in Chapter 9, include sensory neurons, interneurons, and motor neurons. Nerves, or bundles of neurons or their parts, are of the sensory, motor, or mixed type. Nerves are specialized for the transmission of impulses over long distances. The human nervous system has two divisions: (1) the central nervous system and (2) the peripheral nervous system.

Central Nervous System

The central nervous system is composed of the brain and spinal cord (see Fig. 15–1). The *spinal cord* is a hollow tube composed of nerve fibers that carry impulses to or from the brain. It is also connected to the peripheral

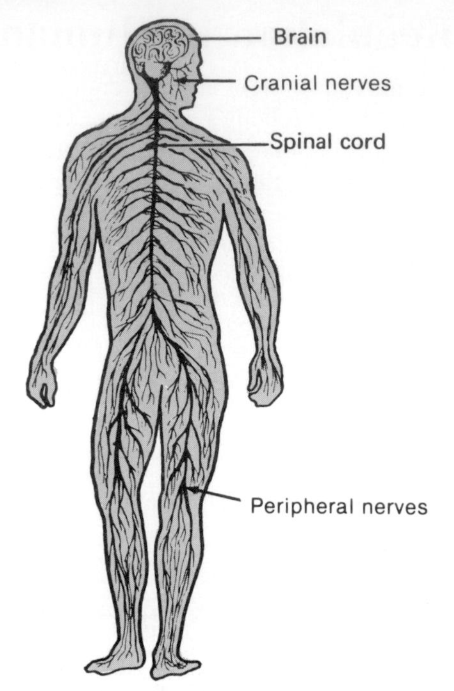

Fig. 15–1. The human nervous system

nervous system and serves as the center for many reflexes. The *brain* is an expanded hollow portion of the spinal cord. Composed of millions of neurons and their synapses, the brain has been likened to a giant telephone switchboard or to a computer. However, the brain does more than merely connect neurons. In some as yet unexplained manner, it enables humans to have sensations, to make judgments, to initiate action, and to think creatively. The brain is protected by the bony *cranium* of the skull and by three membranes called *meninges*. The three main portions of the brain are the *cerebrum*, the *cerebellum*, and the *medulla*. These are shown in Figure 15–2.

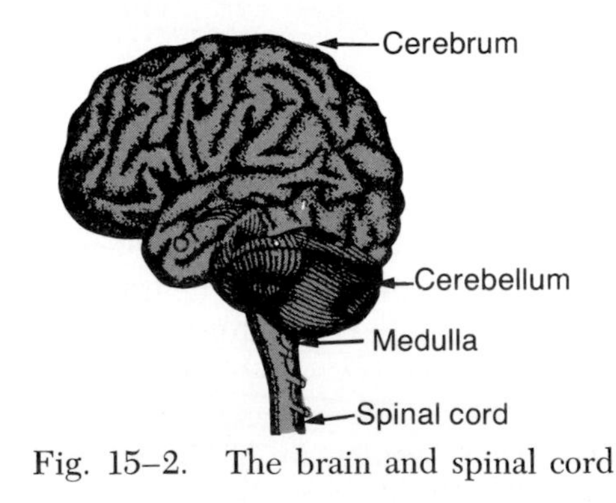

Fig. 15–2. The brain and spinal cord

The Cerebrum The cerebrum is more highly developed in humans than in any other animals. The surface of the cerebrum has ridges and folds called *convolutions*. These greatly increase the cerebrum's surface area. The *cortex* is the outer portion of the cerebrum. This region is composed of cytons (see Chapter 9) and numerous synapses which comprise the *gray matter*. The inner portion of the cerebrum consists chiefly of axons with fatty sheaths which make up the *white matter*.

Compared to other animals, the superior thinking abilities of human beings has been attributed to the extensive development of the gray matter of the cerebrum. According to one theory, as impulses are passed from neuron to neuron, new pathways come into use that result in memory, thought, and voluntary action.

Although the eye receives the stimulus of light, the *sensation* of sight occurs in the cerebrum of the brain. For example, if the optic nerves leading from the eyes are stimulated in some manner (such as by pressure or electrical stimulus), the sensation of sight occurs in the cerebrum. Each of the sense organs and each part of the skin has a special part of the cerebral cortex where its impulses are received and interpreted. Furthermore, regions of the cerebral cortex control specifically the voluntary muscles of the body: a right arm region, a left toe region, etc. The higher functions of coordination—reasoning, memory, emotion—are controlled mainly by the front part of the cerebrum.

During surgery on the cerebrum under local anaesthesia, the stimulation by a probe of specific regions causes the patient to recall long forgotten events, words, and songs from early childhood. The patient seems to be actually reliving previous experiences as though played back by a tape recorder. But, we do not yet know what chemical or physical changes take place in or between neurons during learning, memory, or thought.

Memory. Humans have two kinds of memory, short-term and long-term. Short-term memory is the recall of events that occurred within the last few minutes or hours. This is maintained by impulses circulating within areas of the brain. Long-term memory seems to involve the synthesis of protein molecules. Elderly people tend to forget recent events but are fond of recalling happenings from long ago. Short-term memory decreases with age.

Habits. *Habits* are complicated acts that are examples of conditioned behavior. Habits may be good or bad. Good habits are useful, for they make us more efficient by saving time and energy. The following are involved in the formation of a good habit:

- A desire to form the habit.
- Performing the act in the correct manner from the start.
- Repeating the act many times.
- Satisfaction. Each performance of the act should result in satisfaction. Satisfaction can be achieved through reward or through withholding of punishment. An *intrinsic* reward is one that follows naturally from the performance of the act; for example, brushing one's teeth results in healthy beautiful teeth. An *extrinsic* reward is an artificial reward, such as giving a child a toy for brushing the teeth regularly.
- Persistence. Never allow an exception to the performance of the act.

The human brain has more than 10^{10} nerve cells, each of which is connected, on the average, with 10^3 others! Memory or learning seems to involve two kinds of alterations: (1) change in the function of existing neurons and (2) formation of new synapses. Repetition establishes pathways for the transmission of nerve impulses which permit rapid automatic responses to be made.

The Cerebellum

When you swing a tennis racket and top the ball at just the right moment, it is your cerebellum that is coordinating the action of several muscles. Located below the rear part of the cerebrum, the cerebellum coordinates and controls all voluntary activities and some involuntary ones. It also gathers information from receptors in the inner ear and sends motor impulses to maintain balance.

The Medulla

The medulla connects the spinal cord to other parts of the brain. It is the control center for various involuntary functions that are essential for life. These functions include control of breathing, heartbeat, blood pressure, muscle contractions in blood vessels and the digestive tract, and swallowing. Injury to the medulla is likely to be more threatening to life than an injury to the cerebrum.

The Spinal Cord

The spinal cord is a tubular structure containing a hollow space, the *spinal canal.* In humans the spinal cord is protected by 26 vertebrae, which make up the spinal column, and by three membranes. A cross section of the spinal cord is shown in Figure 15–3.

The diagram reveals a center H-shaped darker region, the gray matter. This is the region where synapses occur between neurons. The white matter, in the outer areas, contains bundles of nerve tracts which carry impulses up and down the spinal cord. The spinal cord is filled with cerebrospinal fluid which also occupies the cavities of the brain.

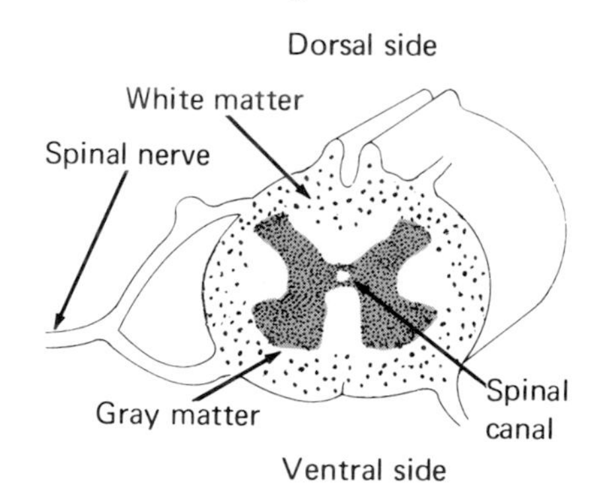

Fig. 15–3. Spinal cord. One spinal nerve is shown; 31 pairs of spinal nerves are present.

Reflexes

In addition to coordinating activities between the brain and other body structures, the spinal cord is the center for reflex action. Chapter 9 described the three kinds of neurons that compose the reflex arc. These are the *sensory neuron*, the *interneuron* (formerly known as the association neuron), and the *motor neuron.* A reflex is a simple, innate form of behavior that is involuntary. When you pull your finger from a hot stove, you have already removed your finger by the time you feel pain. Such reflex actions are rapid because it takes only a moment for the impulse to travel to the spinal cord and back. The reflex arc is short, with few time-consuming synapses. Interneurons in the spinal cord also make connections leading to the brain. In this case, a fraction of a second later you feel pain and may voluntarily decide to take some action. Other examples of reflexes are coughing, sneezing, and blinking. When a doctor taps your knee with a hammer, he or she is checking on your knee-jerk reflex.

Characteristics of reflexes are:

- Reflexes are inborn (present from birth).
- Reflexes are automatic (do not require thought; are not voluntary).
- Reflexes protect the body.

Functions of the Brain and Spinal Cord

Part	Function
Cerebrum	Creative thought. Memory. Judgment. Sensation. Voluntary Action. Habits.
Cerebellum	Coordination of voluntary activities. Control of balance.
Medulla	Controls reflexes in upper regions of the body and such involuntary activities as heart action, breathing, coughing, swallowing, sneezing, movements of digestive system.
Spinal cord	Regulates reflexes such as pulling a finger from a hot stove and the knee jerk. Carries nerve impulses between various parts of the body and the brain.

(B) The Peripheral Nervous System

The peripheral nervous system has two parts: the somatic nervous system and the autonomic nervous system. The peripheral nervous system consists of nerves that carry impulses between the central nervous system and the various parts of the body. All nerves outside the brain and spinal cord that extend throughout the body are part of the peripheral nervous system.

Twelve pairs of nerves connecting with the brain are *cranial nerves.* Thirty-one pairs of nerves connecting with the spinal cord are *spinal nerves.* Among the cranial nerves are the *olfactory nerves* to the nose, the *optic nerves* to the eyes, and the *auditory nerves* to the ears.

Figure 15–3 shows that a spinal nerve joins the spinal cord by means of two roots. The posterior root carries sensory impulses *to* the spinal cord, and the anterior root carries motor impulses *from* the spinal cord. Within a spinal nerve itself, however, some neurons carry impulses in one direction and others in the opposite direction. A spinal nerve, therefore, is a *mixed nerve* with sensory and motor components.

...he Autonomic ...rvous System

The autonomic nervous system controls many of the automatic (involuntary) activities of the body including the functioning of internal organs. This system maintains homeostasis by keeping the circulatory, respiratory, and digestive systems going at the proper rates for working in unison. The autonomic nervous system consists of two divisions: the *sympathetic nervous system* and the *parasympathetic nervous system.* Both systems have nerves leading to the same organ, but here they have opposite effects. Sympathetic nerves produce the responses needed for periods of stress; parasympathetic nerves produce the responses appropriate for the following periods of calm. For example, during battle the sympathetic system sends much blood to the large muscles of the body, but not to the digestive system. The sympathetic system is known as the "fight or flight" system.

The autonomic nervous system is linked by nerves to the spinal cord and brain (see Fig. 15–4). Thus, the central nervous system and the autonomic nervous system are interdependent. The autonomic nervous system includes two vertical chains of ganglia, one on each side of the spinal cord. From these ganglia, nerves lead to many involuntary muscles and glands.

A large group of ganglia constitutes a *plexus* (for example, the solar plexus which lies just above the somach). A plexus resembles a ganglion in serving as a relay center containing numerous interneurons. However, a plexus is larger than a ganglion and is a sheetlike mass of nervous tissue. Why can a blow to the solar plexus be dangerous?

How can sympathetic and parasympathetic nerves have opposite effects

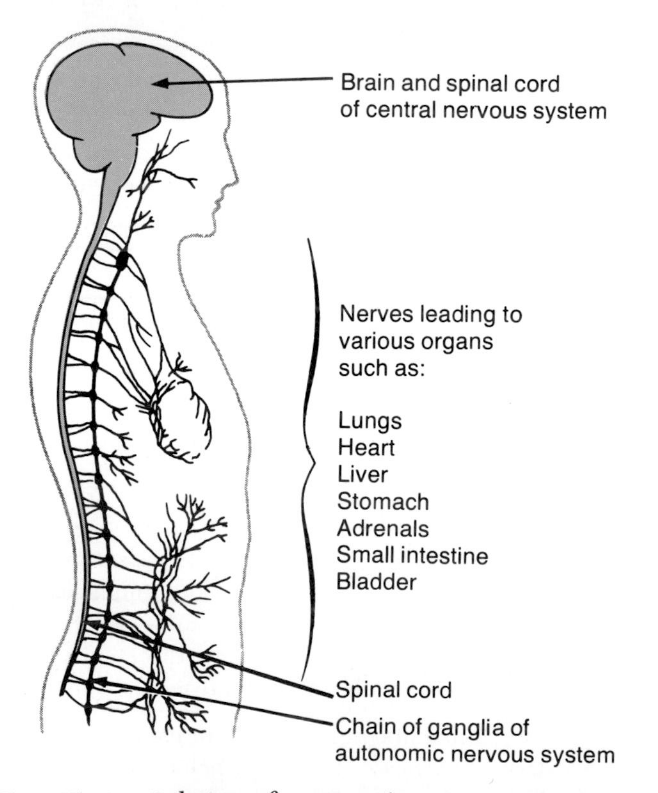

Fig. 15–4. Relation of autonomic nervous system to central nervous system

on the same organ? It is because they release different neurotransmitters. Sympathetic nerves release noradrenaline; parasympathetic nerves release acetylcholine. We have already seen that the effect of each neurotransmitter depends on the nature of its target. For example, acetylcholine inhibits the action of heart muscle but stimulates the action of intestinal muscle. Accordingly, during periods of calm, the heart beats more slowly but digestive action increases. During periods of stress, noradrenaline from sympathetic nerves speeds the heart but slows digestion. When the endocrine system is discussed, you will see that the hormone adrenaline has effects similar to those of the sympathetic nervous system. Does the sympathetic nervous system change liver glycogen to blood glucose, or does it promote the reverse action?

The autonomic nervous system contains only motor neurons while the somatic nervous system contains both sensory and motor neurons. The somatic nervous system controls the activity of skeletal muscles which are under conscious control and are used to run, sing, or draw. This system permits us to react to the outside world while the autonomic nervous system is more concerned with homeostasis, self-regulatory mechanisms within the body.

Some Malfunctions of the Nervous System

Cerebral palsy. Cerebral palsy is a form of paralysis caused by damage to motor areas of the brain. The injury may occur before or during birth or by injury or infection after birth. Cerebral palsy is characterized by involuntary movements and by difficulty in coordinating voluntary muscles. Great progress has recently been made in treating this condition.

Meningitis. Meningitis is an inflammation of the meninges, the membranes surrounding the brain and spinal cord. The disease is caused by a bacterium, the meningococcus, or by a virus. The symptoms include severe headache and stiffness of the neck. Because the infection is so close to the fibers of the central nervous system, meningitis may be fatal. Bacterial meningitis is now successfully controlled by the use of antibiotics.

Stroke. If a part of the brain's blood supply is cut off, the resulting damage to brain cells is a stroke. The interruption of the blood supply may be caused by a hemorrhage (a bursting of a blood vessel) or by a blood clot. The symptoms depend upon the part of the brain affected. Paralysis of part of the body or difficulty with speech are common symptoms. With a program of rehabilitation, a stroke victim may recover use of paralyzed body parts.

Polio. The full name of this disease, *anterior poliomyelitis,* indicates that the infecting virus affects the anterior (motor) roots of spinal nerves. The resulting paralysis most often affects the arms and legs but can be life threatening because it often interferes with breathing. Another name for this disease is *infantile paralysis.* Polio, a much-feared disease for children in the 1950s, has been brought under control by immunization. The Salk vaccine, developed by Jonas Salk, consists of killed virus particles that are injected; the Sabin vaccine, developed by Albert Sabin, is made from weakened live virus particles that are taken orally.

Reasoning Exercises

1. Explain two similarities of the nervous system and the endocrine system.
2. What part of the brain is involved in studying for a test? walking a tightrope?
3. Trace a reflex action from touching a hot stove to pulling your hand away from the stove.
4. Why do the sympathetic nervous system and the parasympathetic nervous system have opposite effects on the digestive system?

D

The Human Endocrine System

The human endocrine system consists of more than a dozen glands and groups of cells located in various parts of the body (see Fig. 15–5). The secretions of these glands are called *hormones*. Endocrine glands influence each other and thus form an interrelated system. The endocrine system helps to (1) coordinate life processes and (2) maintain homeostasis despite changes in the external and internal environment.

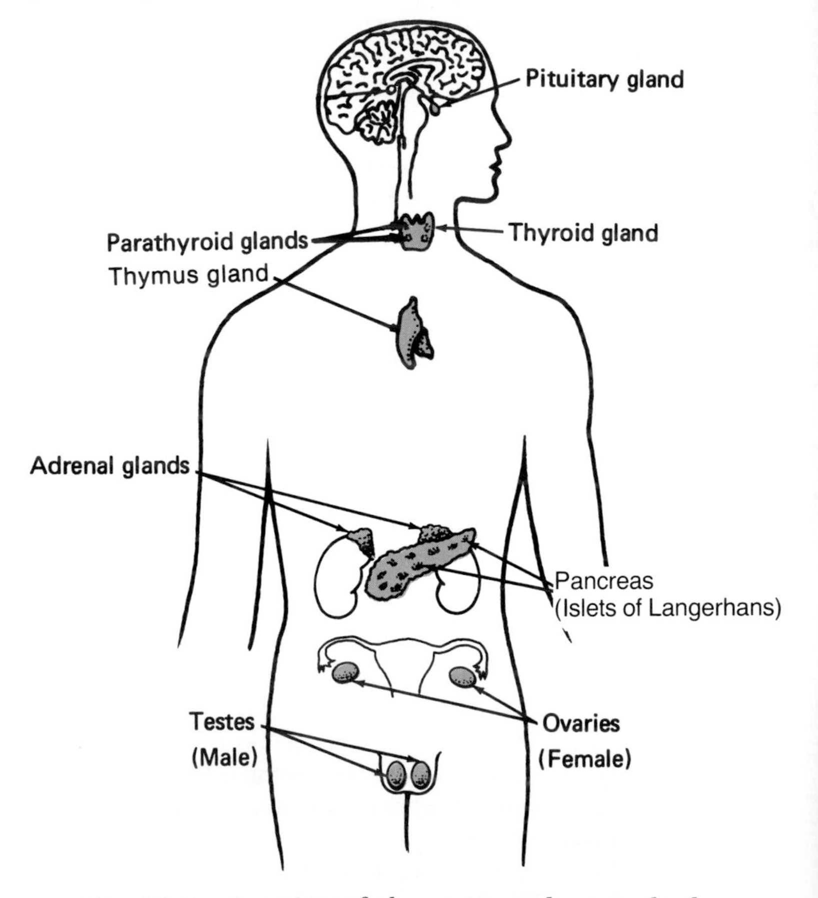

Fig. 15–5. Location of the major endocrine glands. Endocrine glands are ductless glands that pass their secretions to the blood.

ypothalamus

The hypothalamus is a tiny structure of the brain located near its base. Although the hypothalamus is part of the central nervous system, it has an endocrine function. The pituitary gland, one of the major glands of the endocrine system, is connected to the hypothalamus by a stalk. The hypothalamus produces some brain hormones that flow to the pituitary gland by means of a network of capillaries and other hormones that pass by way of nerve fibers and are stored in the pituitary gland until released. These relationships between the hypothalamus of the brain and the pituitary gland of the endocrine system demonstrate the link between the nervous system and the endocrine system.

The Pituitary Gland

The pituitary gland has been called "the master gland of the body" because it produces hormones that affect many other endocrine glands. The title master gland, however, is misleading, it does not take into consideration that other glands produce hormones which in turn affect the pituitary gland. Many of the endocrine glands stimulate and inhibit one another in an interrelated fashion. In this way, they assist the nervous system in coordinating the functions of the body.

The pituitary gland is the size of a large pea and is attached by a stalk to the underside of the brain. The pituitary gland is composed of two sections: the anterior lobe and the posterior lobe. Each releases its own hormones.

Hormones of the anterior pituitary. The *growth hormone* increases growth of the body by promoting the growth of bone and muscle. Hypersecretion (oversecretion) of growth hormone in childhood causes *giantism,* a condition in which the individual grows very tall, but the various parts of the body are in proper proportion. Hyposecretion (undersecretion) of growth hormone in childhood results in *dwarfism.* In this condition, the individual is small but well-proportioned and has normal intelligence. Many circus midgets are pituitary dwarfs.

In 1970, biochemists first prepared *human growth hormone* (HGH) in the laboratory. Now it is being produced experimentally by the process of genetic engineering. Human genes for the production of HGH are introduced into the gene makeup of bacteria or yeasts. When grown in mass culture, these organisms produce the hormone in large quantities. If this process becomes feasible, large quantities of HGH will be available for treating children suffering from a lack of this hormone.

The *thyroid-stimulating hormone* (TSH) stimulates the thyroid gland to produce its own hormone, thyroxin.

The *follicle-stimulating hormone* (FSH) stimulates certain structures in the ovaries, the follicles, to develop at the proper time in the reproductive cycle. This hormone also affects activity in the testes. Other hormones involved in reproduction will be considered in the chapter on human reproduction.

The name *adrenocorticotrophic hormone* (ACTH) means the "hormone that affects the adrenal cortex." ACTH stimulates the adrenal cortex to liberate the hormone *cortisol.* Both ACTH and cortisol has been used for treating a variety of ailments including arthritis.

Hormones of the posterior pituitary. The posterior pituitary releases two hormones: *oxytocin,* which causes contractions of the uterus, and antidiuretic hormone (ADH), which affects water balance. Both oxytocin and ADH are produced in the brain's hypothalamus but are stored in and released from the posterior pituitary.

The thyroid gland is an H-shaped structure located in the neck on both sides of the trachea. It produces the hormone *thyroxin* which contains large amounts of *iodine*. Thyroxin increases the general rate of the body's metabolism, and is essential to normal growth.

Hypothyroidism. *Hypothyroidism* is an undersecretion of thyroxin; *hyperthyroidism* is an oversecretion of thyroxin. In hypothyroidism, the rate of metabolism is lowered. A hypothyroid individual is less physically active and less mentally alert than normal. There are several forms of hypothyroidism. Among these are:

Cretinism. A cretin is a person who has had a deficiency of thyroxin since birth. Such an individual may be physically and mentally retarded. He or she may be a dwarf whose body parts are out of proportion.

Myxedema. This disease of adults is characterized by a slowing of mental processes, lowered metabolic rate, and a puffy swelling of the face and body.

Endemic goiter. A goiter is an enlargement of the thyroid gland. In endemic goiter the swelling is caused by lack of iodine in the diet. The gland swells in the attempt to produce a sufficient amount of thyroxin. This type of goiter is prevalent in (endemic to) regions of the world where the drinking water lacks sufficient iodine. Endemic goiter can be prevented by using iodized salt. This is table salt to which an iodine compound has been added.

Hyperthyroidism. In hyperthyroidism, the individual's rate of metabolism is increased; he or she is energetic and restless. Hyperthyroidism may result in *exophthalmic goiter where* the thyroid gland swells and the eyeballs protrude. This disease may be treated by surgical removal of a portion of the thyroid gland or by various new drugs. If the goiter is cancerous, it may be treated with radioactive iodine, I-131. This is given by mouth. The thyroid gland picks up the radioactive iodine from the bloodstream. The radiations are more destructive to the cancerous cells than to the normal cells of the thyroid.

To determine whether an individual is suffering from abnormal thyroxin production, a doctor may give a *basal metabolism test.* This test measures the rate at which the person takes in oxygen and gives off carbon dioxide while completely at rest. Comparisons are made with average individuals of the same sex, age, and size. A relatively new diagnostic procedure is a blood test for the amount of *protein-bound iodine.*

The parathyroids are a group of four tiny glands located on the lobes of the thyroid gland. The hormone they secrete, *parathormone,* regulates the amount of calcium in the blood and the rate at which calcium is deposited in the bones. A shortage of parathormone results in transfer of calcium from blood to bones. The ensuing lowered calcium in the blood produces violent involuntary muscular contractions and convulsions, called *tetany.* The proper metabolism of calcium is also needed for nerve function, blood clotting, and proper growth of bones and teeth.

Islets of Langerhans

From your study of the digestive system you know that the pancreas secretes digestive enzymes through a duct that leads to the small intestine. The pancreas, however, also contains cells that secrete hormones into the bloodstream. The pancreas is thus both a duct gland and a ductless gland.

In 1869, the German physician Paul Langerhans examined the microscopic structure of the pancreas. He noted certain groups of cells that appeared different from the others adjacent to them. They stood out as little islands in the mass of other tissue. These cells were named the *islets of Langerhans.* We now know that two kinds of these islet cells secrete the hormones *insulin* and *glucagon.*

Insulin (from the Latin for "island") is secreted in response to a rise in the level of blood glucose, as occurs after a meal. Insulin lowers blood sugar in two ways: (1) it promotes the conversion of glucose to glycogen to be stored in the liver and muscle; (2) it helps cells throughout the body to take in glucose from the blood and to oxidize it.

An excess of blood glucose is called *hyperglycemia;* a lack is called *hypoglycemia.* The condition *diabetes mellitus* is a hyperglycemia resulting usually from insulin deficiency. The concentration of blood glucose is so great that much of the glucose that diffuses into the kidney tubules cannot be reabsorbed. Excess glucose is excreted with the urine. An excess of glucose in the blood or in urine is detected in the laboratory by heating with the common laboratory reagent, Benedict's solution. Diabetics can also test their urine at home with chemical indicators contained in special strips of paper or tablets.

In diabetes, the loss of glucose excreted in the urine is accompanied by a loss of water from the body. The resulting dehydration can cause a failure of blood circulation due to a drop in blood pressure, which is one of the causes of death in an untreated diabetic.

Methods for treating diabetes include: control of carbohydrate intake in the diet; injections with a long-lasting form of insulin; and administration of certain medicines that can be taken orally.

Insulin for treating diabetes is extracted from the pancreas glands of sheep and pigs. This insulin differs slightly from human insulin, and it may cause allergic reactions in some individuals. However, by splicing human genes into bacteria, the new science of genetic engineering has now developed bacteria that produce human insulin in large quantities. Such bacteria-produced insulin is already commercially available.

The other pancreatic hormone, *glucagon,* is produced by different islet cells than those responsible for insulin. Glucagon's effect is opposite to that of insulin: it *increases* the level of blood sugar. One way it does this is by promoting the breakdown of the liver's glycogen to glucose.

The Adrenal Glands

There are two adrenal glands, one on top of each kidney (*ad renal* means "on the kidney"). Each gland consists of two parts: (1) the medulla, or inner part, and (2) the cortex, or outer layer.

The adrenal medulla. The inner part of the adrenal gland produces the hormones *adrenaline* (or epinephrine) and *noradrenaline* (or norepinephrine). The adrenal medulla provides another example of the relationship between the nervous and endocrine systems: release of adrenaline from the adrenal medulla is stimulated by a nerve fiber of the sympathetic nervous system.

Adrenaline's effects reinforce those of the sympathetic nervous system. The adrenal medulla has been called "the gland of combat" because many of adrenaline's specific effects help the body meet emergency situations:

- It increases the rate and strength of heartbeat.
- It stimulates respiration.
- It dilates the respiratory air passages. (Accordingly, adrenaline is used to combat attacks of asthma.)
- It affects muscles in arteriole walls in a way that diverts blood from the digestive system to skeletal muscles and to the brain. This effect is a reason for making mealtimes pleasant occasions in restful surroundings. Noise and minor arguments cause the release of small amounts of adrenaline that interferes with peristalsis and digestion.
- It promotes activity of the enzymes that break down glycogen to glucose. In this way adrenaline cooperates with glucagon (from the pancreas) in *raising* the level of blood sugar. Adrenaline, thus, causes increased amounts of glucose and oxygen to be brought to muscle cells during emergencies. Remarkable muscular feats can be explained by the effects of adrenaline throughout the body.

The adrenal cortex. The adrenal cortex secretes several *steroid* hormones. A steroid hormone is a complex molecule, but it is smaller than hormones which are proteins. One of these steroid hormones is *cortisol.* Cortisol raises the level of glucose in the blood by converting *protein and fat* (not glycogen) of body tissues into glucose. *Cortisone* is a breakdown product of cortisol, formed in the liver.

Cortisol and cortisone prevent inflammation. A synthetic form of cortisone is used medically to reduce pain and swelling in conditions such as arthritis. However, cortisone's side effects limit its usefulness.

Another type of steroid hormone produced by the adrenal cortex has its effect in the kidney tubules. Here it promotes the reabsorption into the bloodstream of sodium and chloride ions. This activity affects the water balance and helps maintain blood pressure.

The secretion of cortisol is stimulated by the hormone ACTH (adrenocorticotrophic hormone) produced by the anterior pituitary gland. An excess of cortisol, however, shuts off the supply of ACTH by *negative feedback* on the hypothalamus and the anterior pituitary similar to that shown in Figure 15-7.

Small amounts of steroid *sex hormones* are also produced by the adrenal cortex. A tumor of the adrenal cortex may cause the development of masculine characteristics in females, such as the growth of a heavy beard.

The Gonads

The gonads are the two testes (in the male) and the two ovaries (in the female). In addition to producing sperm or ova, these glands also produce *sex hormones*. These hormones play an important role in the sexual cycle.

The sex hormones produced in the gonads are responsible for development of the *secondary sex characteristics*. The ovaries secrete the female sex hormones *estrogen* and *progesterone*. Estrogen causes enlargement of the breasts, broadening of the pelvic region, and growth of hair in the armpits and around the reproductive organs. The male sex hormones are collectively called *androgens*. *Testosterone* is the principal male sex hormone secreted by the testes. Male secondary sex characteristics include enlargement of the genitals, deepening of the voice, and growth of hair on the face, in the armpits, and around the genitals. *Puberty* is the period when the body becomes sexually mature and when the secondary sex characteristics develop.

Mechanisms of Endocrine Action

Endocrine glands often work together to control body functions. We shall consider two examples—glucose metabolism and the pituitary-thyroid relationship.

Glucose metabolism. The concentration of glucose in the blood remains fairly constant although some body processes remove while others add this sugar to the blood. A state of equilibrium (homeostasis) is maintained by the combined action of insulin, glucagon, and adrenaline. Insulin and glucagon are secreted by the pancreas, and adrenaline is secreted by the adrenal medulla. The interrelationships are shown in Figure 15–6. Insulin removes glucose from the blood and stores it in the liver as glycogen. Insulin also removes glucose from the blood for use by cells of the body. When the level of glucose in the blood is too low, however, adrenalin and glucagon draw upon the bank of glycogen in the liver and convert glycogen to glucose.

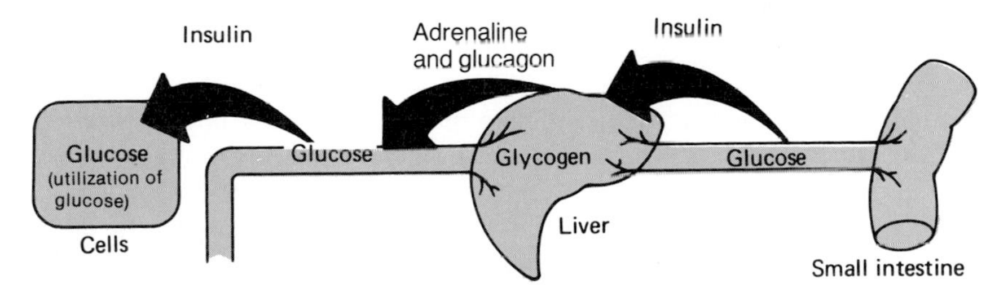

Fig. 15–6. Cooperation among insulin, glucagon, and adrenaline maintains a steady level of glucose in the blood.

Pituitary-thyroid feedback. The speed of a steam engine is regulated by a governor. Excessive speed of rotation raises the governor to shut off the engine's power. This is an example of negative feedback, to maintain a constant condition. A home thermostat is also a feedback device. In a similar manner, the level of thyroxin in the blood is kept constant by a feedback system that involves the anterior pituitary and thyroid glands. This relationship is diagrammed in Figure 15–7.

In this diagram a line with an arrowhead represents production or stimulation, a line with a roadblock (||) represent inhibition or the blockage of action.

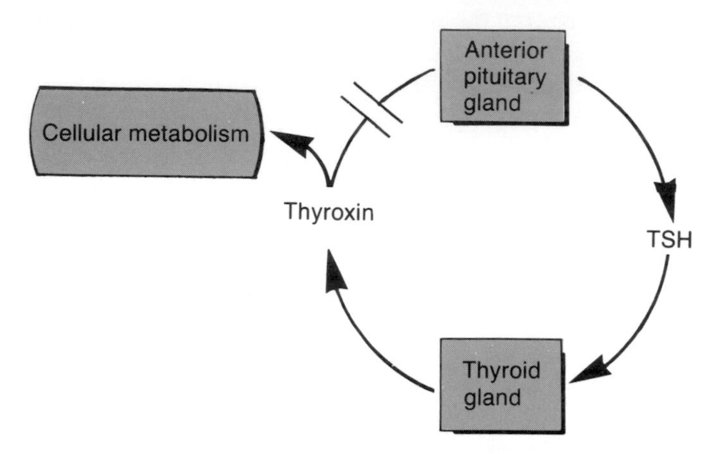

Fig. 15–7. Negative feedback in pituitary-thyroid relationship

Locate the anterior pituitary gland in the diagram. This gland secretes a hormone called TSH (thyroid-stimulating hormone). TSH stimulates the thyroid gland to liberate thyroxin. Thyroxin increases the rate of cellular metabolism. However, a high level of thyroxin in the blood *inhibits the anterior pituitary* from producing TSH. With less TSH now present in the blood, the thyroid gland decreases its output of thyroxin. In this way, there is a negative feedback mechanism. An excessive amount of thyroxin, operating through the anterior pituitary, reduces its own level. Moreover, the rate of metabolism remains constant, an example of homeostasis.

How Hormones Work

As hormones circulate through the body, how can they tell which cells to affect? That is, how do they recognize the cells of their target organs? Also, how do hormones produce their effects on these cells?

On or within the cell membranes of target cells are specific *receptor* molecules. The shape of the receptor molecule fits the shape of the appropriate hormone molecule, and the two molecules combine. Hormones are of two types: small steroid molecules and large protein molecules. Small steroid molecules pass through the cell membrane, (see Fig. 15–8A) and form a hormone-receptor combination within the cell. This combination moves to the nucleus. Here it affects genes that produce certain enzymes. These enzymes, then, catalyze the chemical reactions that we attribute to the hormone.

Large protein molecules, (see Fig. 15–8B) do not penetrate the cell membrane. Instead, they attach to specific receptor molecules on the cell membrane. This combination on the cell membrane promotes the formation of a *second messenger* molecule within the cell. (The hormone itself is the first messenger.) The second messenger, then, affects gene action in the nucleus to cause the hormone's effects. The second messenger moves to the cell's nucleus. Prostaglandin is an intermediary molecule within the cell membrane. The second messenger has been identified as cAMP (cyclic adenosine monophosphate), a derivative of ATP.

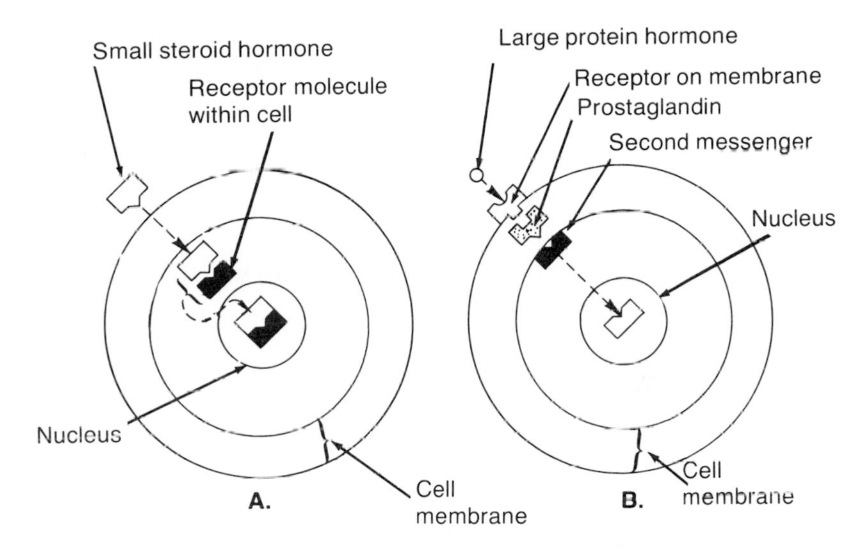

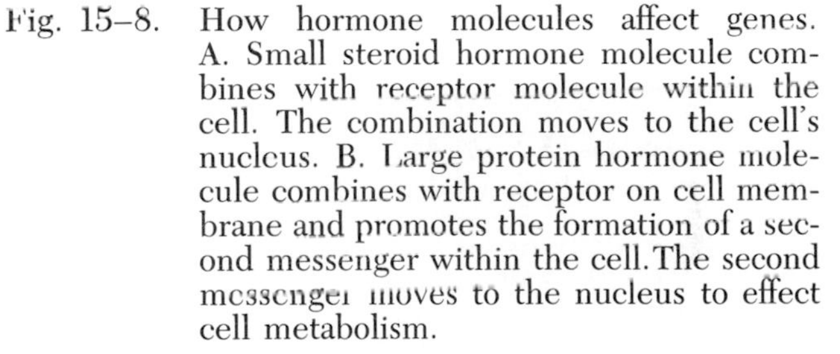
Fig. 15–8. How hormone molecules affect genes. A. Small steroid hormone molecule combines with receptor molecule within the cell. The combination moves to the cell's nucleus. B. Large protein hormone molecule combines with receptor on cell membrane and promotes the formation of a second messenger within the cell.The second messenger moves to the nucleus to effect cell metabolism.

Diabetes in adults is caused not by lack of insulin but by a lack of receptor binding sites for insulin on target cells. As you would expect, such adult diabetics are treated most effectively by diet, rather than by administration of insulin.

Prostaglandins. Prostaglandins in the cell membrane play a role in the formation of the second messenger. Prostaglandins are a group of recently discovered chemicals (originally found in the prostate gland) that have many effects within the body. One of these effects is to cause inflammation, as in rheumatoid arthritis. Aspirin is useful for treating arthritis and for lowering fever because it *inhibits* prostaglandin activity.

Inasmuch as the brain responds to pain-killing drugs such as opium and morphine, it must have receptors for these chemicals. But why should the human brain have receptor sites for foreign substances made by plants? Biologists reasoned that the brain must produce its own substances that resemble opium and morphine. It was found that brain cells do indeed release pain-killing compounds. These are small chains of amino acids called *neuropeptides*. Diffusing from their site of release to affect distant brain cells that have the appropriate cell membrane receptors, the neuropeptides act like neurotransmitters. Opium molecules have their effect because they are analogs (imitators) of the natural neuropeptides.

Two classes of neuropeptides are *endorphins* and *enkephalins*. These molecules bind to receptors located in pleasure centers and pain centers of the brain. They increase the sensation of pleasure and decrease the sensation of pain.

Some Common Hormones

Source	Hormone	Effect
Anterior pituitary	Human growth hormone (HGH)	Increases rate of growth during childhood
	Thyroid stimulating hormone (TSH)	Stimulates thyroid to secrete thyroxin
	Adrenocorticotrophic hormone (ACTH)	Stimulates adrenal cortex to secrete its hormones
	Luteotrophic hormone (LTH) (also called prolactin)	Causes corpus luteum of ovary to secrete progesterone Stimulates production of milk
	Gonadotrophins (FSH, LH)	Affect gonads (testes and ovaries) and their secretions during the sexual cycle
Posterior pituitary	Oxytocin	Stimulates contraction of muscles of uterus. (Produced in hypothalamus and stored in posterior pituitary)
	Antidiuretic hormone (ADH) (also called vasopressin)	Stimulates kidney to reabsorb water back into the blood. (Produced in hypothalamus and stored in posterior pituitary)
Thyroid	Thyroxin	Increases rate of metabolism in body cells
Parathyroids	Parathormone	Regulates calcium metabolism
Thymus	Thymosin	Helps development of immunity
Adrenal medulla	Adrenaline and noradrenaline (also called epinephrine and norepinephrine)	Stimulates various organs to cope with stress and emergencies, including change of liver glycogen to glucose
Adrenal cortex	Cortisol	Regulates level of sugar in blood
	Cortisone	Reduces inflammation

Some Common Hormones (continued)		
Source	**Hormone**	**Effect**
Pancreas (islets of Langerhans)	Insulin	Reduces level of glucose in blood by (1) storing it as glycogen in liver and muscle, (2) promoting its use in body cells
	Glucagon	Increases level of glucose in blood by changing stored liver glycogen to glucose
Cells of stomach lining	Gastrin	Stimulates secretion of gastric juice
Cells of small intestine lining	Secretin	Stimulates secretion of pancreatic juice and bile
Ovaries	Estrogen	Stimulates development of female secondary sexual characteristics Prepares uterus for pregnancy
	Progesterone	Maintains uterus during pregnancy
Testes	Testosterone	Stimulates development of male secondary sexual characteristics

Reasoning Exercises

1. Define the term *hormone*.
2. Name three hormones and explain their effects.
3. How does the relationship between the hypothalamus and the pituitary gland illustrate the link between the nervous system and the endocrine system?
4. What is the relationship between diabetes and hyperglycemia? between goiter and hypothyroidism?
5. Explain the negative feedback mechanism between cortisol and ACTH.

Completion Questions

A

1. The two main divisions of the human nervous system are the central nervous system and the . . . . . . nervous system.
2. The portion of the brain that controls balance is the . . . . . .
3. The sensation of hearing occurs in the part of the brain called the . . . . . .
4. The hollow space inside the spinal cord is called the . . . . . .
5. The membranes that protect the brain are called the . . . . . .
6. The part of the brain that controls breathing is the . . . . . .
7. Neurons that relay nerve impulses between sensory and motor neurons are called . . . . . .
8. Complex learned acts that become automatic through repetition are called . . . . . .

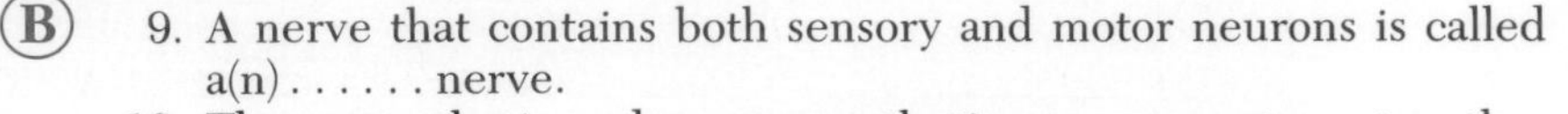

Ⓑ 9. A nerve that contains both sensory and motor neurons is called a(n) . . . . . . nerve.
10. The sympathetic and parasympathetic nervous systems together make up the . . . . . . nervous system.
11. The part of the autonomic nervous system that controls responses to stressful situations is the . . . . . . nervous system.
12. Parasympathetic nerves release the neurotransmitter . . . . . .
13. Nerves outside the central nervous system that extend throughout the body are part of the . . . . . . nervous system.

Ⓒ 14. A stroke may result in difficulty with speech or . . . . . .
15. An inflammation of the meninges caused by a virus or meningococcus bacteria is . . . . . .
16. Cerebral palsy can be caused by early injury or infection to the . . . . . . areas of the cerebrum.
17. The full name of polio is . . . . . .

Ⓓ 18. Giantism is caused by an excess of hormones from the . . . . . . gland.
19. Lack of iodine in the diet may result in the condition . . . . . .
20. An H-shaped endocrine gland located on both sides of the trachea is the . . . . . .
21. The structure of the brain that exerts some control over the pituitary gland is the . . . . . .
22. Diabetes mellitus in children is due to a lack of the hormone . . . . . .
23. A hormone produced by the pituitary that stimulates activity in the ovaries and testes is . . . . . .
24. A hormone that lowers the level of blood sugar is . . . . . .
25. Coordination between parts of the body to reduce an excess supply of a substance is known as . . . . . .
26. Two recently discovered classes of natural pain killers released in the brain are . . . . . . and . . . . . .

Multiple-Choice Questions

[A] *Base your answers to questions 1 and 2 on the information below and on your knowledge of biology.*

A barefoot boy walking down the road stepped on a sharp stone. He immediately jerked his foot up, cried out in pain, and inspected the injury.

1. The jerking of his foot is an example of a (1) learned response, (2) conditioned response, (3) simple reflex, (4) habit.
2. The boy's awareness of pain was centered in the brain at the (1) cerebrum, (2) cerebellum, (3) medulla, (4) spinal cord.
3. Homeostasis in humans is regulated by the action of (1) the nervous system only, (2) the endocrine system only, (3) both the nervous and endocrine system, (4) neither the nervous nor the endocrine system.
4. A severe injury to a person's head caused a temporary loss of memory. The structure most probably affected by the injury was the (1) pituitary gland, (2) cerebrum, (3) medulla, (4) cerebellum.
5. Reflexes are (1) inborn and voluntary, (2) inborn and automatic, (3) learned and voluntary, (4) learned and automatic.

(B)

6. The involuntary beating of the human heart is controlled by (1) the autonomic nervous system, (2) a pair of fused ganglia, (3) the nerve net, (4) the spinal cord.
7. The olfactory nerve is a kind of (1) cranial nerve, (2) spinal nerve, (3) sympathetic nerve, (4) auditory nerve.
8. The posterior root of a spinal nerve carries (1) sensory impulses from the spinal cord, (2) motor impulses from the spinal cord, (3) sensory impulses to the spinal cord, (4) motor impulses to the spinal cord.
9. The system that maintains homeostasis by keeping the circulatory, respiratory, and digestive systems working at proper rates is the (1) sympathetic nervous system, (2) parasympathetic nervous system, (3) central nervous system, (4) autonomic nervous system.

(C)

10. A clot in a blood vessel of the brain can cause (1) a stroke, (2) meningitis, (3) cerebral palsy, (4) polio.
11. An inflammation of the membranes surrounding the brain and spinal cord causes (1) meningitis, (2) hemorrhage, (3) polio, (4) stroke.

(D)

12. Insulin and glucagon are both produced in the (1) liver, (2) pancreas, (3) muscle cells, (4) adrenal glands.
13. Which hormone does *not* participate directly in controlling the amount of sugar in the blood? (1) parathormone, (2) glucagon, (3) insulin, (4) adrenaline.
14. The glucose content of the blood is regulated by (1) nerve stimulation alone, (2) insulin alone, (3) adrenaline alone, (4) combined action of insulin and adrenaline
15. The "emergency gland of combat" produces (1) adrenaline, (2) thyroxin, (3) estrogen, (4) parathormone.
16. Hormones from the adrenal cortex have been found useful in treating certain forms of (1) anemia, (2) diabetes, (3) arthritis, (4) myxedema.
17. A hyperthyroid condition is usually associated with (1) mental retardation, (2) high blood sugar, (3) low blood pressure, (4) increased rate of metabolism.
18. Cretinism results from (1) an excess of adrenaline, (2) a deficiency of adrenalin, (3) an excess of thyroxin, (4) a deficiency of thyroxin.
19. A very high level of calcium in the blood suggests a malfunction of the (1) liver, (2) pancreas, (3) parathyroids, (4) thyroid.
20. Brain cells were found to release pain-killing compounds called (1) morphine, (2) enkephalins, (3) oxytocin, (4) opium.

Base your answers to questions 21 and 22 on Fig. 15-5 on page 260.

21. Which endocrine gland might be affected by an abdominal injury? (1) pituitary, (2) thymus, (3) pancreas, (4) testes.
22. Which endocrine gland does not occur as a pair of glands? (1) pituitary, (2) parathyroid, (3) adrenal, (4) ovary.

Chapter Test

1. In humans, impulses are transmitted from receptors in the skin to the spinal cord by (1) sensory neurons, (2) motor neurons, (3) interneurons, (4) mixed neurons.
2. Which best indicates the pathway that nerve impulses travel in a simple reflex? (1) spinal cord → interneuron → sensory neuron, (2) sensory neuron → motor neuron → spinal cord, (3) motor neuron → spinal cord → interneuron, (4) sensory neuron → spinal cord → motor neuron
3. A type of self-regulation such as the relationship between the pituitary gland, TSH (thyroid-stimulating hormone), the thyroid gland, and thyroxin is known as (1) negative feedback, (2) cyclosis, (3) synapsis, (4) voluntary control.
4. A similarity of the human nervous and endocrine systems is that both normally (1) secrete chemical messengers, (2) have the same rate of response, (3) have the same duration of response, (4) secrete hormones that travel by way of neurons.
5. In which part of the human nervous system does the reasoning process take place? (1) cerebellum, (2) cerebrum, (3) spinal cord, (4) medulla
6. Difficulty in coordinating the action of voluntary muscles is a symptom of (1) stroke, (2) cerebral palsy, (3) meningitis, (4) polio.
7. The Salk and Sabin vaccines provide immunity to (1) meningitis, (2) typhoid fever, (3) cerebral palsy, (4) polio.
8. A person was admitted to the hospital with abnormally high blood sugar and abnormally high sugar content in the urine. Which gland most likely caused this condition by secreting lower than normal amounts of its hormone? (1) pancreas, (2) parathyroid, (3) salivary, (4) thyroid
9. The cells of the human body receive endocrine secretions through the activity of which system? (1) respiratory, (2) digestive, (3) excretory, (4) circulatory
10. Undersecretion by the islets of Langerhans usually results in an increased (1) oxidation of glucose, (2) blood sugar concentration, (3) energy output of the organism, (4) rate of growth.
11. Hormones recognize their target cells because these cells have the correct (1) prostaglandins, (2) receptor molecules, (3) DNA, (4) second messenger.
12. Which is true of both the nervous system and the endocrine system? (1) They bring about rapid responses to stimuli. (2) They send messages by impulses. (3) They assist in the maintenance of homeostasis. (4) They are under the direct control of the cerebellum.
13. All is true of the hypothalamus *except* it (1) is a part of the pituitary gland, (2) is a link between the nervous and endocrine systems, (3) secretes hormones, (4) is a part of the central nervous system.
14. Inflammation of the membranes surrounding the brain and spinal cord is called (1) neuritis, (2) cerebral palsy, (3) meningitis, (4) poliomyelitis.
15. Secretions from ductless glands are known as (1) enzymes, (2) hormones, (3) lachrymal fluids, (4) excretory fluids.

Chapter 16 Locomotion in Humans

As vertebrates, humans have a body plan for locomotion that differs in a fundamental way from that of arthropods, such as grasshoppers. Although both organisms have a skeleton, the parts of which are moved like levers to gain speed, humans have a living endoskeleton whereas grasshoppers have a nonliving exoskeleton. Human locomotion involves the interaction of living tissues such as bone, cartilage, muscle, tendon, and ligament.

A Structures and Functions in Locomotion

Bone

Bone, which forms the major part of the adult human endoskeleton, is a living tissue. It contains bone cells which are arranged in a circular pattern around minute branches of the circulatory system (see Fig. 16–1). The material between the cells is the *matrix*. This contains calcium phosphate which helps to make the matrix hard and strong. For building strong bones, you must include adequate amounts of calcium and phosphorus in your diet. You must also have vitamin D to assist in the proper utilization of calcium.

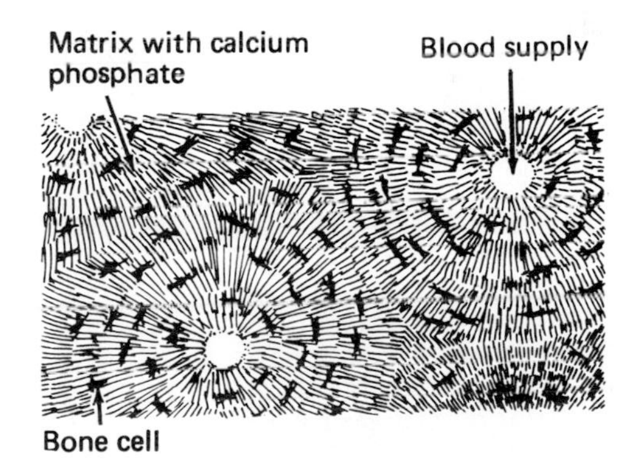

Fig. 16–1. Bone tissue

An important function of bones, as discussed in Chapter 10, is to *provide leverage for body movement.* One end of a muscle orginates in a bone which is the *anchorage site* for the muscle action; the other end is inserted into the bone that is moved. Another function of bones is the *production of blood cells* in bone marrow. The most readily apparent function of bones however, is the *support and protection* of other structures and organs of the human body. For example, a frail jellyfish floating in the sea has its organs buoyed by the water, but the organs of a human would collapse into a heap if there were no bony structure to support and suspend them in their proper positions.

The Human Skeleton

The human skeleton consists of the vertical axis and the appendages, the arms and legs (see Fig. 16–2). The *vertical axis* includes the skull, the spinal column, and the ribs. There are about 206 bones in the human skeleton. These bones are of many different shapes and sizes. The skull, which protects the brain and parts of the eye, consists of 29 bones, including the bones of the ear which are the smallest bones in the body. The *spinal column,* or backbone, consists of 26 bones called *vertebrae,* which protect the spinal cord (see Fig. 16–3). The *ribs* are attached to the backbone in the rear and to the *sternum* or *breastbone* in the front. They form the chest cavity and protect the heart and lungs.

The arms are attached to a group of bones which form the *pectoral* girdle. The legs are attached to the bones of the *pelvic girdle.* The thigh

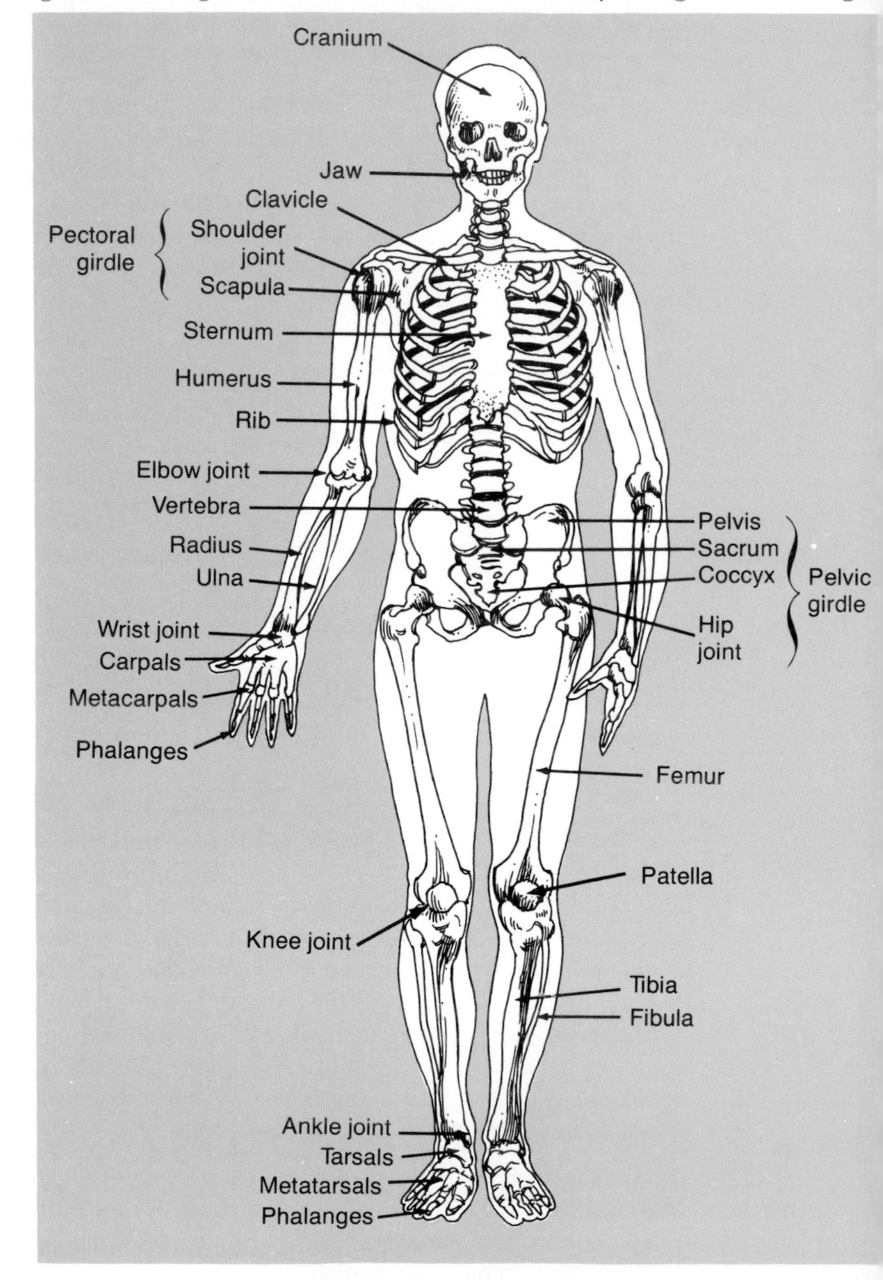

Fig. 16–2. The human skeleton

bone (femur) of the leg is the largest bone and accounts for almost one-fourth of the weight of the human body.

Cartilage Although the adult human skeleton consists mainly of bone, it has another kind of tissue, *cartilage*, which also provides support and protection (Figure 16–4). Cartilage consists of nearly spherical cells in a rubbery matrix which contains strengthing fibers. Cartilage may be flexible, fibrous, or elastic. In the adult, cartilage provides flexible support for the tip of the nose, for the ears, for the larynx and for the trachea (you can feel the rings of cartilage in the front of your throat). Cartilage is also found at the ends of bones and between vertebrae where it functions as a cushion.

Much of the skeleton of the early human embryo is composed of cartilage. By adulthood, much of this cartilage has been replaced by bone.

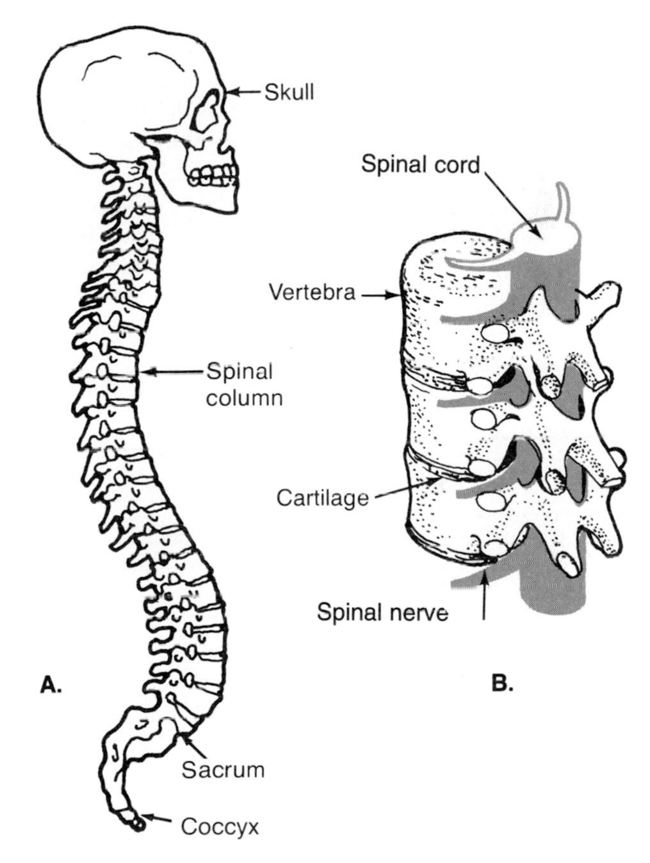

Fig. 16–3. The spinal column, side view. A. Twenty-six vertebrae fit together to form the spinal column or backbone which joins the skull at the top. B. View showing how the vertebrae fit together to form the spinal column and are cushioned by pads of cartilage between them. Each vertebra has an opening through which the spinal cord passes; in this way, the spinal *column* protects the spinal *cord*.

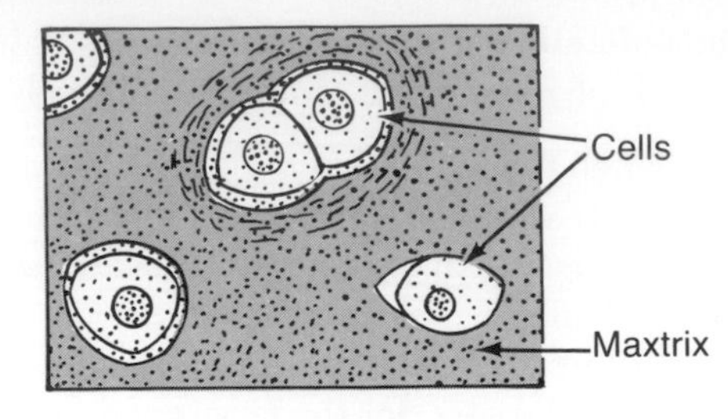

Fig. 16–4. Cartilage. The intercellular matrix of cartilage is rubbery or elastic, not stiff as in bone. The matrix may also contain strengthening fibers, (not shown in the drawing).

The functions of cartilage are to provide support with flexibility and to provide cushioning at joints and between vertebrae.

The Muscles

Humans have three major types of muscle: (1) visceral muscle, (2) skeletal muscle, and (3) cardiac muscle (see Fig. 16–5). *Visceral muscle* is so called because it is found in many of the viscera (organs) of the body. Visceral muscle consists of distinct cells, each with its own nucleus. These spindle-shaped cells fit together in such a manner that the tissue appears smooth when viewed under the microscope. For this reason, visceral muscle is often called *smooth muscle.* There are no cross stripings or striations in these muscle cells. Visceral muscle tissue cannot ordinarily be consciously controlled and is therefore *involuntary muscle.* Visceral muscle forms layers in the walls of the digestive tract, other internal organs, and blood vessels.

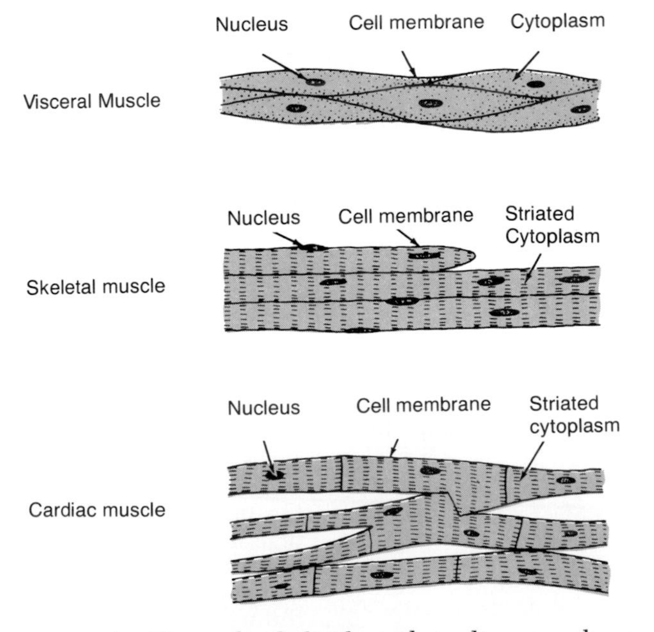

Fig. 16–5. Visceral, skeletal, and cardiac muscle as seen under the light microscope

Skeletal muscle, which is controlled by the nervous system, moves the bones of the skeleton—hence the name skeletal. Skeletal muscle tissue consists of long fibers with many nuclei arranged around their periphery. Cross stripings, or *striations*, are visible under the light microscope. Of the three types of muscle, skeletal muscle contracts the most rapidly. Because skeletal muscle can be consciously controlled, it is *voluntary muscle*.

Muscles do their work by *contracting;* they cannot exert a push. Skeletal muscles function in opposable pairs—when one contracts the other relaxes. In Figure 16–6, a pair of skeletal muscles causes movement at the elbow joint. The muscles are the biceps, in front of the arm, and the triceps at the back of the arm. When the biceps muscle contracts (and the triceps relaxes) it pulls the lower arm up to close, or flex, the joint. The biceps is therefore called a *flexor* muscle. When the triceps contracts (and the biceps relaxes) the lower arm is extended to open the joint. The triceps is therefore called an *extensor* muscle. Flexors and extensors are found at all hinge joints in the body.

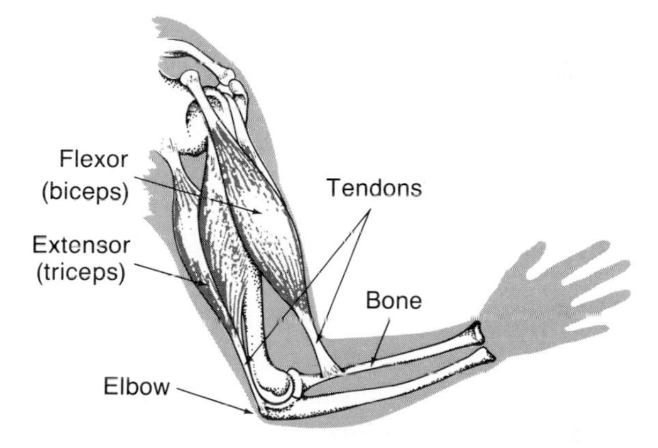

Fig. 16–6. The flexor and extensor muscles in the upper arm and the tendons that attach them to bone.

During vigorous activity, the blood may not bring sufficient oxygen to skeletal muscle cells. This oxygen deficiency may stop cellular respiration at the end of the anaerobic phase, with the accumulation of *lactic acid.* Lactic acid is associated with fatigue.

Cardiac muscle is a special type of muscle found only in the heart. As this tissue contracts and relaxes, it produces the pumping action of the heart. Cardiac muscle resembles visceral muscle in that the nuclei occur within the cytoplasm instead of being arranged around the outside of the fiber as in skeletal muscle. Like visceral muscle, its function is *involuntary.* Cardiac muscle resembles skeletal muscle in that it is *striated* and has one nucleus for each branched cell.

Tendons and Ligaments

Connective tissue is characterized by the presence of tough fibrils in the matrix, among the cells. Two kinds of sturdy connective tissue are tendons and ligaments. *Tendons* are tough, inelastic fibrous cords that *attach muscles to bones.*

Types of Human Muscle Cells		
Visceral	**Skeletal**	**Cardiac**
involuntary	voluntary	involuntary
not striated	striated	striated

The numerous small bones that constitute the skull, or cranium, are held together in an immovable manner. However, many other bones are connected at movable joints by *ligaments*. Ligaments *connect bones to bones*. Among the ligament tissue are many strong, somewhat elastic fibers. Ligaments *connect bones* at movable joints such as at the elbows, knuckles, knees, and vertebral column.

Movable joints are lubricated by a thin yellow fluid. This fluid helps the joint move easily and prevents wear. With age, the amount of fluid decreases and the joints tend to become stiff.

Reasoning Exercises

1. Explain how the body plans for locomotion in humans and grasshoppers are similar and how they are different.
2. Explain three main functions of bones in humans.
3. Explain the functions of cartilage in the human body.
4. Identify and describe the three types of muscle in the human body.
5. How are tendons and ligaments alike? How are they different?

(B) Some Malfunctions Associated with Locomotion

Arthritis. An inflammation of the joints that can cause stiffness, swelling, soreness, or pain is called *arthritis*. Chronic arthritis has three main forms: osteoarthritis, rheumatoid arthritis, and gout.

Osteoarthritis, resulting from wear and tear on the cartilage at the joints, is called "old age rheumatism." *Rheumatoid arthritis* can occur at any age and causes swelling and pain. The joints may then stiffen in a deformed position. *Gout* is caused by deposits of uric acid crystals in the joints, resulting in pain and swelling. Cortisone and related compounds are used in the treatment of various forms of arthritis.

Tendonitis. *Tendonitis* is an inflammation of a tendon near the point at which it connects to the bone. People may feel the pain of tendonitis in the wrist or ankle after unusual exertion. Although this condition is often the result of playing tennis or engaging in other athletic endeavors, it may also be caused by so mundane a pursuit as shoveling snow.

Completion Questions

A

1. The matrix of human bone is hardened by the presence of the compound . . . . . .
2. Muscles interact with each other in . . . . . . pairs.
3. Bones are attached to bones by tissue called . . . . . .
4. The arms of humans are attached to the . . . . . . girdle.

5. Voluntary muscle is also called . . . . . . muscle.
6. Muscles are attached to bones by tissue called . . . . . .
7. Two types of striated muscle are cardiac and . . . . . .
8. Two types of involuntary muscle are cardiac and . . . . . .
9. The vertebrae enclose and protect the . . . . . .
10. The hardened material between bone cells is called the . . . . .

(B)

11. A general name for conditions of inflammation of the joints is . . . . . .
12. An inflammation of the tendon where it joins the muscle that it pulls is called . . . . .

Multiple-Choice Questions

[A]

1. The function of tendons in the human body is to (1) join muscles to bones, (2) connect bones to bones at joints, (3) coordinate body movements, (4) protect internal organs.
2. A substance *not* found in the human skeleton is (1) calcium, (2) matrix, (3) cellulose, (4) living tissue.
3. A tough tissue that connects parts of the human skeleton is (1) ligament, (2) tendon, (3) epithelium, (4) chitin.
4. The spinal cord is protected chiefly by the (1) bones of the skull, (2) ribs, (3) blood, (4) vertebrae.
5. In the human body the levers for movement are (1) muscles, (2) tendons, (3) bones, (4) ligaments.
6. Muscles that are voluntary are (1) skeletal and cardiac, (2) smooth and cardiac, (3) smooth only, (4) skeletal only.
7. A muscle that closes the bones at a joint is a(n) (1) cardiac muscle, (2) visceral muscle, (3) flexor muscle, (4) extensor muscle.

Base your answer to question 8 on Fig. 16-6 on page 277.

8. When the extensor muscle in the upper arm contracts, (1) the shoulder moves up, (2) the shoulder moves down, (3) the hand moves up, (4) the hand moves down.

(B)

9. Gout is caused by deposits in the joints of (1) cortisone, (2) calcium, (3) uric acid crystals, (4) vitamin D.
10. Arthritis is a collective term for any inflammation of (1) the skeleton, (2) the spinal column, (3) any joint, (4) any tendon.

Chapter Test

1. For strong bones, your diet must have adequate amounts of vitamin D, phosphorus, and (1) blood, (2) nitrogen, (3) calcium, (4) iron.
2. The living bone in the human body makes up the structure that is called the (1) exoskeleton, (2) endoskeleton, (3) ligament, (4) cartilage.
3. The human skeleton consists of the appendages and the (1) spinal column, (2) pectoral girdle, (3) vertical axis, (4) pelvic girdle.
4. The spinal column consists of a set of bones called (1) vertebrae, (2) ribs, (3) sternum, (4) pelvic girdle.

Base your answers to questions 5 and 6 on Fig. 16-2 on page 274.

5. The arms are attached to a group of bones in the human skeleton called the (1) pelvic girdle, (2) vertebrae, (3) ribs, (4) pectoral girdle.
6. In the human skeleton, the legs are attached to the (1) ribs, (2) pelvic girdle, (3) pectoral girdle, (4) vertebrae.
7. The adult human skeleton consists of bone and (1) ribs, (2) ligaments, (3) cartilage, (4) vertebrae.
8. Muscle that cannot be consciously controlled is (1) skeletal, (2) involuntary, (3) voluntary, (4) flexor.
9. Visceral muscle is often called (1) cartilage, (2) striated muscle, (3) smooth muscle, (4) ligament.
10. Because skeletal muscle can be consciously controlled, it is called (1) voluntary muscle, (2) involuntary muscle, (3) cardiac muscle, (4) visceral muscle.
11. Muscle fatigue is associated with the accumulation of (1) oxygen, (2) blood, (3) lactic acid, (4) striations.
12. Cardiac muscle is a special type of muscle found only in the (1) skeleton, (2) brain, (3) stomach, (4) heart.
13. Connective tissue is characterized by the presence of tough fibrils in the (1) matrix, (2) nucleus, (3) endoplasmic reticulum, (4) cytoplasm.
14. Connective tissue that connects bones to bones is called (1) ligament, (2) cardiac muscle, (3) tendon, (4) cartilage.
15. Connective tissue that connects muscles to bones is called (1) ligament, (2) cardiac muscle, (3) tendon, (4) cartilage.

Unit 3 Human Physiology

Portfolio Project

1. Cut a photograph of an athlete in action from a newspaper or magazine. Choose one part of the athlete's body that is in motion. Identify the bones and joints that are involved in the motion. Describe the motion of the bones that you have identified.
2. Create a chart with 3 columns. Label the columns as follows:
   Digestion in the Mouth
   Digestion in the Stomach
   Digestion in the Small Intestine
   Obtain 3 Nutrition Facts labels from food packages. Study the ingredients listed. Identify which ingredients undergo some digestion in the mouth, in the stomach, or in the small intestine. Write these ingredients into the appropriate column in your chart.

UNIT FOUR REPRODUCTION AND DEVELOPMENT

The life processes we have studied thus far maintain the single cell and the individual organism. But for life to continue, cells must replicate, that is, make copies of themselves. Individual organisms must reproduce to continue the species. In this unit we consider the processes through which life continues.

An essential feature of reproduction is the transmittal of the hereditary information that is carried in the nucleic acid DNA found in every cell and in every organism. Since DNA is the main component of the chromosomes, our study will include examination of DNA replication as well as the distribution of chromosomes from parent to offspring.

There are two kinds of reproduction: sexual and asexual. In sexual reproduction, new individuals result from the fusion of two sex cells called gametes. In sexual organisms, the gametes are made in specialized organs. Usually, the gametes come from two different parents, and two different sexes, the male and the female, are present in the species. There are, however, a number of plants and animals in which one parent produces both male and female sex cells.

Asexual reproduction does not involve fusion of gametes. A single parent produces offspring. In asexual reproduction, the offspring are duplicates of the parent. We begin this unit by considering asexual reproduction.

Chapter 17 Asexual Reproduction

Cell division in a single-celled organism, such as an ameba, is an example of asexual reproduction. Each daughter cell receives a set of chromosomes containing DNA. These chromosomes are identical to those of the parent cell. Cells in multicellular organisms must also divide, though this is not asexual reproduction. Nevertheless, all cells share fundamental activities concerned with replication and division. These activities can best be described as part of the cell cycle. The events in the cell cycle involve all levels of cellular organization, from the molecular level through the organelles to the entire cell itself. We will concentrate on features of the cell cycle in the eukaryotic cell.

(A) The Cell Cycle

When a cell replicates and divides, it is essential that the daughter cells get an exact copy of the parent's DNA, the hereditary material. For eukaryotic cells, this means that the number and types of chromosomes must be exactly the same in the daughter cells as in the parent.

Stages of the cell cycle. The cell cycle has two main stages: interphase and mitosis. Interphase includes several events such as growth of the cell and replication of DNA. Mitosis is separation of the chromosomes and their distribution from the parent cell to the daughter cells.

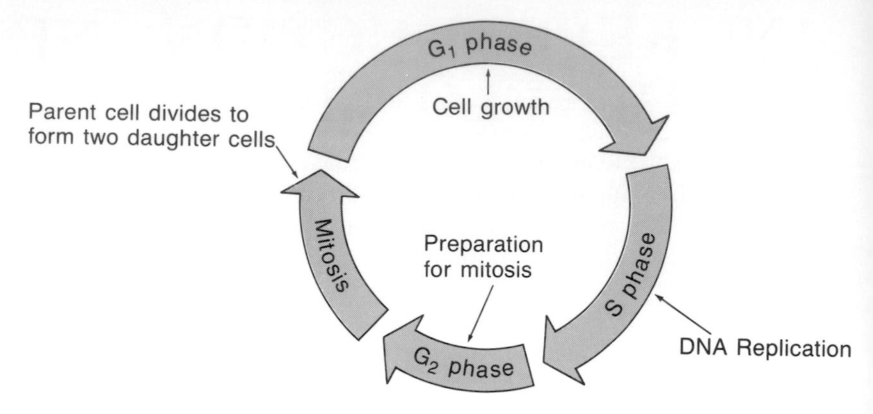

Fig. 17–1. The cell cycle

Interphase has three important phases. During the first, or G1 phase, the cell builds its supply of enzymes and other molecules it will need to carry out activities in the rest of the cycle. Then the cell replicates, or copies, its DNA in a period called the S phase. During this phase, the cell also builds proteins found with the DNA in the chromosomes. The centriole also replicates itself during the S phase. Next the cell builds the spindle fiber proteins that later play a role in separation of chromosomes during mitosis. During this time, called the G2 phase, the cell has two full sets of chromosomes.

Chromosome structure. Before we look closely at DNA replication and mitosis, let us briefly consider what makes up a chromosome in a eukaryotic cell. Chromosomes contain both nucleic acid and protein. Most of the chromosome is made up of DNA and globular proteins called histones. The DNA molecule coils tightly around clusters of histone molecules. Chromosomes also contain enzymes and nuclear RNA. Chromosome structure is called supercoiled. This means that it is wound into large coils, and each large coil has smaller coils within it.

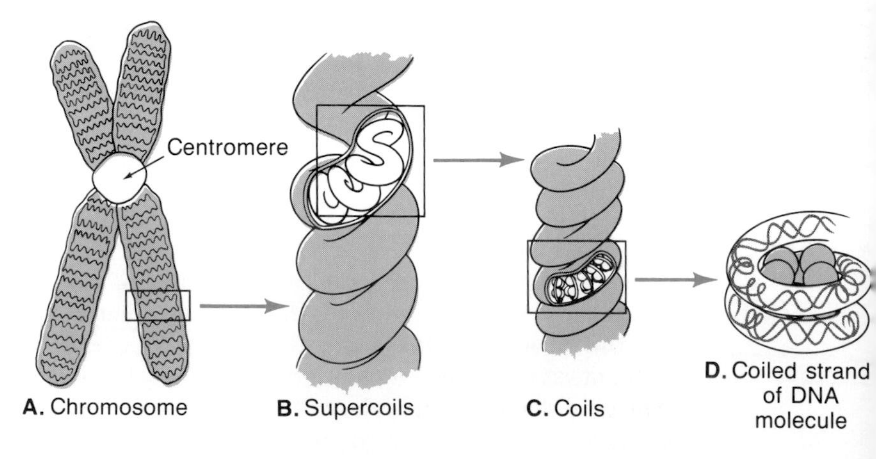

Fig. 17–2. A chromosome is a highly coiled structure containing DNA and various proteins.

DNA replication Replication of DNA is a complex process that involves enzymes, free nucleotides, and the DNA molecule. Recall from Chapter 4 that the DNA molecule is a double strand. It has two coiled chains of nucleotides, side by side. Replication begins with an enzyme that opens the two strands. Think of the two linked strands of a zipper coming apart in the middle to form an opening. At each of the points where the zipper comes apart, another enzyme, a DNA polymerase, assembles a new strand next to one of the original strands. A polymerase is an enzyme that builds a polymer, or long chain. DNA polymerase does this by joining free nucleotides together.

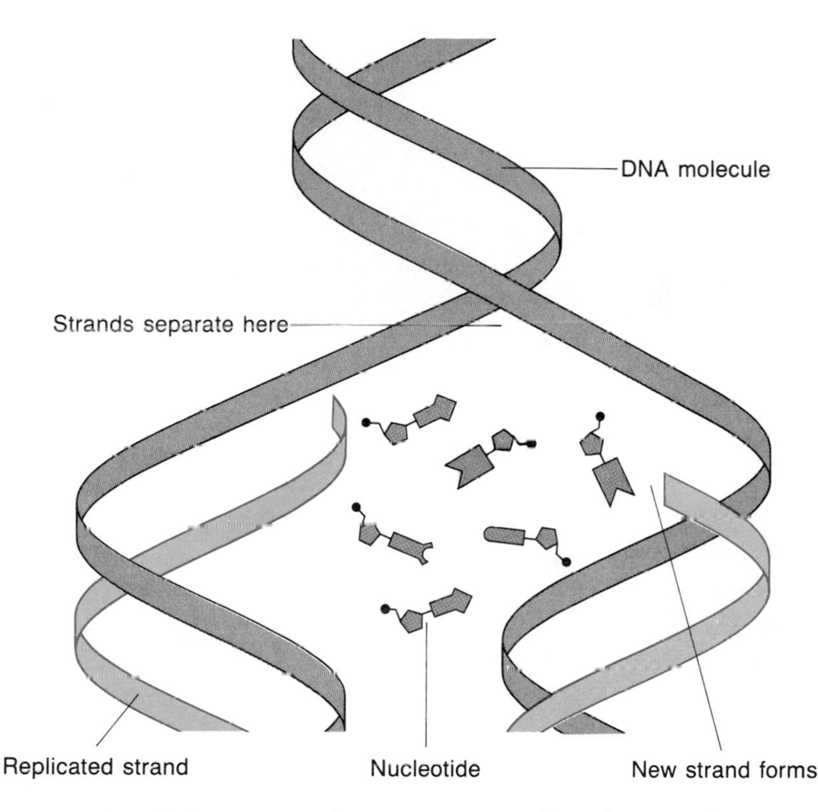

Fig. 17–3. DNA replication: An opening forms between the two strands so that a copy of each strand may be assembled from free nucleotides.

The new strand is complementary to the original one. As you learned in Chapter 4, each nitrogen base forms a rung in the ladder-like structure of DNA by joining with its complementary base. Each new double-stranded DNA molecule is formed from one strand of the original molecule, and one new strand that is assembled next to it. Several replication openings may form in a DNA molecule at one time, so that DNA polymerase may build new strands of nucleotides at several different places along the original DNA. These sections of new strands are joined by another enzyme, called DNA ligase.

Some molecular biologists suspect that once a cell enters the S phase of DNA replication, it is committed to entering and completing the mitosis phase of the cell cycle. This begins after the G2 phase.

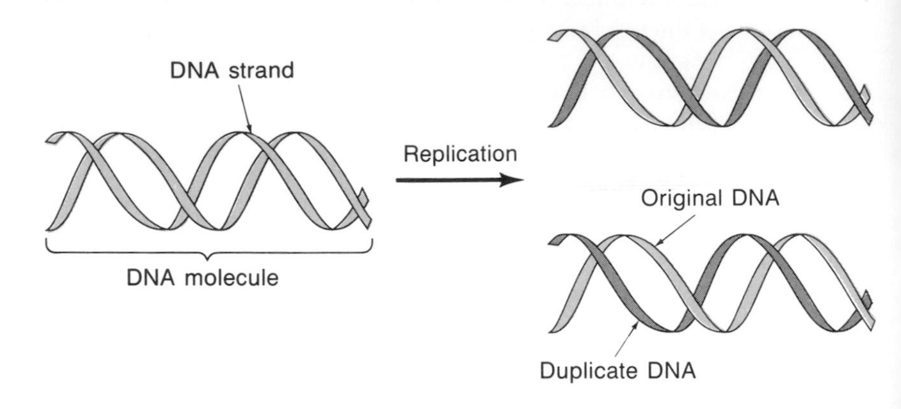

Fig. 17–4. DNA replication: The two strands of DNA become separated. Each new molecule has one original and one duplicate strand.

B

Mitosis

While mitosis is a continuous process, biologists have identified four main phases which we use to describe the sequence of events in mitosis. The names of the stages are based on key indicators or events seen through the light microscope.

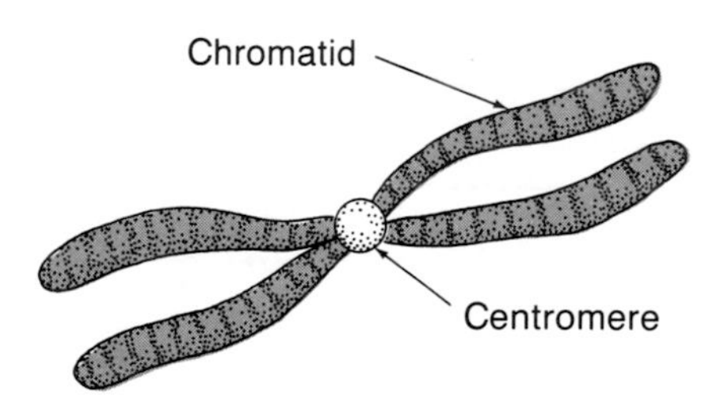

Fig. 17–5. When mitosis begins, each chromosome contains two chromatids joined at the centromere.

Prophase. The first stage of mitosis is marked by supercoiling and thickening of chromosomal material in the nucleus. The chromosomes can be seen, and continue to thicken until they assume a rod-like shape. Each chromosome consists of paired strands, called chromatids, held together by a tiny structure called a centromere. The nuclear membrane disintegrates. The centrioles begin to move to opposite ends, or poles, of the cell. Thread-like structures, called spindle fibers, appear and extend between the centrioles. Biologists don't yet clearly understand the relationship between the centrioles and the spindle fibers. In higher plants there are no centrioles, but there are spindle fibers.

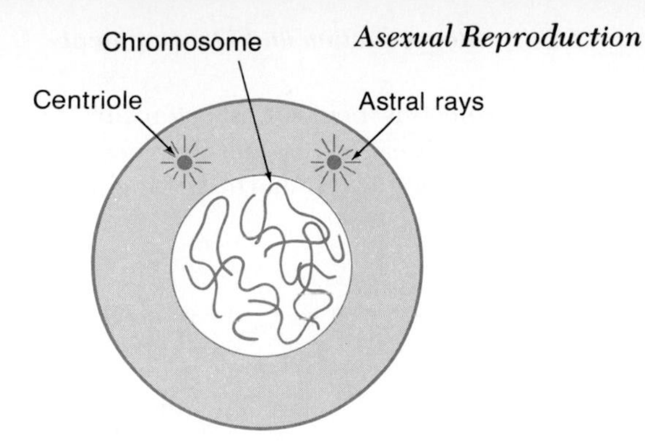

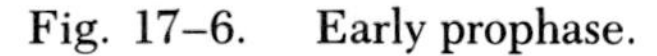
Fig. 17–6. Early prophase.

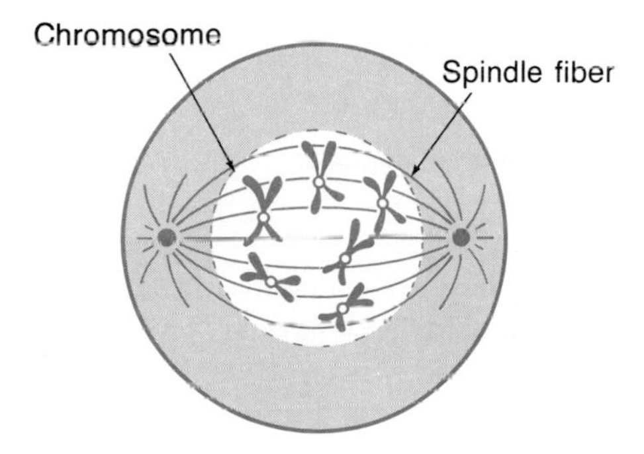

Fig. 17–7. Late prophase.

Metaphase. The major indicator of this phase is that the thickened chromosomes align along the equator, or middle, of the cell. "Meta" means mid or middle. Each chromosome is attached to a spindle fiber at

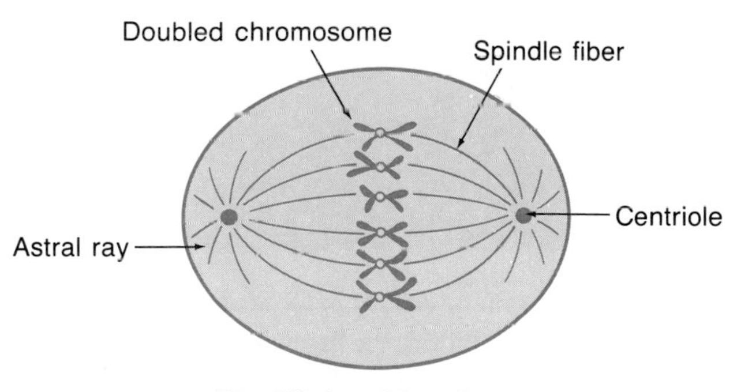

Fig. 17–8. Metaphase.

the centromere. The precision of chromatid separation depends upon this attachment. Metaphase chromosomes have such a distinctive shape that they are used in a procedure to identify each chromosome in a cell. You will read about this procedure, called karyotyping, in Chapter 22.

Anaphase. Anaphase is marked by the separation of the chromatids from each other. Each chromatid moves away from the equator of the cell, attached to a spindle fiber as it does so. The exact mechanism for this is not completely known. Biologists do know that the spindle fibers attached to chromatids begin to shorten and thicken. The separated chromatids, correctly called chromosomes now, move toward opposite poles of the cell. This phase is the shortest of the four.

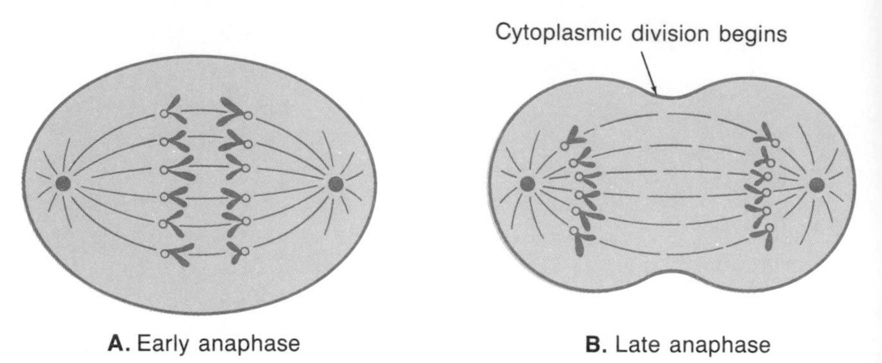

Fig. 17–9. Anaphase.

Telophase. During this phase the tightly coiled and thickened chromosomes unfold and lengthen. They begin to resemble the chromatin that is characteristic of interphase. Two new nuclear membranes form as well. The spindle fibers disappear, and the parent cell begins to divide. Cell division is called cytokinesis. In animal cells this happens by a pinching in of the cell membrane until the cytoplasm is split roughly in half. This pinching in or furrowing of the membrane is not seen in plant cells, where a cell plate grows across the cell to divide it in two.

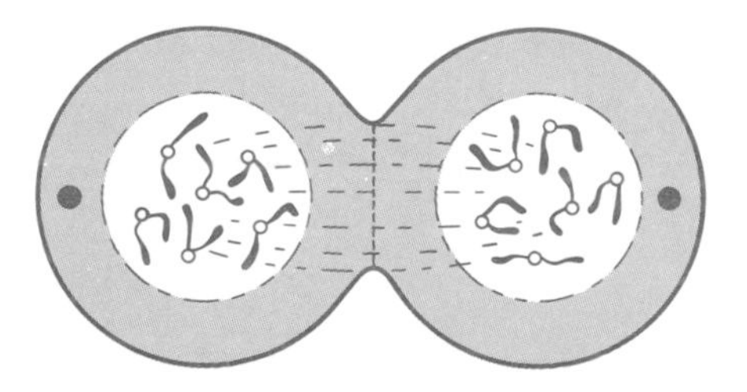

Fig. 17–10. Telophase.

Control of the cell cycle

Cells contain information to guide the duration of each phase in the cycle. This is evident because in each species the phases remain fairly constant in duration. Cells also contain substances that signal the cell's machinery when to start a phase, and when to stop it. Recent research has shown that key enzymes control reactions that regulate the phases of the cycle.

For example, a particular enzyme adds phosphates to protein polymers in the nuclear membrane. The addition of phosphates, which come from ATP, causes the membrane to break down. This is one of the reactions that triggers the start of mitosis. It is becoming clear that many enzyme complexes control the cell cycle by starting and stopping each of its phases.

Some cells do not follow repeated cycles but remain fixed at one stage. Examples in multicellular animals include nerve and striated muscle cells.

Cell division and cancer

Sometimes cell division continues again and again in a rapid and unregulated way. This produces tumors, which are swellings consisting of the rapidly dividing cells. Sometimes tumor cells spread to other parts of the body and continue to divide in an uncontrolled way. This is cancer. Cancer cells don't seem to follow the controls that regulate the cell cycle. Another possibility is that the substances that initiate cell division override the factors that inhibit division. Cancer cells interfere with normal function of the tissues in which they grow.

Biologists have identified many carcinogens, or cancer-causing substances. These include many artificial and natural chemicals in the environment, as well as ionizing radiation.

Reasoning Exercises

1. In what way does reproduction differ from the other life processes?
2. Distinguish between sexual and asexual reproduction.
3. What two main processes occur during cell division?
4. Name the phases of mitosis, and describe events in each.
5. Why must DNA replication take place before mitosis can occur?
6. During which phase of mitosis do the double chromosomes separate into two single chromosomes?
7. How does mitosis in a plant cell differ from mitosis in an animal cell?
8. Give three results of mitotic cell division.

C

Asexual Reproduction

In asexual reproduction, new individuals are produced from a single parent. Methods of asexual reproduction include binary fission, budding, spore formation, regeneration, and vegetative propagation.

Binary Fission

In *binary fission*, a one-cell organism undergoes cell division to form two one-celled organisms. Since the nuclear changes occur by mitosis, the daughter cells have the same heredity that the parent cell had. If the organism is motile, the daughter cells swim apart. If it is nonmotile, the daughter cells may adhere to each other for a time.

Binary Fission in Ameba. An ameba that reaches a certain size reproduces by binary fission. The nucleus duplicates itself exactly by mitosis, and each nucleus moves to opposite sides of the cell (Fig. 17–11). The ameba then divides by constricting in the middle and pulling apart. The cytoplasm is divided between the two new cells in approximately equal portions. In this way, two new Amebas are produced from the parent cell.

Binary fission Paramecia. Paramecia are more complex in structure than amebas. As you may recall, it has two nuclei—a macronucleus and a micronucleus. The macronucleus seems to regulate the cell's metabolism. During cell division (Fig. 17–12), the macronucleus seems merely to pinch in half. Only the micronucleus divides by mitosis. During cytoplasmic division, new organelles appear as needed. Paramecia also undergo conjugation, a form of sexual reproduction.

Budding

Budding is a type of asexual reproduction in which a new organism de-

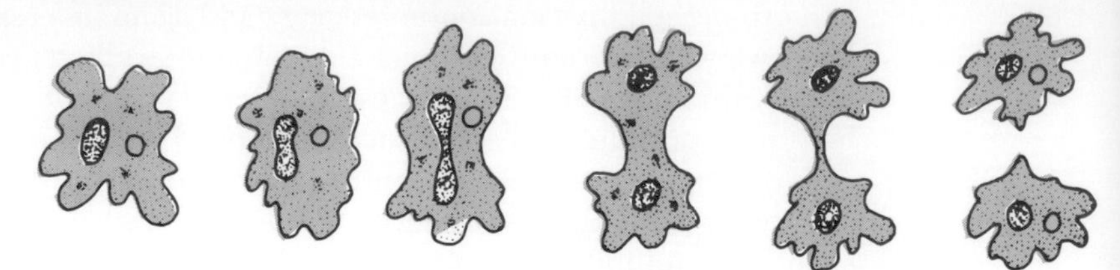

Fig. 17–11. Binary fission in Ameba. The nucleus divided equally by mitosis. The cytoplasm divides into approximately equal portions. The daughter cells move apart.

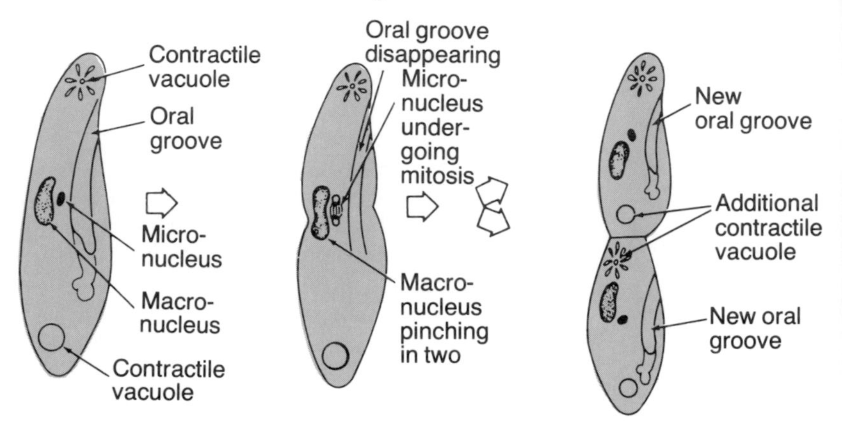

Fig. 17–12. Binary fission in Paramecium.

velops as an outgrowth of an older one. The new individual is called a *bud*.

Budding in one-celled organisms resembles binary fission in that the nucleus divides into equal portions by mitosis. Budding differs from binary fission in that the cytoplasm does not divide equally. The bud is smaller.

Budding in yeast. A yeast cell is an example of a one-celled protist that reproduces by budding (Fig. 17–13). In this process, *the nucleus divides equally* by mitosis, forming two identical nuclei. However, *the cytoplasm divides unequally.* The new cell that protrudes is smaller. The bud then increases in size and eventually breaks away. Sometimes, however, the bud remains attached to the parent cell and may even develop buds of its own.

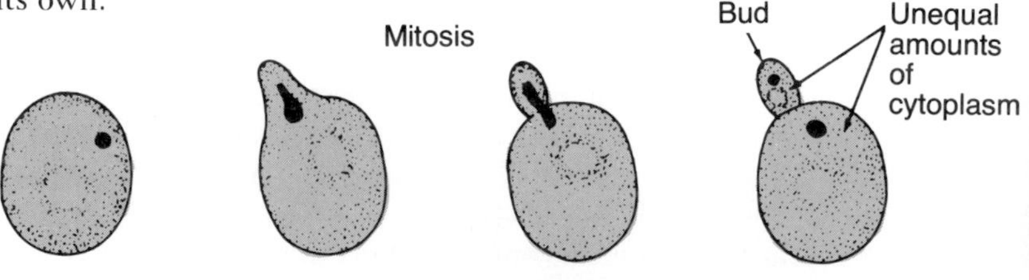

Fig. 17–13. Budding in yeast.

Budding in Hydra

Budding in Hydra. Simple many-celled animals make smaller copies of themselves in a process that is also called budding. In *Hydra*, a multicellular bud grows out of the side of the parent (Fig. 17–14). The bud develops a mouth and tentacles. Later, the bud breaks away from its parent to live an independent life. A culture of well-fed *Hydra* may contain many specimens that have several buds. *Hydra* also reproduces sexually.

Spore Formation (Sporulation)

Molds that grow on bread or fruit are spread to new locations by spores. Spores are asexual cells having a protective wall that prevents drying of the protoplasm.

Under favorable conditions of food, warmth, and moisture, spores germinate to produce a new mycelium (mass of hyphae). Bread mold also reproduces sexually by conjugation.

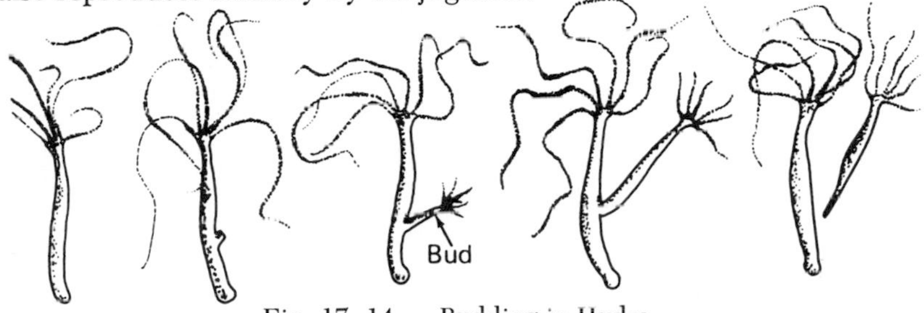

Fig. 17–14. Budding in Hydra.

Regeneration

Regeneration is the growing back of missing parts. Oystermen used to cut starfish in half and toss them back into the water. To their dismay, they learned that each half regenerated an entire starfish (Fig. 17–15). Even a single arm that has part of the central disc can regenerate a whole organism.

Fig. 17–15. Regeneration in starfish and in Planaria.

The flatworm, *Planaria*, has great powers of regeneration. A single worm can regenerate three or more pieces (Fig. 17–15). However, a rear portion that is too small will not regenerate a whole planarian. Invertebrate animals generally possess more *undifferentiated* cells than do vertebrate animals. As a result, the invertebrates exhibit a higher degree of regeneration than most vertebrates. Although a starfish can regenerate an entire arm, you cannot regenerate a fingertip.

Vegetative Propagation

The major organs of a plant are the root, stem, leaf, and flower (Fig. 17–16). The flower produces seeds during the process of sexual *repro-*

duction. The other three organs have functions pertaining to growth and maintenance. They are called *vegetative structures*. When vegetative structures produce entire new plants, such a method of asexual reproduction is called *vegetative propagation*. Vegetative propagation is asexual reproduction by means of roots, stems, or leaves.

Vegetative propagation occurs by natural methods. It is also artificially induced by humans to hasten the formation of new plants.

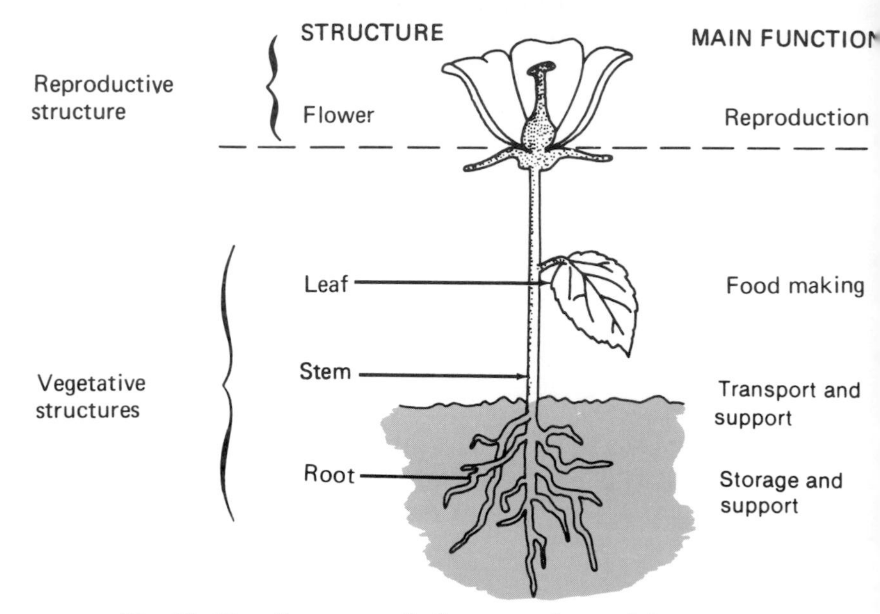

Fig. 17–16. Structures of a flowering plant and their major functions.

Natural Vegetative Propagation

We shall discuss bulbs, tubers, runners, and rhizomes as examples of vegetative propagation by natural means.

Bulbs. A bulb is a short underground *stem* with thick, fleshy *leaves* that contain stored food. (See Fig. 17–17). A plant may produce several bulbs underground. In the spring, the fleshy leaves supply the growing shoot

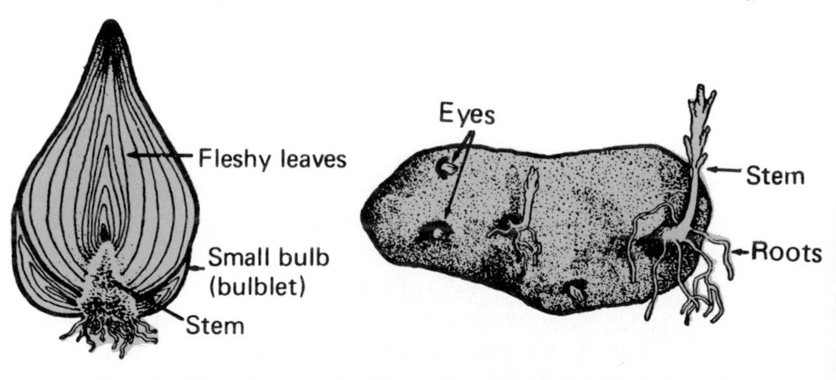

Fig. 17–17. Left: Bulb of the tulip plant. Right: The tuber of the white potato.

with food until it produces leaves that carry on photosynthesis. Bulbs are formed by onions, tulips, daffodils and lillies.

Tubers. A tuber is a fleshy underground *stem* which has buds. As the potato plant grows above ground during the summer, it produces several underground tubers. Here the plant stores food. The "eyes" of a potato are actually *buds* on a fleshy underground stem (Fig. 17–17).

When planting potatoes, the farmer cuts the tuber into pieces, each of which has at least one bud. The buds sprout to produce new plants.

Runners. A *runner* (Fig. 17–18) is an overground *stem*. The stem grows or "runs" along the surface of the ground and produces new roots and upright stems.

As many as a dozen runners may spread from a single strawberry plant in one season.

Some valuable lawn grasses spread rapidly by means of runners. However, many garden weeds also reproduce quickly by runners.

Rhizomes. If you wish to plant irises, your garden store may sell you short pieces of woody, underground stems. These are *rhizomes*. They store food. When planted, shoots for new plants arise from swollen regions of the rhizome (Fig. 17–19). During the summer, the rhizome lengthens and the following spring you will have an increased number of iris plants. Other plants that reproduce vegetatively by rhizomes include ferns, cat-tails, and poison ivy.

Fig. 17–18. Runners of a strawberry plant.

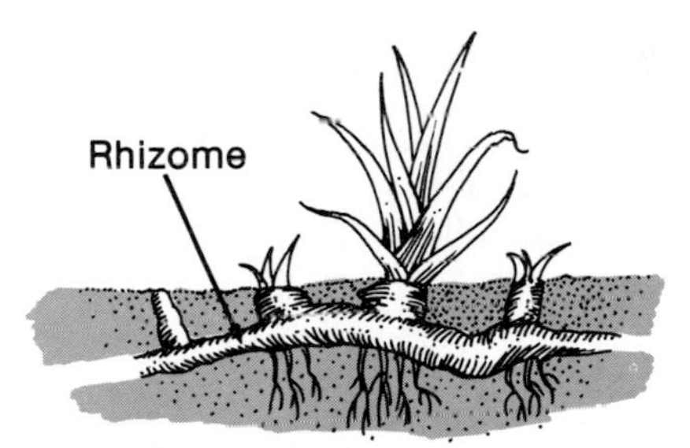

Fig. 17–19. Rhizome of an iris plant.

Artificial Vegetative Propagation

In addition to using nature's own ways of vegetative propagation, humans have developed artificial methods for producing new plants from roots, stems, and leaves. The techniques include *cuttings*, *layering*, and *grafting*.

Cuttings. A piece of a stem, called a *cutting* or *slip*, is cut from the plant and placed in water or moist sand (Fig. 17–20). Soon the cutting develops roots and leaves to become a new, independent plant. It may then be transplanted to soil. Plants that reproduce in this manner include the coleus, geranium, hydrangea, rose, ivy, and grape.

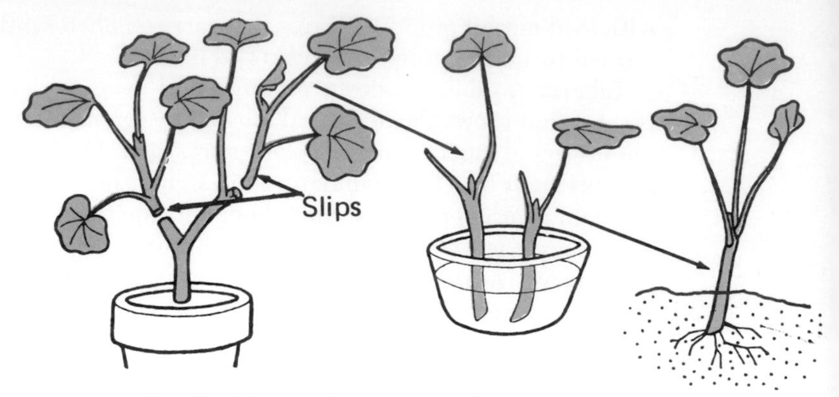

Fig. 17–20. Making cuttings from a geranium plant.

Leaf cutting. When a leaf of the *Bryophyllum* plant is placed on moist soil, tiny plants, complete with roots, stem, and leaves, develop at the notches of the leaf (Fig. 17–21). As the old leaf dies, several new independent plants are formed. Begonia may also be propagated by leaf cuttings.

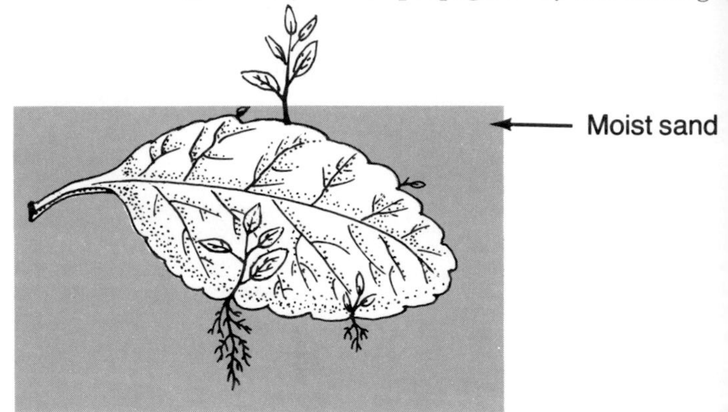

Fig. 17–21. Leaf cutting of *Bryophyllum*.

Layering. The woody stems of the raspberry plant grow about waist-high and then bend over. The farmer bends the stem further and secures the tip underground. Each root tip then grows into a complete new plant (Fig. 17–22). Blackberry plants are also propagated by layering.

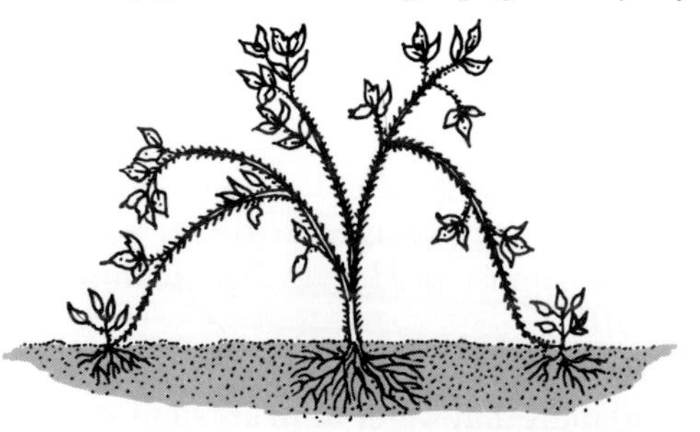

Fig. 17–22. Layering in the raspberry plant.

Grafting. In *grafting*, a stem is cut from one plant and attached to the stem of another plant (Fig. 17–23). The top portion is the *scion*. The

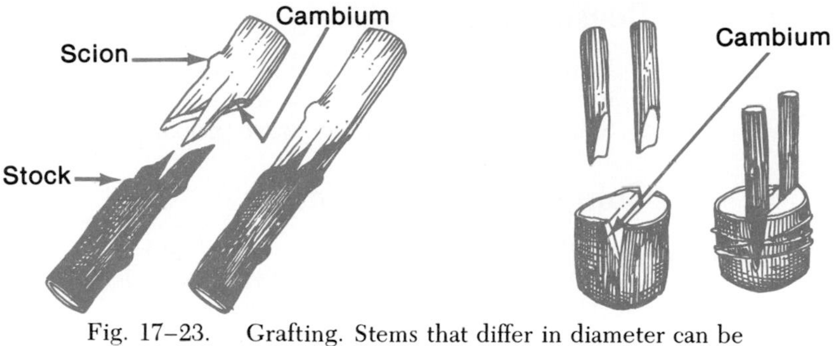

Fig. 17–23. Grafting. Stems that differ in diameter can be spliced in a variety of ways—so long as the two cambiums make contact and the union is mechanically secure.

stem which remains attached to its roots is the *stock*. In order for a graft to "take," the cambium layers of the scion and stock must make contact. They must also be cut in such manner that the pieces will fit snugly. After the scion is placed in position, the two sections are fastened with cord, and wax is applied to prevent infection.

All plant parts that grow above the graft, from the scion, *have the hereditary characteristics of the scion*. (Why is this so?) *There is no mixing or blending of hereditary characteristics in grafting*. For a graft to be successful, however, the two plants must be closely related.

Grafting permits the grower to combine desirable characteristics of two plant varieties in a single plant. For example, the stock may have roots which are resistant to soil pests, whereas the scion may bear a desirable kind of fruit.

For ornamental or gastronomical purposes, the home gardener may purchase an apple tree bearing scions of many different kinds of apples. In this manner, Macintosh, Greening, Baldwin, and Delicious apples can all be grown on one tree.

Advantages of Vegetative Propagation

No variations. When plants are grown from seeds, the undesirable characteristics of remote ancestors may appear. However, in vegetative methods there are no ancestral throwbacks. Since the new cells develop by mitosis there is no change in heredity. The grower can be sure of getting exact copies of the parent plant.

Speed. When a scion is grafted to a stock which possesses a well-developed root system and a thick stem, a mature, fruit-bearing tree develops soon. This is faster than using seeds.

Certainty. The stored food in a bulb, tuber, or rhizome gives the new plant a good start. By contrast, many seeds fail to germinate.

Seedless fruits. Plants whose fruits lack seeds can be reproduced only by vegetative propagation. Examples are seedless oranges, bananas, and grapes.

Combination of desirable characteristics. Grafting permits the combination in one plant of the desirable qualities of the root (stock) and the desirable qualities of the stem, leaf, flower, and fruit (scion). In grafting, however, there is no "mixing" of the heredity of the scion and stock.

Reasoning Exercises

1. Why do offspring produced by asexual means have the same heredity as their parents?
2. State 5 advantages of vegetative propagation to plant growers.

Completion Questions

(A)

1. The cell cycle has . . . . . . main stages.
2. The main stages of the cell cycle are called . . . . . . and . . . . . .
3. During the G2 period of interphase, ... fiber proteins are synthesized.
4. The formation of an exact copy of a chromosome is known as . . . . . .

[B]

5. The structure that holds two chromatids together is the . . . . . .
6. A cell with eight chromosomes divides to form two daughter cells, each of which has . . . . . . chromosomes.
7. In animals, the final step in telophase involves a pinching of the . . . . . .
8. In a plant cell, cytoplasmic division requires formation of a . . . . . .

[C]

9. Reproduction from a single parent is called . . . . . . reproduction.
10. Bread mold reproduces asexually by the process of . . . . . .
11. The process by which a starfish grows back a missing arm is called . . . . . .
12. The production of a new plant by use of roots, stems, or leaves is known as . . . . . .
13. Short underground stems with thick, fleshy leaves are called . . . . . .
14. The eyes of a potato are actually . . . . . .
15. The rooted portion of a graft is the . . . . . .
16. The portion of a plant that grows above a graft has the heredity of the . . . . . .

Multiple Choice Questions

(A)

1. During the cell cycle, DNA is synthesized during (1) the G1 period, (2) the S period, (3) the G2 period, (4) mitosis.
2. The synthesis of a double-stranded chromosome from a single-stranded chromosome is known as (1) cell division, (2) alignment, (3) replication, (4) regeneration.
3. Mitosis directly follows (1) the G1 period, (2) the S period, (3) the G2 period, (4) DNA replication.
4. Which of the following cells never divide once fully grown? (1) skin cells, (2) bone cells, (3) nerve cells, (4) leaf cells.

[B]

5. The first phase of mitosis is called (1) anaphase, (2) telophase, (3) prophase, (4) metaphase.
6. The shortest phase of mitosis is (1) anaphase, (2) telophase, (3) prophase, (4) metaphase.

7. Which occurs in a plant cell but not in an animal cell? (1) formation of spindle fibers, (2) chromosome division, (3) formation of a cell plate, (4) cytoplasmic division.
8. In a *Paramecium*, which is true of a daughter cell produced by binary fission? (1) it has one-half as many chromosomes as the parent cell, (2) it has twice as many chromosomes as the parent cell, (3) it is the same size as the parent cell, but has fewer chromosomes than the parent, (4) it is smaller than the parent cell, but has the same number of chromosomes as the parent.
9. A spindle fiber is attached to a chromosome at the (1) arm, (2) centromere, (3) centriole, (4) nucleolus.
10. Chromatids separate and move toward opposite poles during (1) prophase, (2) metaphase, (3) anaphase, (4) telophase.
11. During which mitotic phase does the nuclear membrane disappear? (1) prophase, (2) metaphase, (3) anaphase, (4) telophase.

C

Base your answer to question 12 on Fig. 17-11 and 17-13 on page 288.

12. Budding in one-celled organisms differs from binary fission in one-celled organisms in that (1) the cytoplasm does not divide equally in budding, (2) the cytoplasm does not divide equally in binary fission, (3) the nucleus does not divide into two new nuclei, (4) the nucleus divides into two equal portions.
13. Vegetative propagation is a method of reproduction which (1) occurs in some multicellular plants, (2) is commonly called sexual reproduction, (3) results in genetically unlike offspring, (4) is found in unicellular organisms.
14. A farmer found that one tree in his pear orchard had especially delicious fruit. Which method would most quickly provide a large crop of these pears? (1) planting seeds from this tree, (2) crossing this tree with another tree in the orchard, (3) grafting from this tree to other healthy pear trees, (4) giving the tree special fertilizer.
15. A stem that grows along the surface of the ground is called a (1) rhizome, (2) runner, (3) cutting, (4) stock.
16. Which of the following is not a vegetative structure? (1) flower, (2) root, (3) stem, (4) leaf.
17. Which method is used to grow Macintosh and Delicious apples on the same tree? (1) layering, (2) cuttings, (3) grafting, (4) planting bulbs.

Chapter Test

1. The process of mitosis ensures equal distribution of the (1) mitochondria, (2) cytoplasm, (3) chloroplasts, (4) chromosomes.
2. Which life function is not needed for survival of individuals but is essential for the survival of the species? (1) synthesis, (2) reproduction, (3) digestion, (4) circulation.
3. As a result of mitosis and cell division, a cell with 20 chromosomes gives rise to two cells each of which has a chromosome number of (1) 10, (2) 20, (3) 40, (4) 5.
4. A red rose scion growing on a white rose stock normally produces roses that are (1) white only, (2) red only, (3) pink, (4) red and white.

5. Which method of reproduction is carried on by both yeast and *Hydra*? (1) budding, (2) binary fission, (3) sporulation, (4) multiple fission.
6. Which organelle contains hereditary factors and controls most cell activities? (1) nucleus, (2) cell membrane, (3) centriole, (4) endoplasmic reticulum.

Base your answers to questions 7 and 8 on the procedure described below:

A leaf of the Bryophyllum plant was placed on moist sand. Several weeks later, it was observed that young plants were growing from the edges of the leaf.

7. Which method of reproduction is demonstrated by this procedure? (1) binary fission, (2) regeneration, (3) vegetative propagation, (4) sexual reproduction.
8. The technique described above is called (1) cutting, (2) grafting, (3) layering, (4) stocking.

Chapter 18 Sexual Reproduction in Animals

Asexual reproduction, as we have seen, preserves hereditary characteristics from generation to generation. Sexual reproduction, in contrast, results in considerable variation among the offspring. This is partly because the offspring receive chromosomes from two parents instead of one. Also, there is significant variation in the *gametes*, or sex cells, produced by each parent. The great variety that results from sexual reproduction makes it more likely that a population will be able to adapt to changing environments. It is a factor in evolution.

A Sexual Reproduction: Gametogenesis

Sexual reproduction involves the joining of gametes (specialized sex cells), usually from two different individuals. The two gametes are the male gamete, or *sperm*, and the female gamete, or *ovum* (plural—*ova*). The size and structure of male and female gametes are quite different. Sperm are small and swim by beating a long, whiplike tail. Ova are larger and do not swim. Far more sperm are produced than ova. Sperm cells contain much less stored energy than do ova, which usually have more cytoplasm than sperm. In many vertebrate animals, the ovum contains yolk, which is a stored food supply to provide energy for later development.

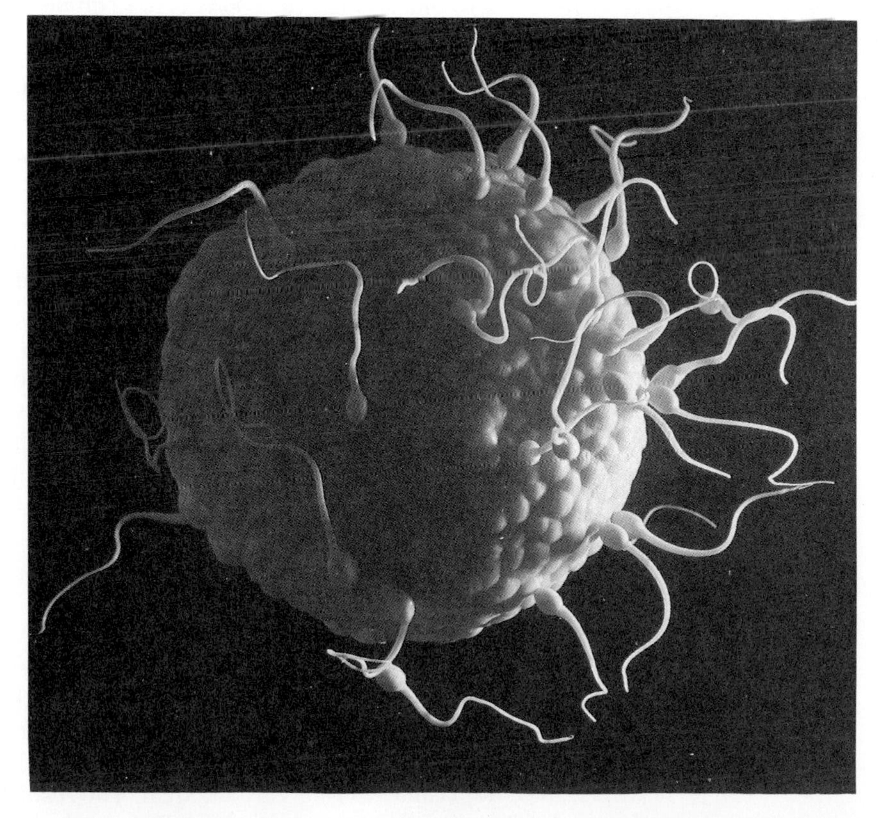

Fig. 18–1. This model shows sperm cells and an ovum.

Gametogenesis

Gametogenesis is the process by which gametes are produced. Gametogenesis occurs in organs called *gonads*. The male gonads that produce sperm are the *testes* (singular—testis). The female gonads that produce ova are the *ovaries*. *Spermatogenesis* is the production of sperm in the testes. *Oogenesis* is the production of ova in the ovaries.

Some animals, such as the earthworm, have both testes and ovaries. Such animals are called *hermaphrodites*. Animals that produce only sperm cells are *males*; those that produce only ova (or egg cells) are *females*. In most species, males and females differ in several physical characteristics. For example, among humans, the mature males are usually larger and develop more body hair. Mature females develop a slightly thicker layer of fat beneath the skin than do males.

B

Meiosis

The number of chromosomes per cell varies from one species to another. Humans have 46 chromosomes in each body cell. Fruit flies have eight. Some species have several hundred chromosomes in each cell. Chromosomes exist in pairs. Each member of a pair has the same shape as its partner. The two members of a pair are called *homologous chromosomes*, and each is referred to as a *homolog*. Both homologs carry genes governing the same hereditary traits. Humans, with their *chromosome number* of 46, have 23 pairs of chromosomes in each body cell. Fruit flies have four pairs.

Maintaining the Chromosome Number

The human chromosome number of 46 means that each body cell has 46 chromosomes. If gametes also had 46 chromosomes, their fusion would produce a cell with double this number, or 92 chromosomes. All cells produced from this parent cell by a series of mitotic cell divisions would also contain 92 chromosomes. Accordingly, you might expect all the cells of the offspring to have double the chromosome number of their parents. And in the next generation, double again! Why doesn't this happen? Because when the gametes are formed, their chromosome number is reduced to half the number in the parent cells. This *reduction division* occurs during a special set of cell divisions called *meiosis*. Meiosis produces gametes with half the chromosome number of the original cell.

The double number of chromosomes that is characteristic of a species and is found in all body cells is called the *diploid number*, or 2n. The single number that is found in the sperm and egg is called the *monoploid number*, or n. In humans, the diploid (2n) number is 46 and the monoploid (n) number is 23. If a fruit fly has eight chromosomes in a cell of its intestine, what is its diploid number? How many chromosomes are present in a fruit fly ovum?

Meiosis occurs during spermatogenesis and oogenesis (when sperm and ova—the gametes—are produced). In both processes, the distribution of chromosomes to the four resulting monoploid gametes is the same. There are, however, differences in the sizes of the gametes that are produced.

In spermatogenesis the cytoplasmic divisions are equal. In oogenesis, however, the cytoplasmic divisions are unequal. The result, in oogenesis, is the production of one large and three small monoploid cells. The large

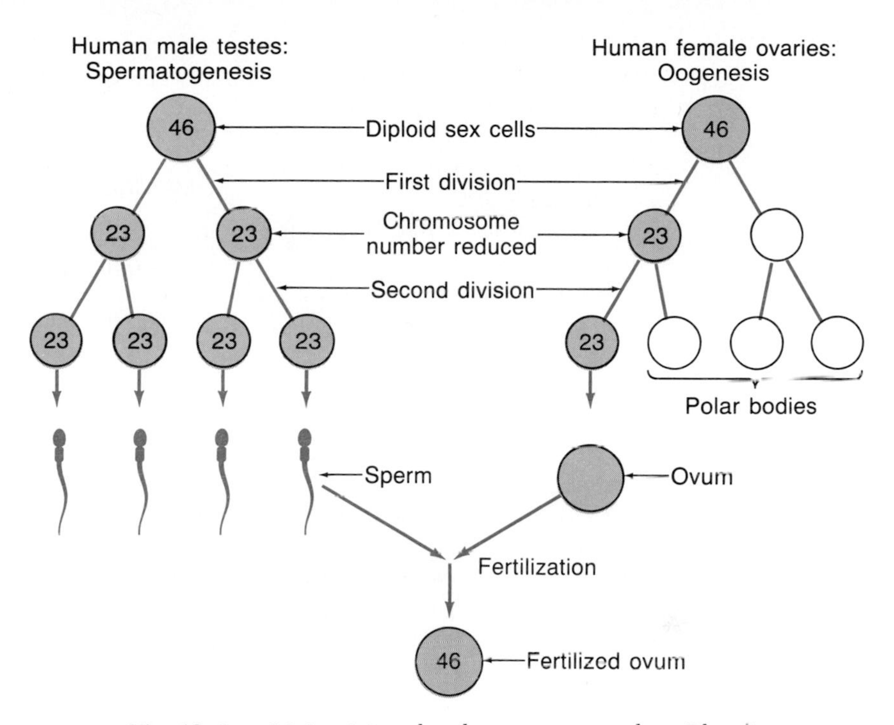

Fig. 18–2. Maintaining the chromosome number: The diploid number of chromosomes is reduced in half during formation of sperm and ova. Fertilization restores the diploid number.

cell becomes the ovum and the three small cells become *polar bodies*. The polar bodies serve as receptacles for the excess chromosomes and they later disintegrate.

When ovum and sperm fuse, the diploid number of chromosomes is restored. Accordingly, the chromosome number is maintained from generation to generation.

teps of Meiosis

Meiosis occurs only in those cells of the gonads that produce gametes. These are called *primary sex cells* and have the diploid number of chromosomes.

Meiosis differs from mitosis in that it involves two cell divisions rather than one. The two divisions yield four cells instead of two. Also, the chromosome number is reduced from diploid to monoploid.

We shall trace the formation of gametes from a single primary sex cell. Gonads, however, may have many thousands of primary sex cells. The number of gametes formed at one time differs among various animals, and according to the sex and the age of an animal. We will follow the steps of meiosis in a cell with six chromosomes. Instead of presenting all the details of the various phases, we shall focus upon the distribution of chromosomes and chromatids. Follow the series of diagrams in Figure 18–3 as you read the description.

Step 1. We start with a primary sex cell having the diploid number of chromosomes.

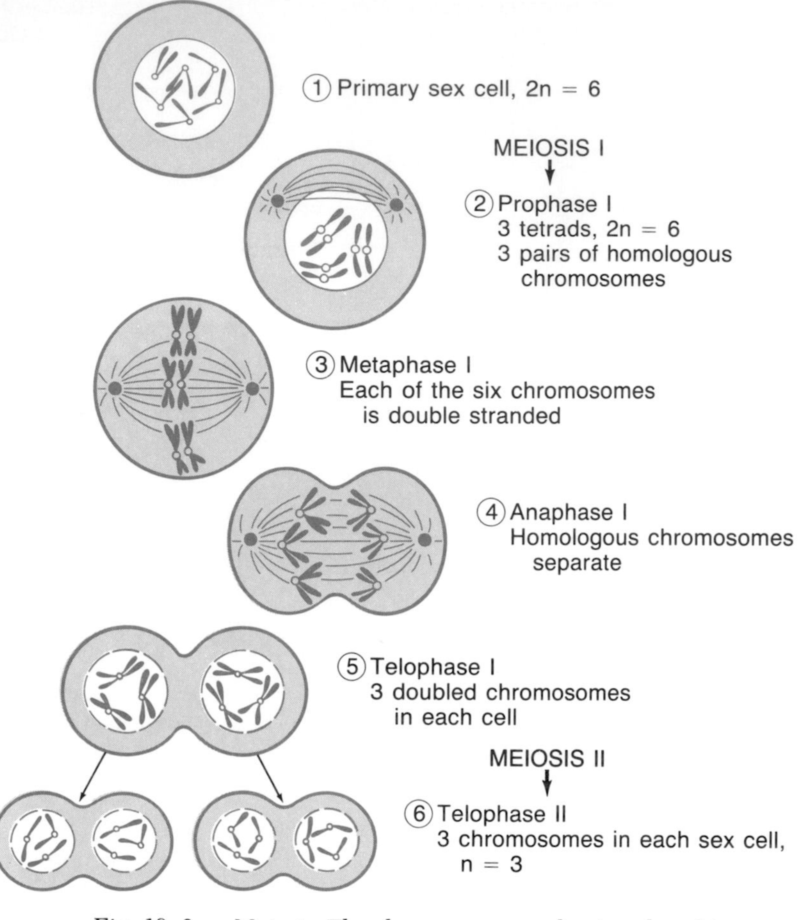

Fig. 18–3. Meiosis. The chromosome number is reduced in Meiosis I. In Meiosis II, the monoploid number of chromosomes is conserved.

Step 2. This cell has six chromosomes arranged as three pairs of homologous chromosomes. Because replication has already occurred, each chromosome is a doubled chromosome consisting of two chromatids, so there is a total of 12 chromatids.

Step 3. The doubled chromosomes line up at the equator in homologous pairs. (This is unlike mitosis, where the doubled chromosomes form a single line at the equator.) For each pair of homologous chromosomes there are four chromatids. The four chromatids make up a *tetrad*. When homologous chromosomes come together it is called *synapsis*. At synapsis, there may be an exchange of chromatid segments—a process known as *crossing-over.* A description of crossing-over will follow.

Step 4. During the first division of meiosis, each doubled chromosome separates from its homolog.

Step 5. Each cell that results from the first division has the monoploid number of chromosomes. Thus, the first division is a reduction division. Notice, however, that the chromosomes are still doubled chromosomes consisting of a pair of chromatids.

The two sex cells then undergo the second division. The chromatids of each doubled chromosome separate and move in opposite directions, as in a mitotic division.

Step 6. Each chromatid is now a chromosome. Each of the four cells has the monoploid chromosome number. The second division is like mitosis in that the chromosome number is conserved.

Crossing-Over

During synapsis, when four chromatids lie alongside each other as a tetrad, they often exchange segments. This interchange, called crossing-over, is shown in Figure 18–4. In this diagram, the black chromosomes are the ones that, long before, originated from the male parent. The white chromosomes originated from the female parent. As you trace the interchange of chromosomal material and the subsequent distribution of chromatids, you can see that four different chromosomes are distributed to the gametes. By contrast, in the absence of crossing-over only two different chromosomes go to the gametes.

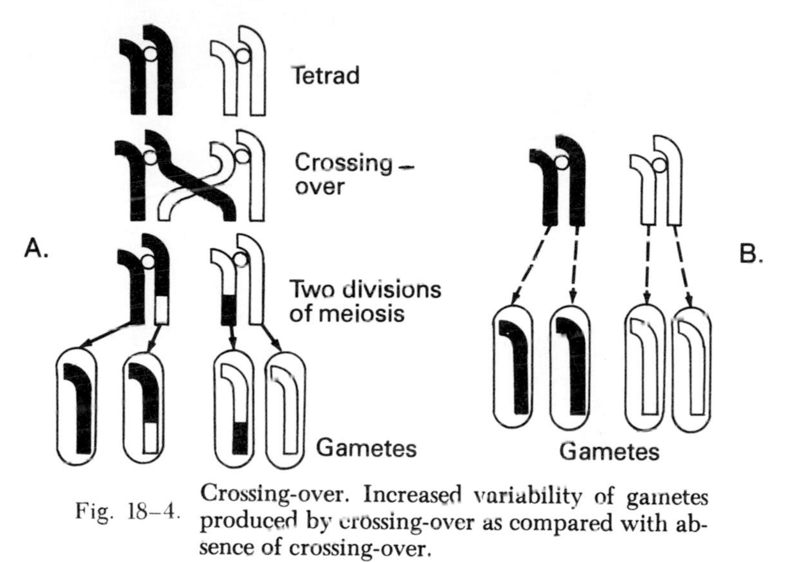

Fig. 18–4. Crossing-over. Increased variability of gametes produced by crossing-over as compared with absence of crossing-over.

The human primary sex cell has 23 pairs of chromosomes. Crossing-over in many of these homologous chromosomes greatly increases the variety of gametes that are produced by a single pair of parents. No wonder that each human child inherits so many traits that differ from those inherited by other siblings.

This variability among gametes leads to great diversity among offspring—an evolutionary advantage of sexual reproduction over asexual reproduction.

C

Fertilization and Conjugation

Fertilization is the union of a monoploid sperm nucleus with a monoploid egg nucleus. The fusion of their nuclei produces a fertilized egg cell, or diploid *zygote*. As a result of fertilization, the species' diploid number of chromosomes (2n) is restored.

Of the millions of sperm that are attracted chemically to the ovum, only one gains entrance. The others are kept out by the immediate formation of a fertilization membrane and by chemical action. Only the head of the sperm enters the ovum; its tail remains on the outside.

Internal versus External Fertilization

External fertilization occurs outside the body of the female. *Internal fertilization* occurs inside the body of the female. With internal fertilization, the gametes and zygotes are protected from the outside environment. With external fertilization, the gametes and zygotes are usually exposed to hazards in the environment, such as being eaten by other animals.

In most kinds of fish, the female deposits eggs and the male deposits sperm in the same place in the water. Fish and amphibians generally reproduce by external fertilization.

Fig. 18–5. External fertilization of eggs takes place when these frogs mate.

Animals such as reptiles, birds, and mammals reproduce by internal fertilization. In this method, the sperm are introduced into the female's body. Then they swim to the moist environment of the oviduct where they unite with the ovum or ova.

Eggs deposited in the water have less chance of being fertilized than eggs fertilized internally. However, animals that reproduce by external fertilization produce more eggs than animals that reproduce by internal fertilization. The production of a large number of eggs balances the low probability that any one egg will be fertilized.

Conjugation

Though protozoans usually reproduce asexually by means of binary fission, they also use a simple form of sexual reproduction, called conjugation. It involves the exchange of nuclear material between two individuals. In *Paramecium*, for example, two individuals become attached to each other, sometimes for hours. During this time, nuclear material from each individual travels to the partner. There it fuses with nuclear material in the partner's cell.

A similar form of conjugation occurs in some bacteria. In this case a part of the chromosome of one bacterium is donated to the partner bacterium. The chromosomal material travels from one cell to the other via a tiny bridge of cytoplasm.

Like the sexual reproduction of the multicellular animals, conjugation brings about a shuffling of the hereditary characteristics. Following conjugation the protozoans may reproduce asexually by binary fission hundreds of times before conjugation again occurs.

Reasoning Exercises

1. Identify the advantages of sexual reproduction over asexual reproduction.
2. Compare sperm and ovum as to size, motility, and stored energy.
3. How does oogenesis differ from spermatogenesis?
4. What is a hermaphrodite?
5. How is a constant chromosome number maintained from generation to generation?
6. An animal has 7 chromosomes in a polar body. What is its diploid number?
7. What is the advantage to the species of crossing-over?
8. Distinguish between conjugation and fertilization.
9. Why is it important to the survival of the species that an animal whose eggs are fertilized externally produce a large number of eggs?

(D)

---

evelopment

Early velopment of the Embryo

After fertilization, the fertilized egg begins a lengthy series of mitotic cell divisions to produce the embryo and then the adult. The study of embryo development is known as *embryology* or *developmental biology*.

Figure 18–6 shows the stages in the development of a frog embryo. These drawings show the division of the large fertilized ovum into a solid ball of small cells. This series of stages is called *cleavage*. The solid ball of cells resulting from cleavage is called the *morula* (morula = bunch of grapes). As the embryo develops, each cell has the same number of chromosomes as the fertilized egg—the diploid number.

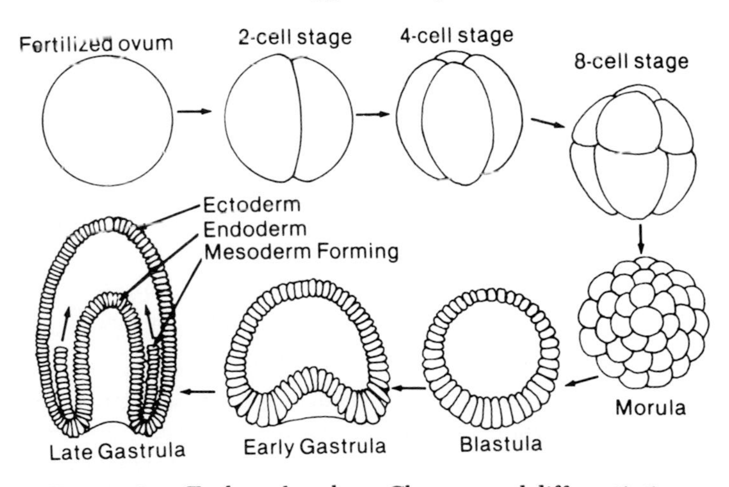

Fig. 18–6. Early embryology. Cleavage and differentiation in the frog. Is a mesoderm cell n or $2n$?

As the multiplying cells press against one another, they form a hollow ball of cells called the *blastula*. Further pressure by dividing cells causes an in-pushing, which results in the *gastrula* stage (gastrula = stomach). The *early gastrula*, in three dimensions, has the appearance of a soft hollow ball that has been pushed in by a finger.

As the gastrula increases in size, it elongates to form a pouch. A new layer of cells begins to fill the old cavity of the blastula stage. Notice that the *late gastrula* has three layers of cells. These are known as the *primary germ layers* and consist of (1) the *endoderm*, a lining on the inside, (2) the *mesoderm*, forming a middle layer, and (3) the *ectoderm*, or outer layer.

Differentiation

Embryologists have traced the development of all the body systems and organisms from the three primary germ layers. By marking the cells of an embryo with dyes and noting their movement, scientists have determined that the digestive tract and related structures of an organism generally come from the endoderm. The organs near the body surface structures generally come from the ectoderm, while the mesoderm usually gives rise to those structures that lie within the body cavity. The differentiation of the three primary germ layers into the body systems is indicated in the table below.

Differentiation of Primary Germ Layers

Ectoderm	Mesoderm	Endoderm
Nervous system	Skeleton	Digestive tract
Epidermis of skin	Muscles	Respiratory system
	Circulatory system	Liver, pancreas
	Gonads	Bladder

One of the great mysteries of development is how a single fertilized egg is able to generate all the different types of cells of an organism. A common nematode, the roundworm *Caenorhabditis elegans*, gives scientists clues to the answer. *C. elegans* is an excellent model for study because it grows from embryo to adulthood in three days, always has exactly 959 cells as an adult, and has transparent flesh that enables scientists to see into its body and watch its cells divide. Scientists have mapped the fate of each cell of this roundworm and are able to say what parts of the early embryo have gone on to form the head, the nervous system, the muscles, and the rest of the adult organism. While the mechanisms that determine the ultimate fate of cells is still not completely understood, research indicates that organelles in the cytoplasm of the cell, present at fertilization, play a key role. Scientists studying the roundworm have also located genes that seem to "mastermind" differentiation.

Protection and Nutrition of the Embryo During Development

A developing embryo must receive food, have a proper environment, and be protected from enemies.

The fertilized eggs of amphibians and of most fish develop externally in the water in which they were fertilized. The food for the embryos is the yolk stored in the egg. Generally there is little or no parental care. The

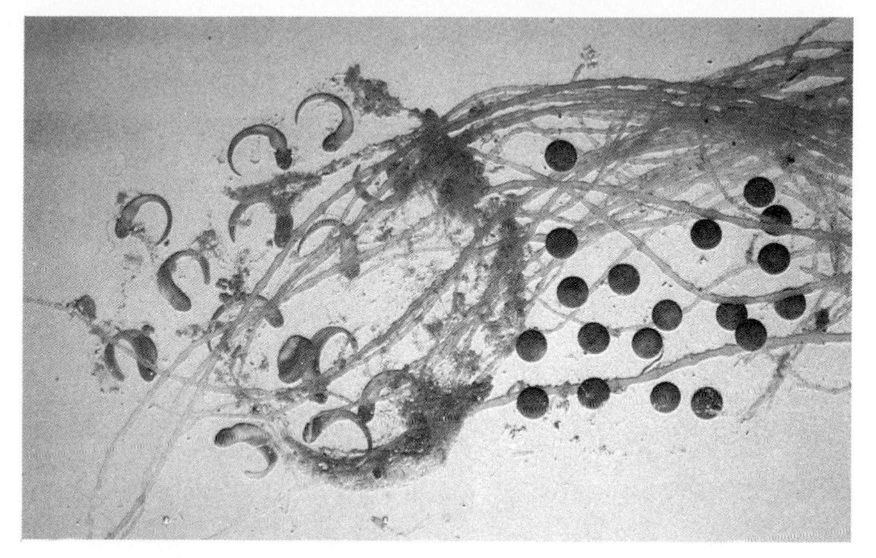

Fig. 18–7. Fertilized frog eggs, on the right, develop in water. Frog embryos, on the left, develop into swimming forms called tadpoles.

large number of eggs produced by fish and amphibians serve to maintain the species despite the losses caused by predators.

The fertilized eggs of reptiles and birds usually develop externally, on land. Food for the developing reptile and bird embryos consists of the large amount of yolk in the eggs. Birds protect their eggs and their young in nests. Birds and reptiles produce far fewer eggs than do fish and amphibians.

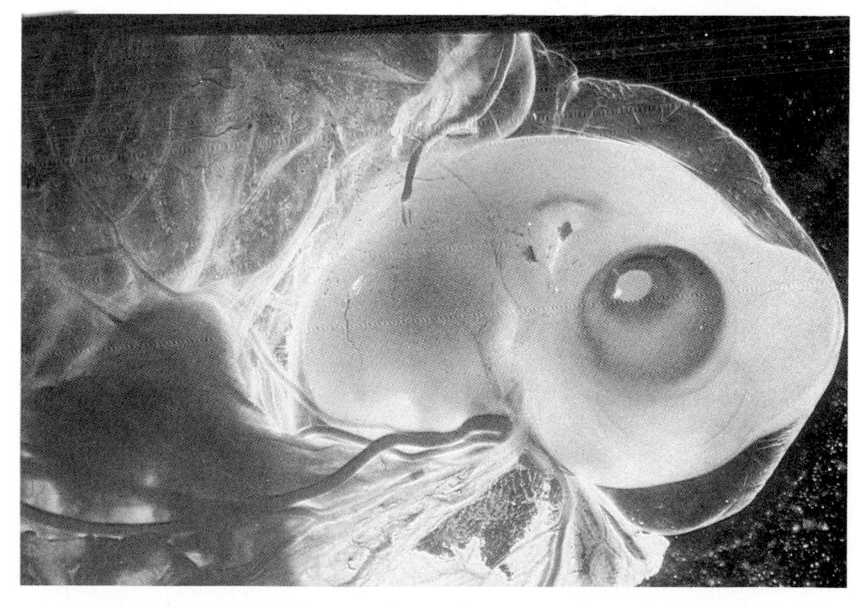

Fig. 18–8. Chicken embryo after seven days of development.

Adaptations for External Development in Birds

The development of bird embryos in a land environment required the evolution of a number of adaptations.

Shell. The eggs of birds, as well as of reptiles, have a shell. The calcium-containing shell of the bird egg provides protection. This shell is porous enough to permit the passage of gases into and out of the egg.

Embryonic membranes. The developing bird embryo has four membranes that help to provide a favorable environment for its development. These are the yolk sac, the amnion, the allantois, and the chorion. Notice these membranes in Figure 18–9.

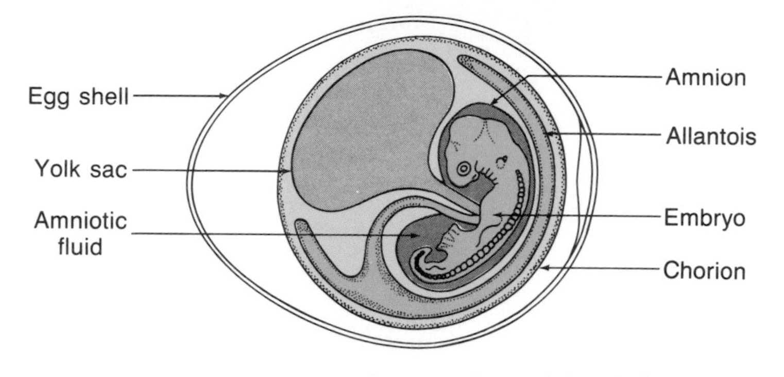

Fig. 18–9. Developing embryo of the chicken.

The *yolk sac* protrudes from the digestive tract of the embryo and encloses the yolk. Blood vessels transport the stored food from the yolk sac to the developing embryo.

The *amnion* is a sac enclosing the embryo in a watery fluid, the amniotic fluid. This fluid provides a liquid environment for the embryo and protects it against mechanical shock.

The *allantois* is a saclike structure that protrudes from the digestive tract and lies against the shell. Well-supplied with blood vessels, the allantois carries on an exchange of gases with the external environment through the shell. The allantois serves the embryo as an organ for respiration and excretion. Nitrogenous wastes are excreted from the embryo into the allantois in the form of insoluble deposits of uric acids.

The *chorion* forms a moist membrane just inside the porous shell. It helps to exchange respiratory gases between the outside and the blood vessels of the allantois.

E

Internal Development

We have seen that the oviduct is the tube that carries ova from an ovary toward the outside of the organism. Some fish and snakes retain their fertilized eggs in the oviduct and development occurs there, internally. If you raise tropical fish, you may be familiar with "live-bearers." These are fish whose young emerge from the oviduct as young fish, rather than as eggs. In these fish, the developing embryo obtains food from the yolk of the egg, not from its mother.

In mammals the oviducts lead to a muscular chamber, the *uterus*. In the uterus, an egg that has been fertilized in the oviduct develops into an embryo. The embryo is attached by the *umbilical cord* to a mass of tissue

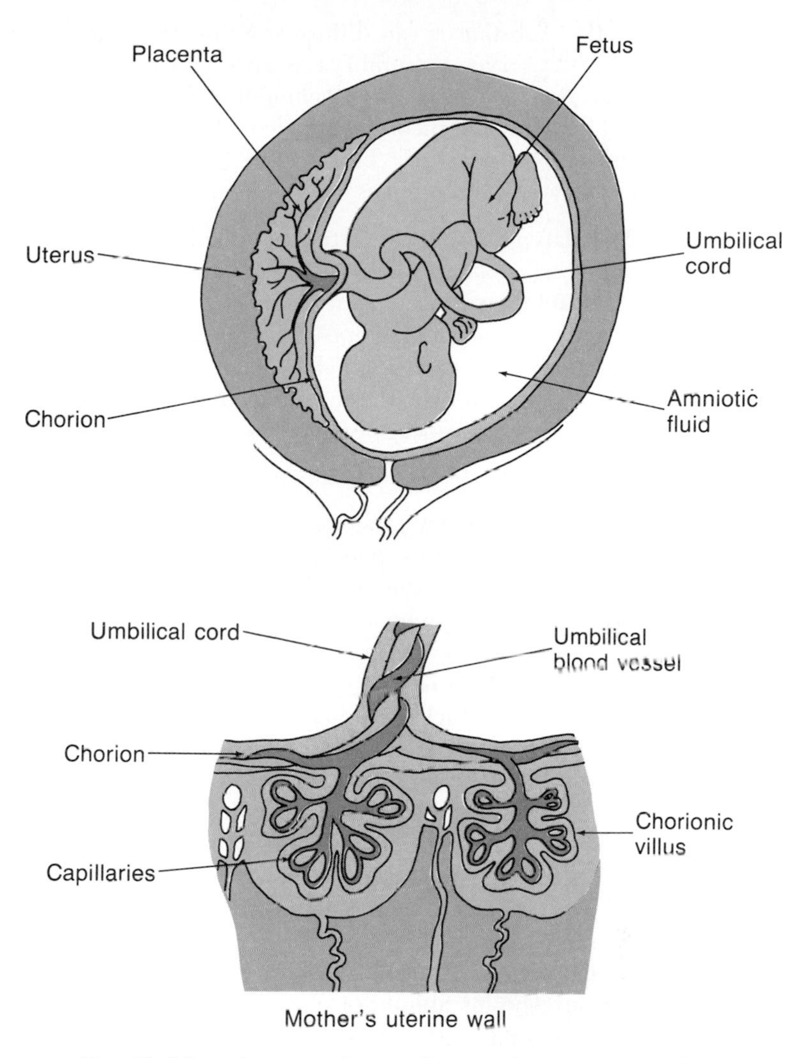

Fig 18-10. At top is a human fetus in the uterus. Note that the umbilical cord and the placenta attach the fetus to the uterus. The diagram at bottom shows the capillaries where the exchange of food, oxygen, carbon dioxide, and waste products between mother and fetus takes place.

called the *placenta*. The placenta develops from the lining of the uterus and from the outermost embryonic membrane, the chorion. The embryo obtains food by diffusion from the bloodstream of the mother at the placenta. Mammalian eggs lack yolk and are microscopic in size. As we have seen, the eggs of fish, frogs, reptiles, and birds have relatively large amounts of yolk. The egg of an elephant (a mammal) is microscopic, whereas the egg of a frog is several millimeters in diameter.

At the placenta, food and oxygen diffuse from the mother's blood, by means of the umbilical cord, into the blood of the embryo. The two blood systems are separate—little or no blood of the mother flows into the blood system of the embryo. However, the two blood systems are close enough so that substances can diffuse from one system to the other. Thus, the placenta serves the embryo as an organ for nutrition, respiration, and excretion, as well as for attachment.

Drugs such as nicotine and alcohol can also diffuse from the mother to the embryo and may be harmful to a developing embryo. For these reasons, such substances carry warnings against use during pregnancy.

Development in Primitive Mammals

The platypus is a mammal that has no placenta. It lays eggs, like a reptile, and is called a *non-placental mammal*. Intermediate between true mammals and the primitive non-placental mammals are the *marsupials*, such as the kangaroo and the opossum. Their placenta is poorly developed and their eggs have some yolk. The young are so tiny that a half-dozen can fit in a teaspoon. After birth, the young climb up the mother's fur to its *marsupium*. This is a "pocket" where the young get milk, shelter, and warmth.

(F)

Reproduction in Humans

Male Reproductive Structures

Figure 18–11 shows the structures of the male reproductive system. Notice that the testes, paired oval structures, lie in an outpocketing of the body wall, called the *scrotum*. Temperature in the scrotum is 2 to 4 degrees lower than body temperature. This slightly lower temperature is advantageous for the production and storage of sperm. The sperm are produced in a series of highly coiled tubes within the testes.

The sperm duct of humans is called the *vas deferens*. In addition to carrying sperm, the vas deferens collects fluid from several glands, including the *seminal vesicles* and the *prostate gland*. This liquid medium for the sperm is an adaptation that provides transport, lubrication, energy for swimming, and protection from the acidic environment of the female's genital tract. The mixture of sperm and fluid is called *semen*.

The vas deferens empties into the *urethra*, which conducts semen out of the body through the *penis*. During sexual excitement, tissues of the penis become filled with blood, making this organ larger and erect. A release of semen contains about 200 million to 350 million sperm in a volume of about 3.5 ml. Although the urethra also carries urine from the urinary bladder, semen and urine do not flow at the same time. During the release of semen, the exit from the bladder is closed off.

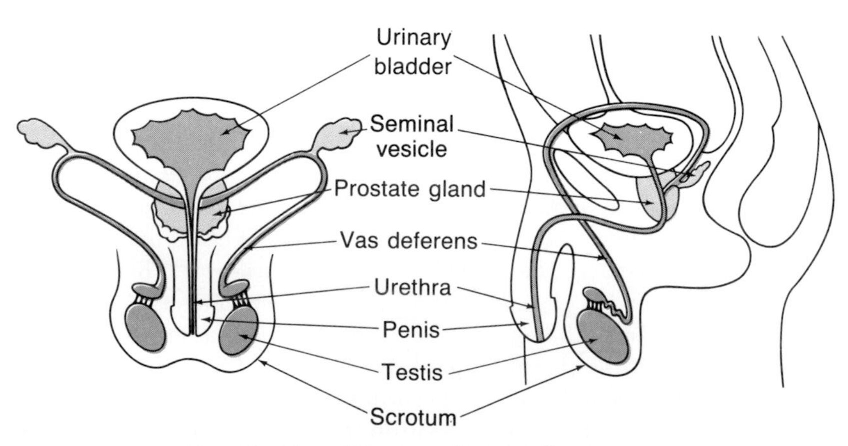

Fig. 18–11. Human male reproductive system.

Female Reproductive Structures

Figure 18–12 shows the structures of the female reproductive system. Notice the ovaries—paired, walnut-sized structures located in the lower part of the abdominal cavity. They are partially surrounded by funnel-like openings of the oviduct. In humans, the oviducts are called the *Fallopian tubes*.

The Fallopian tubes lead to the thick-walled, muscular uterus, or womb. This is where, if fertilization has taken place, the embryo develops. At the bottom of the uterus is a muscular ring, the *cervix*. The cervix extends partially into the *vagina*. The vagina is a muscular tube that leads from the uterus to the outside. It receives semen during mating. The urethra, in the female, carries only urine, not gametes. The vagina is also called the birth canal.

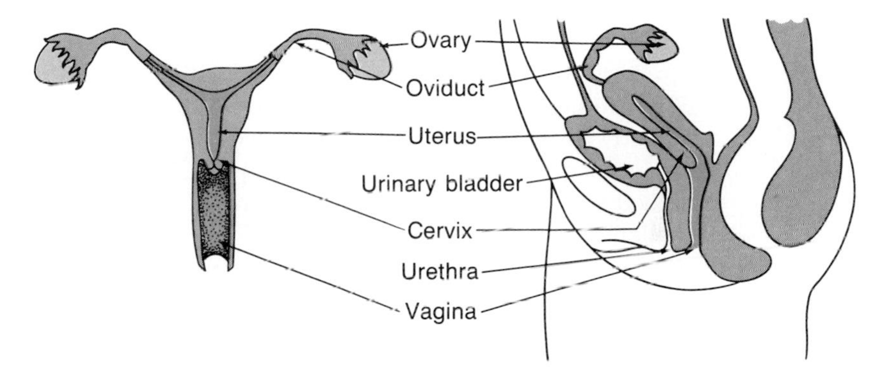

Fig. 18–12. Human female reproductive system.

The Menstrual Cycle

Human males produce large numbers of sperm continuously from puberty until old age. Females, however, release a single gamete (an egg, or ovum) at intervals of approximately 28 days from puberty (about age 12) until the female menopause (about age 50).

The release of an egg from an ovary is one of the four stages of the *menstrual cycle*. The menstrual cycle consists of a series of changes in the ovaries and uterus controlled by the interaction of hormones.

Follicle stage. The ovary contains many thousands of follicles. Each follicle is a cluster of cells that encloses an egg cell, or ovum. During this stage, follicle-stimulating hormone from the pituitary gland stimulates the follicles to grow. As they grow, the follicles secrete the hormone estrogen. Eventually, only one follicle continues to grow and fill with fluid; the other follicles stop growing.

Ovulation. The enlarged follicle ruptures through the wall of the ovary and ejects its egg. This step is called *ovulation*. The egg enters by the opening of the Fallopian tube. Usually one egg is released each month, with the ovaries alternating production.

Corpus luteum stage. After ovulation, the cavity of the follicle becomes filled with yellow tissue called the *corpus luteum* (corpus = body; luteum = yellow). The corpus luteum produces the hormones *progesterone* and *estrogen*.

Menstruation. The hormones estrogen and progesterone (produced by the ovary) cause the build-up of the lining of the uterus. This build-up

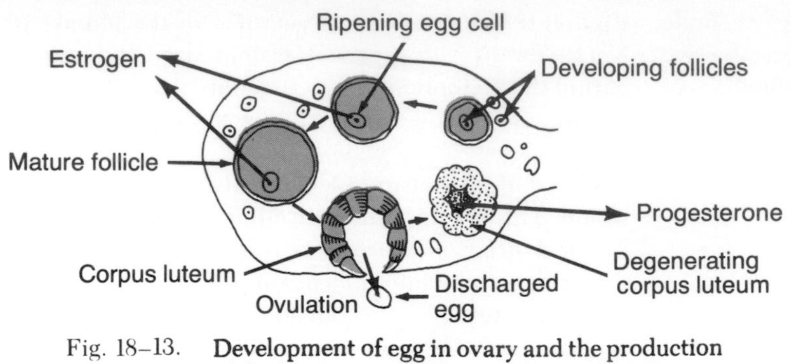

Fig. 18–13. **Development of egg in ovary and the production of the hormones estrogen and progesterone.**

prepares the uterus to receive the embryo—if fertilization has occurred. The lining becomes thick, soft, and moist. Its blood supply increases greatly. However, if no embryo has become implanted, the rich lining of the uterus breaks down. The tissue and a slight to moderate amount of blood is then discharged from the vagina. The flow of tissue and blood is called *menstruation*. The unfertilized egg is discharged with the menstrual flow. On the average, ovulation occurs on or about the 14th day after the onset of menstruation, but the number of days may vary from woman to woman, or even in the same woman from month to month.

After menstruation, hormonal action causes the uterine wall to rebuild in preparation for the next possible embryo. Thus, in the absence of fertilization, the menstrual flow occurs periodically, on the average about every 28 days.

If an embryo implants, however, the embryo itself produces hormones. These promote the continued existence of the uterine lining that supports and nourishes the embryo. The menstrual cycle ceases. Accordingly, the absence of menstruation at the expected time is a sign of possible pregnancy. Normal individuals, however, vary in the regularity of menstruation. Moreover, menstruation may be delayed by illness or emotional disturbance. A more reliable indication of the onset of pregnancy is the appearance of certain hormones in the urine.

Pregnancy

The period of time during which the mother carries the developing embryo is known as the *period of gestation*, or *pregnancy*. After the first eight weeks, in humans, the embryo is called a *fetus*. The length of gestation varies in different mammals. Some approximate times are shown in the table below.

Periods of Gestation

Human	280 days	Dog	60 days	Whale	360 days
Mouse	21 days	Cat	60 days	Elephant	22 months
Rabbit	32 days	Horse	350 days		

Birth Birth is the separation of the placenta and the fetus from the mother's uterine lining and their passage to the outside. The process of birth begins when hormones promote repeated contractions of the muscles of the uterus. These contractions push the fetus through the vagina. Shortly thereafter, further contractions of the uterus expel the placenta.

During pregnancy, hormone-induced changes occur in the mammary glands. Soon after birth these glands are ready to secrete milk for the nourishment of the infant.

Hormones and Reproduction The interaction of numerous hormones regulates gamete formation in both males and females as well as the events of menstruation, pregnancy, and birth. We shall consider only a few of these hormones.

Pituitary Hormones. One part of the pituitary gland releases *FSH* and *LH*. FSH, the *follicle-stimulating hormone*, stimulates the growth of the follicle in the ovary. LH, the *luteinizing hormone*, stimulates the growth of the corpus luteum in the ovary.

Ovarian Hormones. The ovary produces *estrogen* and *progesterone*. Estrogen is produced by the follicle during its growth in the ovary. This hormone promotes the early steps in the build-up of the uterine lining. Progesterone is produced by the corpus luteum, the yellow tissue that fills the cavity of the follicle. Progesterone promotes the further build-up of the uterine lining. If pregnancy occurs, the continued secretion of progesterone maintains this lining to support the embryo.

LTH and Oxytocin. *LTH*, the *luteotrophic hormone*, also released by the pituitary gland, promotes the secretion of milk in the breasts. *Oxy-*

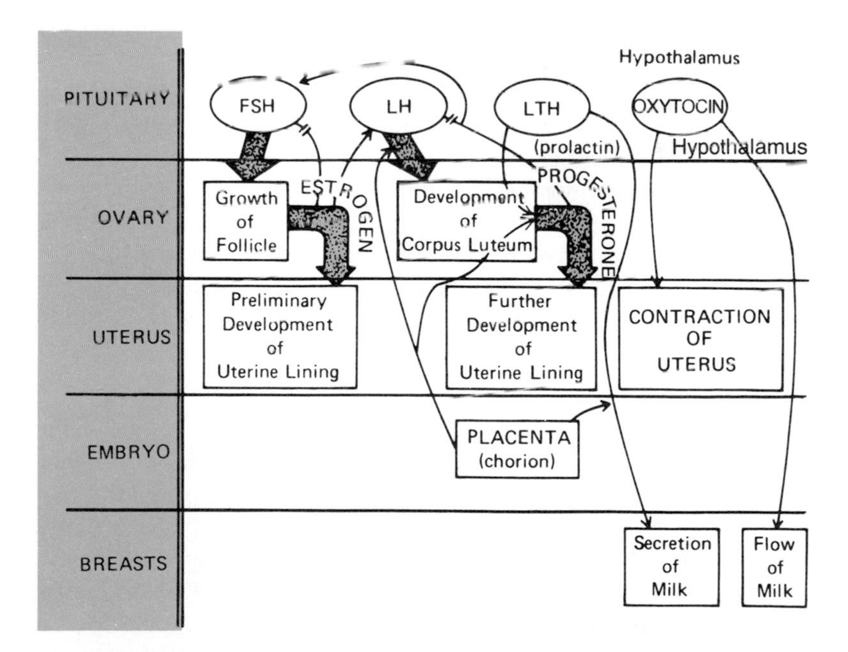

Fig. 18–14. **Hormones in reproduction. An arrowhead indicates stimulation; a road block sign (—┫ ┣—) indicates inhibition.**

tocin, secreted by the *hypothalamus*, a region of the brain, promotes contraction of the uterus during childbirth. It also causes the flow of milk under the stimulus of the infant's first suckling.

Hormone Interaction

Considerable stimulation and negative feedback occur during the menstrual cycle and pregnancy. Some of these interactions are shown in Figure 18–14. In this diagram, an arrowhead indicates stimulation and a roadblock (—┤├—) indicates inhibition. For example, a high level of estrogen in the blood acts upon the pituitary to reduce its release of FSH.

Secondary Sexual Characteristics

The production of sperm and eggs is a primary sexual characteristic. Hormones, however, also promote the development of secondary sexual characteristics. The hormones produced by the testes are categorized under the general term *androgens*. An important androgen is *testosterone*. Testosterone promotes the development of such secondary male characteristics as the beard, body and pubic hair, a deep voice, and broad shoulders. Estrogen promotes such secondary female sexual characteristics as the broader pelvis, mature breasts, and a thicker layer of fat under the skin.

Both males and females produce estrogens and androgens. In females the concentration of estrogens is high and the concentration of androgens is very low. In males the opposite condition prevails.

Human Fertility

Fertilization takes place in the upper portion of the Fallopian tubes. Sperm cells introduced into the vagina reach this region by swimming, aided by contractions of the uterus and oviducts. They may reach the oviducts within fifteen minutes after mating has occurred. It takes as many as 130 million sperm to ensure fertilization of one egg. The sperm secretes an enzyme that helps form an entry-way in the outer membrane of the egg. The outer membrane then changes so that no additional sperm can enter.

An egg that has not been fertilized lives for about a day. Sperm cells may survive in the oviduct for about two days. Accordingly, fertilization may occur even if mating is not on the day of ovulation.

As the zygote passes down the oviduct to the uterus it begins its embryological development. The embryo is a small mass of cells when it implants in the wall of the uterus. This occurs between the sixth and tenth day following fertilization.

Conditions of Infertility

Infertility is a condition in which two people mate yet are unable to produce a child. However, either the male or the female may be physically able to produce offspring with another partner.

A disorder of the male reproductive system is the primary cause of about two-fifths of all cases of infertility. Such cases often involve a low sperm count (insufficient number of sperm) or a high percentage of sperm that function abnormally.

Disorders of the female reproductive system account for about three-fifths of all cases of infertility. One such disorder involves blockage of the Fallopian tubes, which prevents eggs from entering the uterus. *Anovula-*

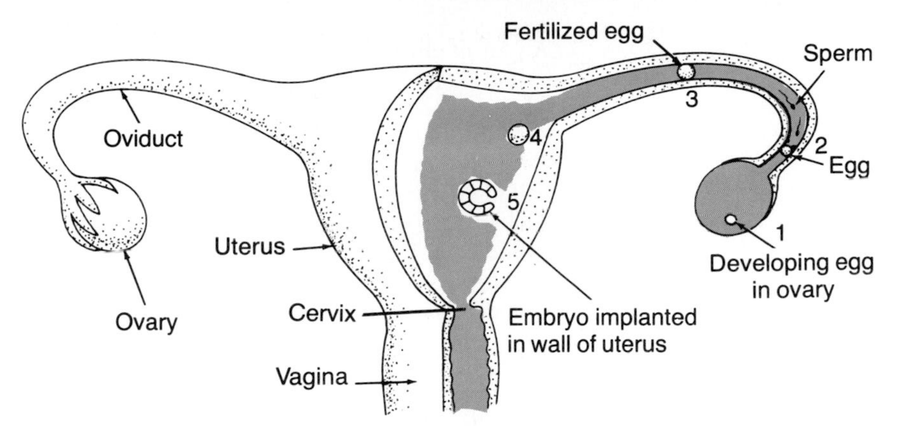

Fig. 18-15. Structure of the human female reproductive system, showing fertilization of the egg in the oviduct and implantation of the embryo in the wall of the uterus. What may happen if both ovaries produce an egg at the same time, or if an ovary produces several eggs?

tion, a disorder in which the ovaries fail to release eggs, also prevents fertilization. A third female disorder is *endometriosis*, a disease of the reproductive system in which a certain kind of tissue grows in an abnormal location, such as on the ovaries and other reproductive organs.

Treatment of Infertility

Cases of male infertility can be treated by hormone treatment or by microsurgery. If these treatments are ineffective, semen from a male donor may be injected into a woman's uterus, a procedure called *artificial insemination*. Sometimes sperm from the woman's partner and the donor are mixed before being injected into the female's uterus.

In cases of female infertility, surgery may correct structural disorders of the reproductive system such as blocked Fallopian tubes. Anovulation may be helped by drugs that trigger ovulation. Endometriosis can sometimes be treated successfully by drugs or surgery.

If these techniques are ineffective, artificial fertilization can be attempted. *In vitro fertilization* (IVF) is a procedure in which eggs are removed from a female's ovaries and fertilized with her partner's sperm in a laboratory dish. The fertilized eggs are then inserted into the woman's uterus, where one or more may develop into a fetus. The term "test tube babies" is not accurate because only fertilization and the very earliest stages of embryonic development take place outside the mother.

Completion Questions

A

1. Reproduction by means of gametes is called . . . . . . (sexual, asexual) reproduction.
2. The motile gamete is the . . . . . .
3. The male gonads are called . . . . . .
4. The processes of forming sperm and ova are called, respectively, ... and . . . . . .

B

5. A pair of chromosomes that regulate the same traits are called . . . . . . chromosomes.
6. The number of chromosomes in a single set of homologs is th . . . number.
7. Four similar chromatids that come together during synapsis a called a(n) . . . . . .
8. The pairing of chromosomes that occurs during meiosis is called . . . . . .
9. The interchange of portions of chromatids during synapsis is called . . . . . .
10. The number of cell divisions occurring during meiosis is . . . .

C

11. Animals that live on land generally reproduce by . . . . . . (ext internal) fertilization.
12. The exchange of chromosomal material via movement of cyto between two cells is called . . . . . .
13. Birds have . . . . . . (external, internal) fertilization.

D

14. The stage of cleavage characterized by a solid ball of cells is the . . . . . .
15. The cup-shaped stage in the development of an embryo is the . . . . . .
16. The membrane that supplies food to the bird embryo is the . . . . . .
17. The bird embryo develops in a fluid called . . . . . . fluid.

E

18. The mammal embryo develops within a chamber called the . . . . . .
19. The sperm duct and the oviduct of humans are called, respec the . . . . . . and the . . . . . .
20. The process by which tissue and blood are discharged from th uterus is called . . . . . .
21. The time required for a mammal embryo to develop is called period of . . . . . .

F

22. A hormone that promotes the development of male secondary ual characteristics is . . . . . .
23. Two female sex hormones produced by the ovaries are . . . . . and . . . . . .
24. Fertilization in humans occurs in the structure called the . . .
25. The condition in which two people, as a couple, are unable to duce a child is known as . . . . . .

Multiple-Choice Questions

A

1. Sexual reproduction involves (1) budding, (2) fusion of gamete (3) regeneration, (4) spore formation.
2. The reproductive cell that is produced in the male gonad is th (1) sperm, (2) ovum, (3) zygote, (4) pollen.

3. Eggs and sperm are similar in that both (1) develop in specialized organs called gonads, (2) have adaptations for locomotion, (3) have the same relative amount of cytoplasm surrounding their nuclei, (4) are produced in approximately the same numbers.
4. Hermaphrodites are organisms that (1) are females with nonfunctioning ovaries, (2) are males with nonfunctioning testes, (3) are unable to reproduce sexually, (4) have functional male and and female gonads.
5. As compared with the sperm, the egg contains more (1) chromosomes, (2) mitochondria, (3) cytoplasm, (4) centriole.

B

6. Meiosis occurs during (1) embryo formation, (2) oogenesis, (3) budding, (4) replication.
7. A single primary sex cell may produce four gametes. These gametes are known as (1) diploid egg cells, (2) monoploid egg cells, (3) polar bodies, (4) sperm cells.
8. Replication occurs in (1) fertilization, (2) mitosis only, (3) meiosis only, (4) meiosis and mitosis.
9. If gametes were formed solely as a result of mitosis, each time that fertilization occurred the species' chromosome number would be (1) reduced by half, (2) unchanged, (3) doubled, (4) quadrupled.
10. The diploid number (2n) of chromosomes is restored during (1) meiosis, (2) fusion of gametes, (3) mitosis, (4) cleavage.
11. In a certain species of fruit fly, the diploid number of chromosomes is 8. How many chromosomes are normally found in each mature sex cell produced by these flies? (1) 8, (2) 2, (3) 16, (4) 4.
12. As a result of which process do daughter cells contain one-half the chromosome number of the parental cell? (1) budding, (2) meiosis, (3) fission, (4) conjugation.
13. To the species involved, a major advantage of sexual reproduction over asexual reproduction is that sexual reproduction results in (1) larger offspring, (2) greater variety of offspring, (3) more rapid development of offspring, (4) greater number of offspring.
14. In the human female, the number of gametes normally produced from one primary sex cell is (1) 1, (2) 2, (3) 3, (4) 4.
15. That a sample of tissue has come from the testis of a cat and not from its kidney can be determined by the presence of cells (1) in various stages of mitosis, (2) which lack nitrogenous wastes, (3) with yolk, (4) with the monoploid number of chromosomes.

Base your answer to question 16 on Fig. 18-2 on page 299.

16. Spermatogenesis and Oogenesis are similar in that (1) they produce diploid sperm and ova (2) they produce polar bodies (3) the first division reduces the chromosome number in half (4) they produce diploid sex cells.

20. In a species that reproduces sexually, the two events most responsible for the maintenance of the chromosome number from generation to generation are (1) cleavage and differentiation, (2) pollination and fertilization, (3) gamete production and zygote formation, (4) fission and regeneration.

C

21. Fertilization is accomplished when (1) an egg nucleus and a sperm nucleus have fused, (2) a mature egg meets a mature sperm, (3) a sperm enters the uterus, (4) a sperm penetrates the membrane of an egg.
22. Animals that produce one or two egg cells during a single reproductive cycle are most likely to have (1) external fertilization and much parental care of the young, (2) external fertilization and little parental care of the young, (3) internal development and little parental care of the young, (4) internal fertilization and much parental care of the young.
23. In frogs, zygote formation normally occurs in the (1) ovary, (2) oviduct, (3) external environment, (4) internal environment.
24. Generally, animals that carry on external fertilization (1) produce more eggs than animals carrying on internal fertilization, (2) have much parental care of the young, (3) have little yolk in the eggs, (4) live on land.
25. Which is an important adaptation for reproduction among land animals? (1) fertilization of gametes outside the body of the female, (2) fertilization of gametes within the body of the female, (3) production of sperm cells with thick cell walls, (4) production of sperm cells with thin cell walls.
26. Which is an advantage of internal fertilization? (1) More of the eggs produced will probably be fertilized. (2) It is not necessary for sperm to swim to the egg. (3) The organism involved has a shorter life cycle. (4) Only one parent is involved.
27. The development of internal fertilization accompanied the evolution of (1) land animals, (2) water animals, (3) invertebrates, (4) monoploid animals.
28. A primitive method of sexual reproduction is (1) regeneration, (2) budding, (3) conjugation, (4) fission.
29. Which of the following choices generally characterizes animals in which fertilization is external? (1) They live in or near the water. (2) They give extensive care to their newborn. (3) They have fewer offspring than animals in which fertilization is internal. (4) They produce nonmotile male gametes.

D

30. Which is the correct sequence in the development of an animal embryo? (1) cleavage, blastula, fertilization, gastrula, (2) gastrula, fertilization, blastula, cleavage, (3) fertilization, cleavage, blastula, gastrula, (4) fertilization, cleavage, gastrula, blastula.
31. From which human embryonic layer do the epidermis of the skin and the nervous system develop? (1) ectoderm, (2) blastula, (3) mesoderm, (4) gastrula.
32. The membrane that forms a fluid-filled sac that serves as protection for a developing bird embryo is the (1) chorion, (2) placenta, (3) allantois, (4) amnion.

33. What is a function of the placenta in a mammal? (1) It surrounds the embryo and protects it from mechanical shock. (2) It joins the maternal and fetal blood vessels. (3) It permits the passage of nutrients and oxygen from the mother to the fetus. (4) It pumps blood until the fetus is born.
34. During the development of a chicken egg, which embryonic membrane is used for both respiration and excretion? (1) amnion, (2) allantois, (3) placenta, (4) yolk sac.
35. The endoderm of the gastrula gives rise to the (1) blood and blood vessels, (2) muscles, (3) brain and nervous system, (4) digestive system.
36. Of the following, the smallest eggs are produced by the (1) sparrow, (2) elephant, (3) codfish, (4) ostrich.
37. The hollow ball that is formed at one stage in embryo development is called the (1) blastula, (2) morula, (3) gastrula, (4) mesoderm.
38. When a cell divides during the process of cleavage, each resulting cell, compared with the parent cell, has (1) more cytoplasm, (2) less cytoplasm, (3) more chromosomes, (4) fewer chromosomes.
39. The cells of an animal blastula are characterized by (1) frequent mitotic divisions, (2) frequent meiotic divisions, (3) monoploid chromosome numbers, (4) crossing-over at synapsis.
40. Which group of animals stores the least amount of food in its eggs for its developing embryos? (1) fish, (2) birds, (3) placental mammals, (4) non-placental mammals.
41. A placenta is usually associated with which group? (1) amphibians, (2) reptiles, (3) birds, (4) mammals.
42. Which is true of most of the carbon dioxide produced by a chicken embryo? (1) It is not excreted. (2) It is destroyed by a chemical process. (3) It is released through the shell. (4) It combines with the yolk.

E

Directions (43–47): Questions 43 through 47 describe structures associated with mammalian reproduction and development. For *each* description in these questions, write the *number* preceding the name of the structure, *chosen from the list below*, that is most closely associated with that description.

Structures

(1) Allantois
(2) Amnion
(3) Gonad
(4) Oviduct
(5) Placenta
(6) Uterus
(7) Yolk sac

43. Meiotic division normally occurs in this structure.
44. This structure is formed from a combination of maternal and embryonic tissues.
45. Internal fertilization usually takes place in this structure.
46. This structure becomes modified by hormonal action in preparation for the implantation of an early embryo.
47. This structure contains a watery environment for internal embryonic development.
48. If a scientist removed a patch of ectoderm from a salamander's developing gastrula, which system would fail to develop completely in this embryo? (1) nervous, (2) digestive, (3) reproductive, (4) respiratory.

49. How does the human embryo receive most of its nourishment? (1) by a secretion from the walls of the uterus, (2) by diffusion from the mother's blood into its own blood system, (3) by absorption from the yolk, (4) directly from the mother's blood, which circulates through the embryo.

(F)

50. The term gestation refers to the period of time (1) between fertilization and birth, (2) that the zygote is in the oviduct, (3) during which the lining of the uterus is replaced, (4) during which the secondary sex characteristics develop.
51. Which of the following structures *least* affects the human female menstrual cycle? (1) pituitary, (2) ovarian follicle, (3) pancreas, (4) corpus luteum.
52. Which represents the typical sequence in the human menstrual cycle?
    (1) follicle formation—corpus luteum stage—menstruation—ovulation.
    (2) follicle formation—corpus luteum stage—ovulation—menstruation.
    (3) follicle formation—menstruation stage—ovulation—corpus luteum stage.
    (4) follicle formation—ovulation—corpus luteum stage—menstruation.
53. In human females, which two structures mainly produce the hormones that control reproduction? (1) pituitary gland and thyroid glands, (2) pituitary gland and the ovaries, (3) adrenal gland and the ovaries, (4) adrenal glands and the thyroid gland.
54. The gestation period is the period between (1) ovulation and fertilization, (2) fertilization and birth, (3) adolescence and adulthood, (4) birth and death.
55. The first development of secondary sex characteristics in human females is most closely associated with (1) menopause, (2) gestation, (3) zygote formation, (4) puberty.
56. In humans, which structure is most closely associated with the protection of the developing embryo from mechanical shock? (1) chorion, (2) allantois, (3) amnion, (4) placenta.
57. Which hormone is directly responsible for the development of male secondary sex characteristics? (1) testosterone, (2) interstitial cell-stimulating hormone, (3) adrenaline, (4) luteinizing hormone.
58. Which observable stage of a menstrual cycle does *not* take place if zygote formation occurs? (1) follicle stage, (2) ovulation, (3) menstruation, (4) corpus luteum stage.
59. In human reproduction, a follicle is a cavity where (1) an egg cell is produced, (2) a zygote attaches to the uterus, (3) an egg cell is fertilized, (4) a zygote begins to undergo cleavage.
60. In humans, the process of fertilization normally takes place in the (1) ovary, (2) vagina, (3) Fallopian tube, (4) uterus.
61. Fertilization in humans may occur (1) for about a day after ovulation occurs, (2) only within 15 minutes of mating, (3) only on the day sperm are introduced into the vagina, (4) only if mating occurs on the day of ovulation.

62. A disorder in which ovaries fail to release eggs is (1) endometriosis, (2) anovulation, (3) artificial insemination, (4) oogenesis.
63. In vitro fertilization is a technique in which (1) babies develop in test tubes, (2) eggs are fertilized in lab dishes, (3) a female is injected with semen from a male donor, (4) a female surrogate is used as a donor.
64. The general term for the inability of a couple to produce a child is (1) infertility, (2) blockage, (3) low sperm count, (4) insemination.

Chapter Test

Directions for questions 1 through 5: Complete each statement by using the expressions LESS, GREATER, or THE SAME.

1. Compared to the number of chromosomes in the zygote, the number of chromosomes in each cell of the blastula of the same organism is normally
2. Compared to the amount of yolk in an egg of an organism which has external development, the relative amount of yolk in an egg of an organism which has internal development is . . . .
3. Compared to the number of types of cells in the three embryonic layers, the number of types of cells in the differentiating embryo is . . . .
4. Compared to the number of offspring produced by animals that provide little parental care, the number of offspring produced by organisms that protect their young is . . . . . .
5. Compared to the number of functional sperm developed from a primary sex cell in a testis, the number of functional eggs developed from a primary sex cell in an ovary is . . . .

Directions (6-10) For *each* phrase in questions 6 through 10, select the *number* of the structure, *chosen from the list below*, which best fits the description. [A number may be used more than once or not at all.]

1 Oviduct	3 Ovary	5 Testes
2 Scrotum	4 Uterus	6 Vagina

6. Paired structure which produces sperm
7. Channel that leads to the outside of the body
8. Structure in which the fetus develops
9. Outer pouch of the body which contains sex glands
10. Organ in which the corpus luteum develops
11. A major advantage of sexual reproduction over asexual reproduction is that sexual reproduction results in (1) more rapid production of offspring, (2) a greater number of offspring, (3) greater variety of offspring, (4) larger offspring.
12. Which part of the differentiating embryonic cell seems to be most important in determining its ultimate fate? (1) the cell membrane, (2) the cytoplasm, (3) the yolk, (4) the follicle.
13. Which is classified as sexual reproduction? (1) conjugation, (2) budding, (3) sporulation, (4) vegetative propagation.
14. When a cell divides during the process of cleavage, each daughter cell, compared with the parent cell, has (1) less cytoplasm, (2) more cytoplasm, (3) more chromosomes, (4) fewer chromosomes.

15. Which structure most directly makes nutrients and oxygen available to the human embryo? (1) uterus, (2) placenta, (3) oviduct, (4) ovary.
16. Which will a developing human embryo normally *not* receive from the mother? (1) red blood cells, (2) calcium, (3) glucose, (4) oxygen.
17. Embryos of both sea and land animals develop in a watery environment. The fluid for the developing land animal is found within the (1) umbilical cord, (2) yolk sac, (3) amnion, (4) allantois.
18. Variety in the characteristics of offspring depends greatly on (1) regeneration, (2) asexual reproduction, (3) crossing-over, (4) mitosis.
19. The umbilical connection between the developing embryo and the placenta greatly reduces the significance of the (1) amnion, (2) yolk sac, (3) shell, (4) ovary.

Chapter 19 Sexual Reproduction in Plants

Is a tomato a fruit or a vegetable? "Who cares?" you may ask. But to a man who was importing tomatoes many years ago, it made a big difference in dollars. Fruits he could import free of duty, but if they were vegetables he would have to pay 10% to the government.

The case went before a judge. The judge agreed that to a *botanist* tomatoes, cucumbers, and beans are fruits. "But to *ordinary people*," he continued, "these are not fruits. Fruits are desserts that are eaten at the end of a meal. Vegetables, however, are grown in kitchen gardens and are eaten during the meal. I side with ordinary people. Tomatoes, as well as cucumbers and beans, are vegetables. Case closed. Pay the duty."

Why do botanists persist in calling tomatoes, cucumbers, and beans fruits? In this chapter on sexual reproduction in plants, you will learn the answer.

A The Flower

The reproductive structure of angiosperms is the flower. This is a stem with highly specialized leaves. Fertilization and meiosis both take place within the flower.

Structure of the Flower

Figure 19-1 is a diagram of a generalized flower. There are many variations on this general plan.

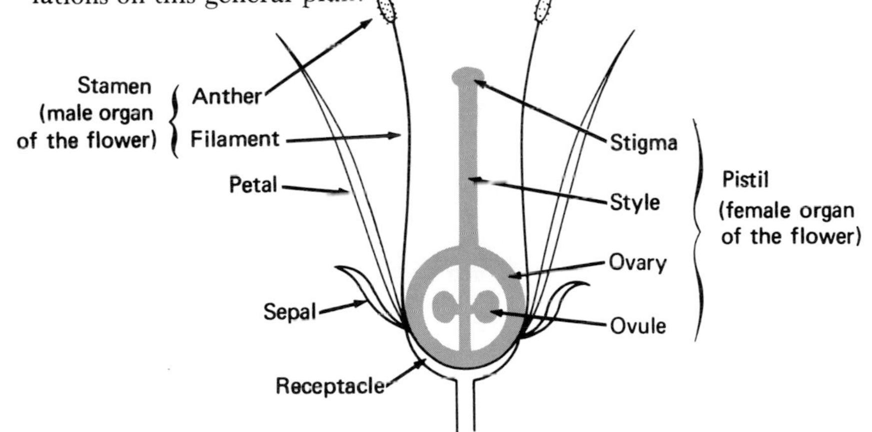

Fig. 19-1. Diagram of a generalized flower.

The parts of the flower are as follows:

Receptacle. The receptacle, or base, is the enlarged part of the stem. It supports the entire flower structure.

Sepals. The sepals are flower leaves that form an outer circle at the base. All the sepals together make up the *calyx*. The sepals protect the flower before it opens, when it is a bud. Typically, the sepals are green, but they may be as brightly colored as the petals.

Petals. The petals are the inner circle of flower leaves. All the petals together constitute the *corolla*. The petals of many flowers have bright colors, odors, or sugars that attract insects.

Stamens. Located inside the corolla is a ring of stamens. The *stamens* may be considered as the *male organs* of the flower because they ultimately give rise to the sperm nucleus. A knob-like sac at the top of the stamen is the *anther*, which produces pollen. The *filament* is a thread-like stalk that supports the anther.

Pistil. Inside the circle of stamens is the pistil. The *pistil* may be considered as the *female organ* of the flower because it ultimately gives rise to the egg nucleus. The pistil consists of three parts: (1) The *stigma*, an expanded, sticky top that receives the pollen; (2) the stalk-like *style*, that connects the stigma with the ovary; and (3) the enlarged base of the pistil, the *ovary*.

A flower may have several pistils. Inside the ovary are one or more *ovules*, attached to the ovary. Some flowers may have over a hundred ovules. The ovules within the ovary later become seeds. The ovary itself later becomes the fruit.

The *essential organs* of a flower are the stamens and pistils. The *accessory organs* are the petals and sepals.

Types of Flowers

A flower that possesses all four parts—calyx, corolla, stamens, and pistil—is a *complete* flower. If any of these parts is missing, the flower is *incomplete*. A *staminate flower* has only stamens among its essential organs. A *pistillate flower* has only a pistil or pistils. A *male plant* has only staminate flowers and a *female plant* has only pistillate flowers. A corn plant carries both staminate and pistillate flowers.

Much of the pleasure derived from studying flowers lies in observing the many variations from the generalized diagram presented here.

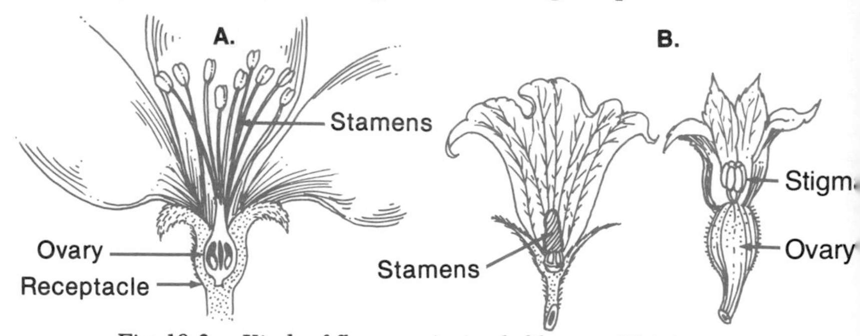

Fig. 19-2. Kinds of flowers. A. Apple blossom. This is a perfect flower containing all essential and accessory organs. Note that the ovary is below the sepals and petals, deep within the receptacle. The apple that you eat develops from the wall of the receptacle as well as the wall of the ovary. B. Squash. A single squash plant bears both staminate flowers (left) and pistillate flowers (right).

Development of the Pollen Grain

Cells of the plant and its flower have the diploid ($2n$) chromosome number. During the development of the pollen grains within the anther, *meiosis* occurs. As a result, the nucleus that develops within the pollen grain has the monoploid (n) chromosome number. When the pollen grains are ripe, the anther splits, leaving a huge number of pollen grains. The pollen grains also provide a protective shell to the sperm that prevents dehydration.

Development of the Ovule Diploid cells within the ovule undergo *meiosis* and other changes to form an oval-shaped *embryo sac*. Within this chamber there develop at least three monoploid nuclei. These are the *egg nucleus* and two *polar nuclei*. Figure 19-3 shows an ovule at the time of fertilization. The ovule walls have a minute opening, the *micropyle*. Near the micropyle is the stalk that attaches the ovule to the ovary.

As you can see, the female gamete lies within the embryo sac, that is within the ovule, that is within the ovary, that is part of the pistil, of a flower.

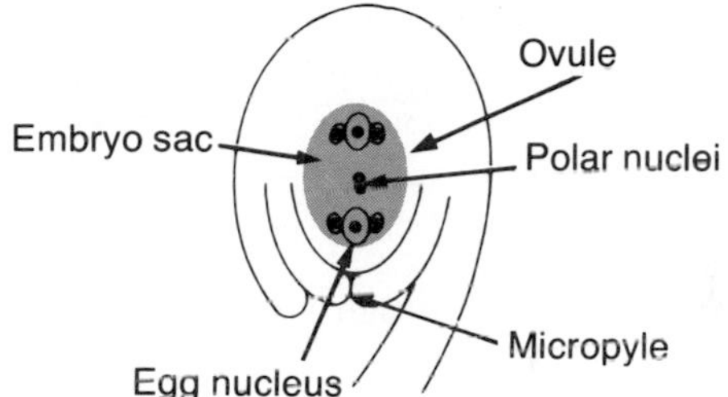

Fig. 19-3. The ovule at time of fertilization.

Pollination *Pollination* is the transfer of pollen from an anther to a stigma. When the anthers burst, they release pollen. Pollen grains may be carried by the wind to the stigmas of other flowers. This type of pollination is called *wind pollination*.

Some flowers are adapted for insect pollination. Insects that enter the flower in search of nectar pick up pollen on their bodies and carry the pollen to other flowers. Many farmers keep beehives in their orchards to insure pollination of the flowers of their fruit trees.

When pollen from an anther falls on the stigma of a flower on the same plant, the process is called *self-pollination* (Fig. 19-4). When pollen is transferred to the stigma of another plant of the same kind, the process is called *cross-pollination*.

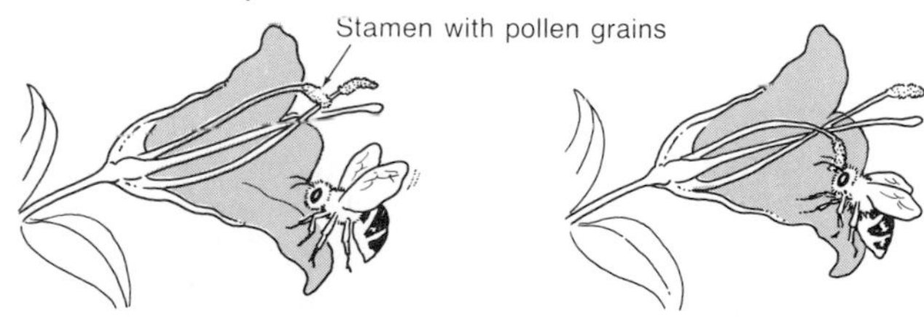

Fig. 19–4. Left: A bee lands on a flower. Right: The insect brushes against a stamen and picks up pollen. It later transfers this pollen to another flower.

Pollination may be accomplished by wind, water, insects, wandering animals, and birds. In *artificial pollination*, humans use a brush or the anther itself to transfer pollen from an anther to a stigma.

The thick wall of the pollen grain prevents dehydration of its contents during its transfer to the female reproductive organ. In this way, flowering plants solve the problem of reproduction in a dry external environment.

Growth of the Pollen Tube

Pollen grains that land on the stigma of a flower are held there by a sticky, sugary secretion. The pollen grain absorbs food and water from the stigma and develops a long *pollen tube* (Fig. 19-5). This digests its way through the stigma and style to the ovary.

Within the pollen tube three monoploid nuclei develop (Fig. 19-5). These are the *tube nucleus* and two *sperm nuclei.* The tube nucleus regulates growth of the pollen tube. One of the sperm nuclei will fertilize the egg nucleus that has developed within the ovule.

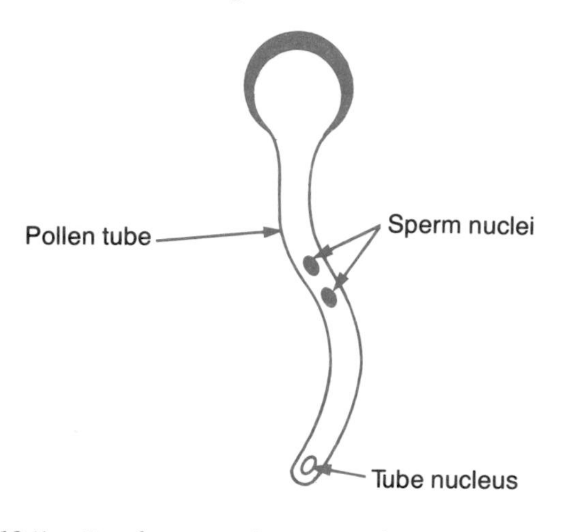

Fig. 19-5. Development of sperm nuclei within the pollen tube.

B

Fertilization

The pollen tube enters the ovule through the micropyle and discharges its two sperm nuclei into the embryo sac. Note that the sperm do not swim through water to reach the egg. Two fertilizations result (Fig. 19-6).

1. One sperm nucleus (n) unites with the egg nucleus (n). The diploid zygote resulting from this fertilization begins a series of mitotic cell divisions that ultimately result in the diploid embryo of the new plant.

2. The other sperm nucleus (n) unites with the two polar nuclei to form a triploid ($3n$) *endosperm nucleus.* Cell divisions from this nucleus result in the *endosperm.* This tissue provides food for the developing embryo. In many plants, the endosperm disappears and its function of storing and supplying food is taken over by a structure called the *cotyledon*, or seed leaf.

Fertilization in flowering plants is known as *double fertilization* because one sperm nucleus unites with the egg nucleus and the second sperm nucleus unites with the two polar nuclei.

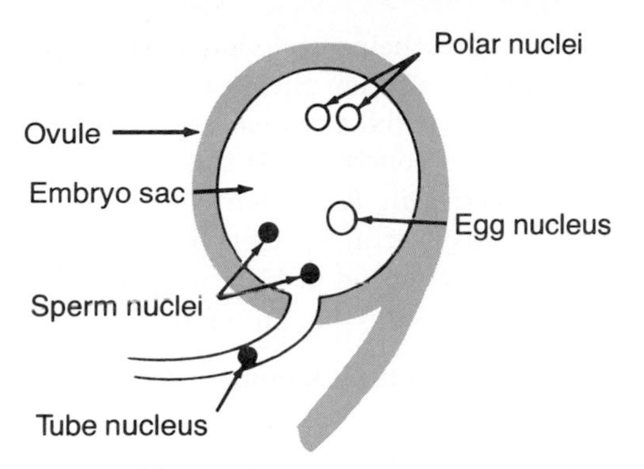

Fig. 19-6. Double fertilization. One sperm nucleus unites with the egg nucleus; the other sperm nucleus unites with the two polar nuclei.

C

The Seed and Fruit

In the flower, you recall, ovules are located within the ovary. After fertilization, *the ovules develop into seeds* and *the ovary develops into a fruit.*

Development of the Seed. As shown in Figure 19-7, a seed has three main parts:

(1) *The embryo.* The embryo develops by a series of mitotic divisions from the fertilized egg nucleus. The embryo has two main parts: the *hypocotyl* and the *epicotyl.* The hypocotyl later develops into the *roots* and part of the stem of the new plant. The epicotyl develops into part of the stem and the *leaves.*

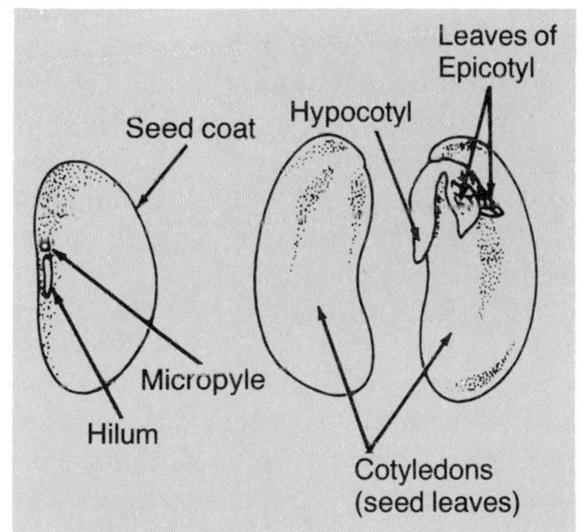

Fig. 19-7. Lima bean seed. External and internal views. Near the scar where the seed was attached to the fruit can still be seen the micropyle by which the pollen tube entered the ovule.

(2) *Food for the embryo.* The endosperm develops from the second fertilization and stores food for the embryo for a time. In most seeds, however, the function of the endosperm is taken over by a new tissue, the *cotyledon(s).* The two halves of a bean seed or of a peanut, for ex-

ample, are their cotyledons. The angiosperms are divided into two groups based upon their number of cotyledons. The *dicots* have two cotyledons and the *monocots* have one cotyledon. The major portion of a corn seed consists of its single cotyledon endosperm.

(3) *Seed coat.* The outer walls of the ovule become the *seed coat.* This hardened covering protects the embryo within from loss of water during the lengthy period of time until the seed is planted. When you soak a lima bean seed, you can see its wrinkled seed coat.

Development of the Fruit

While the ovule is ripening into the seed, changes are also occurring in the ovary that surrounds it. Generally, the ovary gets larger, develops a thick wall, and stores food and water. The specific changes which occur depend upon the type of plant. The ovaries of different plants develop in different ways for protection and dispersal of the seeds within.

A *fruit* is an enlarged ovary with its seeds and any parts of the flower which remain attached. An apple, an orange, or a bean pod are familiar examples of fruits, but a fruit need not be edible. For example, the "polly-noses," which develop on maple trees in the springtime are fruits, as are the "stickers" of the cocklebur plant, which catch on clothing in the autumn. Moreover, biologists do not recognize the distinction between "fruits and vegetables" made in the food market. A fruit is the ripened ovary of a flower; consequently, tomatoes and cucumbers are fruits. The major functions of the fruit are to protect and disperse seeds.

Seed Dispersal

Fruits have a variety of adaptations to ensure dispersal of their seeds to favorable locations. Seeds may be spread by (1) wind, (2) water, (3) animals, and (4) mechanical means. The fruits of the maple tree have wings. Dandelion seeds have parachutes. Milkweed seeds have tufts to help them float through the air. The light fibers of the coconut enable this fruit to float to distant shores. If you brush by the touch-me-not, leaves twisted by drying shoot the seeds a short distance. (A better name for this plant would be the "please-touch-me." Why?) The cocklebur and the burdock have hooks that catch on clothing or on animal fur. Edible fruits such as the cherry, peach, and apple are eaten by animals which spread the seeds.

Germination of the Seed

The embryo inside a seed is in a period of dormancy. It renews its growth (germinates) when the seed receives water, warmth, and oxygen. Many seeds do not germinate unless they have passed through a period of coldness. Growth takes place by rapid cell division in undifferentiated cells called meristem. The meristem at the tips of roots and stems is called *apical meristem.* Cell division is followed by cell elongation and then by differentiation into specialized tissues.

The bean seedling (Fig. 19-8) emerges from the ground in an interesting way. An arch of the root pierces the soil from below. This arch then acts as a spring to pull the rest of the embryo and the cotyledons above ground. The cotyledons spread apart and are sometimes called *seed leaves.* As the cotyledons provide food for the growing seedling they gradually shrink and wither. Meanwhile the epicotyl develops the first true, chlorophyll-bearing leaves and the new plant assumes its independent existence.

(D)

Alternation of Generations

During their lifetime, diploid *animals* produce monoploid gametes that fuse to produce, finally, the next generation that is diploid like their parents. *Plants*, however, have two different and distinct generations in their life cycle. One kind of individual is diploid and the other is mono-

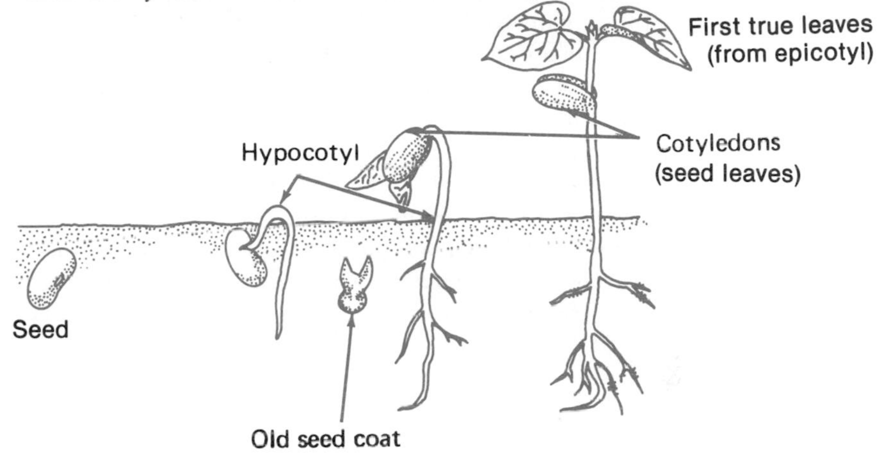

Fig. 19-8. Germination of a bean seed.

ploid. This sequence of diploid and monoploid generations is called *alternation of generations*. The two kinds of individuals that occur during the life cycle of a plant are called the *sporophyte* and *gametophyte* generations.

(1) The *sporophyte generation is diploid (2n)*. By *meiosis* these individuals produce monoploid (*n*) *spores*. The sporophyte thus reproduces *asexually*. Its monoploid spores develop into the gametophyte generation.

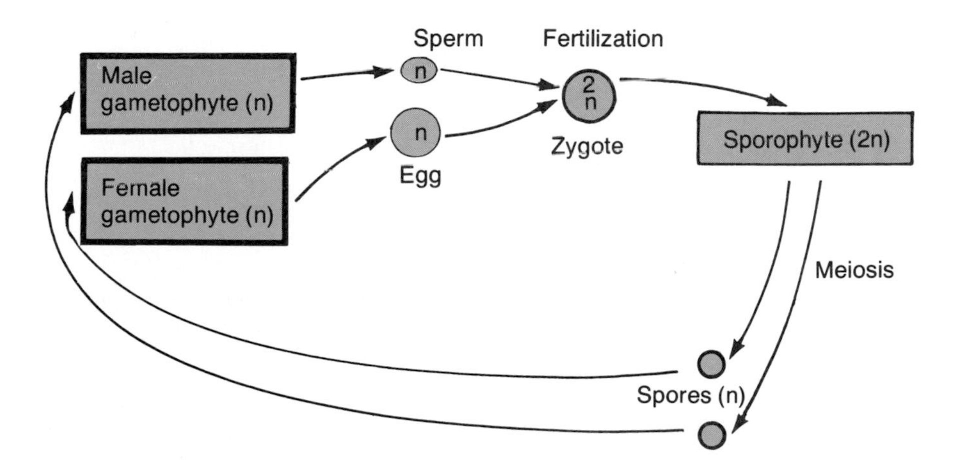

Fig. 19-9. Alternation of generations in a moss.

(2) The gametophyte generation is monoploid (n). These individuals produce monoploid *(n) gametes* by mitosis. The gametophyte, thus, reproduces *sexually.* The gametes fuse to form the zygote *(2n)* which develops into the sporophyte *(2n)* generation, and the cycle is completed.

Mosses

The details of this cycle vary in different plants but we shall consider the moss as an example in simple plants. In Fig. 19-9, we start at the left with the gametophyte generation. This is the familiar moss plant that you see as a carpet in moist places. Mosses have two kinds of gametophytes. One is the *male gametophyte* (*n*) and the other is the *female gametophyte* (*n*). By mitosis, these produce sperm (*n*) and eggs (*n*) respectively. The sperm swim through water to the eggs and fertilize them to produce the *zygote* (2*n*). The zygote develops mitotically into the sporophyte (2*n*). As shown in Fig. 19-10, the moss sporophyte grows up out of the female gametophyte as a slender thread, having a spore capsule at the top. By *meiosis*, the diploid sporophyte produces monoploid spores. These are of two kinds. One develops into the male gametophyte (*n*) and the other into the female gametophyte (*n*), completing the cycle.

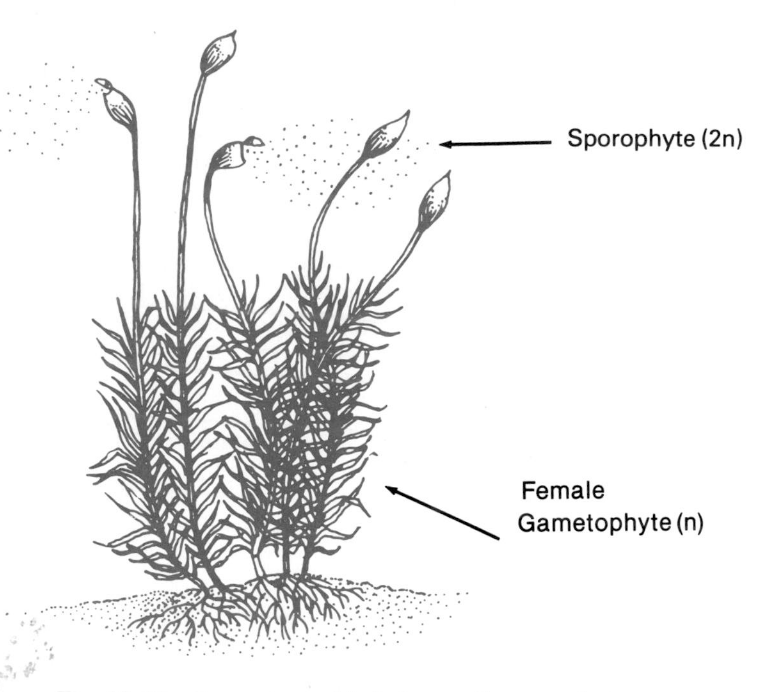

Fig. 19-10. In a common kind of moss, the sporophyte grows out of the female gametophyte.

In mosses, the gametophyte is the dominant, conspicuous generation whereas the sporophyte is less conspicuous and dependent. To emphasize the dominance of the gametophyte generation, this generation has bold outlines in Figure 19-9.

In ferns, the dominance is reversed. (See Fig. 19-11.) Here, the large, conspicuous fern plant that you see is the *sporophyte* ($2n$), not the gametophyte (n). On the underside of the leaves of some ferns, you may have noticed tiny brown dots. These are the location of sporangia that produce monoploid spores (n) by meiosis. These spores develop into the gametophyte (n). In ferns, the gametophyte is an inconspicuous, leaf-like structure that grows flat on the ground. Within special structures, the fern gametophyte produces eggs and swimming sperm by mitosis. Fertilization results in the zygote ($2n$) that develops into the large, diploid sporophyte plant that you recognize as a fern.

Flowering Plants

The trend toward the *ascendancy of the sporophyte* and the suppression of the gametophyte reaches a climax in the angiosperms, whose repro-

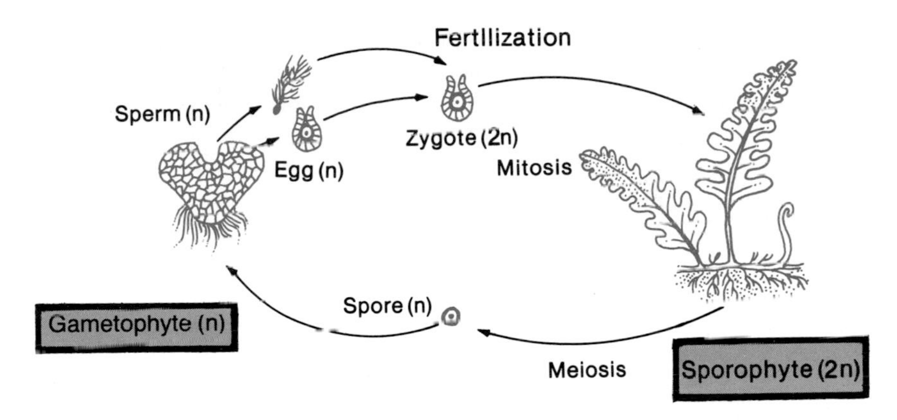

Fig. 19-11. Alternation of generations in the fern plant.

duction you have just studied. The large bean plant or maple tree that you see is the sporophyte ($2n$). Within the anther and the ovule of the flower are spores ($2n$) of two different sizes. *Meiosis*, and further changes from these spores, produce the male and female gametophytes (n). These are the *microscopic*, dependent pollen tube and embryo sac.

Is the gradual ascendancy of the diploid sporophyte generation associated with evolutionary survival value? Many biologists think so. They theorize that the presence of a *double set of chromosomes* in sporophyte individuals might provide insurance in the event of damage to one of the chromosomes of the homologous pairs. Damage to the monoploid gametophyte, however, is more likely to yield defective offspring which fail to survive.

Completion Questions

A B C

1. The male organ of the flower is the...... and the female organ is the ......
2. The three parts of the pistil are the......, ..., and......
3. What part of the stamen produces pollen?
4. The accessory organs of the flower are the...... and......
5. A flower having only pistils is a...... flower.

6. In pollination, a pollen grain is transferred to the. . . . . . of a pistil.
7. The sperm nuclei develop within the. . . . . .
8. The egg nucleus develops within the embryo sac that is found in the. . . . . .
9. The opening in the ovule wall is the. . . . . .
10. A seed is a ripened. . . . . .
11. A fruit is a ripened. . . . . .
12. The part of the embryo which develops into the roots is the. . . . . .
13. The part of the embryo which develops into the leaves is the. . . . . .
14. The process in which a seed starts to grow is called. . . . . .
15. Before green leaves are produced, the seedling is supplied with food by the . . . . . .

(D) 16. The cycle of switching between sexual and asexual generations is called. . . . . .
17. Gametes are produced by the. . . . . . generation.
18. The asexually-reproducing generation is the. . . . . . generation.
19. The dominant generation in simple plants such as mosses is the. . . . . . generation.
20. The evolution of complex plants is associated with the ascendancy of the. . . . . . generation.

Multiple-Choice Questions

Base your answers to questions 1 through 5 on the diagram below.

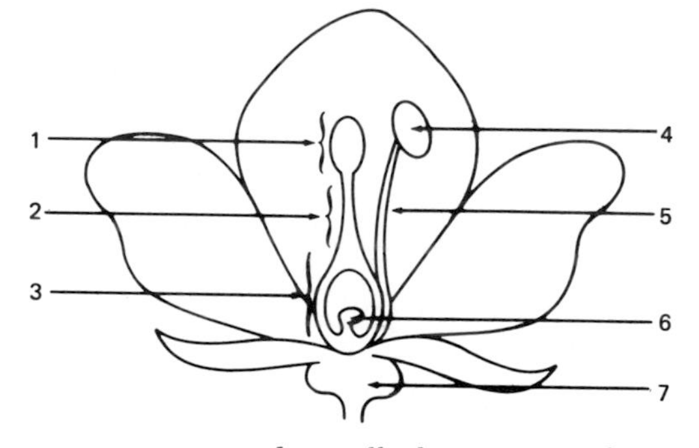

1. Which two structures produce cells that carry on the process of meiosis? (1) 1 and 2, (2) 2 and 5, (3) 6 and 7, (4) 4 and 6.
2. Which structure contains a female gamete? (1) 1, (2) 2, (3) 6, (4) 4.
3. Which structure may develop into a seed? (1) 1, (2) 6, (3) 7, (4) 4.
4. On which structure does a pollen grain normally begin to germinate? (1) 1, (2) 7, (3) 3, (4) 4.
5. Which structure may develop into a fruit? (1) 1, (2) 5, (3) 3, (4) 4.
6. The male reproductive organ of a flowering plant is the (1) pistil, (2) ovary, (3) stigma, (4) stamen.
7. Which structure includes the other three? (1) stigma, (2) pistil, (3) ovary, (4) ovule.
8. In a flowering plant, the process of meiosis occurs in the (1) ovules of the flowers, (2) cells of the root tips, (3) cells of the cambium, (4) developing plant embryos.
9. In which structure would you be most likely to find monoploid nuclei?

(1) yolk of a chicken egg, (2) seed coat of a bean seed, (3) ovule of a bean plant, (4) wall of a rabbit uterus.

10. Except for male and female gametes, the cells in a geranium plant are generally (1) monoploid, (2) diploid, (3) triploid, (4) polyploid.
11. Pollen tubes serve as passageways for (1) pollen grains, (2) sperm nuclei, (3) ovules, (4) egg nuclei.
12. If a plant has large colorful flowers, it is probably (1) wind pollinated, (2) insect pollinated, (3) self-pollinated, (4) water pollinated.
13. The stamen is to the sperm nucleus as the pistil is to the (1) stigma, (2) ovary, (3) embryo sac, (4) egg nucleus.
14. Which represents an adaptation in higher plants for reproduction in a dry land environment? (1) production of gametes with flagella, (2) protection of the male gametes inside pollen grains, (3) evolution of a placenta and umbilical cord, (4) development of an embryonic membrane known as the amnion.
15. Self-pollination can be prevented by removing the flower's (1) anthers, (2) petals, (3) sepals, (4) epicotyls.
16. In flowering plants, which represents the order of events for sexual reproduction? (1) fertilization, pollination, growth of pollen tube, formation of pollen; (2) formation of pollen, pollination, growth of pollen tube, fertilization; (3) growth of pollen tube, formation of pollen, pollination, fertilization; (4) growth of pollen tube, formation of pollen, fertilization, pollination.
17. The monoploid egg nucleus in flowering plants is produced in the (1) ovary, (2) filament, (3) stigma, (4) anther.
18. Germinating pollen grains of a plant contain (1) male gametes, (2) female gametes, (3) zygotes, (4) ovules.
19. In flowering plants, fertilization takes place in the (1) pollen tube, (2) stigma, (3) pollen grain, (4) ovule.
20. A pollen grain does *not* normally germinate until (1) a zygote is formed, (2) cleavage has occurred, (3) pollination has occurred, (4) a diploid nucleus is formed.

Base your answers to questions 21 through 24 on the diagram below of the internal structure of a bean seed.

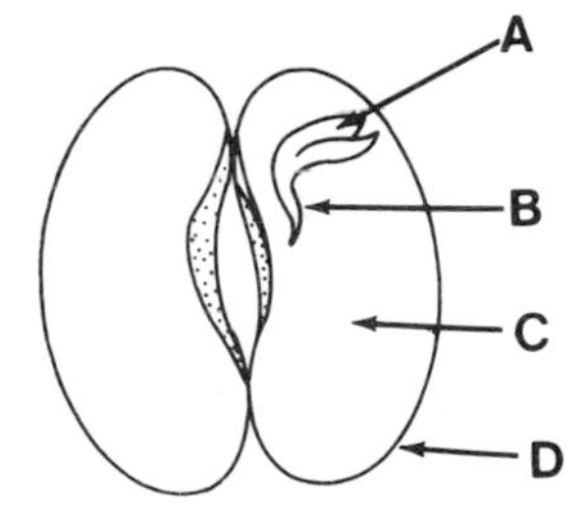

21. Which part would most probably turn blue-black if treated with iodine solution? (1) *A*, (2) *B*, (3) *C*, (4) *D*.
22. Which part of the seed is known as the epicotyl? (1) *A*, (2) *B*, (3) *C*, (4) *D*.
23. Which part of the seed develops into the lower part of the stem and roots? (1) *A*, (2) *B*, (3) *C*, (4) *D*.
24. Bean seeds of this type do *not* ordinarily germinate in seed packets because they lack (1) water, (2) light, (3) chlorophyll, (4) food.
25. The ripened ovary of a jewelweed plant pops open when it is touched.

This is an example of adaptation for (1) protection, (2) seed dispersal, (3) self-pollination, (4) cross-pollination.

26. Which three conditions are necessary for most plant seeds to germinate? (1) light, proper temperature, fertile soil; (2) oxygen, carbon dioxide, proper temperature; (3) fertile soil, oxygen, light; (4) moisture, proper temperature, oxygen.
27. Which structure in seeds has a function similar to that of the yolk in animal eggs? (1) epicotyl, (2) cotyledon, (3) hypocotyl, (4) ovule.
28. The cotyledon of a developing bean plant is most similar in function to the (1) yolk of a robin's egg, (2) shell of a robin's egg, (3) uterus in a cat, (4) umbilical cord in a cat.

Chapter Test

1. The opening in the ovule is the (1) embryo sac, (2) micropyle, (3) calyx, (4) pollen tube.
2. In dicot embryos food is stored in the (1) hypocotyl, (2) radicle, (3) epicotyl, (4) cotyledons.
3. Fertilization in higher plants takes place in the (1) ovule, (2) pollen tube, (3) stigma, (4) style.
4. If a plant has large colorful flowers, it is probably (1) wind pollinated, (2) insect pollinated, (3) self-pollinated, (4) water pollinated.
5. The stamen is to the sperm nucleus as the pistil is to the (1) stigma, (2) ovary, (3) embryo sac, (4) egg nucleus.
6. Which structure is found in bean seeds but *not* in fern spores? (1) embryo, (2) cell membrane, (3) nucleus, (4) chromosome.
7. The fruit is to the ovary as the seed is to the (1) ovule, (2) embryo, (3) stigma, (4) pollen tube.
8. The ripened ovary of a jewelweed plant pops open when it is touched. This is an example of adaptation for (1) protection, (2) seed dispersal, (3) self-pollination, (4) cross-pollination.
9. As seeds germinate, the starch they contain is converted to sugar. This process is necessary because (1) the enzyme used aids digestion, (2) only soluble materials may enter a living cell, (3) starch contains no energy, (4) amino acids are necessary for growth.
10. Pollen tubes serves as passageways for (1) pollen grains, (2) sperm nuclei, (3) ovules, (4) egg nuclei.

Unit 4 Reproduction and Development

Portfolio Project

Obtain a variety of flowers from a local florist. Dissect a flower and attach the parts to a large sheet of paper. Label each of the parts involved in sexual reproduction. Create a bulletin board display with the different types of flower parts. Compare the size and shape of parts that perform the same function but that are from different flowers.

UNIT FIVE GENETICS

Even in ancient days, people noticed that offspring tend to resemble their parents. They saw, however, that offspring may also differ from their parents; for example, brown-eyed parents may have blue-eyed children. To the medieval nobleman trying to breed sturdier war-horses, or to the farmer trying to obtain more eggs from his chickens, there seemed to be no pattern by which traits are passed from one generation to the next. Most people thought inheritance was carried through the blood. The expressions "blood relatives," and "bad blood" still persist in our language.

Today, we know that biological traits are carried by the DNA of chromosomes. DNA carries chemical instructions to cells in the form of a genetic code. We know that an individual's heredity consists of the code combinations received through the gametes of his or her parents. The branch of biology that studies the process of heredity is called *genetics*.

Chapter 20 Patterns of Heredity

Every day, it seems, DNA makes newspaper headlines. Transferring human DNA to bacteria puts these microorganisms to work, producing a plentiful and inexpensive source of human insulin and other hormones. Biologists may soon be able to alter human DNA to prevent hereditary diseases. Knowledge of DNA sheds new light on basic aspects of heredity and embryological development.

Long stretches of DNA in chromosomes are the units of heredity that we call *genes*. We shall return to DNA later in this unit. First, however, we will consider the general principles by which traits are passed from parents to offspring. Most of these principles were discovered by Gregor Mendel in the mid-1800s—over a century ago.

A Basic Mendelism

Gregor Mendel

When writing a scientific paper, a scientist thoroughly searches the literature to describe previous reports on that topic. That is how, in 1900, three investigators in three different countries of Europe brought to light the discoveries of Gregor Mendel—a third of a century after he reported them in 1866. The new group found that Mendel had long before predicted and explained some of their results. Mendel had discovered important principles of heredity. Many years after his death, Gregor Mendel was acclaimed as "The Father of Genetics."

Gregor Mendel (1822-1884) was born to peasants and received his education at a monastery in Brunn, Austria. After two years studying mathematics and science at the University of Vienna, he returned to the monastery as a teaching brother and eventually became abbot.

In the monastery garden, Mendel performed experiments on the inheritance of several plants, including the garden pea. Well aware of contemporary scientific theories, Mendel was probably seeking to determine if *new species* can arise through hybridization. His inconclusive results about new species received little attention when reported to a local scientific society or when published in 1866. Most biologists of that day, untrained in mathematics, could not understand his reasoning or were otherwise uninterested in his conclusions concerning hybridization.

One of Mendel's major contributions was to demonstrate that inherited characteristics are carried by *discrete units* (He called them "unit characters"). These are reassorted in different ways in each generation. Hybridization, thus, is like mixing billiard balls, not paint. These discrete units eventually became know as *genes*.

Reasons for Mendel's Success

Although Mendel knew of sperm and egg cells, chromosomes and their role in gamete formation had not been discovered. What were the reasons for Mendel's success in discovering basic principles of heredity?

1. **Use of favorable material.** The garden pea is easy to cultivate, produces a number of generations in a reasonably short time, and exists in several easily recognizable varieties. Because the plants are self-pollinating, the offspring usually have the same heredity as the parent.

When Mendel wished to mate two plants that differed in a trait, he would *cross-pollinate them*. For example, in mating a tall plant with a short one, he removed the anthers from a flower of the short plant before its own pollen was mature. He then dusted onto the stigma of this flower pollen from a flower growing on a tall plant. He also cross-pollinated in the opposite direction. Mendel was careful to prevent any stray pollination.

2. **Use of pure strains.** Mendel reasoned that a tall pea plant resulting from several generations of self-pollination by tall pea plants would be unlikely to carry heredity for shortness. That is, it is probably *pure* tall. Starting with pure strains provided good controls for all of Mendel's experiments.

3. **Careful choice of traits.** Some people are definitely tall and others are definitely short. But a complete range exists between these extremes. Height in humans, thus, is a *continuously* varying trait. Mendel, however, studied *discontinuous* traits. A short garden pea plant is a low-growing herb, but a tall one is a vine that needs support. Pea seeds are either green *or* yellow. They are either smooth *or* wrinkled. While only a few traits vary discontinuously, they are the simplest to study. Much of Mendel's success was due to this choice. Fortunately, as we now know, each trait he studied is carried on a different pair of chromosomes.

4. **Study of one trait at a time.** Experiments by Mendel's contemporaries usually considered many traits of an organism at the same time. Mendel's first experiments, however, focused on only a single trait at a time. This procedure simplified his problem.

5. **Use of mathematics and large numbers.** Instead of studying only a

few offspring resulting from a single mating. Mendel made the same kind of cross hundreds of times. One experiment had over 8,000 offspring. Mendel thus, had large numbers to work with.

Instead of merely noting, in a general way, the kind of offspring produced, Mendel counted the numbers of different kinds of offspring. He was thus able to calculate the ratios of offspring and to use these ratios in a mathematical manner to determine general principles.

The Principle of Dominance

When Mendel crossed pure *tall* pea plants with pure *short* pea plants, hundreds of seeds resulted. When planted, *all (100%) of these seeds developed into tall plants.* Similarly, in the six other experiments wherein he crossed plants which differed for a trait, *only one* of the alternative forms appeared in the next generation. For example, a cross between pure *yellow*-seeded plants and pure *green*-seeded plants resulted only in *yellow*-seeded plants. Accordingly, Mendel formulated the *Law of Dominance: In a cross between two pure contrasting traits only one of these traits appears in the next generation; this trait is the dominant trait and the one that does not appear is the recessive trait.*

In garden peas, the trait of tallness is dominant to shortness, the trait of yellow seeds is dominant to green seeds, and the trait of round seeds is dominant to wrinkled seeds. Other dominant traits found in garden peas are shown in the second vertical column of the table below.

Mendel's Results in Crossing Garden Peas for Two Generations

Parental Generation	F_1 Plants	F_1 Self-Pollination	F_2 Plants	F_2 Ratio
tall × short stems	all tall stems	tall × tall	787 tall stems 277 short stems	2.84 : 1
yellow × green seeds	all yellow seeds	yellow × yellow	6,022 yellow seeds 2,001 green seeds	3.01 : 1
round × wrinkled seeds	all round seeds	round × round	5,474 round seeds 1,850 wrinkled seeds	2.96 : 1
colored × white seed coats	all colored seed coats	colored × colored	705 colored seed coats 224 white seed coats	3.15 : 1
axial × terminal flowers	all axial flowers	axial × axial	651 axial flowers 207 terminal flowers	3.14 : 1
inflated × wrinkled pods	all inflated pods	inflated × inflated	882 inflated pods 229 wrinkled pods	2.95 : 1
green × yellow pods	all green pods	green × green	428 green pods 152 yellow pods	2.82 : 1

Today, we speak of genes with dominant and recessive alleles, not traits, and in many cases the principle of dominance does not apply.

Making Diagrams of Crosses

When heredity is traced for several generations, the following symbols are used: P = parental generation; F_1 = first filial generation; F_2 = second filial generation. ("Filial" is from the Latin word *filius* for son and refers to offspring.) In Mendel's experiments, the dominant traits appeared in the F_1 generation, the recessive traits did not.

Mendel then allowed the tall plants of the F_1 generation to self-pollinate themselves. The resulting seeds developed into the F_2 generation consisting of 787 tall plants and 277 short plants. This is a ratio of 2.84 tall to 1 short, or *approximately 3 tall to 1 short*. The results in all seven types of cross are shown in the table on the previous page.

In each case, the F_2 generation had a ratio of approximately 3 : 1. Mendel's results on the length of stem, for example, may be summarized as follows:

P pure tall × pure short
F_1 100% tall
F_2 tall, tall, tall, short (75% tall : 25% short)

Today, we interpret Mendel's results on the basis of what we know of chromosomes, meiosis, and fertilization. Figure 20-1 shows a pair of homologous chromosomes in a diploid cell. The genes are represented as filled circles in a line. At one *locus* (position) on these chromosomes is the gene controlling height. A gene may occur in alternative forms called *alleles*. In this case, there are two alleles of the gene for height: T represents the dominant allele for tallness and t represents the recessive allele for shortness. The capital first letter of the dominant trait symbolizes the dominant allele, while the recessive allele is symbolized by the same letter in lower case. T and t are also referred to as an allelic pair of genes.

As chromosomes separate during meiosis, their genes are carried into different gametes, as shown in the figure. The drawing at the right side of Fig. 20-1 merely uses symbols for the alleles being studied. **Tt** represents a plant all of whose body cells carry the alleles for T and t. **T** and **t** represent the two kinds of gametes formed by meiosis.

Pure and Hybrid

If both alleles are alike, the organism is *pure* or *homozygous* for that trait. All its gametes carry the same allele. If the alleles differ, the organism is *hybrid* or *heterozygous* for that trait. Half its gametes carry one allele and half carry the other allele. Thus, Fig. 20-1 represents a hybrid (heterozygous) plant.

Genotype and Phenotype

The *genotype* refers to the genetic makeup of an individual and can be ascertained by knowing its genes. The *phenotype* refers to the observable characteristics of an individual. The difference between these two terms is shown in the table below.

Comparing Genotype with Phenotype

Genes	Genotype	Phenotype
TT	pure tall	tall
Tt	hybrid tall	tall
tt	pure short	short

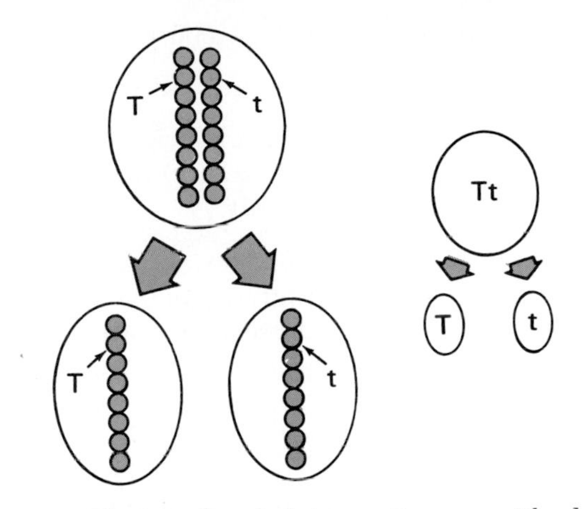

Fig. 20-1. The use of symbols in genetic crosses. The drawing at the left indicates an allelic pair of genes on homologous chromosomes which separate during meiosis. The drawing at the right merely uses the symbols for the gene's alleles.

Note that a pea plant whose phenotype is short must be *pure* short. If it were a hybrid, it would possess a dominant gene for tallness and consequently would not be short.

A Mendelian Experiment

With this background, you are now ready to consider some of Mendel's experiments in terms of genetics diagrams. We start with the cross between *pure tall* and *pure short* pea plants. Study Fig. 20-2. In the left group of drawings, the curved arrows show all the possible combinations of sperm cells and egg cells. If the F_1 generation consists of 500 offspring *all* are Tt. The genotype ratio is *100% hybrid tall*; the phenotype ratio is *100% tall.*

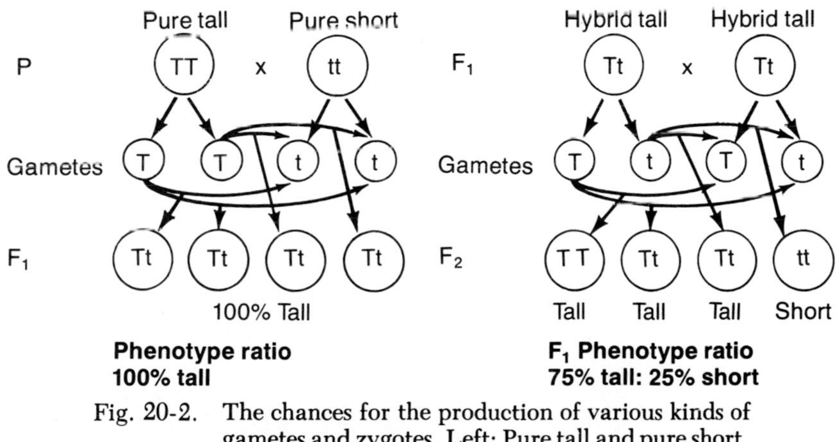

Fig. 20-2. The chances for the production of various kinds of gametes and zygotes. Left: Pure tall and pure short. Right: Hybrid tall.

What ratios can be expected from self-pollination of the F_1 hybrids? We show this cross at the right side of Fig. 20-2. We see that if 4,000 offspring are produced, 1,000 will probably be TT, 2,000 will be Tt, and 1,000 tt.

The genotype ratio is:
25% pure tall 50% hybrid tall 25% short
The phenotype (appearance) ratio is:
75% tall 25% short

The Law of Segregation

In the above set of problems, the recessive trait of shortness disappeared in the F_1 generation but reappeared in the F_2 generation. Why is this so? Mendel explained this reappearance of the recessive trait in the F_2 generation with his *Law of Segregation*. In modern terms, this law may be stated as follows: *During gamete formation, the two genes responsible for each trait separate from each other so that each gamete contains only one gene for each trait.* It is a tribute to Mendel's genius that he understood this principle without knowing about chromosomes and meiosis.

The Punnett Square, or Checkerboard Method

Sample problem 1. What is the expected ratio of offspring produced in crosses between hybrid tall pea plants and pure tall pea plants? (See Fig. 20-3 and Fig. 20-4 for the solution)

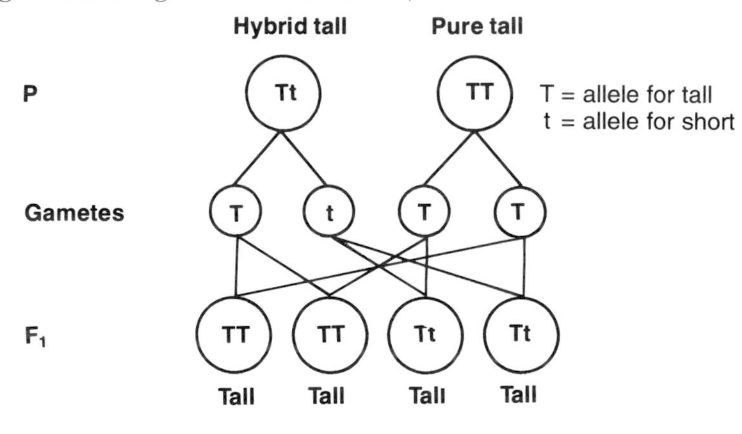

Fig. 20-3. Solution to sample problem 1. Unless the genotype ratio is specifically requested in the problem, only the phenotype ratio need be given as the answer.

In Fig. 20-4 we use lines drawn from the various gametes to show the possible fertilizations. It is more convenient to use the *Punnett square*, or *checkerboard method* to solve problems in genetics. Accordingly, in Fig. 20-4, we solve the same problem as in Fig. 20-3, using the Punnett square.

Note that the two kinds of sperm are placed at the top of the square and the two kinds of eggs at the side. Then carry the letters from the top of the square to each box below. Similarly, carry the letters from the side of the box to each box at the right. As a result, each box has two letters. These indicate the different kinds of zygotes formed — and how many of each kind there are.

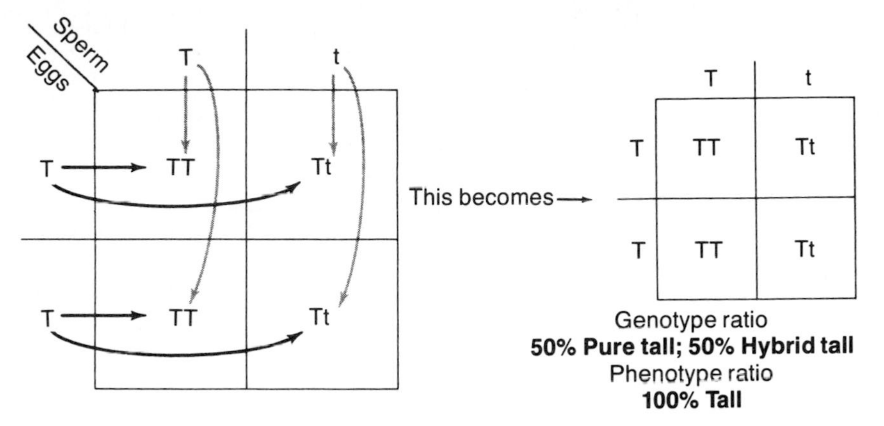

Fig. 20-4. Solution to sample problem 1 using the Punnett square or checkerboard method.

Sample problem 2. What ratios can be expected in the offspring of a cross between hybrid tall pea plants and short pea plants? (See Fig. 20-5 for solutions.)

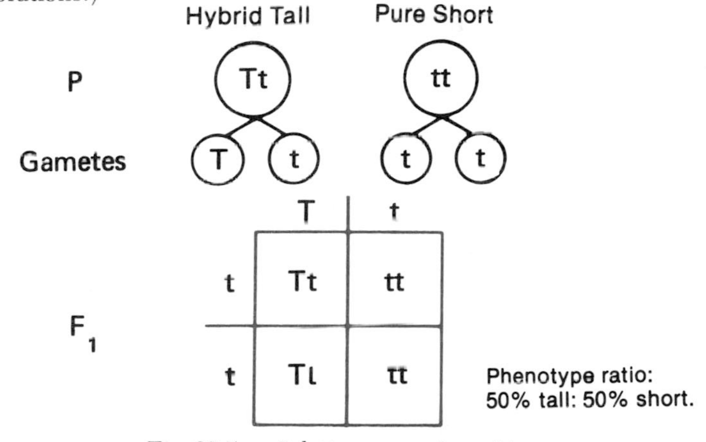

Fig. 20-5. Solution to sample problem 2.

This problem can be solved by inspection, merely by noting that it represents a cross between a hybrid and a recessive. The ratios produced are the same as for a cross between *Tt* and *tt* as shown in Fig. 20-6. The detailed solution is shown in Fig. 20-7.

Segregation Ratios

Note that the three problems shown in Figs. 20-2, 20-3, and 20-5 include all of the possibilities involved in crossing *hybrid* plants. The phenotype ratios determined are shown in the table of segregation ratios of Fig. 20-6.

Sample problem 3. Mendel found that wrinkled-seeded plants crossed with pure round-seeded plants resulted in 100% round-seeded plants. What ratio can be expected in crosses between wrinkle-seeded plants and hybrid round?

Tt × Tt	hybrid × hybrid	⟶	75% dominant: 25% recessive
Tt × TT	hybrid × pure dominent	⟶	100% dominant: 0% recessive
Tt × tt	hybrid × recessive	⟶	50% dominant: 50% recessive

In addition, the following ratios are apparent:

TT × TT	pure dominant × pure dominant	⟶	100% dominant
tt × tt	recessive × recessive	⟶	100% recessive
TT × tt	pure cominant × recessive	⟶	100% dominant

Fig. 20-6. Summary of segregation ratios obtained in various crosses. This is a useful tool for solving problems quickly by inspection. The top group indicates all cases where there is a hybrid. The phenotype ratios are shown on the right.

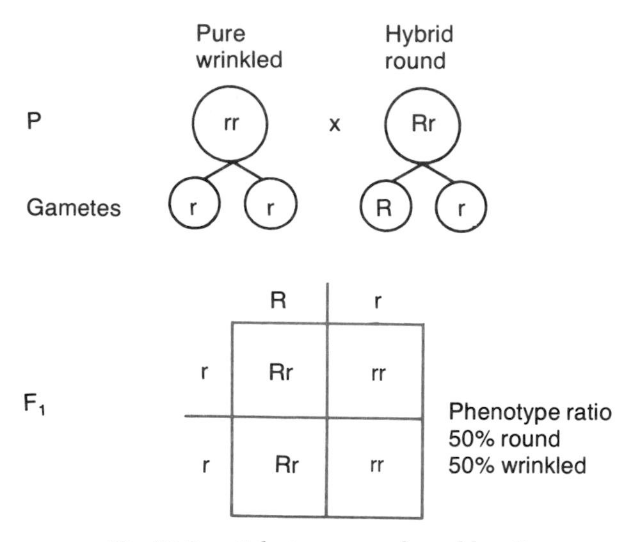

Fig. 20-7. Solution to sample problem 3.

The Need for Large Numbers

In tossing a coin, there is a 50% chance that a head will turn up. However, it is quite possible for you to toss a coin 10 times and obtain 8 heads and 2 tails. But if you tossed a coin *1,000* times and obtained 800 heads and 200 tails, you would suspect the coin to be "loaded"—that the laws of probability were not operating. As the number of trials increases, the ratios obtained are closer to those predicted by the laws of chance (or the laws of probability).

Which kinds of sperm and eggs unite at any mating is also a matter of chance. Consequently, the expected Mendelian ratios are more likely to appear when many offspring are produced.

Sample problem 4. Black coat color is dominant over white coat in guinea pigs. A cross between two black guinea pigs resulted in four offspring, all of which were black. Could both parents be hybrids?

The results of mating black parents can be represented by three possibilities (A, B, and C):

(A) *Bb* x *Bb* → 75% black: 25% white
(B) *BB* x *BB* → 100% black
(C) *Bb* x *BB* → 100% black

Answer: Yes, as in possibility (A). Although the first four offspring were black, the next few offspring could be white. Then the 75 : 25 ratio would become apparent. Four offspring constitute too small a number to rule out the possibility of the (A) mating.

The Test Cross (Back Cross)

A student wishes to determine whether a black guinea pig is pure black or hybrid black. What cross could be made to find out?

Recall that, in guinea pigs, the color black is dominant and the color white is recessive. If the student selects a *white* guinea pig for mating with a black one, the genotype of at least one of the parents is known—the white one must be *pure white*. The student can use this pure recessive to make a test. The two possibilities are shown in Fig. 20-8.

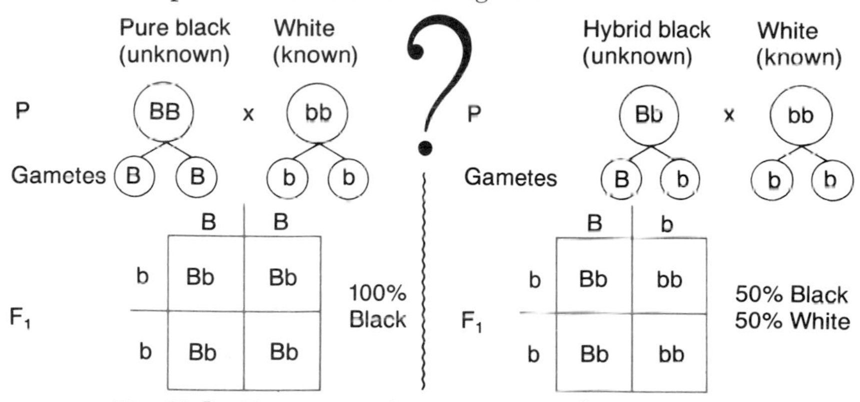

Fig. 20-8. Test cross with guinea pigs. Make many crosses between the unknown black and a (pure) white. If the offspring are *100% black* (as at the left), you know that the unknown is *pure* black. If the offspring are *50% black: 50% white*, (as at the right) you know that the unknown is *hybrid* black. The *first* time that a white offspring appears, you know that the unknown is a hybrid. *Why?*

The more black offspring that are obtained, the more likely it is that the unknown is pure black.

A *test cross*, or *back cross*, is a method for determining the genotype of an organism by mating it with a pure recessive.

Dihybrids and the Law of Independent Assortment

Until now, we have considered only a single trait at a time. For example, we have considered the trait of height in pea plants and the trait of fur color in guinea pigs. Let us now consider a cross in pea plants that differ in *two traits*—in *height* and *seed color* (See Fig. 20-9).

Sample problem 5. Show the results of a cross between pea plants that are pure *tall* and pure *yellow* for seed color with pea plants that are *short* and have *green* seeds.

The genes for height and for seed color are carried on different chromosomes, as shown in Fig. 20-9. As shown in the diagram, when gametes are produced by a plant which is pure for both tallness and for yellow color of seeds, each gamete receives an allele for tallness and an allele for yellow seed color.

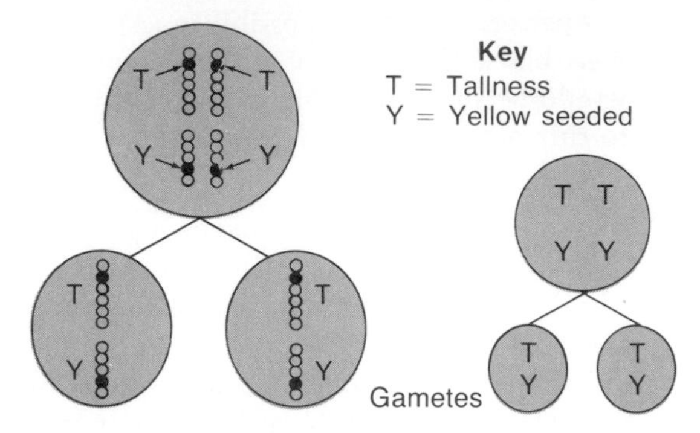

Fig. 20-9 Loci of genes for height and for seed color. These genes are carried by different chromosomes.

Now we are ready to diagram the cross of sample problem 5. This is done in Fig. 20-10. The results show the F_1 offspring to be hybrid for both height and for color. Such an individual is a *dihybrid*. An individual that is hybrid for only one trait is a monohybrid.

Let us proceed to the next generation. What can we predict from a cross between the F_1 dihybrids? This cross is started in Fig. 20-11.

When the homologous chromosomes line up and then separate during meiosis, two kinds of gametes formed are *TY* and *ty*. However, if the chromosomes line up differently during synapsis, there is an equal chance for the formation of the gametes *Ty* and *tY*. Consequently, a dihybrid may produce equal numbers of *four* different kinds of gametes, as shown in the diagram.

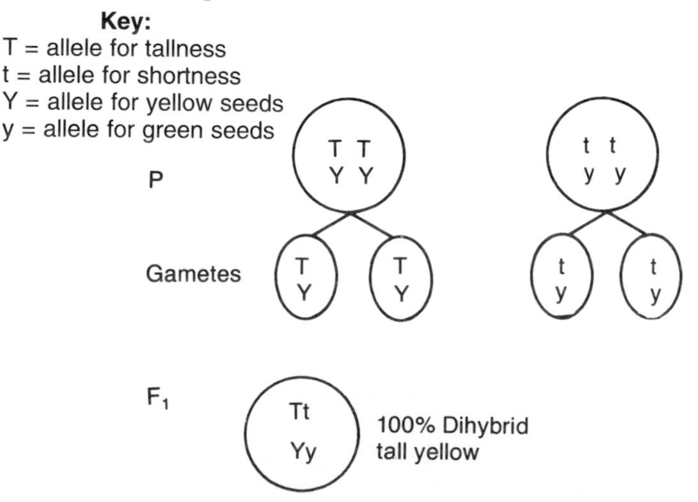

Fig. 20-10. Pure tall yellow × short green.

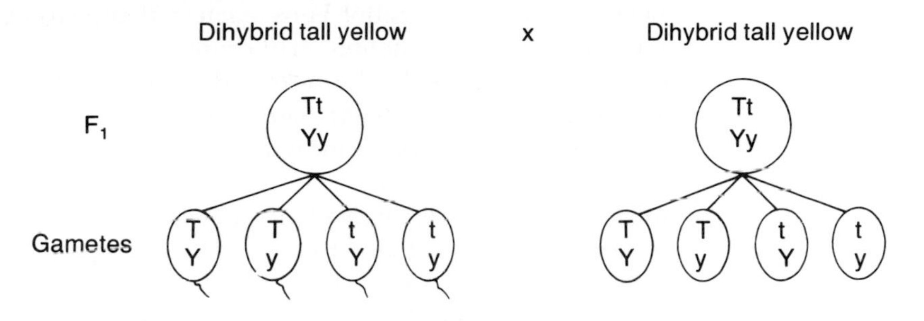

Fig. 20-11. Gametes produced by a dihybrid. Equal numbers of *four* kinds of gametes may participate in fertilization.

To represent the possible fertilizations, we again use a Punnett square. Now, however, the square must be large enough to accommodate the four different kinds of male and female gametes. This square is shown in Fig. 20-12.

	T Y	T y	t Y	t y
T Y	T T Y Y	T T y Y	t T Y Y	t T y Y
T y	T T Y y	T T y y	t T Y y	t T y y
t Y	T t Y Y	T t y Y	t t Y Y	t t y Y
t y	T t Y y	T t y y	t t Y y	t t y y

Fig. 20-12. Punnett square for dihybrid cross.

Four different kinds of phenotypes are produced as shown below. In italics, we indicate how many of each phenotype we can expect.

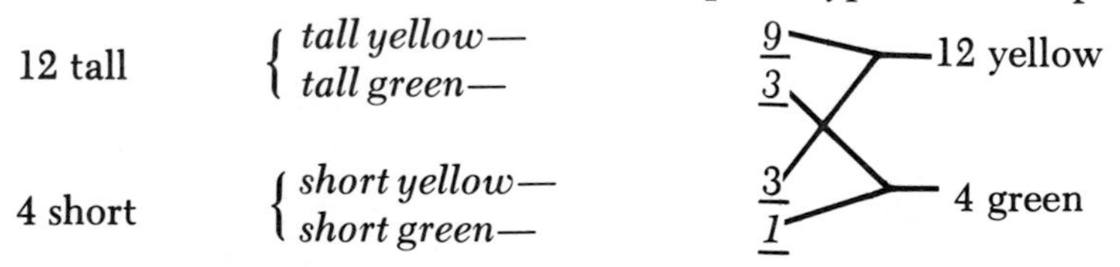

Thus, *a cross between two dihybrids yields a 9:3:3:1 ratio.*

Of additional interest, however, is that fact that there are 12 tall plants to 4 short plants. The 3 : 1 ratio of tall to short still appears in this dihybrid cross. Similarly, there are 12 yellow-seeded plants to 4 green-seeded ones—again the 3 : 1 ratio! Thus, each trait appears in the same ratio as if it were alone in a monohybrid cross.

His results with dihybrid crosses led Mendel to formulate his third law, the *Law of Independent Assortment: When dihybrid plants are crossed, the factor for each trait is distributed independently of the factors for all other traits.*

Alleles of genes that are located on different chromosomes are distributed independently because the chromosomes carrying these genes segregate independently during meiosis. This law applies only if the genes involved are on different chromosomes. It is a remarkable coincidence that 5 of the genes for the 7 traits studied by Mendel are on different chromosomes, while the other 2 genes are on opposite ends of yet another chromosome in the pea!

Incomplete Dominance

In the Japanese Four O'Clock plant, red-flowered plants crossed with red-flowered plants produce red-flowered offspring. Similarly, white-flowered plants crossed with white-flowered plants produce white-flowered offspring. What is the result of crossing *red* with *white?* Examine Fig. 20-13. The F_1 generation is 100% pink! Obviously, this cross represents a different type of heredity—one wherein the Law of Dominance does not operate. This type of heredity, in which the hybrid is noticeably different from both purebred parents, is known as *incomplete dominance.*

Apparently, it takes two "doses" of the gene for red to produce the red color. If there is only one gene for red, the amount of pigment produced is less, and the petals are pink.

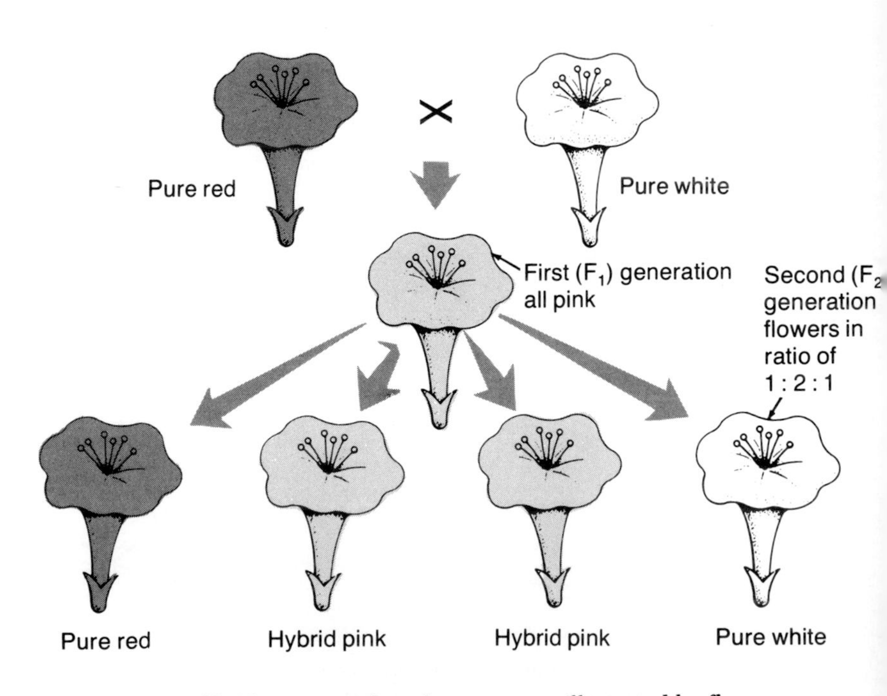

Fig. 20-13. Incomplete dominance as illustrated by flowers of Japanese Four-O'clock plant.

We analyze this cross in Fig. 20-14 using this key:

Key: *R*— allele for red *W*— allele for white *RW* = pink (phenotype)

Since neither red nor white is dominant, we use the capital initial letter for each allele. Pink results from the combined influence of the alleles for red and white.

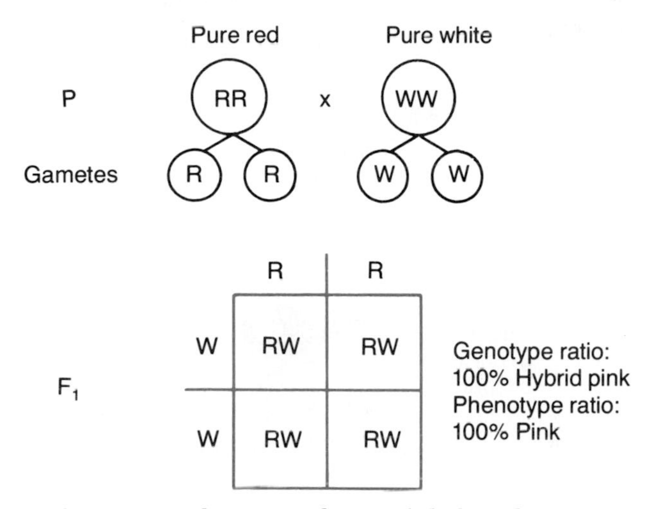

Fig. 20-14 Cross between red Four O'Clocks and white Four O'Clocks.

Sample problem 6. What ratios may be expected in a cross between pink flowered Japanese Four O'Clocks? (Fee Fig. 20-15.)

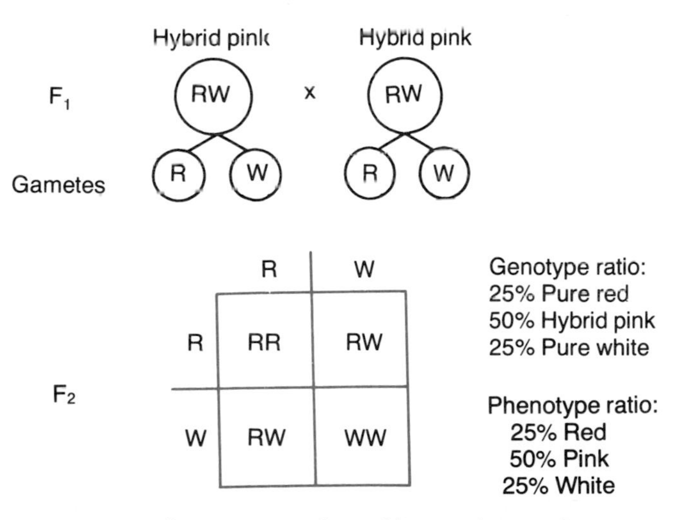

Fig. 20-15. Solution to sample problem 6. (Note: The genotype ratio is the same as the phenotype ratio: 25% pure red : 50% hybrid pink : 25% pure white.)

Another well-known example of incomplete dominance is feather color in the Andalusian fowl. These highly prized roosters and chickens from the Andalusian section of Spain may be pure black, pure white, or a speckled blend of black and white. This speckled blend appears *blue*. When blue Andalusian fowls are mated, their offspring occur in the ratio of 25% black : 50% blue : 25% white (Fig. 20-16).

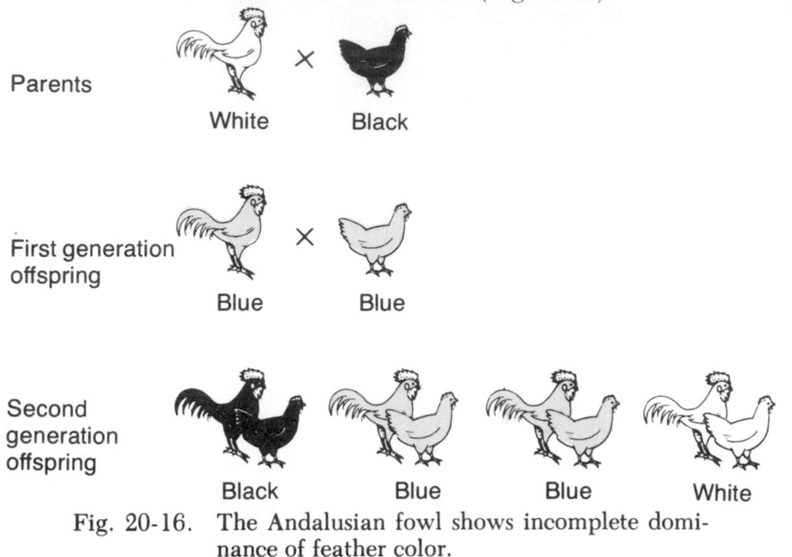

Fig. 20-16. The Andalusian fowl shows incomplete dominance of feather color.

Codominance

Roan Cattle. Matings between red shorthorn cattle and white ones produce offspring with an intermediate coat color known as *roan*. The roan appearance is due to a mixture of red hairs and white ones. This pattern of inheritance involves the expression of two dominant alleles and is known as *codominance*. The homozygous red color may be symbolized as C^RC^R, the homozygous white color as C^WC^W, and the heterozygous roan as C^RC^W. Examples of codominance in humans are sickle-cell anemia and blood type.

Reasoning Exercises

1. Show by means of keyed and labeled diagrams the ratio of offspring expected in each of the following: (A) A cross between hybrid tall garden pea plants and pure tall garden pea plants. (B) A cross between hybrid tall and short. (C) A cross between hybrid tall and hybrid tall.
2. Summarize the ratios obtained in problem 1 by extending each of the following: $Tt \times Tt \rightarrow$ $\quad Tt \times tt \rightarrow$ $\quad TT \times tt \rightarrow$
   $Tt \times TT \rightarrow$ $\quad TT \times TT \rightarrow$ $\quad tt \times tt \rightarrow$
3. Black coat color in guinea pigs is dominant over white coat color. (A) By means of keyed and labeled diagrams, show the results of crossing a hybrid black with a white. (B) Show the results of crossing a pure black and a hybrid black.
4. In pigs, the white color *W* is dominant; the black color *w* is recessive. Using diagrams, show the expected results of the following crosses: (A) A pure white pig is mated with a black pig. (B) A hybrid pig is mated with a hybrid pig.
5. What were the parents of the following groups of offspring from guinea pig crosses? Give all possibilities, assuming that the laws of chance operate:
   (A) One-half of the offspring are black.

(B) Three-fourths of the offspring are black.
(C) One-half of the offspring are hybrid black.
(D) All of the offspring are black.
(E) All of the offspring are white.
(F) One-half of the offspring are white.
(G) One-fourth of the offspring are white.

6. Explain with the aid of keyed and labeled diagrams how you would determine whether a squirrel is pure gray or hybrid gray. (Gray is dominant over black.)
7. After several matings of tan-colored birds, the following offspring resulted: 23 white, 26 brown, 53 tan. By means of keyed and labeled diagrams, show each of the following: (A) A cross that would produce 50% of all offspring brown. (B) A cross that would produce 100% of all offspring tan.
8. There are three types of radishes: round, oval, and long. A breeder made three crosses, and obtained the results indicated below. Using keyed and labeled diagrams, show the crosses in each.
   (A) *First cross:* Long with round gave 342 oval.
   (B) *Second cross:* Long with oval resulted in 48 long and 52 oval.
   (C) *Third cross:* Oval with round resulted in 141 oval and 137 round.
9. A black guina pig was crossed with a white guinea pig. All of the individuals in the F_1 generation were black. These individuals were then crossed among themselves, resulting in 30 black guinea pigs and 10 white guinea pigs.
   (A) How many of the black pigs in the F_2 generation would be (1) pure dominant? (2) hybrid?
   (B) How many of the white pigs in the F_2 generation would be (1) reessive? (2) hybrid?
10. What ratios may be expected in a cross between a red-flowered Japanese Four O'Clock plant and a pink one?
11. What ratios may be expected in a cross between a white-flowered Japanese Four O'Clock and a pink one?
12. What ratios may be expected in a cross between a blue Andalusian fowl and a black one?

B

The Drosophila Era

It was not until the early 1900s that Mendel's principles were interpreted in terms of the distribution of chromosomes during meiosis. Shortly thereafter, great advances in genetics resulted from experiments performed on the fruit fly, *Drosophila*, by Thomas H. Morgan and his associates at Columbia University. Many of the ideas that we shall discuss in this section were an outgrowth of experiments on *Drosophila*, performed in many laboratories, in the first third of this century.

Characteristics of Drosophila

Drosophila melanogaster, the fruit fly, is a tiny fly which is often found around grapes and rotting bananas. (See Fig. 20-17.) *Drosophila* possesses the following characteristics which made it an ideal organism for experimental studies in genetics:

1. **Short life cycle.** Its entire life cycle is only 14 days. Thus, many generations can be bred within a short period of time.
2. **Many offspring.** One pair of parents may produce over 300 off-

spring. Thus, the large numbers required for accurate ratios are easily obtained.

3. **Small size.** A half-pint milk bottle can accommodate several hundred individuals.

4. **Modest food requirements.** Corn meal and molasses, with a little agar added, is a commonly used culture medium.

5. **Few chromosomes.** *Drosophila* has only four pairs of chromosomes. These are recognizable by their size and shape (Fig. 20-17).

6. **Giant chromosomes.** In the salivary glands of one stage of the *Drosophila* larvae were found greatly enlarged chromosomes—the *giant chromosomes* of *Drosophila* (Fig. 20-17). Light staining and dark staining bands on these chromosomes permitted the study of fine detail.

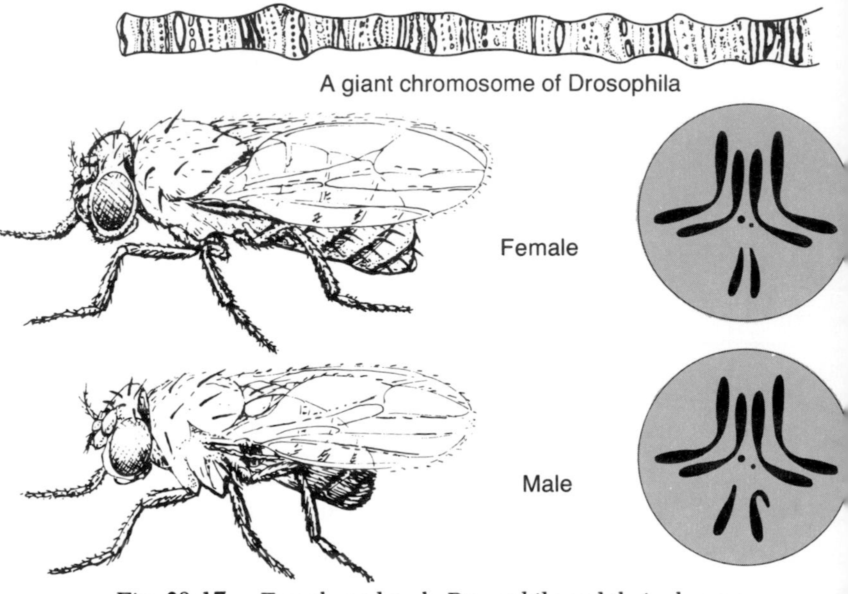

Fig. 20-17. Female and male *Drosophila* and their chromosomes.

7. **Mutant forms.** Sometimes new traits appeared in *Drosophila* cultures. The new trait, if passed on to succeeding generations by heredity, is called a *mutation*. Morgan was able to locate the genes for many mutations on gene maps which he prepared of the chromosomes of *Drosophila*. Some of the mutant forms of *Drosophila* are shown in Fig. 20-18.

Although *Drosophila* remains an active subject for research, it has largely been supplanted by bacteria and by molds (such as *Neurospora*). These organisms are much smaller than *Drosophila;* they reproduce more rapidly, and they are good subjects for studying the biochemical reactions caused by genes.

Linkage

According to the *Law of Independent Assortment*, each trait is inherited independently of other traits. Geneticists, however, began to find exceptions to this rule. Some traits seemed to stick together with other traits. Traits that are inherited together are said to be *linked*. In the fruit fly *(Drosophila)*, four large groups of traits were found to be linked.

Drosophila has four pairs of chromosomes, corresponding to the number of linkage groups. The concept emerged, therefore, that when traits are linked it is because the genes which determine these traits are present on the same chromosome.

As previously stated, Mendel was fortunate in that the traits which he studied were on different chromosomes. He did not have to face the complexities of linkage.

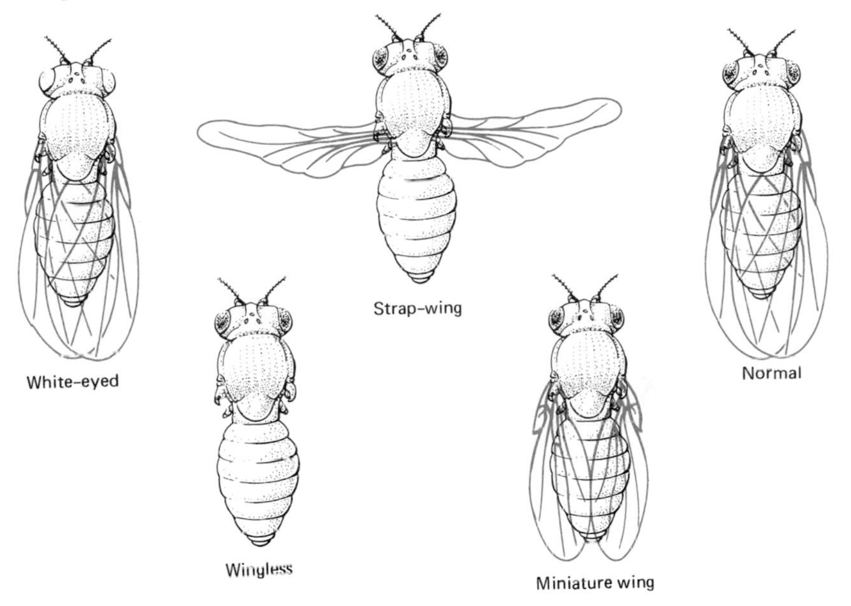

Fig. 20-18. Mutant forms of *Drosophila* compared with the normal "wild type."

Crossing-Over

Linkage is an exception to independent assortment; crossing-over is an exception to linkage. *Crossing-over* is the breaking of linkage groups and the exchange of these linkage groups between homologous chromosomes. This exchange occurs during meiosis when homologous doubled chromosomes pair during synapsis to form tetrads. Crossing-over was described in Chapter 18, without mention of genes. Figure 20-19 shows how new gene combinations are produced by crossing-over. Crossing-over occurs frequently and increases the variety of gametes—and zygotes—that are produced by sexually reproducing organisms.

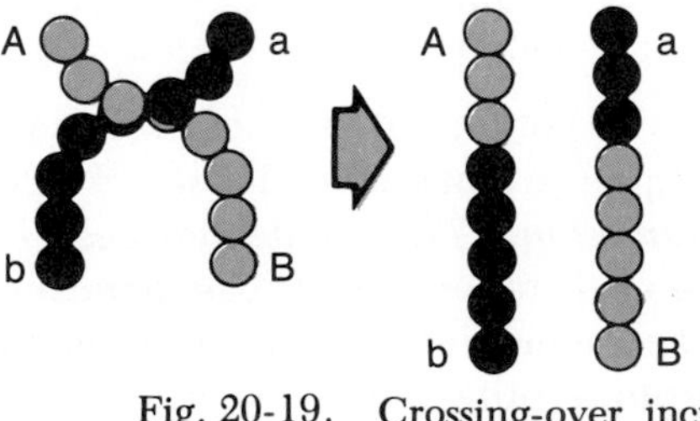

Allele A, which was linked to allele B, is now linked to allele b; and allele a, which was linked to allele b, is now linked to allele B.

Fig. 20-19. Crossing-over increases the variability of the gametes.

Theory of the Gene Morgan and his associates were largely responsible for developing the theory of the gene. By the late 1930s, this theory included the following concepts:

1. Genes in a chromosome are arranged in a row, like the cars of a train.
2. Traits which are inherited together are controlled by genes which are linked on the same chromosome.
3. Linkage groups may be broken by crossing-over.
4. The position of genes on a chromosome may be determined and may be indicated on gene maps.

For his contributions to genetics Morgan was awarded the Nobel Prize in 1933. Since then, the theory of the gene has been greatly expanded, especially since the discovery of DNA and its structure.

Sex Determination Figure 20-20 is a *karyotype* showing an orderly arrangement of human chromosomes. This figure was made by photographing through a microscope the contents of a ruptured human diploid cell during metaphase. Then the photograph was enlarged and the chromosomes cut out with scissors. The chromosomes were paired by shape, and arranged in order of decreasing size. Each pair of chromosomes is given a number from 1 to 22, except for the last pair.

Male karyotype | Female karyotype

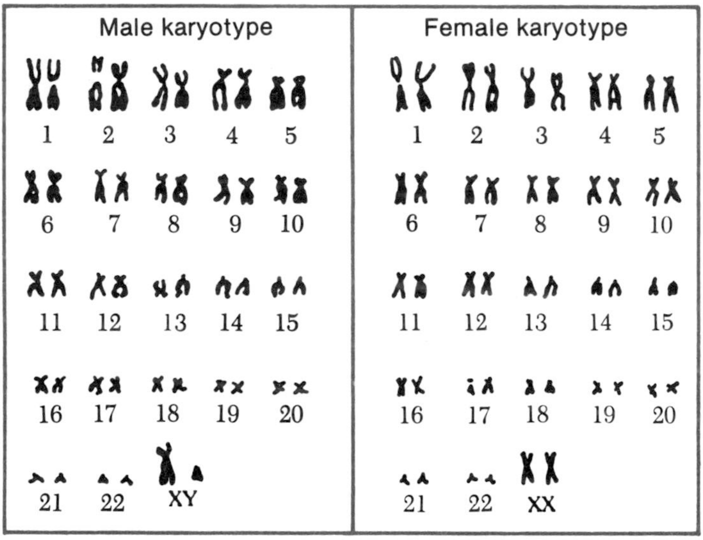

Fig. 20-20. Human karyotypes.

Compare the male karyotype with that of the female. In the male, the members of the last pair are not alike. These are called the *X chromosome* and the *Y chromosome. The female, however, has two X chromosomes*. This last pair of chromosomes are called the *sex chromosomes* because they determine the individual's sex. The other 22 pairs of chromosomes, which determine other body characteristics, are called *autosomes*.

Disregarding the autosomes, we can represent a mating as shown in Fig. 20-21.

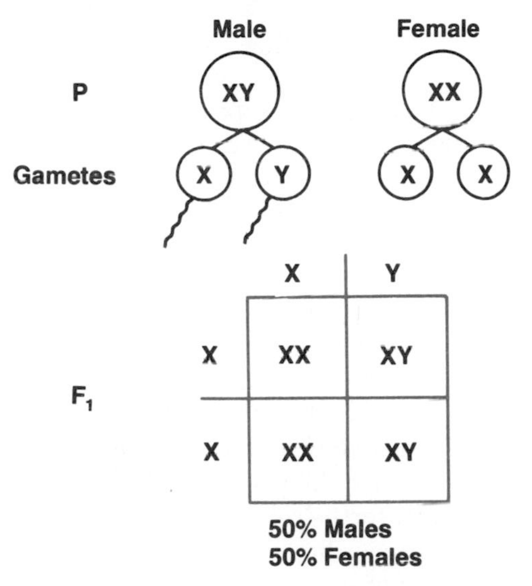

Fig. 20-21. Male × female.

This pattern of sex determination, that is followed in most animals, was discovered by Morgan and his co-workers in their study of *Drosophila*. In *Drosophila*, which has only 4 pairs of chromosomes, the sex chromosomes are relatively easy to identify (Fig. 20-23).

The symbol ♂, representing Hermes' sword and arrow, is used to designate males; and the symbol ♀, representing Aphrodite's looking glass, is used for females.

At any one mating, millions of sperm enter the oviducts, Half of the sperm carry the X chromosome; half carry the Y chromosome. All the ova carry the X chromosome. If an X-carrying sperm fertilizes an ovum, the fertilized egg develops into a female if a Y-carrying sperm fertilizes the ovum, a male results. The sex of an individual is thus determined at the time of fertilization by the X or Y chromosome donated by the male. (See Fig. 20-22.)

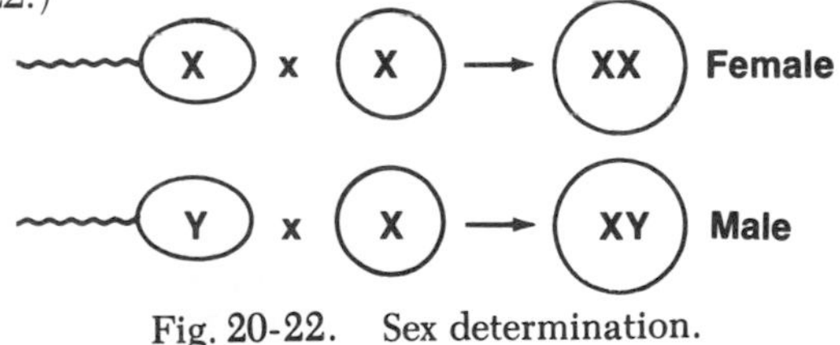

Fig. 20-22. Sex determination.

On the basis of chance, we expect that in a large number of human offspring there would be a 50:50 ratio of boys to girls. Birth statistics for the entire United States, however, depart from the ideal ratio. The ratio at birth is 106 boys:100 girls. Moreover, if the larger number of prenatal deaths of male fetuses is taken into account, the ratio at conception is about 114:100. This disparity is large enough to have statistical

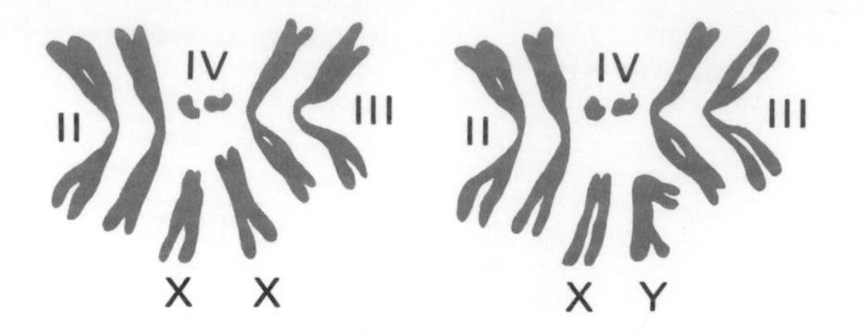

Fig. 20-23. The chromosomes of female and male *Drosophila*. Each chromosome is a doubled chromosome composed of a pair of chromatids.

significance and indicates an advantage of the Y-carrying sperm ove the X-carrying sperm. Experiments have shown that the Y-sperm ar generally speedier than the X-sperm. The two groups in a mixture hav been separated on the basis of their speed.

Conditions of alkalinity and acidity favor one kind of sperm over th other. Since the pH of the female reproductive tract varies during th monthly fertile period, the date of conception can affect the attained se ratio. Accordingly, some success has been achieved in improving th chances of having a child of the desired sex.

Sex Linkage Why are more men than women color-blind? Why is *hemophili* (bleeder's disease) found more frequently in men than in women Such traits that occur more often in one sex than the other are example of *sex-linked inheritance*. They are carried by the sex chromosome rather than by the autosomes.

Hemophilia. *Hemophilia* is a hereditary condition in which the bloo clots very slowly. Prolonged bleeding can result from the slightes scratch. This disease was common in several royal families of Europe one of which traces its lineage back to Queen Victoria of England. To day, it is found in nonroyalty as well. Hemophilia is found more fre quently in males than in females and the gene for the disease is carrie in the sex chromosomes.

In Fig, 20-24, we represent the X chromosome as a bar and the chromosome as a shorter bar with a hook to help identify it. The sma circle represents the normal allele which causes blood to clot properly. Not that this gene is located *in that portion of the X chromosome which*

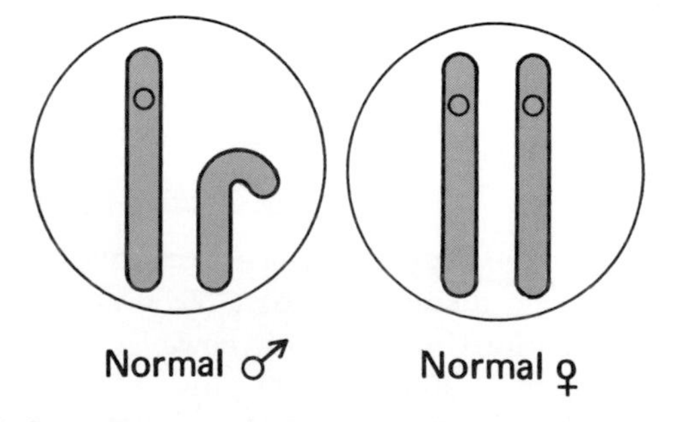

Fig. 20-24. Genes and chromosomes in sex-linked inheritance.

absent in the shorter Y chromosome. Sex-linked inheritance is controlled by genes having such a location. Only one normal allele is required to produce the chemicals that cause the blood to clot properly. Thus, the male represented in the diagram is a normal male.

The normal female has a normal allele on each of her X chromosomes.

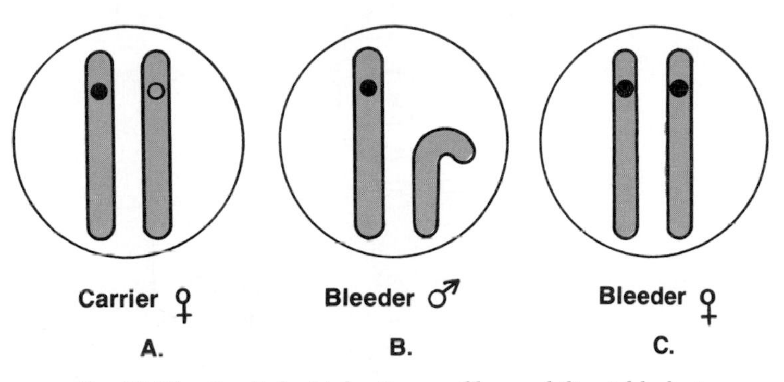

Fig. 20-25. Sex-linked inheritance of hemophilia. A black circle indicates a defective allele. A single normal allele in the genotype is sufficient to produce an individual whose blood clots normally.

In Figure 20-25A, the black circle represents a defective allele. This *allele* fails to lead to the production of chemicals for normal blood clotting. Because *only one normal allele is needed* for normal blood clotting, this female does not have hemophilia. However, because she can transmit the defective allele to her offspring, she is a *carrier.*

The male shown in Fig. 20-25B has a defective allele on his X chromosome. The Y chromosome is short and lacks the gene entirely. Not having even a single normal allele, this male is a *bleeder* or *hemophiliac.* Note that in the male genotype, the presence of a single defective allele results in a bleeder.

The female shown in Fig. 20-25C has defective alleles on both X chromosomes *and is a bleeder.* Note that, in the female genotype, two defective alleles are necessary to produce a bleeder.

The chromosome drawings shown above are awkward for use in solving genetics problems. Instead we shall use the following symbols:

X = X chromosome carrying the normal allele for blood clotting
$\not{X}$ = X chromosome carrying the defective allele for bleeder
Y = Y chromosome

Thus, XX = normal ♀ $\quad$ $\not{X}$X = carrier ♀
XY = normal ♂ $\quad$ $\not{X}\not{X}$ = bleeder ♀
$\not{X}$Y = bleeder ♂

Sample problem 7. What ratios can be expected in matings between a bleeder male and a normal female? (See Fig. 20-26.) Note that in problems involving sex-linkage it is useful to give the ratios for each sex, separately. If these parents have five daughters, and a nonbleeder desires

to marry one of these daughters, he knows that she *must* be a carrier. What ratios could this young couple expect in their offspring? This is the subject for sample problem 8.

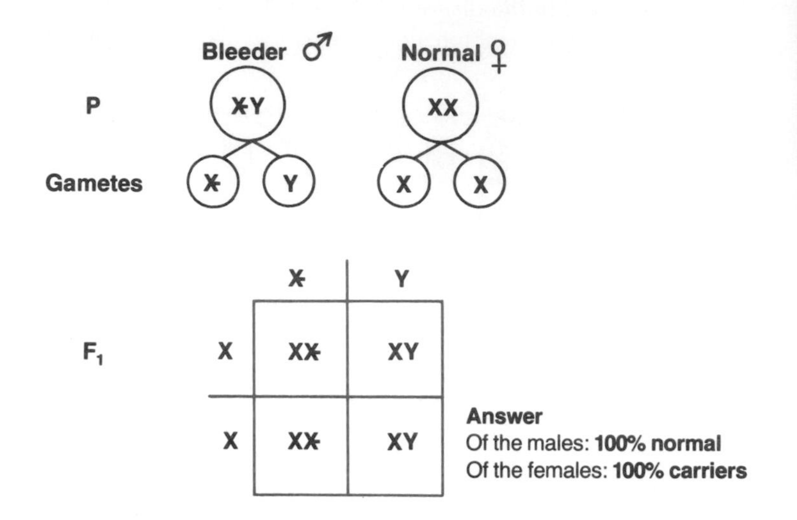

Fig. 20-26. Solution to sample problem 7.

Sample problem 8. What ratios can be expected from a mating of a normal male and a carrier female? (See Fig. 20-27.)

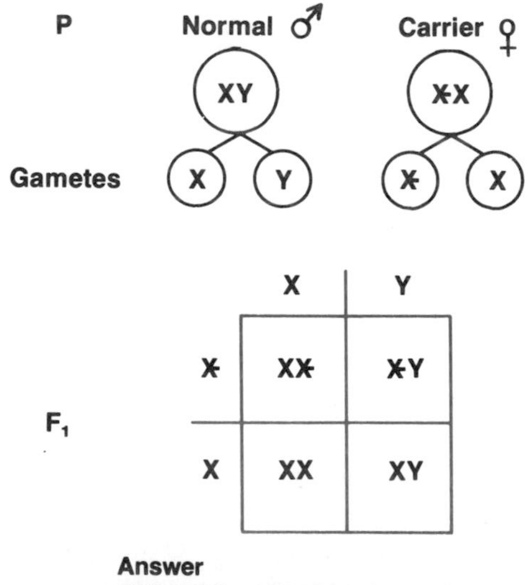

Answer
Of the males: **50% bleeders, 50% normal**
Of the females: **50% carriers, 50% normal**

Fig. 20-27. Solution to sample problem 8.

Now let us consider the results of problems 7 and 8 in sequence. They show that a bleeder male transmits this trait, *through his daughters*, to one-half of his grandsons.

With modern methods for treatment, males with hemophilia can have long lives. It is rare for hemophiliac females to be produced because, in relation to the entire population, the chances are against a hemophiliac male mating with a carrier female.

Other Sex-Linked Traits

White eyes in Drosophila. Normal *Drosophila* have red eyes. The condition of white eyes is sex-linked, more frequently found in males than in females. White eyes in *Drosophila*, discovered by T.H. Morgan, was the first analysis made of sex-linked inheritance.

Color blindness in humans. A type of color blindness known as red-green color blindness is sex-linked. This explains why color blindness is relatively rare in females.

Sample problem 9. What heredity must the parents have in order to produce a color-blind daughter? (See Fig. 20-28.)

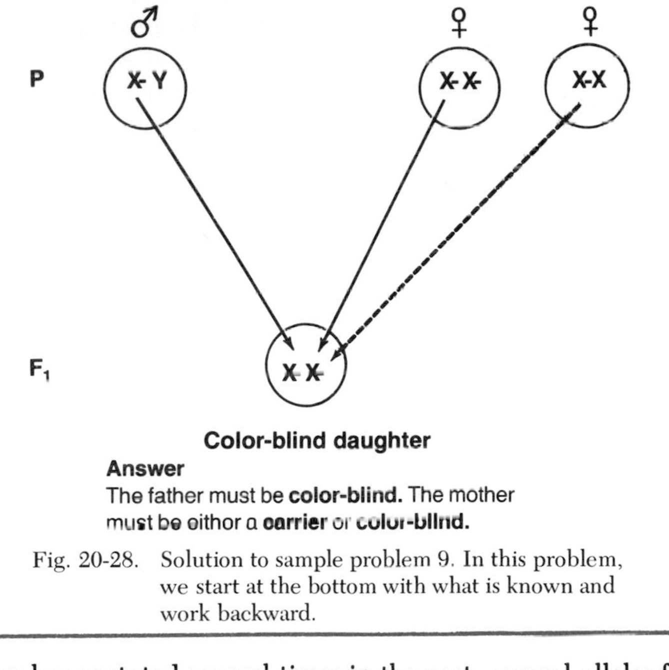

Fig. 20-28. Solution to sample problem 9. In this problem, we start at the bottom with what is known and work backward.

C Multiple Alleles

If a gene has mutated several times in the past, several alleles for this gene may exist among individuals of the population. *Multiple alleles* are several varieties of genes for a given trait, any of which may occur at the same locus (position) on a chromosome.

Blood Types

In Chapter 12, we described the human blood types and their importance in blood transfusions. We saw that on the surface of the red blood cells there may be present two kinds of proteins called antigen A and antigen B. Now we examine how the A-B-O blood types are inherited.

We shall use the symbols *A*, *B* and *O* to represent three alleles governing blood type. (These are also called I^A, I^B, and i.)

Allele *A* produces antigen A on the red blood cells and allele *B* produces antigen B. Allele *A* and allele *B* are equally powerful as in codominance. Allele *O* produces no antigen. It is recessive to both alleles A and B.

This combination of codominance and dominance may be indicated as follows:

$$A = B > O$$

This means that *A* and *B* are equally powerful and that each is dominant to allele *O*.

Summary of Possible Phenotypes and Genotypes		
Phenotypes	**Genotypes**	**Symbols**
Blood Type O	OO	ii
Blood Type A	AA or AO	I^AI^A or I^Ai
Blood Type B	BB or BO	I^BI^B or I^Bi
Blood Type AB	AB	I^AI^B

What ratios can be expected from matings of blood type A and blood type B? Since we do not know the genotypes of the parents, the various possibilities are shown in Fig. 20-29. As you can see, a cross between a type A and a type B individual can produce as many as four different blood types, depending upon the genotypes of the parents.

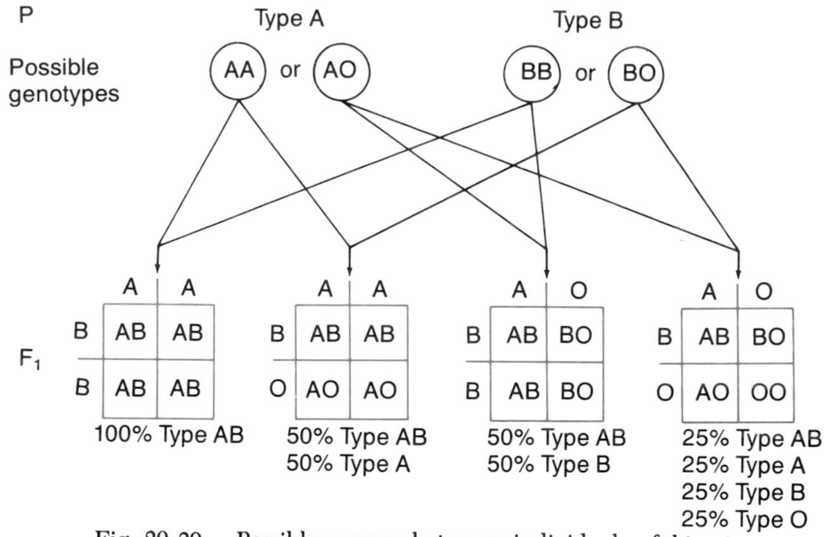

Fig. 20-29. Possible crosses between individuals of blood type A and blood type B.

The Problem of the "Switched Baby"

Occasionally, parents of a newborn baby believe that an error was made in the hospital and that the infant which they brought home is not their own. This belief might be deepened when blood tests reveal that the father is blood type A, the mother is blood type B, and the baby is blood type O. The parents could readily understand how the baby might be type A (like the father), or type B (like the mother), or even type AB (a blend of the two parents). But something entirely different like type O!

Sample problem 10. Could type A and type B parents have a type O offspring? (See Fig. 20-30.).

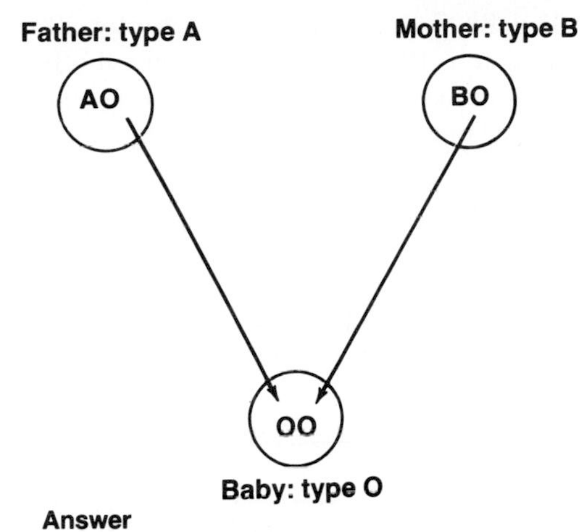

Fig. 20-30. Solution to sample problem 10. Start at the bottom with the baby's genotype and then work upward.

Paternity Suits

Courts of law sometimes have to rule on cases such as the following: A mother who is blood type A has a baby who is blood type AB. She accuses a man who is blood type O of being the child's father and asks for financial support of the child. Could this man be the father?

Sample problem 11. If the mother is blood type A, could a man of blood type O be the father of a baby with blood type AB? (See Fig. 20-31).

Although courts, of course, consider such scientific evidence, they make paternity decisions that primarily protect the rights of the infant.

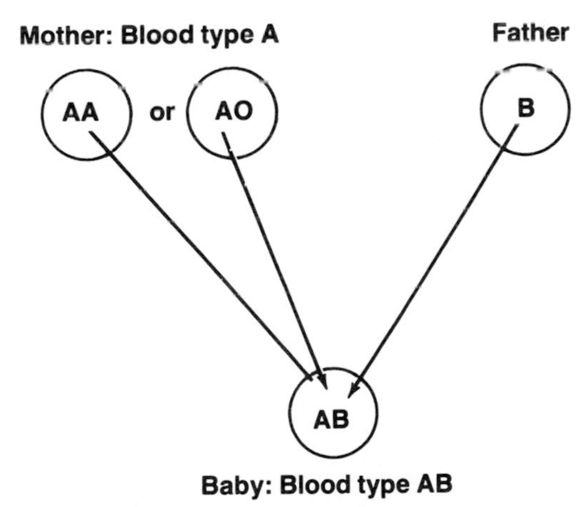

Fig. 20-31. Solution to sample problem 11.

The Rh Factor The Rh factor, you saw in Chapter 12, may be troublesome when the mother is Rh-negative (Rh−) and the baby is Rh-positive (Rh+). How is the Rh factor inherited? Numerous antigens and multiple alleles are involved but following is a simplified explanation:

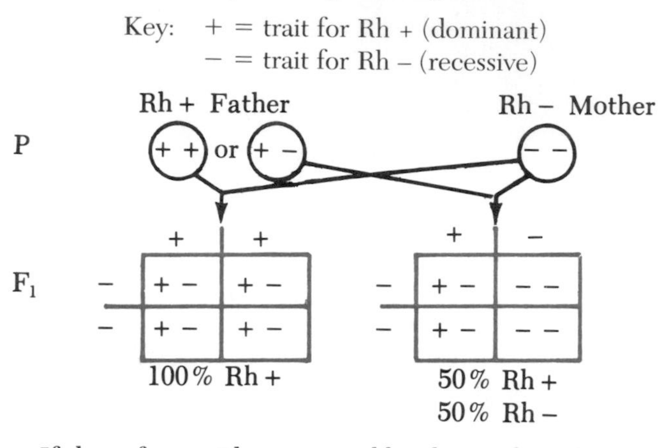

If the infant is Rh-negative, like the mother, there will be no problem of Rh disease at birth. Which genotype of the father will provide a 50 : 50 chance of having an Rh-negative infant? What hereditary information would be helpful in learning the father's genotype? Families concerned with this problem should consult a *genetic counselor* for more precise information than can be supplied here.

Reasoning Exercises

1. **What ratios can be expected in a cross between a bleeder male and a carrier female?**
2. **(A) Show by keyed and labeled diagrams the results of a cross between a normal male and a female carrier of color blindness. (B) What combination of parents could result in a color-blind female?**
3. **By means of keyed and labeled diagram, show how a color-blind man passes the trait of color blindness through his daughters to some of his daughters' children.**
4. Nine of ten children in a family are right-handed. Right-handedness is a dominant trait. Assume that this trait is controlled by a single pair of alleles and answer these questions:
   (A) What is the genotype of the left-handed child?
   (B) What are the possible genotypes of the right-handed children?
   (C) What are the possible genotypes of the parents?
   (D) Could these parents have produced only right-handed children? Explain.
   (E) If these parents had produced only one child would this child have been left- or right-handed? Explain.
5. In shorthorn cattle, the hornless condition is dominant over the horned condition. Indicate by keyed and labeled diagrams the results of the following crosses: (A) Hybrid crossed with hybrid. (B) Hybrid crossed with recessive.

D Mutations

Almost daily, it seems, we are warned of agents in our environment that can change the heredity of our cells. Radiation from an accident at a nuclear power plant, excessive exposure to sunlight or X-rays, observing atom bomb tests, and even taking in chemicals in our food and drinking water may cause mutations that are potentially harmful. In this section, we discuss the various kinds of mutations.

A mutation, simply stated, is a sudden change in heredity. Two broad classes of mutation are *germ line mutations* and *somatic mutations*. Germ line mutations affect sex cells in the gonads and are passed along to future generations. *Somatic* mutations affect body cells. Passed along to daughter cells by mitosis, somatic mutations may cause extensive damage to the exposed person's body but are not passed along to offspring. For example, a mutation that causes skin cells to become cancerous does not affect the gametes.

Mutations can also be classified according to whether they affect entire chromosomes or only those segments of DNA that we call genes. Accordingly, we speak of *chromosome mutations* and *gene mutations*.

Chromosome Mutations

A chromosome mutation is a change in the number of chromosomes or of their structure.

Ploidy. During meiosis, homologous chromosomes may fail to separate (disjoin) from each other. If both sets of chromosomes pass to one side, some of the resulting gametes are diploid ($2n$) instead of monoploid (n). A $2n$ sperm fertilizing a $2n$ egg then results in offspring that are *tetraploid* ($4n$). Various multiples are possible. The formation of cells having *extra whole sets* of chromosomes is called *ploidy* (or polyploidy).

Ploidy in plants is artificially induced by use of the chemical *colchicine*. This chemical interferes with proper spindle-fiber formation.

Polyploid plants are usually larger than ordinary specimens. Many of the giant-sized fruits, vegetables, and flowers that you see on the market were developed by use of chemicals such as colchicine.

Nondisjunction. The term *nondisjunction* is used when *only one pair of homologous chromosomes* fails to separate during meiosis. The resulting gametes have an ($n \pm 1$) chromosome number. Fertilization of an $n \pm 1$ gamete with a normal n gamete results in an individual whose body cells are $2n \pm 1$.

In humans, if the extra chromosome is number 21, the resulting condition is known as *Down syndrome*. Children with Down syndrome are mentally retarded, have short, stocky bodies with thick necks and, often, internal abnormalities. With training, however, these individuals can hold responsible jobs. Because the eyefold may appear somewhat oriental, Down syndrome was formerly called mongolism. Down syndrome occurs most frequently in the offspring of older mothers.

Nondisjunction of the sex chromosomes may result in such genotypes as an *X* female and an *XXY* male. Such individuals are sterile and may have abnormal secondary sexual characteristics.

Changes in chromosome structure. Abnormalities during meiosis may cause profound changes in the structure of chromosomes. Changes in chromosome structure often result in marked changes in the offspring because many genes are involved. Probably many stillbirths in humans and other animals are due to such abnormalities.

Gene Mutation

A gene mutation is a change in that portion of a DNA molecule that we call a gene. Examples of such changes will be considered in our discussion of DNA.

Causes of Mutation. Radiation and chemicals are the main external causes of chromosome and gene mutations. Some mutations also arise from spontaneous errors during meiosis and mitosis.

(1) X-rays. These shortwave radiations are used for medical diagnosis. Recognition of the potential danger from X-radiation has promoted the development of apparatus and procedures that lessen exposure of the body. A form of sonar that uses high frequency *sound* waves has recently been introduced. In some cases, the sonograms provide more information to the physician than do X-ray plates.

(2) Radioactive isotopes. As pointed out in Chapter 4, radioactive isotopes are unstable atoms of elements that release radiation while decaying from one kind of atom to another.

Radioisotopes, such as cobalt 60 and iodine 131, are used to treat some forms of cancer. The physician carefully weighs the benefits versus the risks of such treatment and carefully regulates the dosage.

Radioactive isotopes play an essential role in the operation of nuclear power plants that produce electrical energy. An accident at the Three Mile Island nuclear power plant near Harrisburg, Pennsylvania, in 1979 released a small amount of radiation and radioactive isotopes into the nearby environment. Apparently no individual received a harmful dose of radiation, but from this much discussed accident have emerged stricter regulations for the design, operation, and inspection of nuclear power plants.

Nuclear explosions and the aboveground testing of atomic weapons also release radioactive isotopes. One of these, strontium 90, may be carried around the earth by air currents, to descend as *fallout*. Taken up by microorganisms in the sea, and by land plants, the strontium 90 eventually enters the human body with food. Since strontium chemically resembles the element calcium, it is absorbed by bones and teeth. Here, for years, it continues to emit radiation. Surveys indicate that teeth extracted from children are showing increasing amounts of strontium 90.

(3) Cosmic rays. These are short wavelength radiations that enter the earth's atmosphere from outer space. Cosmic rays were probably responsible for most hereditary changes in living things during the early history of life on earth. But the ozone (O_3) layer now present in the upper atmosphere serves as a partial shield against cosmic rays. People liv-

ing on mountaintops have slightly greater exposure to cosmic radiation than people living in valleys.

(4) Other radiation. Ultraviolet rays are somewhat shorter than the violet rays of visible light. They are used in tanning lamps, decorative 'black light' lamps, and germicidal laboratory lamps. *Microwaves* are very short radio waves. Microwave ovens cook food from within by causing rapid vibration of food molecules. Federal agencies regulate the design and construction of microwave ovens to ensure that they do not leak unsafe amounts of *mutagenic* (causing mutation) radiation. On request, governmental consumer agencies test home microwave ovens for safety. *Radar* also works by means of microwaves.

Radiation that may affect the chemistry of DNA molecules is known as *ionizing radiation.* As these rays pass through living things, they strip electrons from atoms to form ions.

(5) Chemical mutagens. Chemicals cause gene mutation by altering components of the DNA molecule. Many *carcinogens*—chemicals known to cause cancer—also cause mutations in bacteria. Consequently, the preliminary screening of a host of environmental chemicals for carcinogenicity is accomplished by means of laboratory tests that determine if they cause mutation in bacteria.

Many industrial chemicals that were formerly discharged into rivers as wastes are now known to cause genetic defects. Among these is a group of chemicals called *PCBs* (polychlorinated biphenyls). Industrial companies are now cleaning such rivers—either voluntarily or under government orders—at great expense.

Chemicals are added to modern processed foods as food additives. These may improve the taste, color, or texture of foods. Many improve the keeping quality of foods that must remain on the shelf or in machines for long periods of time. Some of these additives have been shown to be carcinogenic and their use is forbidden. Others are still under investigation. *Saccharin,* the artificial food sweetener, has been retained by Congress on the permissible list while lengthy tests on its safety are performed.

Nitrites, added to hot dogs, bacon, and luncheon meats, protect food against bacterial decay and also provide the desired red color. The use of nitrites is now questioned because, in the stomach, they may release nitrous acid (or nitrosamines). Nitrous acid removes nitrogen atoms from one of the components of DNA, changing it to a different substance.

Do you read the labels on food packages? The U.S. Food and Drug Administration (FDA) requires that packages list all food additives.

The FDA faces a number of problems in determining whether to ban a suspected mutagen or carcinogen. Some of these are: What will be the cumulative effect of a small, apparently safe dose when used over a lifetime? How well can data obtained by studying laboratory animals be extrapolated (extended) to human beings? How should possible risks be weighed against possible benefits?

Characteristics of Mutations

These are some of the characteristics of mutations:

• *Most mutations are disadvantageous* to the organism or its offspring. An organism's genes work fine—the organism is living. Any change is likely to "upset the apple cart." However, *some mutations may be advantageous* to a population in a changing environment.

• *Mutations are random.* The changes caused by natural mutations cannot be predicted.

• *Most mutations are recessive.*

Plant and Animal Breeding

Breeders apply the principles of genetics to improve plants and animals. Methods used by breeders include the following:

(1) *Artificial selection.* Plants or animals having desired qualities are selected to reproduce their kind. Farmers use the best seed for sowing, not for consumption.

(2) *Hybridization.* Crosses are made between organisms having desirable qualities in the attempt to produce some offspring that incorporate these qualities. To produce cattle that are immune to Texas Fever, cattle breeders made a worldwide search and discovered Brahman cattle, in India, that are immune to this disease. Cross-breeding combined the good beef qualities of the American cattle with the disease resistance of the Brahman cattle.

(3) *Inbreeding.* Inbreeding is the mating of genetically related organisms to produce a pure strain. Inbreeding may bring together desirable alleles in the homozygous condition. But this process may also bring together a double dose of undesirable, or even lethal alleles.

(4) *Vegetative propagation.* Plant breeders have an advantage over animal breeders: in some cases, a desirable mutation, or the product of hybridization, can be propagated swiftly by vegetative means.

Cytoplasmic Inheritance

The importance of the nucleus with its chromosomes and genes is now well established. However, it is now apparent that some organelles in the cytoplasm have a role in determining their own heredity. Mitochondria and chloroplasts, for example, contain DNA and duplicate themselves. Scientists now think that chloroplasts and mitochondria are vestiges of primitive one-celled organisms which entered more advanced cells in the early history of life on earth, and have lived symbiotically within ever since.

Sexual Reproduction and Evolution

An important factor in evolution is the occurrence of variations among offspring. This variability is the raw material for natural selection to work upon. Some factors promoting variations among offspring are:

- independent assortment of chromosomes
- chance mating of different kinds of sperm and eggs
- crossing-over of portions of chromatids
- chromosome mutation
- gene mutation

Ⓔ

Probability in Genetics: The Algebraic Method

Problems in genetics may be solved by using an algebraic method instead of the Punnett square. The algebraic method is based upon the laws of probability. *Probability* is the mathematical science that attemps to predict the chances of an event happening.

In tossing a coin, the chances that the coin will fall head may be expressed as the fraction 1/2. In rolling one die (singular of dice), what is the chance of obtaining a 5? Since there are six numbers on the die, the probability is 1/6. The probability of drawing a spade in a deck of cards is 13/52 or 1/4. With a trick coin, both of whose sides are heads, the chances of its falling head in 1000 trials would be 1000/1000, or 1. The chances of its falling tail in 1000 trials would be 0/1000, or 0. The event, tails, has a *zero probability*—that is, it is impossible.

Now consider two events occurring at the same time. In rolling a pair of dice, what is the probability of obtaining *two* 5s? The probability of obtaining a 5 on one die is 1/6; the probability of obtaining a 5 on the other die is 1/6; the probability of obtaining a 5 on *both* dice is 1/6 × 1/6 = 1/36 or 0.028. *The probability that two independent events will occur together is the product of their probabilities of occurring separately.*

When tossing a coin a large number of times, the probability of obtaining a head is 1/2. However, it is quite possible that the first eight trials all result in tails. What is the probability that the ninth trial will be a head? The answer is still 1/2. *Previous trials do not affect the results of later trials of the same event.* If parents have four male children in succession, the probability that the next child will be a boy (if no other factors are operating) is still 1/2.

In tossing two coins simultaneously, the probability of obtaining
(*a*) 2 heads: is 1/2H × 1/2H = 1/4HH
(*b*) 2 tails: is 1/2T × 1/2T = 1/4TT

What is the probability of obtaining the combination of a head and a tail? There are two ways of obtaining the combination of a head and a tail: The first coin could fall head and the second one tail; the first coin could fall tail and the second one head.

Probability for Heads and Tails

	1st coin		2nd coin	Probability
Two heads	1/2*H*	×	1/2*H*	1/4*HH*
Head and tail	1/2*H*	×	1/2*T*	1/2*HT*
	1/2*T*	×	1/2*H*	
Two tails	1/2*T*	×	1/2*T*	1/4*TT*

Thus, the probability of obtaining a head and a tail is 1/2 (or 0.5).

This problem may also be solved by algebraic multiplication. As you may recall, an expression such as 1/2H + 1/2T is a binomial. (Note on the next page, the procedure for multiplying binomials.) First, state the probabilities for each coin; then multiply the probabilities.

$$
\begin{array}{lllll}
 & 1/2H & + \ 1/2T & & \textit{(probability for 1st coin)} \\
\times & 1/2H & + \ 1/2T & & \textit{(probability for 2nd coin)} \\
\hline
 & 1/4HH & + \ 1/4HT & & \\
 & & \quad\ 1/4HT & + \ 1/4TT & \\
\hline
 & 1/4HH & + \ 1/2HT & + \ 1/4TT &
\end{array}
$$

The probability of obtaining a head and a tail is 1/2.

Let us now turn to *genetics*. If the parent is homozygous with the genotype *AA*, the probable gametes are 1/2A + 1/2A = 1/1A, or all *A*. If the parent is homozygous *aa*, the probable gametes are 1/2*a* + 1/2*a* = 1/1*a*, or all *a*.

If the parent is heterozygous *Aa*, The probable gametes are 1/2*A* + 1/2*a*.

Sample problem 12. What are the probable offspring in a cross between two heterozygous parents *Aa* × *Aa*?

Solution:

$$
\begin{array}{lllll}
 & 1/2A & + \ 1/2a & & \text{(gametes from one } Aa \text{ parent)} \\
\times & 1/2A & + \ 1/2a & & \text{(gametes from other } Aa \text{ parent)} \\
\hline
 & 1/4AA & + \ 1/4Aa & & \\
 & & \quad\ 1/4Aa & + \ 1/4aa & \\
\hline
 & 1/4AA & + \ 1/2Aa & + \ 1/4aa & \textit{Answer}
\end{array}
$$

These results confirm those obtained by use of the Punnett square.

Sample problem 13. What are the probable offspring in a cross when the parents are *Aa* and *aa*?

Solution:

$$
\begin{array}{llll}
 & 1/2A & + \ 1/2a & \text{(gametes from } Aa \text{ parent)} \\
\times & & \quad\ 1/1a & \text{(gametes from } aa \text{ parent)} \\
\hline
 & 1/2Aa & + \ 1/2aa & \textit{Answer}
\end{array}
$$

Complex problems involving dihybrids and trihybrids may be more readily solved by use of the algebraic method than by the laborious construction of gigantic Punnett squares. For example, consider the following problem involving *dihybrids:*

Sample problem 14. What are the expected results in the cross *Ttyy* × *ttYY*?

Solution:

In solving this problem (1) make the computation for one trait, (2) make the computation for the other trait, (3) multiply.

(1) Computation for the *T* trait.

$$
\begin{array}{llll}
 & 1/2T & + \ 1/2t & \text{(gametes of } Tt \text{ parent)} \\
\times & & \quad\ 1/1t & \text{(gametes of } tt \text{ parent)} \\
\hline
 & 1/2Tt & + \ 1/2tt &
\end{array}
$$

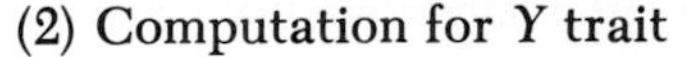

(2) Computation for Y trait

$$\begin{array}{rll} & 1/1y & \text{(gametes of } yy \text{ parent)} \\ \times & \underline{1/1Y} & \text{(gametes of } YY \text{ parent)} \\ & 1/1Yy & \end{array}$$

(3) Multiply. If the inheritance of each pair of alleles is independent of the other, we can now multiply each of the probabilities to determine the probability of their occurring together:

$$\begin{array}{rlcl} & 1/2Tt & + & 1/2tt \\ \times & & & 1/1Yy \\ \hline & 1/2TtYy & + & 1/2ttYy \end{array}$$

Answer. Phenotype ratio: 50% tall yellow, 50% short yellow.

Reasoning Exercises

Sample Problem

Calculate the probable results in the cross $TtYy \times TtYy$. Your results should be: 1/16 $TTYY$, 1/8 $TtYY$, 1/16 $ttYY$, 1/8 $TTYy$, 1/4 $TtYy$, 1/8 $ttYy$, 1/16 $TTyy$, 1/8 $Ttyy$, 1/16 $ttyy$. Collectively adding all the phenotypes results in the 9 : 3 : 3 : 1 ratio previously obtained in solving this problem with the Punnett square:

Tall Yellow:	1/16 + 1/8 + 1/8 + 1/4	= 9/16
Tall Green:	1/16 + 1/8	= 3/16
Short Yellow:	1/16 + 1/8	= 3/16
Short Green:	1/16	= 1/16

1. Calculate the probable results in the cross $TTYy \times TtYy$.
2. Devise a problem involving trihybrids and solve it by means of the Punnett square and the algebraic method.

Completion Questions

A

1. Mendel mated two types of garden peas by the process of......
2. Before starting an experiment, Mendel allowed each kind of pea plant to self-pollinate for several generations in order to obtain......strains.
3. The appearance of the recessive trait in the F_2 generation of a cross between pure parents illustrates Mendel's Law of......
4. When two hybrid tall pea plants are crossed, the ratio of tall to short offspring is......
5. Alternative genes for a trait are known as......
6. If both alleles for a gene are alike, the organism is......for that gene.
7. A ratio of 50% dominant and 50% recessive offspring is obtained in a cross between a pure recessive and a......
8. The expected Mendelian ratios tend to appear when the number of offspring is......
9. In a test cross, the unknown organism is mated with one whose genotype is pure......
10. Black coat color is dominant in rabbits. If a black rabbit crossed with a white rabbit produced a white offspring, the black rabbit must have been......

11. Genes inherited together on the same chromosomes are said to be......
12. The exchange of linkage groups between homologous chromosomes is known as......
13. The lining up of homologous chromosomes in twisted pairs is known as......

B

14. The full scientific name for the fruit fly is......
15. A breeder can determine whether a tall pea plant is pure tall or hybrid tall by crossing it with a......
16. When a human egg is fertilized by a sperm carrying the *Y* chromosome, the sex of the child will be......
17. A color-blind man and a pure normal woman will have sons of whom......percent are normal with respect to color vision.

C

18. If both the father and the mother have blood type A, the baby can have blood type A or blood type......
19. An RH-positive father and an Rh-negative mother can have an Rh-negative baby if the father is ...... for this trait.

D

20. A chemical used to induce polyploidy is......
21. The presence of one extra chromosome in all the body cells of a human may result in the form of mental retardation known as......
22. A radioactive isotope which is readily taken up by bone tissue is......

Multiple-Choice Questions

A

1. If a trait skips a generation, the most probable reason is that this trait (1) is dominant, (2) is recessive, (3) has mutated, (4) is linked.
2. Mendel's Law of Segregation can be best illustrated by the cross (1) *AA* × *aa*, (2) *Aa* × *aa*, (3) *Aa* × *Aa*, (4) *AA* × *Aa*.
3. When experimenting with the factor of height in peas, Gregor Mendel actually obtained this result from one of his series of crosses: 73.97% tall and 26.03% short. The parents were probably (1) hybrid tall peas, (2) hybrid tall peas and pure tall peas, (3) hybrid tall peas and short peas, (4) tall peas and short peas.
4. The phenotype of a mouse's fur color can best be determined by (1) test breeding, (2) looking at it, (3) crossing-over, (4) biochemical techniques.
5. In the cross *Bb* × *Bb*, approximately what percentage of offspring have the same phenotype as the parents? (1) 25% (2) 50% (3) 75% (4) 100%
6. In humans, consider brown eye-color to be dominant to blue eye-color and that this trait is controlled by a single pair of alleles. If two brown-eyed parents have blue-eyed children, the genetic makeup of the parents must be (1) *BB* and *Bb*, (2) *Bb* and *BB*, (3) *Bb* and *Bb*, (4) *BB* and *bb*.
7. In garden peas, the offspring of a cross between two hybrid yellow parents would be (1) 25% yellow, (2) 50% yellow, (3) 75% yellow, (4) 100% yellow.
8. The crossing of dihybrid organisms results in the appearance of traits in the ratio of (1) 9:3:3:1, (2) 3:1, (3) 1:2:1, (4) 1:1.
9. When round squash are crossed with long squash, all offspring are oval in

shape. How many genotypes are produced when round squash are crossed with oval squash? (1) 1, (2) 2, (3) 3, (4) 4.

10. A boy plans to toss a coin ten times. His first four tosses all result in heads. His chances of getting a head on the next throw are (1) 1:10, (2) 1:6, (3) 4:10, (4) 1:2.
11. Pink offspring are produced by crossing a plant bearing white flowers with a plant bearing red flowers. This is evidence of (1) dominance, (2) segregation, (3) incomplete dominance, (4) recessiveness.
12. A cross between two black guinea pigs produces some black guinea pigs and some white guinea pigs. The gene makeup of the two parents is called (1) homozygous black, (2) heterozygous black, (3) heterozygous white, (4) homozygous white.
13. A series of three matings between a hybrid black guinea pig and a white one resulted in 8 black offspring. The most probable explanation is that (1) a mutation occurred, (2) the white parent was also hybrid, (3) the expected ratios are unlikely to appear in small numbers of offspring, (4) the black parent was the result of incomplete dominance.

Base your answers to questions 14 through 16 on the information below:

A purple-flowered plant was cross-pollinated with a yellow-flowered plant of the same species. The offspring (F_1) were all yellow-flowered hybrid plants.

14. If one of the yellow-flowered F_1 plants is cross-pollinated by a purple-flowered plant, approximately what percent of the offspring would be expected to have purple flowers? (1) 25%, (2) 50%, (3) 75%, (4) 100%.
15. The F_1 plants self-pollinated and produced 600 seeds. If all 600 grew, the number of plants with purple blossoms would most likely be (1) 150, (2) 300, (3) 450, (4) 600.
16. The pattern of inheritance illustrated by the plants described in this paragraph is known as (1) crossing-over, (2) independent assortment, (3) transformation, (4) dominance.
17. Some individuals with blood group A may inherit the alleles for blond hair, while other individuals with blood group A may inherit the alleles for brown hair. This can be explained by the principle of (1) dominance, (2) multiple alleles, (3) independent assortment, (4) incomplete dominance.
18. When two four-o'clock plants are crossed, 48 pink four-o'clocks and 52 white four-o'clocks are produced. The phenotypes of the parents are (1) pink and white, (2) pink and red, (3) pink and pink, (4) red and white.
19. The offspring of a cross between $BB \times bb$ illustrates the pattern of heredity known as (1) dominance, (2) segregation, (3) independent assortment, (4) sex-linkage.
20. Genes located at the same position on homologous chromosomes are called (1) genotypes, (2) alleles, (3) linked, (4) recessives.
21. Which pair of Andalusian fowl should be bred to produce only blue fowl? (1) two Andalusian blue fowl, (2) an Andalusian blue fowl and a white fowl, (3) a black fowl and a white fowl, (4) an Andalusian blue fowl and a black fowl.
22. A hybrid black-coated guinea pig produces two million sperm cells. Approximately what number of its sperm cells contain the recessive gene for white coat color? (1) 1 million, (2) 2 million, (3) 0, (4) 0.5 million.

23. Which is an example of codominance? (1) Black and white guinea pigs, when mated, produce all black offspring, (2) Red shorthorn cattle, when mated with white shorthorn cattle, produce roan shorthorn cattle, (3) Rough-haired guinea pigs, when mated, produce both rough-haired and smooth-haired offspring, (4) Tall pea plants with white flowers, when crossed with short pea plants with purple flowers, produce tall plants with purple flowers.
24. In order to determine if an organism is homozygous dominant, it should be crossed with an organism that is (1) recessive, (2) heterozygous, (3) hybrid, (4) homozygous dominant.
25. For a given trait, the two genes of an allelic pair differ. An individual possessing this gene combination is said to be (1) homozygous for that trait, (2) heterozygous for that trait, (3) recessive for that trait, (4) pure for that trait.

B

26. Which hereditary principle probably accounts for the fact that persons who have red hair usually also have freckles? (1) segregation, (2) dominance, (3) linkage, (4) incomplete dominance.
27. The chromosomes that are *not* involved in sex-determination are referred to as (1) centrosomes, (2) centrioles, (3) ribosomes, (4) autosomes.
28. The parents of three sons are expecting their fourth child. What are the chances that they will have another boy? (1) 25%, (2) 50%, (3) 75%, (4) 100%.
29. During which process is the sex of a human determined? (1) synapsis, (2) cleavage, (3) replication, (4) fertilization.
30. A man who is color-blind marries a woman who is not color-blind and is not carrying a gene for it. What is the chance that their sons will be color-blind? (1) 0%, (2) 25%, (3) 50%, (4) 100%.
31. If a color-blind man marries a woman who is a carrier for color blindness, it is most probable that (1) half of their sons will be color-blind, (2) all of their sons will have normal color vision, (3) all of their sons will be color-blind, (4) none of their children will have normal color vision.
32. Linked genes are most often separated by the process of (1) gene mutation, (2) crossing-over, (3) segregation, (4) polyploidy.
33. The number of autosomes and type of sex chromosome normally present in a human egg cell is (1) 44 + *XY*, (2) 44 + *XX*, (3) 22 + *Y*, (4) 22 + *X*.

C

34. A person who is homozygous for blood type A has a genotype which may be represented as (1) I^aI^b, (2) I^aI^a, (3) I^ai, (4) ii.

The following pedigree shows the inheritance of blood types in a family. Use it to answer questions 35 and 36.

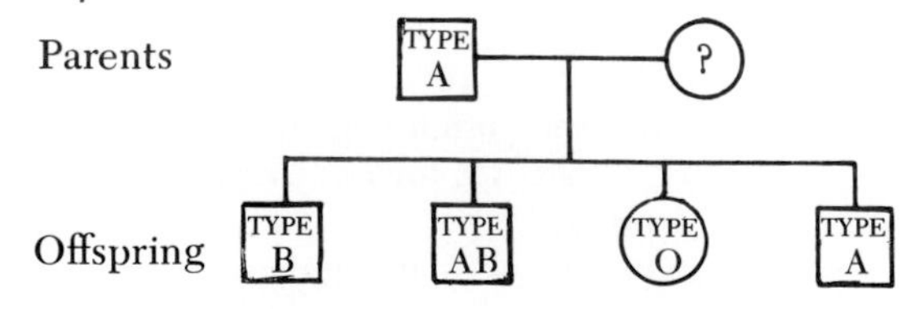

35. The genotype of the type A parent must be (1) I^ai, (2) I^aI^a, (3) ii, (4) I^aI^b.
36. The unknown parental genotype for blood type must be (1) I^ai, (2) I^aI^b, (3) I^bi, (4) I^bI^b.

37. In humans, if the parents have blood types *AB* and *O*, which two blood types may appear in their offspring? (1) *A* and *B*, (2) *A* and *O*, (3) *B* and *O*, (4) *AB* and *O*.

D

38. The failure of homologous chromosomes to separate during meiosis is known as (1) crossing-over, (2) polyploidy, (3) nondisjunction, (4) deletion.
39. One reason why it may take several generations to determine the effects of harmful irradiation on a human population is that (1) humans do not exhibit mutations until adulthood, (2) the majority of mutations are recessive, (3) irradiation of somatic cells causes mutations to occur slowly, (4) irradiation does not cause mutations in sex cells.
40. Exaggerated characteristics in plants, such as those in "double" zinnias, are due to a type of chromosomal mutation called (1) crossing-over, (2) disjunction, (3) polyploidy, (4) breakage.
41. Examples of self-duplicating cellular structures are the (1) mitochondria and chloroplasts, (2) mitochondria and cell walls, (3) cell walls and chloroplasts, (4) vacuoles and chloroplasts.
42. What is the total number of chromosomes in a typical body cell of a person with Down syndrome? (1) 22, (2) 23, (3) 44, (4) 47.
43. Radioactive fallout is dangerous to future generations because radioactive isotopes (1) act as toxins, (2) speed up the mutation rate, (3) have short half-lives, (4) cause somatic mutations.
44. Recent investigations suggest that chloroplasts and mitochondria (1) do not contain genes, (2) are completely controlled by genes located within their nuclei, (3) contain separate genes which are regulated by genes in the centrosomes, (4) contain separate genes which are regulated by genes in the nucleus.
45. A chemical change in a single gene may produce (1) a mutation, (2) polyploidy, (3) loss of chromosomes, (4) doubling of chromosomes.
46. The effects of today's radioactive fallout will probably be more harmful to children of future generations than to children now living because (1) contamination of milk supply is not cumulative, (2) infants are more susceptible to radiation, (3) intensity of radiation increases with age, (4) mutated genes are frequently recessive.
47. Occasionally a person may have only one X chromosome, three X chromosomes, or two X chromosomes and a Y chromosome in each body cell. These abnormal conditions would be due to (1) multiple alleles, (2) nondisjunction, (3) artificial selection, (4) crossing-over.
48. The use of hallucinogenic compounds such as LSD may be dangerous for future generations of human beings because LSD (1) promotes the breaking of chromosomes, (2) promotes resistance to addiction, (3) changes the structure of the ATP molecule, (4) causes a change in the user's blood type.

Chapter Test

1. In comparing a single zygote with a single gamete of a particular species, the ratio of numbers of genes carried would be (1) 3:1, (2) 2:1, (3) 1:1, (4) 1:2:1.
2. A cross between red-flowered and white-flowered four-o'clock plants produces seeds, all of which give rise to pink-flowered plants. If two of these pink-flowered plants are crossed, what is the chance that white-flowered plants will be produced? (1) 0, (2) ¼, (3) ½, (4) ¾.

3. Which of the following is *not* a characteristic of mutations? (1) They are usually recessive. (2) They usually produce an improvement in the organism. (3) They are inherited. (4) They may be caused by chemicals.
4. If dimpled cheeks are dominant over nondimpled cheeks, what proportion of offspring with dimpled cheeks may one expect if two nondimpled individuals are crossed? (1) 0%, (2) 50%, (3) 75%, (4) 100%.
5. In humans, brown eyes seem dominant over blue eyes. A brown-eyed man marries a blue-eyed woman and they have 8 children, all brown-eyed. The *probable* genetic makeup of father, mother and children, respectively, is (1) *Bb*, *bb*, *bb*, (2) *BB*, *bb*, *BB*, (3) *Bb*, *bb*, *BB*, (4) *BB*, *bb*, *Bb*.
6. Which statement concerning an allelic pair of genes controlling a single characteristic in humans is true? (1) Both genes come from the father. (2) Both genes come from the mother. (3) One gene comes from the father and one gene comes from the mother. (4) The genes come randomly in pairs from either the father or the mother.
7. A farmer is told that his black bull is a thoroughbred (pure black). Knowing that black color in cattle is dominant over red color, he decides to determine the purity of the strain by mating the bull with several red cows. If the bull is pure, (1) 100% of the offspring will be red, (2) 100% of the offspring will be black, (3) 75% of the offspring will be black and 25% will be red, (4) 50% of the offspring will be black and 50% will be red.
8. A series of three matings between a hybrid black guinea pig and a white one resulted in 8 black offspring. The most probable explanation is that (1) a mutation occurred, (2) the white parent was also hybrid, (3) the expected ratios are unlikely to appear in small numbers of offspring, (4) the black parent was the result of incomplete dominance.
9. In a breeding experiment in which there are 200 offspring, 50% are *WW*. The parents of the offspring were (1) *RR* and *WW*, (2) *RW* and *WW*, (3) *RW* and *RW*, (4) *RR* and *RW*.
10. Inbreeding is usually used to (1) maintain a desired type, (2) produce new types, (3) insure fertilization, (4) obtain hybrids.

Chapter 21 Molecular Genetics

In Chapter 4 you learned that 20 different amino acids combine to form the proteins found in all organisms. Because amino acids can combine in various amounts and different combinations, there is great variety in the structure and function of proteins in nature. The way amino acids are arranged is of extreme importance. Much as the words on this page are spelled differently and have different meanings, we know that the arrangement of amino acids in a protein determines its function.

At one time biologists theorized that traits were inherited through the transmission of protein molecules from parent to offspring. Over the past several decades, however, biologists have discovered that the molecule of heredity is DNA.

A How DNA Was Discovered to Be the Material of Heredity

The discovery of DNA's role in heredity began over a hundred years ago, when nucleic acids were first isolated from cell nuclei. At that time only protein had been isolated from the nucleus. Further study showed that there were two kinds of nucleic acid, ribonucleic acid or RNA and deoxyribonucleic acid or DNA. The scientists who first found nucleic acids, however, did not know how they functioned in the cell.

In 1928, a British biologist, Frederick Griffith, was trying to find a treatment for the respiratory disease pneumonia. He came upon the first clues pointing to the function of nucleic acids.

Bacterial Transformation

Griffith studied two types of bacteria associated with pneumonia. One of these formed colonies that appeared smooth under the microscope. The other type had colonies with a rough surface. The smooth or S type caused pneumonia, while the rough or R type did not. Griffith's research revealed the following results:

1. Laboratory mice injected with living smooth (S) bacteria developed pneumonia and died. The blood of these mice was filled with living S bacteria.
2. Mice injected with live rough (R) bacteria did not develop the disease. The blood of these mice was filled with living R bacteria, which had no effect on the mice.
3. S type bacteria were killed by extreme heat and injected into mice. The mice did not develop pneumonia.
4. Griffith injected live R bacteria along with S bacteria killed by heat. The mice all developed pneumonia. Much to Griffith's surprise, their blood contained live S bacteria.

Where did the pathogenic, or disease-causing, S bacteria come from? At one time, people thought that living things could arise from nonliving things, an idea we call spontaneous generation. At the time that Griffith performed his experiments, however, most biologists thought that all cells could arise only from previously existing cells. The idea of spontaneous generation had been rejected.

Based on result number 3, Griffith knew that heat killed the S bacteria, so those that were injected into mice could not have caused the disease.

Result 2 showed that the live R bacteria did not undergo mutation and become pathogens. If no other bacteria were present, then it was likely that something from the dead S bacteria had transformed the R bacteria. This would mean that something had changed the traits of the R type, causing them to become pathogens when both the R and S types were injected together. Result number 4 became known as bacterial transformation, or the alteration of the traits of bacteria. Griffith was unable to explain what caused the transformation.

The biologists Oswald Avery, Colin MacLeod, and Maclyn McCarty later isolated and identified the transforming chemical as DNA. In 1944 they showed that DNA had the ability to change the traits of a cell. The scientists concluded that DNA must be responsible for inheritance of traits from generation to generation. But they could not yet explain how nucleic acid in the nucleus could control chemical reactions in the cytoplasm.

B

DNA Structure

In Chapter 4 you learned about the structure of nucleic acids. Remember that DNA is a polymer composed of repeating units called nucleotides. Each DNA nucleotide contains the 5-carbon sugar deoxyribose, a phosphate group, and one of four nitrogen bases (adenine, guanine, thymine, and cytosine). James Watson and Francis Crick first determined the structure of DNA, and suggested how this structure may relate to the function of transmitting information within the cell.

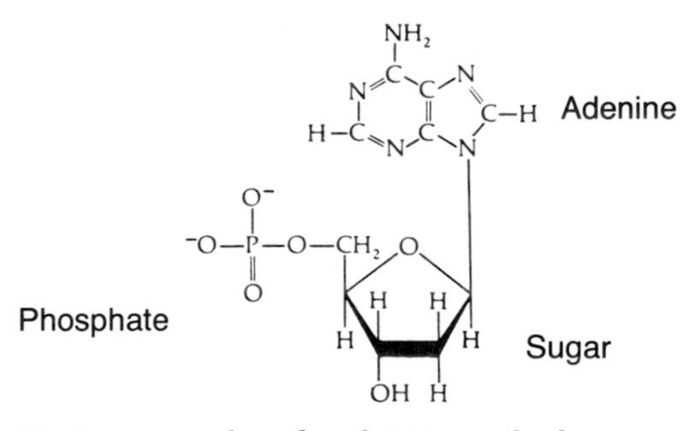

Fig. 21–1. A nucleotide of DNA with the nitrogen base adenine.

Recall one of Watson and Crick's key findings: that the nitrogen base adenine in one strand of DNA always pairs with the base thymine in the second strand. Similarly, guanine and cytosine always pair. This consistent pairing of complementary nitrogen bases means that the sequence of bases in one strand of DNA determines the sequence of bases in the second strand. Recall also that this pairing underlies the replication of DNA, which you read about in Chapter 17. The principle of complementary base pairing is what insures that exact copies of DNA strands are made.

Suppose that a mistake is made during replication. Perhaps the wrong nitrogen base is added to the DNA molecule. To correct this, proofreading enzymes exist that can recognize copying mistakes. This proofreading is so

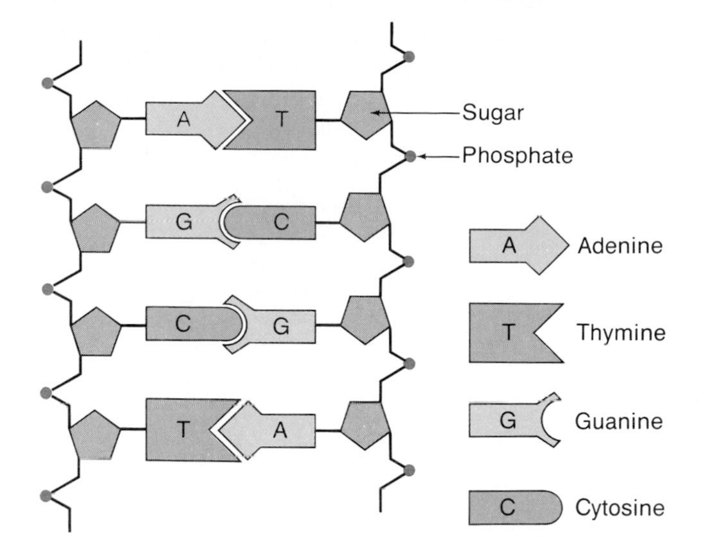

Fig. 21–2. Complementary pairing of nitrogen bases in DNA: This links nucleotides in one strand with those of the other strand.

accurate that generally only one mistake is missed for every 100 million nucleotides copied.

Ⓒ

How DNA Controls Metabolism

A cell's metabolism depends on the workings of many enzymes. Making enzymes, or any other proteins, requires energy from ATP. You learned in Chapter 7, Respiration, that the cell makes ATP when pyruvic acid enters the Kreb's cycle. This is a cycle of reactions catalyzed by enzymes. How does the cell know when to make more ATP, or more of the enzymes that catalyze the reactions in the Kreb's cycle? It is DNA that provides the information the cell needs to coordinate its activities.

DNA Mutation and Enzyme Synthesis. It took a series of classic experiments in the 1940's to prove that there was an essential link between DNA and specific enzymes in cellular metabolism. Working with a common pink mold, called *Neurospora*, the biologists George Beadle and Edward Tatum showed that mutation—a change in the DNA molecule—could inhibit production of a needed enzyme. *Neurospora* is an excellent organism to use because it can be grown on a simple culture medium. It also has a life cycle of only ten days, thus new generations with new traits can be obtained and studied in relatively short periods of time. When *Neurospora* reproduces, it makes eight spores in a narrow sac. Each spore can be isolated, identified, and grown separately to produce a new mycelium, or mass of threads.

Beadle and Tatum used X-rays and ultraviolet (UV) radiation to produce mutations in *Neurospora*. Some of the mutations affected the nutrient requirements of the mold. Figure 21–3 diagrams the experimental results that Beadle and Tatum obtained. These results can be summarized as follows (the numbers refer to the steps in the figure):

Step 1. Normal *Neurospora* survived quite well on a minimal culture medium. This medium contained a carbon source, such as a sugar, and a few minerals as the only nutrients for growth. The mold's enzymes made whatever else it needed to live.

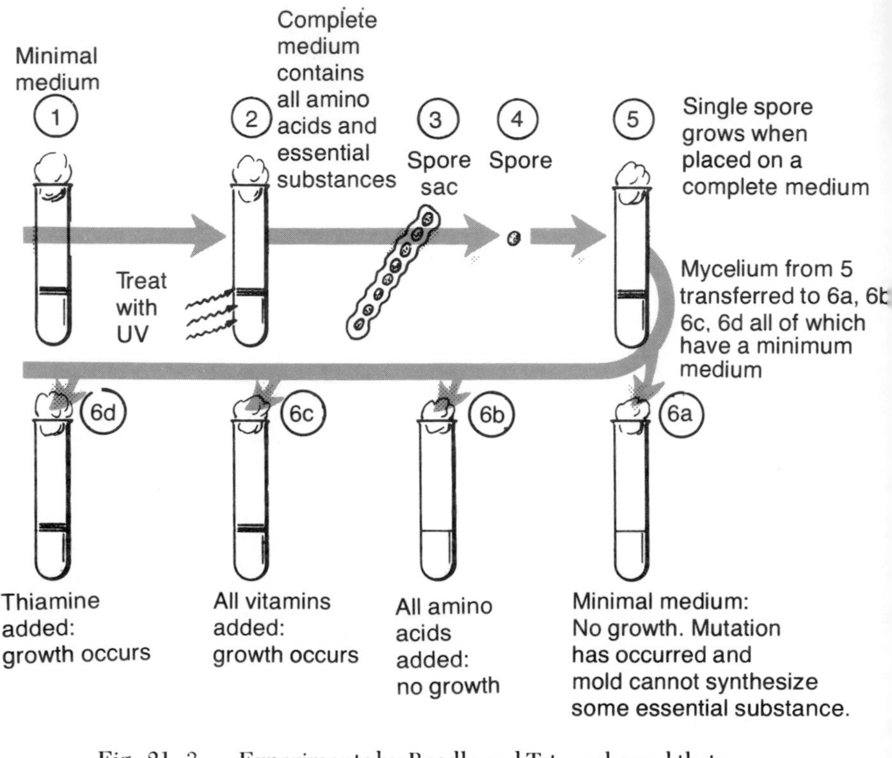

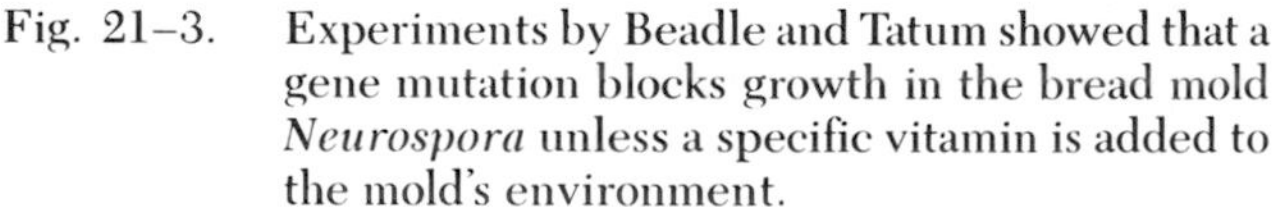

Fig. 21–3. Experiments by Beadle and Tatum showed that a gene mutation blocks growth in the bread mold *Neurospora* unless a specific vitamin is added to the mold's environment.

Step 2. Mold placed in a complete culture medium, with a carbon source as well as all amino acids and vitamins, also grew quite well. This mold culture was exposed to radiation, which can cause mutations.

Steps 3, 4, & 5. The mold produced new spores in sacs. Single spores, each carrying possible mutations, were isolated and transferred individually to a complete medium. New mutant molds grew from these spores. This step assured the biologists that the mutants would survive and grow even if the mutations affected the mold's ability to make nutrients. This is because any nutrients the molds could not make for themselves would be available in the culture medium. Once successful mutant mold colonies had developed, they were transplanted to the minimal culture medium.

Step 6a. Some mutant mold colonies were unable to grow. This demonstrated that a change had occurred preventing the molds from making a nutrient needed for growth. Beadle and Tatum concluded that the mutants required a nutrient not supplied by the culture medium, and could not make it themselves. The next step was to try to figure out which substance in the complete medium was required by each kind of mutant mold. So colonies of mutant molds were grown in a variety of other culture media. The other culture media contained the minimal medium plus all amino acids, minimal medium plus all known vitamins, etc. These culture media with mold colonies are shown in steps 6b–6d in the figure.

Step 6b. Another mutant mold was placed on the minimal medium to which was added all the amino acids. This mold failed to grow. This meant that the change in *Neurospora* did not affect the mold's ability to make amino acids. The inability to grow was caused by the failure of the mold to make something else.

Step 6c. When mutant *Neurospora* was placed in a medium containing all the vitamins, it grew normally. Since the mold did not grow without the vitamins, the change must have affected its ability to make its own vitamins. Beadle and Tatum now needed to find out which specific vitamin or vitamins were not being made by the mutant mold.

6d. Mutant *Neurospora* was transferred to test tubes containing minimal amounts of nutrients plus specific vitamins. This was done to find exactly which vitamin synthesis was affected by the mutation. Mold growth occurred in one test tube, the one with the minimal culture medium plus the vitamin thiamine.

Beadle and Tatum concluded that a mutation to the mold's DNA caused an inability to make an enzyme needed to build the vitamin thiamine.

To understand the significance of this research, think of a long chain of dominos. Suppose you knock over the first domino and the rest fall in a chain reaction. Now suppose that you remove one domino from the middle of the chain, then knock over the first domino again. The dominos fall only up to the point where you have removed one; the rest of the chain remains standing. To synthesize essential molecules in the cell, a series of enzyme-catalyzed reactions must occur in a similar chain-like manner. If just one enzyme in the chain is removed, the series of reactions cannot go from start to finish.

Beadle and Tatum hypothesized that the radiation caused a DNA mutation in *Neurospora*. This resulted in production of a faulty enzyme, which in turn stopped the series of enzyme reactions needed to make thiamine. The biologists concluded that a single mutation affects one gene, which in turn is a piece of DNA that contains the information to make one enzyme.

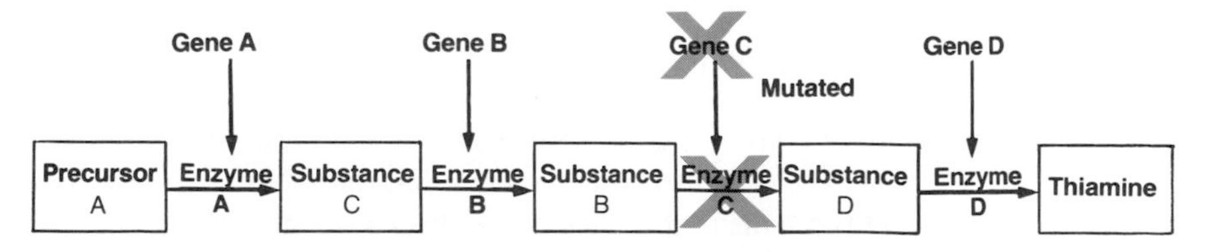

Fig. 21–4. Each gene contains instructions needed to make an enzyme. A gene mutation can block enzyme synthesis, and stop a series of enzyme-catalyzed reactions that build a substance needed for growth.

Beadle and Tatum's hypothesis came to be known as the one gene—one enzyme hypothesis. Over the years, further research has modified this view. We now refer to this idea as the one gene—one polypeptide hypothesis. This change has come about because biologists have learned that a single gene often contains information to make one polypeptide chain only. Recall that a polypeptide is a chain of amino acids, and that all proteins, including enzymes, are made up of polypeptide chains.

(D)

How the Information in DNA Is Organized

The Genetic Code

How is the information for making polypeptides organized within the DNA molecule? Following the discovery of DNA's molecular structure, biologists suspected that the nucleic acid's basic building blocks, the nucleotides, represented a code that contains the information to build peptide chains. By analogy, think of the English alphabet as a code that we have learned to interpret. The 26 letters can be combined in an enormous variety of ways to form words. In DNA, there are only four different nucleotides, which are distinguished from one another by the nitrogen bases A, T, C, and G.

Recall from Chapter 4 that there are 20 amino acids required for life. Let us assume that each amino acid is coded by a particular sequence of nitrogen bases. In this model, we assume that a DNA code, or base sequence, exists for each amino acid. We also assume that the code must consist of the same number of nitrogen bases for all amino acids, otherwise the cell could not interpret the sequences.

Suppose, for example, that each base represented only one amino acid. Only four different codes—A, T, C, & G—could be produced. Twenty amino acids could not be specified this way. Now suppose that a pair of bases represented one amino acid. The number of different codes that can be obtained from combinations of the four DNA bases equals 4^n, where n is the number of bases in one code. When $n = 2$, there are 4^2 or 16 possible codes. The following are the possible codes:

AA	AT	AG	AC	TT	TA	TC	TG
CC	CA	CT	CG	GG	GA	GT	GC

As you can see, this "alphabet" provides only 16 possible words for the DNA code. This is still not enough to code for the 20 essential amino acids. But if three bases are combined to make a single code, then $n = 3$, and $4^3 = 64$. This is more than enough. So biologists investigated the hypothesis that the four bases in combinations of 3 at one time would be the code for building polypeptide chains.

Through elaborate research, biologists created long nucleotide polymers containing one nitrogen base, all adenines, or all guanines, and so forth. They were able to show that the DNA code is indeed a triplet code. This means that sequences of three nitrogen bases at a time code for the 20 essential amino acids. A sequence of 3000 nucleotides in the DNA molecule would code for a polypeptide chain containing about 1000 amino acids.

Eventually biologists deciphered the library of genetic codes. We now know that 61 of the 64 base combinations code for specific amino acids. One of these 61 combinations acts as a promoter, or start signal. The remaining three codes act as terminators, or stop signals. Because there are more triplet codes than there are amino acids, most of the amino acids are coded by two or more base triplets. In DNA, for example, the nitrogen base triplets of CCG, CCA, or CCT all specify one amino acid—glycine. Each triplet of nitrogen bases is called a codon. The genetic code chart shown below contains triplets of nitrogen bases from RNA, not DNA. These triplets are complementary to triplets in DNA. In the next section, you'll discover the role of RNA in the genetic code.

The amazing thing about the genetic code is that it holds true for virtually all organisms studied. Triplet codes have the same meaning in humans, onions, amebas, bacteria, and trees!

The Genetic Code

First Base	Second Base: U		C		A		G		Third Base
	U		**C**		**A**		**G**		
U	UUU	Phenyl- alanine	UCU	Serine	UAU	Tyrosine	UGU	Cysteine	U
	UUC		UCC		UAC		UGC		C
	UUA	Leucine	UCA		**UAA**	**Stop**	**UGA**	**Stop**	A
	UUG		UCG		**UAG**		UGG	Tryptophan	G
C	CUU	Leucine	CCU	Proline	CAU	Histine	CGU	Arginine	U
	CUC		CCC		CAC		CGC		C
	CUA		CCA		CAA	Glutamine	CGA		A
	CUG		CCG		CAG		CGG		G
A	AUU	Isoleucine	ACU	Threonine	AAU	Asparagine	AGU	Serine	U
	AUC		ACC		AAC		AGC		C
	AUA		ACA		AAA	Lysine	AGA	Arginine	A
	AUG	Methionine	ACG		AAG		AGG		G
G	GUU	Valine	GCU	Alanine	GAU	Aspartic acid	GGU	Glycine	U
	GUC		GCC		GAC		GGC		C
	GUA		GCA		GAA	Glutamic acid	GGA		A
	GUG		GCG		GAG		GGG		G

(E)

How DNA's Information Gets to the Cytoplasm

Recall from Chapter 4 that the two forms of nucleic acid in every cell are DNA and RNA. Though DNA contains the coded information for protein synthesis, it does not build proteins itself. This is done in the cytoplasm. Therefore, information from DNA must reach the site of protein synthesis. Since nuclear DNA does not leave the nucleus, there must be a way to transfer the information in DNA to the cytoplasm. This is the role of RNA.

RNA and its functions

RNA, or ribonucleic acid, is a molecule with a single coiled chain of sugars, phosphates, and nitrogen bases. You learned that RNA occurs in the nucleus and in the cytoplasm. Recall also that RNA contains the base uracil instead of thymine. Like thymine, uracil is complementary to adenine.

Biologists have learned that RNA comes in several varieties, each with a different function. Messenger RNA (mRNA) transfers information from the nucleus to the cytoplasm. Ribosomal RNA (rRNA) makes up the cell organelles called ribosomes, which are the sites for assembling polypeptides. Transfer RNA (tRNA) transports amino acids in the cytoplasm to the ribosomes for protein synthesis.

Protein synthesis is a complex process with the following key steps: DNA transfers, or transcribes, its coded information into the structure of the RNA molecule. Then RNA leaves the nucleus for the cytoplasm, where the information can be used. Finally, through the interaction of the three forms of RNA cited above, amino acids are brought to the ribosomes to be assembled into protein molecules. Let us now examine this process in detail.

Transcription of RNA

Recall from Chapter 17 that DNA copies itself when one strand of the double helix serves as a template to make another strand. In the new strand, complementary bases pair up to form the new sequence of nucleotide building blocks. In a similar process, called transcription, DNA specifies the synthesis of RNA.

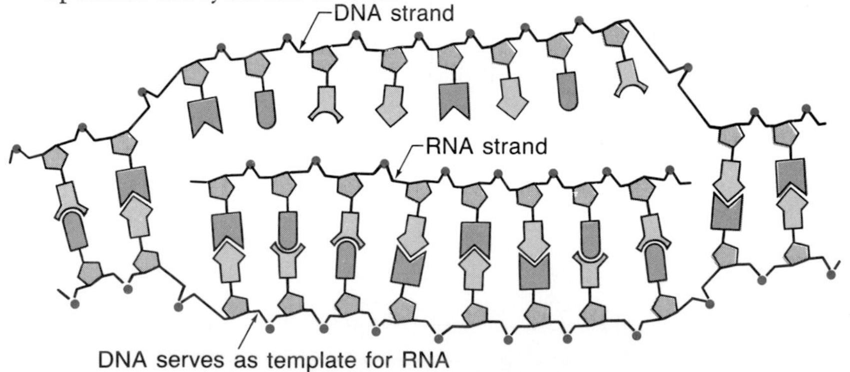

Fig. 21–5. Transcription of RNA by DNA. The RNA molecule is a single strand of nucleotide building blocks.

The DNA molecule "unzips" to expose a sequence of nucleotides. Then an enzyme known as RNA polymerase catalyzes the synthesis of an RNA chain. Free nucleotides are brought to the transcription sites along the

DNA molecule. As in DNA replication, one strand of DNA serves as a template for making a new strand. The nucleotide building blocks are placed in a sequence by the complementary pairing of nitrogen bases between two chains. In this process, the nucleotide uracil is built into the new RNA molecule by bonding with adenine in the DNA chain.

Translation: Protein Synthesis

Following transcription in the nucleus, RNA leaves the nucleus and travels through the cytoplasm to ribosomes. We refer to the RNA from the nucleus as messenger RNA (mRNA) because it carries the genetic code transcribed from DNA. Ribosomes are made of RNA and protein. They serve as binding sites where mRNA and amino acids are brought together. At the ribosomes, the genetic code carried by mRNA will be translated into a sequence of amino acids. Each triplet of nitrogen bases, or codon, on the mRNA chain will specify a particular amino acid.

Before amino acids can be joined to make a polypeptide chain, however, they must be transported to the ribosomes. This is the function of the third form of RNA, transfer RNA (tRNA). The tRNA molecule is folded into a specific shape so that it carries an amino acid molecule at one end.

Another part of the tRNA molecule is called the anticodon. This is a triplet of nucleotides whose nitrogen bases are complementary to an mRNA codon. Suppose, for example, that an mRNA codon contains the bases UGG. This sequence will form a bond with a tRNA that has the sequence ACC as its anticodon. This tRNA carries the amino acid tryptophan. The mRNA codon UGG therefore places tryptophan in a sequence of amino acids.

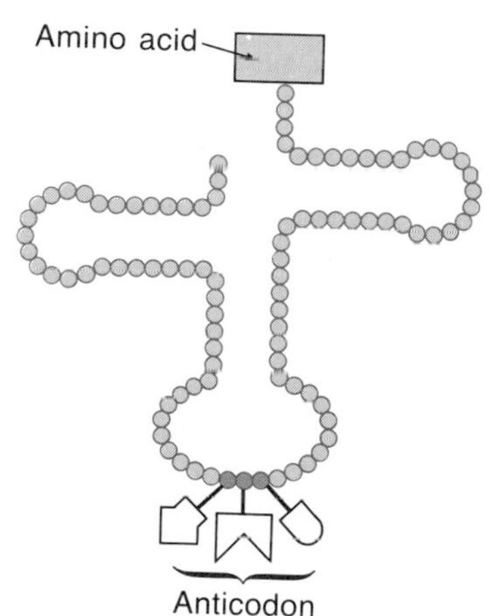

Fig. 21–6. Transfer RNA: The anticodon of this tRNA reads CUA (from right to left). It is complementary to the messenger RNA codon GAU, which codes for aspartic acid.

In order to make a chain of amino acids using the information in the mRNA codons, there must be a way to read the sequence of mRNA codons. This will ensure that the proper sequence of amino acids is assembled. Ribosomes move along the mRNA chain, reading the sequence of codons. Each ribosome is a site where particular tRNA molecules bond with their complementary mRNA codons.

The bond between a tRNA anticodon and a mRNA codon is brief, because many tRNAs must come and go for assembly of an amino acid chain. The shape of tRNA molecules permits enzymes at the ribosome to remove each amino acid from the tRNA that carried it. The enzymes link the amino acids to make polypeptides. After tRNA molecules leave the ribosome, they return to the cytoplasm to pick up more amino acids.

A specific mRNA codon—AUG—is called an initiator because it starts the assembly of a new polypeptide chain. After the initiator codon, the polypeptide grows by addition of amino acids until the ribosome reaches one of the three terminator codons (terminator codons are identified in the genetic code chart). At this point, the polypeptide molecule leaves the ribosome and is transported to the part of the cell that needs it.

The entire process of protein synthesis requires many enzymes and significant amounts of energy. The events described above proceed in a series of steps, each step controlled by a specific enzyme.

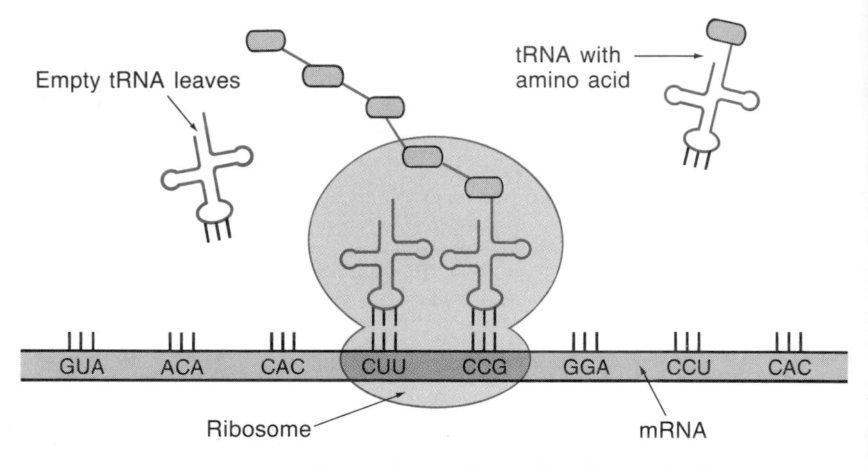

Fig. 21–7. Translation: the synthesis of a polypeptide chain.

(F)

Gene Mutation

In Chapter 20 you read about some of the causes and effects of mutations. We defined gene mutations as those that change the DNA molecule. Understanding the processes of transcription and translation helps you better understand how these mutations affect the cell.

Point mutations are those in which a single nucleotide is affected. There are two types of point mutations: those that add or delete a single nucleotide, and those that substitute one nucleotide for another. These point mutations change the sequence of nitrogen base pairs in DNA, and affect the sequence of nitrogen bases when RNA is transcribed.

To see the effect of point mutations, look at the following sentence:

The dog ate the cat who ate the rat

If a single letter is added to or deleted from the sentence, the result might be as follows:

Addition: The dog ate the cat swh oat eth era t

Deletion: The dog att hec atw hoa tet her at

A substitution might give you this message:

The dog ate the bat who ate the rat.

The changes, which occur at the site of the underlined letter, alter the meaning of the original sentence or make it meaningless.

In a similar way, the addition, deletion, or substitution of a single nitrogen base in DNA will change the sequence of complementary nitrogen bases in RNA. This may, in turn, change a codon, or sequence of codons, in mRNA. This means that a different sequence of amino acids could be assembled to form a protein that differs from what was intended. Let us consider an example.

The human disease sickle-cell anemia affects the production of normal hemoglobin molecules. (You read about hemoglobin in Chapters 7 and 13. You will read more about sickle-cell anemia in Chapter 22.) A gene mutation causes this inherited disease. The substitution of a single base in a nucleotide causes production of abnormal hemoglobin, which contains one wrong amino acid. In abnormal hemoglobin, the amino acid valine substitutes for the amino acid glutamic acid, which is in normal hemoglobin.

Examine the genetic code chart to find the codons that specify these two amino acids. You can see that four codons, all beginning with the mRNA bases GU code for valine. Two codons, both beginning with the mRNA bases GA, code for glutamic acid. Thus the abnormal hemoglobin in sickle-cell anemia results from the substitution of uracil for adenine. This substitution takes place during RNA transcription from the DNA template.

Not all substitutions produce a dangerous mutation. By examining the genetic code chart you can see that some amino acids are specified by several codons. Therefore a substitution may specify the same amino acid as the original codon.

(G) Synthesis of an Artificial Gene

In 1976, Har Gobind Khorana of the Massachusetts Institute of Technology succeeded in synthesizing an artificial gene. When placed into a living cell, the artificial gene functioned normally. The *structural* part of this gene has 126 nucleotides. In addition, there are beginning and ending *regulatory* sections.

Khorana's gene is a small one. A gene may consist of a string of several thousand nucleotides. If all the DNA in a cell could be strung out, it would reach a mile or more.

(H)

Genetic Control: The Operon Model

How do cells "know" when to start and stop producing enzymes to meet their needs? For instance, how does a bacterial cell "know" to produce the enzyme lactase only when the sugar lactose is present in its food supply? Francis Jacob and Jacques Monod proposed the Nobel Prize-winning Operon Model for the control of protein synthesis in bacteria.

According to this model, the genes coding for proteins are called *structural genes.* In prokaryotes, structural genes for enzymes used in a metabolic pathway are organized and transcribed as a unit. A *promoter* gene and an *operator* gene, which do not code for any proteins, control transcription of the adjacent structural genes. Together, the promoter gene, operator gene, and structural genes are called an *operon.* The operator gene allows the enzyme RNA polymerase to transcribe the structural genes. A distant *repressor gene* codes for a *repressor protein* that can block transcription of the structural genes. The repressor protein does this by binding to the operator gene in the operon. When the sugar lactose is present in the cell's food supply, it prevents the repressor protein from binding to the operator gene.

Reasoning Exercises

1. What is the relationship between an amino acid and a messenger RNA codon?
2. Describe the differences between DNA replication and RNA transcription.
3. Describe the steps of protein synthesis starting with transcription.
4. When scientists were trying to figure out the genetic code, why did they use long nucleotide chains that contained just one nitrogen base, such as all guanines, in their research?
5. What might be the relationship between a structural gene and an operon?
6. Why do you think the genetic code is the same in all organisms?

Completion Questions

A

1. The arrangement of amino acids in a protein give it a specific . . . . . .
2. Griffith's experiments showed that something from dead bacteria could change the . . . . . . of live bacteria.

B

3. The DNA molecule is a polymer made of repeating units called . . . . . .
4. The consistent pairing of complementary nitrogen bases ensures that exact copies of DNA strands are made during . . . . . .
5. RNA nucleotides contain the sugar ribose, while DNA nucleotides contain . . . . . .

(C)

6. Beadle and Tatum's research showed that genes are responsible for producing the . . . . . . that control essential chemical reactions.

7. A modified view of Beadle and Tatum's hypothesis is that one gene contains information to make one . . . . . .

(D)

8. Information to coordinate the cell's activities is contained in DNA in the form of . . . . . .
9. The genetic code is expressed by different combinations of three . . . . . . in DNA.
10. Three of the 64 possible base triplets in the genetic code act as . . . . . . instead of coding for specific amino acids.

(E)

11. Uracil forms a complementary pair with the base......
12. Ribosomes consist of protein and......
13. RNA transcription cannot take place without an...... called RNA polymerase.

(F)

14. A gene mutation is any chanage in the nitrogen base sequence of an organism's . . . . . .
15. Mutations in which a single nucleotide is affected are called . . . . . .
16. Sickle-cell anemia results from a change in a single . . . . . . of the . . . . . . molecule.

(H)

17. A repressor gene produces a repressor protein that blocks the transcription of......
18. The control of genes in higher organisms seems to be based on an interaction with the......

Multiple Choice Questions

[A]

1. Bacterial transformation studies showed that (1) DNA is used as a template for messenger RNA production during protein synthesis, (2) DNA is the hereditary material responsible for passing traits from one generation to another, (3) the structure of DNA is a double helix containing the element nitrogen, (4) the interaction between an organism and its environment can change the structure of its DNA.

[B]

2. Suppose that a DNA nucleotide has adenine as its nitrogen base. What would be found in a complementary position in a messenger RNA molecule formed from this DNA template? (1) cytosine, (2) guanine, (3) thymine, (4) uracil.
3. Watson and Crick described the DNA molecule as a (1) straight chain, (2) single strand, (3) double helix, (4) branching chain.

(C)

4. Beadle and Tatum proposed that (1) one gene directs the synthesis of one enzyme, (2) one gene directs synthesis of the B vitamins, (3) one gene directs transcription, (4) one gene directs protein synthesis.

5. Beadle and Tatum's research showed that (1) radiation is needed to make vitamins, (2) molds do not need vitamins to survive, (3) mutation does not affect enzyme synthesis, (4) mutation can upset the cell's ability to make a needed enzyme.

(D)

6. A sequence of DNA that has 3000 nucleotides would produce a polypeptide chain (1) 1000 amino acids long, (2) 3000 amino acids long, (3) 6000 amino acids long, (4) 9000 amino acids long.

(E)

7. RNA contains the nitrogen base uracil instead of (1) guanine, (2) cytosine, (3) adenine, (4) thymine.
8. The main function of transfer RNA is to (1) form peptide bonds in polysaccharides, (2) convert proteins into amino acids, (3) change ATP into DNA, (4) carry amino acids to messenger RNA.
9. The process of interpreting mRNA's message into a polypeptide is called (1) elongation, (2) initiation, (3) translation, (4) termination.
10. The sequence of nucleotides in messenger RNA is determined by the sequence of nucleotides in (1) transfer RNA, (2) protein, (3) amino acids, (4) DNA.
11. Specific proteins produced in a cell are directly related to the (1) number of mitochondria in the cell, (2) type of ribosomes in the cell, (3) nucleotide sequence in the DNA of the cell, (4) sequence of sugars and phosphates in the cell.
12. The anticodon of transfer RNA is (1) a triplet of nitrogen bases complementary to a triplet of nitrogen bases in DNA, (2) a triplet of nitrogen bases that inhibits messenger RNA, (3) a triplet of nitrogen bases complementary to a triplet of nitrogen bases in messenger RNA, (4) a triplet of nitrogen bases that carries an amino acid to the nucleus.

Base your answers to questions 13 through 17 on the diagram below.

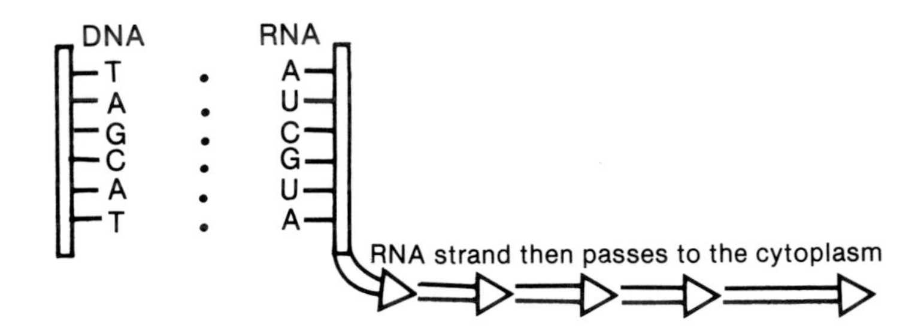

13. The RNA strand shown in the diagram contains (1) 6, (2) 4, (3) 3, (4) 2 codons.
14. In order to make the RNA strand, the DNA strand functions as a(n) (1) enzyme, (2) template, (3) polypeptide, (4) messenger.
15. The process shown in the diagram is called (1) transformation, (2) translation, (3) transcription, (4) termination.
16. At a ribosome in the cytoplasm, the messenger RNA strand shown in the diagram will bind briefly to (1) 6, (2) 4, (3) 3, (4) 2 molecules of transfer RNA.

17. Reading from the lower end of the RNA strand, the first triplet—AUG—will bind to a transfer RNA molecule with the anticodon (1) AUG, (2) UAC, (3) CUA, (4) TAC.

(F)

18. Which process has taken place when the base sequence of a DNA molecule is altered? (1) replication, (2) blending, (3) segregation, (4) mutation.
19. The diagram below shows a point mutation in DNA. This mutation can be described as a(n) (1) substitution, (2) addition, (3) deletion, (4) subtraction.

A T C G A T —X-ray→ A A C G A T

(H)

20. A group of genes whose transcription is controlled as a unit is called a(n) (1) regulator, (2) enzyme, (3) repressor, (4) operon.

Chapter Test

Base your answers to questions 1 through 4 on the diagram below, which represents parts of two nucleic acid molecules.

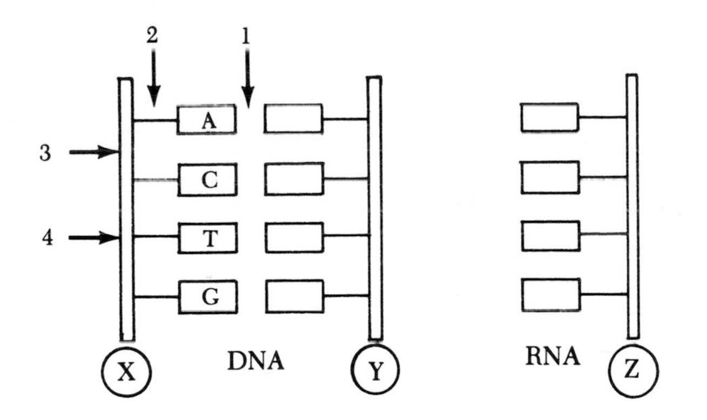

1. What is the nitrogen base sequence in the segment of strand Y shown in the diagram? (1) T-G-A-C, (2) T-A-A-C, (3) U-G-A-C, (4) T-G-U-C.
2. Molecules represented by strand Z move from the nucleus of a cell to cytoplasmic organelles known as (1) mitochondria, (2) vacuoles, (3) ribosomes, (4) centrioles.
3. If strand X serves as a template for the synthesis of strand Z, the base sequence in the segment of Z shown is (1) T-G-A-C, (2) U-G-A-C, (3) A-C-U-G, (4) A-C-T-G.
4. At which location does the DNA molecule "unzip" during transcription? (1) 4, (2) 3, (3) 2, (4) 1.
5. A base pair in DNA could be (1) adenine and guanine, (2) adenine and cytosine, (3) thymine and guanine, (4) guanine and cytosine.

6. The coded information in DNA determines the formation of (1) polypeptides, (2) polysaccharides, (3) lipids, (4) monosaccharides.
7. The coded message carried by mRNA is translated into polypeptides at the (1) nucleus, (2) vacuoles, (3) ribosomes, (4) Golgi bodies.
8. Biochemically, gene mutations are considered to be changes that alter the sequence of (1) nitrogen bases in an organism's DNA, (2) phosphates in ATP molecules, (3) sugars in RNA molecules, (4) hydrogen bonds in messenger RNA.
9. Genes control cellular activity by directing the synthesis of specific (1) enzymes, (2) antigens, (3) organs, (4) tissues.
10. Which would result most directly from chemical alteration of the DNA molecule? (1) crossing-over, (2) gene mutation, (3) nondisjunction, (4) polyploidy.
11. The condition known as sickle-cell anemia is the result of (1) a 2n gamete fusing with an n gamete, (2) exchange of chromatids during meiosis, (3) nondisjunction in a 3n individual, (4) substitution of a single amino acid in a polypeptide chain.
12. How many nitrogen bases code for an amino acid? (1) 1, (2) 2, (3) 3, (4) 4.
13. If a nucleotide in a DNA strand were involved in transcription of RNA, and its nitrogen base was adenine, what nitrogen base would be paired with it? (1) thymine, (2) uracil, (3) guanine, (4) cytosine.
14. If a messenger RNA codon read A-U-G, what would be the complementary transfer RNA anticodon? (1) U-A-C, (2) A-U-C, (3) G-U-A, (4) G-A-U.

Chapter 22 Genetics and People

Much of what we know about heredity comes from studies of organisms like fruit flies, molds, and bacteria. These organisms are ideal for genetic experiments because their offspring mature and reproduce in hours or days and because researchers can control their reproductive mechanisms.

Researchers cannot control human reproduction. Still, much is known about human heredity. In this chapter, we consider how advances in genetics have helped us understand human heredity.

A

Chromosomes in People

Chromosomes are made up of large groups of genes. These genes carry the genetic codes that define the traits of an organism. In Chapters 17 and 18, you learned about chromosome distribution during the processes of reproduction. You will recall that the normal human diploid chromosome number (2n) is 46—22 pairs of autosomes and two sex chromosomes. In females, the two sex chromosomes are a pair of X chromosomes. In males, there is one X chromosome (inherited from the mother) and one Y chromosome (inherited from the father). The Y chromosome is the smallest human chromosome.

In every species, the number and appearance of the chromosomes in the cells are constant and characteristic of the species. In the diploid cells of most organisms, chromosomes can be seen under the light microscope at the metaphase stage of mitosis or meiosis. For ease of study, karyotypes, pictures that represent orderly arrangements of chromosomes, are prepared from photographs or computerized images made during the metaphase stage. For the karyotype, the homologous pairs of chromosomes are rearranged by size and shape, starting with the largest pair and finishing with the smallest. Except for the sex chromosomes, the chromosomes are also numbered. Fig. 22–1 shows a normal human female karyotype.

Unbalanced Chromosome Numbers

Meiosis followed by fertilization (the fusing of two monoploid gametes) maintains the normal diploid chromosome number (2n) from generation to generation. This normal repetition of the chromosome number is referred to as *ploidy.* Normal development of the organism depends on the cells having the characteristic chromosome number and therefore the characteristic number of genes. Sometimes chromosomes fail to separate from each other properly during meiosis, a condition called *nondisjunction.* Nondisjunction leads to the formation of gametes that have extra or missing chromosomes, so that the total number of chromosomes is one too many $(n+1)$ or one too few $(n-1)$. After the abnormal gamete fuses with a normal gamete, the zygote will have more $(2n+1)$ or less $(2n-1)$ than the balanced diploid chromosome number. In other words, the zygote will have an unbalanced chromosome number.

In humans, the most common example of an unbalanced chromosome number is the presence of an extra chromosome number 21. The condition that results is known as *Down syndrome.* Approximately one in every 700 infants born has Down syndrome. The unbalanced triploidy (tri = 3) of

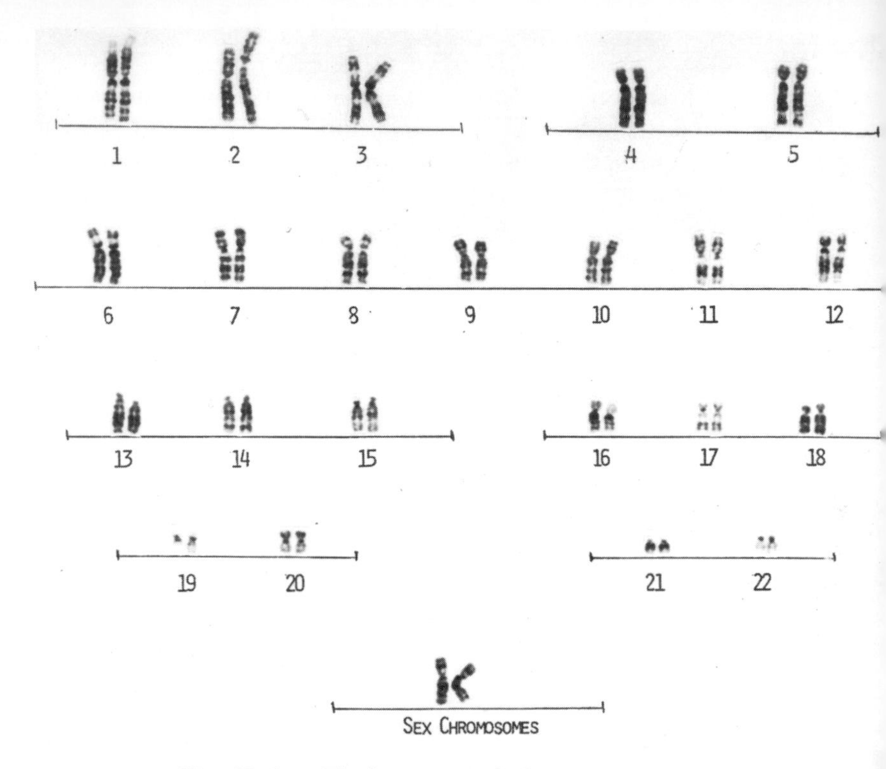

Fig. 22–1. The karyotype of a human female.

chromosome 21 means that the cell has three copies, instead of two, of as many as 1,000 genes. Symptoms of Down syndrome include mental retardation, a short neck, an oval face with upward slanting eyes, and often a protruding tongue. There may also be serious or even fatal disorders of vital internal organs, particularly the heart and the digestive system. With proper medical care and special training, some individuals with Down syndrome can live productive, semi-independent lives.

Down syndrome is also well-known because of the measurable effect of the mother's age on the nondisjunction of chromosome number 21. As women age, the risk that a pair of homologous chromosomes will fail to separate or disjoin normally during meiosis increases. In the overall population the rate of Down syndrome is one in 700. But the rate for women giving birth at age 35 is one in 350. At age 40, the rate is one in 100; and at age 45, the rate is as high as one in 50.

Nondisjunction can occur with all chromosomes. When it occurs with chromosome number 1, the effect of the unbalanced genes is so severe that the gamete or early zygote simply does not function and pregnancy does not result. When nondisjunction occurs with chromosome 16, the imbalance results in *miscarriage*, or loss of the fetus. Nondisjunction of other chromosomes can result in infants born with severe medical disorders. Because of the extra copies of thousands of genes, the infants all have mental retardation and often have fatal physical abnormalities.

Nondisjunction of the sex chromosomes results in such abnormal conditions as a female with a single X chromosome or a male with a Y chromosome *plus two* X chromosomes instead of one. These individuals are sterile and have abnormal development of the sexual features that characterize males and females.

Structural Changes of Chromosomes

A change in the structure of a chromosome can also cause an unbalanced number of genes. Structural changes in chromosomes include *translocations*, *duplications*, *deletions*, and *inversions*.

With translocation, chromosomes exchange pieces. Translocation may not have a visible effect on the individual. But during gametogenesis, when the involved chromosome segregates in the process of meiosis, the resulting gamete may have extra or missing genes.

With *duplications*, extra pieces of chromosomes are inserted, resulting in extra copies of genes. Gene copies may be missing if there are *deletions*, the removal of pieces of chromosomes. In an *inversion*, a piece of a chromosome is turned backward.

Taken together, chromosome changes, either of number or structure, result in medically significant abnormalities in one of every 200 infants born, which amounts to about 20,000 infants each year in the United States. The chart below shows some characteristics of a few of these abnormalities.

Some Chromosome Abnormalities in Humans

Name of Syndrome	Selected Characteristics	Total Chromosome #	Affected Chromosome
Down	MR*, short neck, oval face, slanted eyes, protruding tongue	47	extra 21
Edwards	MR*, overlapping fingers, 95% die before 1 year	47	extra 18
Patau	MR*, cleft lip and palate, 95% die before 1 month	47	extra 13
Turner	Sterile female	45	one X missing
Klinefelter	Sterile male	47	XXY–extra X
Cri-du-chat	MR*	46	part of chromosome 5
Prader-Willi	Obesity, MR*, poor sexual development	46	part of chromosome 15

*MR = mental retardation.

B

Traits Inherited in Humans

In Chapter 20, you read about traits that are inherited in humans, including ABO blood types, Rh factor, and gender. It is likely that many thousands of human traits are inherited in a Mendelian manner. Sometimes disruptions in normal gene activities result in changes in these traits and cause genetic disorders. Some normal human traits and human genetic variations or disorders are shown in the table below.

Trait	Variation or Disorder	Mendelian Inheritance
eye color	dark blue	dominant recessive
hair texture	curly straight	dominant recessive
fingers/toes	polydactyly—extra digits ectrodactyly—fusion or reduced digits	dominant dominant
lips	cleft lip	dominant
color vision	color blindness	sex-linked recessive
hair on head	baldness	sex-influenced dominant

Multifactorial Traits

A trait that results from heredity and is also affected by interaction with the environment is known as a *multifactorial trait*. One such trait is skin color. The amount of *melanin*, or pigment in the skin, is controlled by several pairs of genes. The alleles of these genes show incomplete dominance and each pair of genes is inherited on different chromosomes. The total number of alleles for pigment determines the skin pigment shades from darkly pigmented to lightly pigmented. The absence of the pigment results in albinism. Interaction with the environment—specifically, exposure to sunlight—also affects skin color.

Multifactorial traits are very complicated to study. If Mendel had selected such traits to study in the garden pea, he would not have been able to describe the principles of heredity as he did.

C

Human Genetic Disorders

Human genetic disorders are far more common than is generally realized. Over 6,000 human disorders are known to be inherited. However, some are so rare that many physicians never see anyone who is afflicted with them. In addition, the symptoms of some disorders are difficult to recognize and specialized laboratories may be required to do the tests that diagnose, or confirm, the disorder.

Genetic disorders are *chronic* (long-lasting). Although they are sometimes treatable, none are curable. The diagnosis of an inherited disorder has implications for the affected individual and for the extended family.

Early, accurate diagnosis and treatment can sometimes prevent further complications of the disorder. Family education and counseling may prevent the appearance of the disorder in future family members.

PKU (phenylketonuria)

PKU is an inherited condition that, if untreated, results in mental retardation and disturbances of behavior. Infants with PKU appear healthy and normal at birth. Within a few months on a normal diet, however, symptoms of the disorder begin to appear. Symptoms include an abnormal growth rate and abnormal development, such as the inability to walk or talk.

The name of the disorder, *phenylketonuria*, refers to chemicals known as phenylketones, which appear in the urine of the affected individuals. In a normal person, enzymes convert phenylalanine, one of the 20 amino acids present in many foods, to the amino acid tyrosine. However, individuals homozygous for PKU lack the gene that codes for the enzymes to convert phenylalanine. In their place are recessive alleles that do not code for the enzyme. Thus, in individuals with PKU, phenylalanine cannot be converted to tyrosine. The phenylalanine in the diet is instead broken down to phenylketones and other derivatives that end up in the urine. Still other derivatives accumulate in the body, where they are toxic (poisonous) to the nervous system and result in mental retardation.

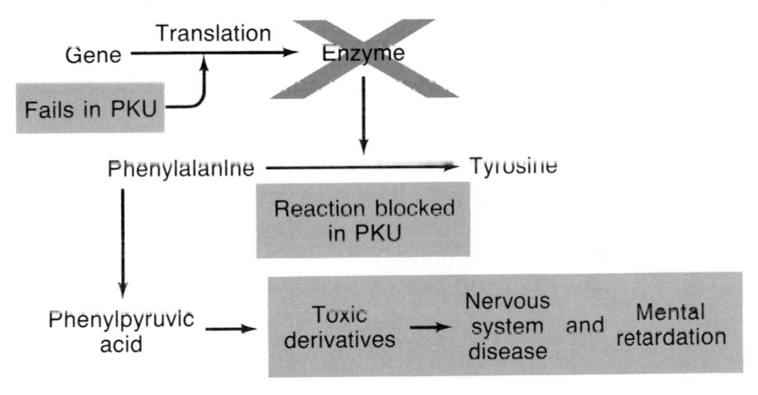

Fig. 22–2. Individuals with PKU lack genes that code for the synthesis of an enzyme needed to convert phenylalanine to tyrosine.

In addition to the harmful accumulation of the breakdown products of phenylalanine, the affected individual suffers from a lack of tyrosine. Tyrosine is an essential amino acid that the body needs for many of its functions, including the production of the pigment melanin.

With early detection, infants can be placed on a special diet low in phenylalanine and supplemented with tyrosine. To be effective, this diet must be started within the first weeks of life. Therefore, early diagnosis of PKU is essential.

Human geneticists have developed and continue to develop tests to diagnose genetic disorders and detect carriers. Application of such tests to populations at high risk or to the population in general is called *screening*. Newborn screening programs test for several genetic disorders, including

PKU and sickle-cell anemia (see page 398). Early detection of such disorders is a benefit of modern biology to humans.

PKU testing is an example of the success of newborn screening programs. There have been no PKU patients institutionalized with mental retardation since such programs started in New York in 1965. Now that women who have received treatment for PKU have reached reproductive age, it has been found that the elevated phenylalanine in their blood is toxic to their fetus during their pregnancy. This makes continuation of the controlled diet even more important.

The lifelong cost of maintaining a PKU patient in an institution can exceed one million dollars. The cost of the newborn screening program is a few dollars per child. Maintenance of the special diet costs about $3,000 a year. From a strictly financial point of view, this public health screening program is "cost effective." Among the issues that still remain are confidentiality of the screening programs and access to good treatment for PKU patients.

Sickle-Cell Anemia

Sickle-cell anemia is so-named because the red blood cells of individuals with the disorder sometimes become shaped like crescents or sickles. The sickle-shaped red blood cells occur where there is a low level of oxygen, such as in the small blood vessels far from the lungs. The sickled cells tend to form plugs that block circulation in these small blood vessels. The blockage causes severe pain and damage in nearby tissues. The abnormal red blood cells survive only 10 to 25 days instead of the usual 120 days. They are destroyed faster than new ones can be made. The resulting shortage of red blood cells is the condition called *anemia*.

As with PKU, an infant born with sickle-cell anemia initially appears healthy and normal. However, by the age of four to six months, a sore throat, cold, or infection may very rapidly become a life-threatening condition. Early treatment with low doses of penicillin can prevent the deadly infections. For this reason, early diagnosis is essential. The same dried-blood spot test used to screen newborns for PKU can be used to screen for sickle-cell anemia.

As children with sickle-cell anemia get older, they may have symptoms of anemia, including fatigue, paleness, and poor appetite. Dehydration, exhaustion, or infection may bring on a *crisis*, a period of severe pain and other symptoms. With early diagnosis, parents and doctors can guard these children against such crises and can provide pain relief and other medical support when they occur. As yet there is no cure for this disorder.

How Is Sickle-Cell Anemia Inherited?

In 1949, Linus Pauling of the California Institute of Technology showed that the cause of the sickling of the red blood cells is an abnormality in their hemoglobin. The abnormal hemoglobin is known as hemoglobin S.

We can use this key for tracing the inheritance of this condition:

β = allele for normal hemoglobin

S = allele for abnormal hemoglobin

Genotypes:

ββ = normal

βS = sickle-cell trait (A carrier of the abnormal allele; the individual makes some abnormal hemoglobin and some normal hemoglobin.)

SS = sickle-cell anemia

Persons with the *sickle-cell trait* (βS) sometimes experience discomfort or pain during activities that reduce the oxygen concentration in the blood. Such conditions or activities might include high altitude or vigorous exercise. Generally, however, persons with the sickle-cell trait lead normal, healthy lives. Many do not suspect that they carry the abnormal allele. The same simple test used to screen newborns for sickle-cell anemia can detect the sickle-cell trait.

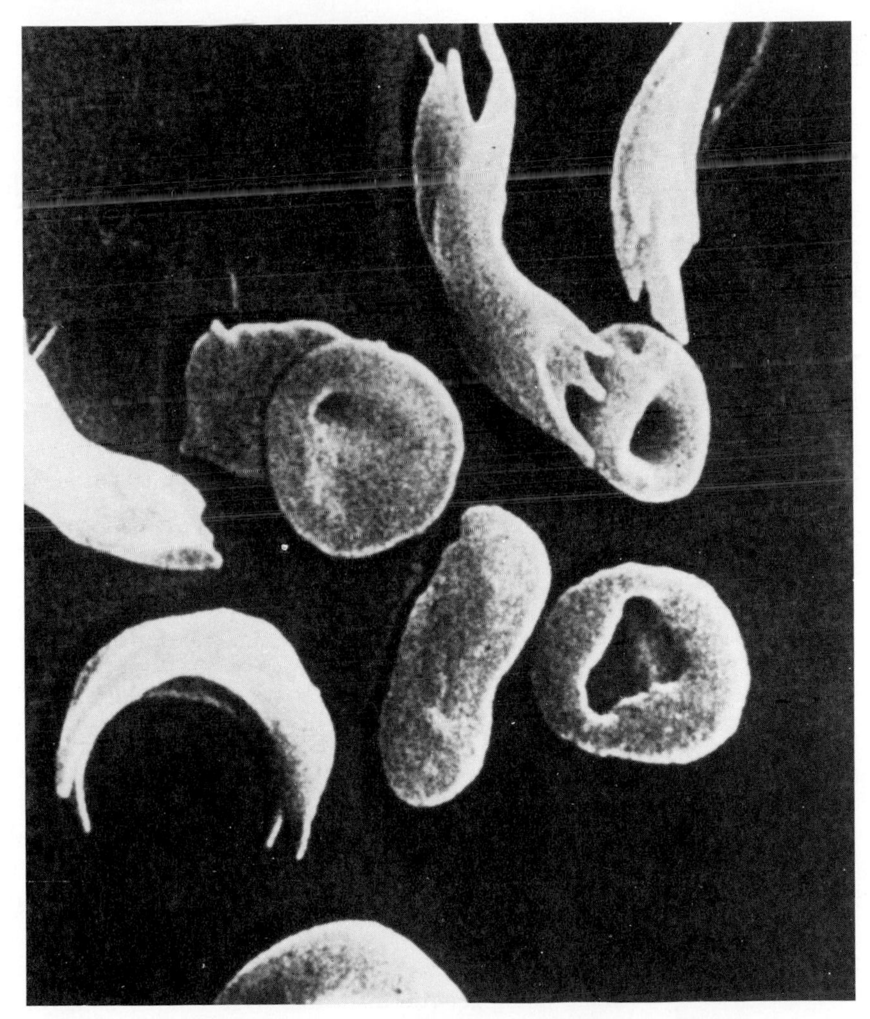

Fig. 22–3. Sickle cells in the blood: Normal red blood cells are disc-shaped; sickle cells have the curved shape of a sickle.

Problem 1. What are the chances that two people having the sickle-cell trait will have a child with sickle-cell anemia? (Complete all diagrams and problems in your notebook; do not write in this book.)

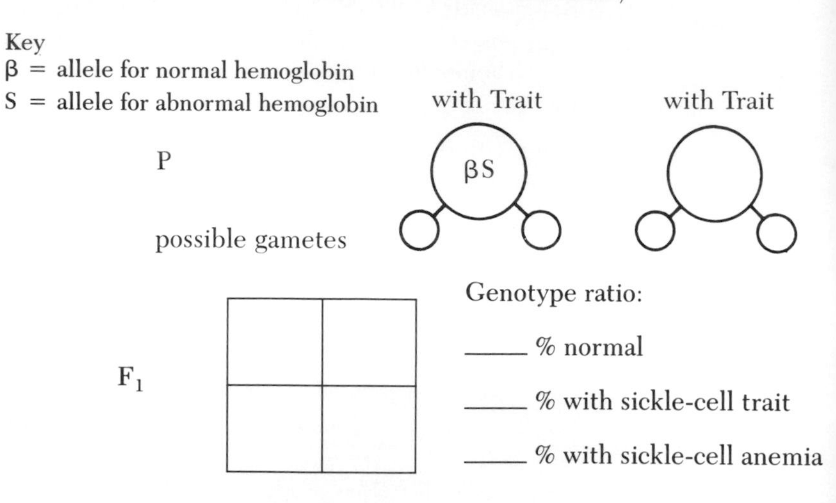

Problem 2. If one parent has the sickle-cell trait and the other parent is normal, what are the chances of their first child having sickle-cell anemia?

Sickle-cell anemia occurs more often in Africans and their descendants. In the United States, it is found mainly in African Americans and Hispanics. The mutation for sickling arose many generations ago in Africa. We might expect that such a harmful allele would have been eliminated from the population through natural selection—that is, by failure of the affected individuals to survive long enough to produce offspring. However, over the centuries, the occurrence of this allele in populations continuously exposed to malaria actually increased. It turns out that the sickling gene provides strong resistance to malaria, a parasitic disease that affects red blood cells. In Africa, the inheritance of the sickle-cell trait was a protection against malaria. Individuals with normal hemoglobin died of malaria or were incapacitated by it. Persons with sickle-cell anemia died or became very ill as a result of the anemia. Individuals with the sickle-cell trait who did not develop anemia were most likely to survive and reproduce.

Today, in the United States, where malaria is under control, the sickle-cell trait no longer has natural survival value to the population. However, with early diagnosis and treatment, sickle-cell anemia is no longer necessarily deadly. About one in every 400 newborn African-American infants in the United States has sickle-cell anemia. In total, more than 50,000 people in this country have the disorder. Moreover, approximately one in every 10 African-Americans have the sickle-cell trait.

Many other genetic disorders have unique racial or ethnic distributions. For example:

PKU: Occurs mainly among whites, but not among eastern and central European Jewish populations.

β-Thalassemia (Cooley's Anemia): Occurs mainly among Greeks, Italians, and other people from the Mediterranean.
α-Thalassemia: Occurs mainly among Southeast Asians.
Cystic fibrosis: Occurs mainly among northern European whites.
Tay-Sachs disease: Occurs mainly among descendants of Ashkenazi Jews, from eastern and central Europe.

Tay-Sachs Disease

Tay-Sachs disease is an inherited disorder caused by an abnormal recessive allele. Thus, an affected individual is homozygous for the condition. Biochemically, the disorder results from the absence of the enzyme *hexosaminidase A (HexA)*, which would be coded for by the dominant gene. HexA breaks down a fatty substance in nerve cells. When the fatty substance cannot be broken down, it accumulates in the lysosomes of the nerve cells and causes their destruction.

As with so many genetic disorders, the affected child appears normal until about six months of age, when symptoms of nervous system destruction begin to appear. These symptoms include progressive blindness, deafness, paralysis, and mental retardation. The disorder results in death, often by the age of four to six years. There is no cure and no effective treatment for Tay-Sachs disease.

A single normal allele (N) is sufficient to produce enough of the needed enzyme, HexA. A person whose genotype has a normal dominant allele (N) and the abnormal recessive allele (n) is a carrier (Nn). Tay-Sachs carriers are normal, healthy individuals.

Chances of having a child with Tay-Sachs disease are greatest for people of Jewish heritage whose ancestors came from eastern Europe. One in every 30 such individuals is a carrier.

Problem 3. What are the chances that two carriers will have a child with Tay-Sachs disease?

Problem 4. If parents who are both carriers have three normal children, what is the chance that the next child will have Tay-Sachs disease?

Carriers of Tay-Sachs disease can be detected by a blood test that measures the enzyme HexA. It is important for individuals in the high-risk group to know if their genotype is homozygous normal (NN) or heterozygous carrier (Nn). This knowledge can help them plan their family and deal with the risks of having an affected child.

Cystic Fibrosis

Cystic fibrosis is as common in the northern European white population as Tay-Sachs disease is among the eastern European Jewish population. One in every 25 white northern Europeans may be a carrier for a recessive cystic fibrosis allele. A homozygous affected child suffers from abnormal cellular secretions. Thick mucus accumulates in the lungs and plugs other ducts, such as those in the pancreas. The result is a susceptibility to respiratory infections and digestive problems. Treatment with antibiotics and pancreatic enzymes and extensive medical care have helped many affected individuals live into adulthood.

In 1987, the cooperative efforts of many researchers identified the gene for cystic fibrosis. Once they had isolated the gene, researchers predicted the protein for which it codes. Then they produced a model of how the protein functions in producing cellular secretions. This elusive protein has now been isolated—an example of the exciting power of the field known as *reverse genetics.* Previously geneticists had to start with visible differences among individuals and work back to the genetic information. With reverse genetics, scientists can work from the genetic information to predict the effect.

The combination of classical genetics and reverse genetics is rapidly lengthening the list of diagnosable genetic disorders.

Other Human Genetic Disorders

Thalassemia. The *thalassemias* are a group of severe anemias resulting from insufficient quantities of hemoglobin, or, in the severest form, from absence of normal hemoglobin. The recessive alleles that produce the thalassemias are found mainly in descendants of populations from the Mediterranean or Southeast Asia. As with sickle-cell anemia, the carriers of these alleles experience a protection against malaria.

Huntington Disease. Unlike the other disorders discussed, *Huntington disease (Huntington's disease)* is the result of a dominant allele. The symptoms of this disorder generally do not appear until the affected individual is 35 to 40 years old. Symptoms include uncontrolled twitching motions and dementia, or bizarre behavior. By the time these symptoms appear, the individual may have had several children who appear to be normal.

Problem 5. If one parent is heterozygous (hybrid) for Huntington disease and develops the symptoms at age 40, what are the chances that any teenage children the parents already have will later develop the condition? The second parent is normal.

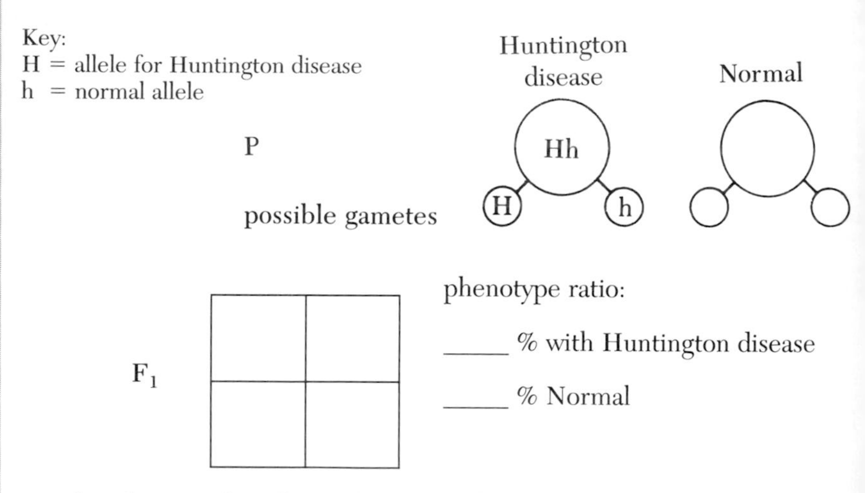

Other human disorders where heredity may play a significant role include heart disease, some mental illnesses, diabetes, and cancer.

D Genetic Counseling

The field of human medical genetics is moving rapidly. Frequent discoveries are leading to diagnosis and potentially improved treatment of more and more genetic disorders. *Genetic counseling* is the process of informing concerned individuals about genetic disorders and their risks of having affected children.

Having a child with a serious genetic disorder can be a distressing event. The emotional effects, provision of care, and financial costs can be severe burdens that can disrupt the lives of the child's parents and brothers and sisters.

Individuals who have relatives with a genetic disorder or who belong to a high-risk population may wish to obtain an accurate diagnosis and family history. The discovery that a person is a carrier usually involves an examination by a physician and blood testing. An accurate family history is a basic tool of genetic counseling. For assessment of individual genetic risk or for diagnosis of a possible genetic disorder, professional advice from a medical genetics team is essential. Once the specific family risks have been defined, the genetic counselor can help the family consider reproductive options.

Amniocentesis The presence of Down syndrome, PKU, sickle-cell anemia, or Tay-Sachs disease can be detected while a fetus is still in the uterus using a process called *amniocentesis*.

In amniocentesis, a sample of amniotic fluid is withdrawn from the pregnant woman by insertion of a needle into the abdomen. The fluid contains cells shed by the growing fetus. The cells can be cultured and tested for all detectable chromosomal abnormalities and for some bio-

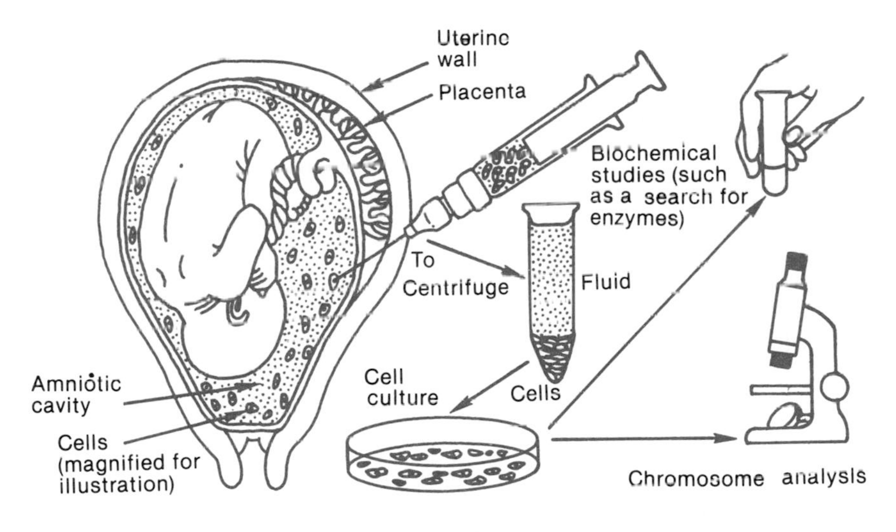

Fig. 22–4. Amniocentesis: Ultrasound sonar helps guide the needle to the amniotic fluid around the fetus. The needle withdraws fetal cells, which can be cultured for examination and testing.

chemical abnormalities as well. Secreted compounds can be detected directly in the fluid. A physician can safely remove amniotic fluid as early as the twelfth to fourteenth week of pregnancy, although amniocentesis is most commonly done at 14 to 16 weeks. A diagnosis can be made even earlier—at 9 to 10 weeks of gestation—by the sampling of certain cells of the placenta. This procedure is known as *chorionic villus sampling*.

Testing of the fetus while it is still in the uterus, such as by amniocentesis, is referred to as *prenatal testing*. Prenatal genetic testing can detect well over 150 serious genetic disorders. Examination of the chromosomes can detect Down syndrome. In testing for Tay-Sachs disease, the presence or absence of the enzyme HexA is measured. For sickle-cell anemia, DNA extracted from the fetal cells can be tested for the presence of the abnormal hemoglobin allele.

When prenatal testing is done for important medical reasons, the sex of the fetus can also be determined. Since the testing procedures are not without some risks and since the laboratory tests are expensive, neither amniocentesis nor chorionic villus sampling is done merely to satisfy a parent's curiosity about the child's sex.

Detection of a disorder during prenatal diagnosis should always be followed by extensive genetic counseling. Counseling helps the family fully understand all their options.

Answers to Problems:

Problem 1: 25% normal, 50% with trait, 25% with sickle-cell anemia.
Problem 2: 0%
Problem 3: 25% normal, 50% carrier, 25% having Tay-Sachs disease.
Problem 4: Still 25%. Previous results do not affect the odds for the next pregnancy.
Problem 5: 50% with Huntington disease, 50% normal.

(E)

History of Applied Genetics

Applied genetics refers to the application of principles of genetics learned in pure research to practical situations. Because humans are not used for genetic experiments, applied genetics is limited to other organisms. Nonetheless, applied genetics has greatly affected the lives of humans. For example, modern agriculture, which has significantly improved the food supply, is largely the result of applied genetics. Several examples follow.

Selective breeding

The *Beltsville turkey* is an example of selective breeding to produce a better food product. A small young turkey normally has little meat compared to the amount of bone. The small *Beltsville turkey*, however, as well as some small chickens developed at the agricultural experiment station at Beltsville, Maryland, has a larger proportion of meat to bone.

Another example of selective breeding to produce an improved food product is *Jersey dairy cattle*. The amount of milk produced by dairy cattle and the milk's butter-fat content are controlled by several different pairs of genes. As with skin pigment in humans, the sum of the alleles determines the amount of milk and the butter-fat content. Selective breeding of cows with bulls known to have fathered offspring that give high milk production further increases the milk production of offspring. The Jersey cow has also been selected over many generations for milk with high butter-fat content—milk for which farmers traditionally received a higher price. With today's enthusiasm for low-fat diets, however, a high butter-fat content may no longer be an advantage. Such quantitative traits take as long to select out of a species as they did to select for.

Polyploid species In mammals, an unbalanced chromosome number is generally deadly. In plants, however, multiple copies of single chromosomes or the entire chromosome set can result in a larger, healthier plant. Most commercially grown wheat, for example, is octoploid (8N).

Hybrids Much of the corn seed now planted by farmers is *dihybrid corn* that has the desirable qualities of four different pure strains of corn. These strains were selected for good taste, regular ear, sturdy stem, and disease-resistant roots. After two generations of hybridization, dihybrid seeds are produced that grow into plants with the four desired qualities. Farmers must purchase new seeds each year. If they plant the seeds produced by self-pollination of the dihybrid plants, the next generation may have many throwbacks to undesirable characteristics of the four ancestral types.

Santa Gertrudis cattle are a breed of cattle developed by crossing English shorthorns with Brahman cattle from India, followed by inbreeding. The offspring combine good beef quality with the ability to withstand the heat of the southeastern and southwestern United States.

(F)

New Genetic Research

The agricultural applications of genetics described above have had major beneficial effects on the human food supply. Breeding new strains of plants and animals, however, is a relatively slow process because it depends on the natural reproductive time of the organism. New developments in modern genetics have the potential for greatly speeding up the development of genetically altered plants and animals.

Two such developments in modern genetics are *cloning* and *genetic engineering* by recombinant DNA.

Cloning In its original usage, the term *clone* referred to genetically identical cells originating from a single cell. For example, bacteria in a colony started from a single bacterium are clones. Today, the term *animal clone* refers to a group of identical, whole individuals.

The complete set of chromosomes of the fertilized egg is repeated in all cells of the resulting organism through the process of mitosis. Each differentiated cell of the offspring has the characteristic number of genes. That number, in a human cell, is approximately 80,000 genes. Accordingly, a cell in the liver has the genes for color vision even though, in the liver, those genes are never turned on.

Similarly, an undifferentiated cell in an early rabbit embryo has a full set of rabbit genes although many of them are not being used. Researchers at the University of Massachusetts successfully produced genetically identical rabbits by the procedures shown in Figure 22-5. First, they removed the set of monoploid chromosomes from unfertilized rabbit eggs. Next, they transplanted the nuclei from an early embryo's cells to these eggs, creating zygotes, and then activated them to continue development. They reimplanted the zygotes in the rabbit for a normal gestation. The result was a litter of genetically identical rabbits—or *clones*. Frogs, cows, sheep and monkeys have been cloned using nuclei from undifferentiated early embryonic cells.

In 1997, scientists reported the first successful cloning of a mammal—a lamb named Dolly—with the nucleus from a differentiated adult cell.

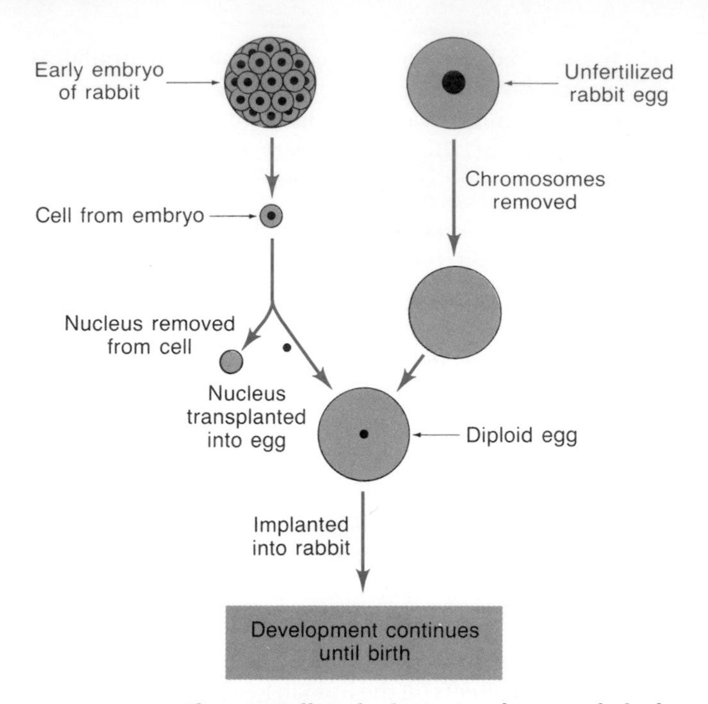

Fig. 22–5. Cloning: Cell nuclei from an embryo are diploid. When such a nucleus is transplanted into an egg without chromosomes, a normal individual can develop. This procedure, when performed many times, can produce a group of genetically identical individuals at birth.

Artificial cloning is becoming a valuable technique for producing genetically identical disease-resistant plants for agricultural purposes and disease-susceptible animals for medical research purposes.

Genetic Engineering

Genetic engineering is the manipulation of DNA to change heredity. The remarkable advances in this field have resulted from the discovery of several special enzymes. *Restriction endonucleases* cut the DNA strands at specific points, and *DNA ligase* joins the cut ends of the DNA strands together.

Using these enzymes, a DNA molecule can be broken and a piece of foreign DNA fitted in. The procedure for accomplishing this is called *gene splicing* and the molecule of combined DNA that results is called *recombinant DNA*.

Researchers use the DNA of common bacteria, such as the human intestinal bacterium *E. coli,* to receive the inserted piece of foreign DNA. In addition to a single chromosome that is not enclosed in a nucleus, bacteria have smaller extra rings of DNA called plasmids. Figure 22-6 shows how foreign DNA is spliced into a plasmid. Subsequent bacterial cell divisions produce a clone of bacteria that carry this foreign genetic information. The foreign DNA can then be isolated by cutting it out with the same restriction endonuclease used to put it in, and used for study or inserted elsewhere.

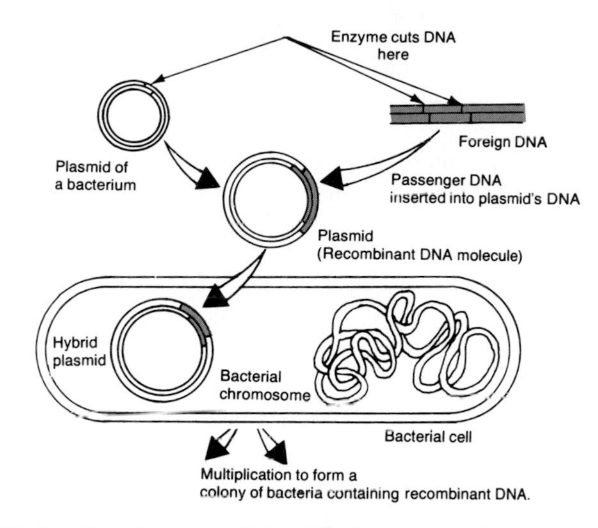

Fig. 22–6. Steps in gene splicing. The bacteria can be manipulated to replicate many copies of the plasmid, thus producing many copies of the recombinant DNA.

When grown in large quantities under special circumstances, the altered bacteria produce the protein coded for by the recombinant DNA. The protein can then be collected from the bacterial culture and used in medicine or research.

Applications of the New Technologies

Gene splicing has promoted pharmaceutical production of human hormones, proteins, and enzymes. *Human insulin,* used to treat diabetes, for example, can be produced by recombinant DNA in bacterial cultures. Prior to the production of the hormone insulin by recombinant DNA, insulin for the nearly 14 million diabetics in this country was obtained from the pancreas of pigs and sheep. Animal insulin is not identical with human insulin and over a long period of use sometimes caused allergic reactions in diabetics. Bacteria with spliced human insulin genes can produce human insulin in large quantities at low cost.

Interferon is a protein produced and released in very small amounts by human white blood cells in response to viral infections. This protein prevents viruses from reproducing by interfering with viral RNA production. Interferon is an important component in the treatment of viral diseases, such as AIDS and herpes. Until its production by genetically engineered bacterial cultures, interferon research proceeded slowly because of the difficulty and expense of obtaining large enough quantities of interferon from human white blood cells.

Other molecules produced by recombinant DNA technology include *human growth hormone,* useful in the treatment of dwarfism; *thymosin,* a thymus hormone; and *somatostatin,* a brain hormone.

Bacteria are not the only organisms that can receive genetic materials and produce useful products. It is possible to insert a foreign gene, by *microinjection,* into the ova of an eukaryote. By a process not yet understood, the foreign gene is incorporated into the host genome. *In vitro* fertilization of the microinjected ova may create a *transgenic* animal that contains a functional copy of the foreign gene in every one of its body cells—both somatic and germline—where it will be both stably expressed and inherited by offspring.

This transgenic animal becomes the parent of a true-breeding line. OncoMice, for example, are a transgenic line of laboratory mice that are susceptible to cancer because they carry a foreign oncogene. Transgenic domestic dairy goats can secrete milligram to gram quantities of pharmaceutical agents in their milk. Soon after the birth of Dolly, the Scottish scientists introduced the first transgenic clone—a lamb named Polly; who carries a human gene for a protein missing in hemophilia and certain bone diseases. This protein will be secreted in Polly's milk, and can then be extracted and administered to hemophiliacs and bone disease sufferers.

The combination of genetic engineering (which allows the isolation and insertion of a single foreign gene into an organism's genome), with cloning (which eliminates the risk of loss, or masking, of desirable traits by meiotic recombination, and allows the sex of the cloned animals to be selected, such as all females in the case of lactating ruminants) holds promise for large-scale production of genetically altered farm and research animals, and will greatly advance pharmaceutical production of therapeutic human proteins. The United States Patent Office has ruled that animals with genetic characteristics different from the original, whether they are bacteria, goats, or other animals, are patentable.

(G)

Genetic Frontiers

All the DNA on a monoploid set of a species' chromosomes is referred to a the *genome* of that species. The undertaking of the *Human Genome Projec* is an example of both the challenge and the promise of the new era of mol ecular genetics. The ultimate goal of the project is to determine the exac nucleotide sequence of the DNA on all the human chromosomes, as well a to construct high resolution physical and genetic linkage maps for each o the 23 human chromosomes.

In order to learn about genomic organization (its gene content, order, anc spacing), scientists are also analyzing the genomes of several model researcl organisms: the bacteria *E. coli,* the yeast *S. cerevisiae,* the roundworm *C. ele gans,* the fruit fly *Drosophila,* and the laboratory mouse. Genes discoverec in these smaller genomes are used as probes to locate and sequence thei human counterpart genes.

During the first half of this project (1990–1998), scientists mapped—tha is, precisely located on chromosomes—over 6,000 (7.5%) of the estimatec 80,000 human genes, and sequenced nearly 4% of the 3 billion nucleotide in the human genome from samples of more than 50,000 genes. In addition the genomes of certain viruses, several bacteria including *E. coli,* and the yeast *S. cerevisiae* were completely sequenced. The human genome is 60C times larger than that of *E. coli.*

The Human Genome Project will affect medical treatment by detecting unknown human genes, facilitating the testing for disease genes. Some ethical dilemmas raised by the new screening tests concern who should be tested, how tests should be paid for, and whether or not employers or insurers should have access to test results. A portion of the Human Genome Project's annual budget is devoted to consideration of ethical issues.

Gene therapy. Perhaps the most exciting prospect of genetic research is the possiblity of treatment or cure of genetic disorders by *gene therapy.* In 1980 scientists injected a gene into mouse cells to correct their hereditary failure to produce a missing enzyme. In 1990 the first such trial in humans was conducted.

In this trial, white blood cells were taken from a child affected by severe combined immune deficiency (SCID) due to the hereditary deficiency of the enzyme adenosine deaminase (ADA). This disorder is lethal by age 5 if not treated. The normal gene for ADA was inserted into the white blood cells using a genetically engineered virus. These cells were then cloned by tissue culture and injected back into the patient where they produced the needed ADA. This procedure must be repeated periodically as the treated white blood cells die out.

Current gene therapy trials target the diseases severe combined immune deficiency, cystic fibrosis, muscular dystrophy, coronary artery disease, rheumatoid arthritis, and Parkinson disease.

Genetics will increasingly impact our lives through medicine, agriculture, and the growing industry of biotechnology. Personal knowledge of your own heredity, ethnic and racial background, and family medical history will enable you to be an informed consumer of biotechnology, medical genetics, and reproductive options.

Reasoning Exercises

1. Explain the rationale for the method used to treat children having PKU.
2. Explain Tay-Sachs Disease in terms of the one gene–one enzyme theory.
3. A man develops the symptoms of Huntington disease at age 40. What hereditary concern does this fact introduce for the healthy children he already has?
4. Give three examples of plants or animals improved by applied genetics.
5. Name four applications of recombinant DNA technology.

Completion Questions

A

1. An orderly display of homologous chromosomes arranged by size is called a . . . . . .
2. The general term for the condition in which chromosomes fail to separate properly in meiosis is . . . . . .

B

3. A trait that results from both heredity and interaction with the environment is known as a . . . . . . trait.

(C)

4. Genes for sickle-cell anemia also provide resistance to the disease ......
5. Giving tests to a population to identify those who may have a disorder is called ......
6. The symptoms of Tay-Sachs disease show an impairment of the ...... system.
7. Tay-Sachs disease is caused by a recessive gene. An affected child must be ...... (pure, hybrid) for this condition.
8. PKU results from failure to produce the amino acid ......
9. Thick mucus forms in the lungs of children having the genetic disorder ......
10. In addition to sickle-cell anemia, another kind of inherited anemia is ......
11. A form of dementia that is carried by a dominant gene is ......

[D]

12. Some genetic disorders can be detected in the uterus by the procedures of amniocentesis and ......

(E)

13. Dihybrid corn incorporates the desirable qualities of ...... (how many?) ancestral strains.
14. Commercially grown wheat is an example of a healthier than normal plant that results from the presence of extra ......

(F)

15. A line of genetically identical cells which was once a single cell is

Base your answers to questions 16 and 17 on Fig. 22-6 on page 401.

16. DNA produced by gene-splicing is known as ...... DNA.
17. A ring of DNA present outside a bacterium's chromosome is called a(n) ......
18. A nonspecific defensive protein, produced by cells that have been attacked by a virus, is called ......
19. Nitrogen-fixing bacteria normally live only on the roots of plants in the ...... family.

(G)

20. A genome that has been totally sequenced is that of a(n) ......

Multiple-Choice Questions

[A]

1. Down syndrome results from (1) an extra chromosome, (2) translocation, (3) a missing chromosome, (4) ploidy.
2. Nondisjunction of the sex chromosomes usually results in (1) a nonfunctional zygote, (2) an extra chromosome number 21, (3) sterility, (4) a protruding tongue.

[B]

3. An example of a trait that is not the result of Mendelian principles is (1) eye color, (2) hair texture, (3) number of fingers, (4) skin color.

(C)

4. A hereditary disorder in which the red blood cells have an abnormal shape is (1) PKU, (2) thalassemia, (3) Tay-Sachs disease, (4) sickle-cell anemia.
5. What are the chances that two people who have the sickle-cell trait will have a child having the disorder? (1) 0%, (2) 25%, (3) 50%, (4) 100%.
6. A hereditary disorder most often found in people of African descent is (1) PKU, (2) thalassemia, (3) Tay-Sachs disease, (4) sickle-cell anemia.
7. A genetic disorder caused by a dominant gene is (1) sickle-cell anemia, (2) cystic fibrosis, (3) thalassemia, (4) Huntington's chorea.
8. Mental retardation is a symptom of (1) PKU, (2) sickle-cell anemia, (3) cystic fibrosis, (4) Rh disease.

D

9. The extra chromosome causing Down syndrome can be detected in the uterus by the procedure of (1) cloning, (2) amniocentesis, (3) nitrogen-fixation, (4) gene-splicing.
10. If a person has a grandmother who died of a genetic disorder, the best thing for that person to do is (1) not have children, (2) see a genetic counselor, (3) have a Bacterial Inhibition Assay (BIA) test, (4) nothing, since the grandmother's genes would have no effect on the person's offspring.
11. Prenatal testing for Tay-Sachs disease looks for (1) an extra chromosome, (2) normal hemoglobin, (3) the enzyme HexA, (4) a chorionic villus.

(E)

12. Which did not originate through a planned breeding program? (1) Beltsville turkey, (2) dihybrid corn, (3) seedless orange, (4) Santa Gertrudis cattle.
13. In producing the best corn, breeders rely on (1) hybridization, (2) inbreeding, (3) mutation, (4) self-pollination.

(F)

14. A bacterium's plasmids are composed of (1) DNA, (2) mRNA, (3) tRNA, (4) protein.

(G)

15. The goal of the Human Genome Project is to (1) determine the nucleotide sequence of the DNA on human chromosomes, (2) treat all human genetic disorders by the year 2100, (3) screen all newborns for PKU, (4) provide genetic counseling to all carriers of genetic disorders.

Chapter Test

1. Genes for skin color produce the pigment (1) melanin, (2) chlorophyll, (3) phenylalanine, (4) guanine.
2. A person having the trait for sickle-cell anemia has the genotype for (1) pure recessive, (2) homozygous recessive, (3) hybrid, (4) homozygous dominant.

3. The genes for sickle-cell anemia also confer resistance to (1) typhoid fever, (2) malaria, (3) Tay-Sachs disease, (4) PKU.
4. A person who is trained to advise a couple of their chances of having a child with a genetic disease is a(n) (1) obstetrician, (2) pediatrician, (3) guidance counselor, (4) genetic counselor.
5. A hereditary disease found most often in Jews of eastern-European ancestry is (1) PKU, (2) thalassemia, (3) Tay-Sachs disease, (4) sickle-cell anemia.
6. The chances of two carriers of Tay-Sachs disease having a child who has the disease is (1) 0%, (2) 25%, (3) 50%, (4) 100%.
7. The failure to metabolize phenylalanine results in (1) Down's syndrome, (2) sickle-cell anemia, (3) PKU, (4) cancer.
8. Of the following, prenatal testing does not detect (1) the sex of the fetus, (2) Down syndrome, (3) the sickle-cell trait, (4) malaria.
9. Bacteria that produce human insulin were developed by (1) genetic counseling, (2) amniocentesis, (3) gene-splicing, (4) nondisjunction.
10. Interferon may become useful in treating disease caused by (1) protozoa, (2) insects, (3) fungi, (4) viruses.

Unit 5 Genetics

Portfolio Project

1. Prepare a research report on the responsibilities of a genetic counselor. Describe the kinds of knowledge that a genetic counselor must have. Describe the situations in which the advice of a genetic counselor should be sought. Explain why this profession is of value to society.
2. Prepare a model of a DNA strand that has at least 12 base pairs. Prepare a similar model of a strand of RNA that would be transcribed from your DNA model. Label the base pairs in all nucleotides on both strands.

UNIT SIX EVOLUTION

The geneticist Theodosius Dobzhansky has said, "Nothing in biology makes sense except in terms of evolution." Now that you have studied genetics you are ready to study the theories that attempt to explain *how* evolution may have occurred.

Scientists have developed theories to explain the probable *mechanisms* of evolution. But a theory in science is not just a theory, or a wild guess. A scientific theory coordinates information and ideas from many fields into a meaningful overall explanation. This information is based upon verified data, controlled experimentation, and logical thought. A valid theory can predict future occurrences and can help direct scientists to meaningful areas of new research.

To be considered as a scientific theory, an explanation must meet two criteria: (1) It must be based upon the cause-and-effect relationships known as *natural law*. Supernatural explanations might possibly constitute truth, but they are not part of science. Art, music, religion, and much of philosophy are outside the domain of science. (2) It must be *falsifiable*. This means there must be some way of determining if it is false. A scientist does not propose an explanation that cannot be tested.

Science, moreover, is not a system of beliefs. Scientists do not believe in a theory. Rather they accept or deny the explanation on the basis of the supporting evidence.

Scientific theories may change in the light of new evidence. As you study evolutionary theory, note the modifications that have been made as new evidence has been discovered.

Chapter 23 Evidences and Theories of Evolution

The study of biology would be largely the recital of a host of unrelated facts were it not for the *Theory of Organic Evolution* which provides a unifying theme. Simply stated, evolution means that living things have *changed* from ancestors that they have in common.

The *evidences* supporting the concept of evolution are distinct from the *theories* that attempt to explain *how* evolution might have occurred. The theories are continually being modified as new ideas are developed.

A Evidences for Evolution

Evidence from Rocks and Fossils

A *fossil* is any record of an organism that lived in the geologic past. Remains, impressions, and traces of organisms of past geologic ages have been preserved in the earth's crust as fossils.

It is impossible to discover all of the previous forms of life that existed because not all of them became fossils. Most organisms are consumed or decomposed after death. While the number of fossils discovered somewhat limits the biologist's investigation of the past, the ones we do have throw great light upon the history of life on earth.

The *remains of hard parts* of organisms, such as bones, teeth, and shells can resist the action of weathering for long periods of time. Fossils are preserved much longer when their environment is dry. For example, the fossil bones of dinosaurs were preserved for 100 million years in the hot desert sands of Mongolia.

Sometimes, the soft parts of extinct organisms were preserved by *refrigeration.* Frozen remains of wooly mammoths, found in North America and Siberia, resemble today's elephants. One 40,000-year-old baby mammoth was so well preserved that its tissues could be studied by immunological methods. These studies showed that the protein albumin is almost identical in extinct mammoths and in today's elephants.

Imprints are the impressions left by plants and animals (see Fig. 23–1). Tracks and tunnels made in soft mud by prehistoric animals were preserved when the mud hardened into rock. Biologists can study the footprints left by dinosaurs 120 million years ago as they walked in regions that are now Texas and Connecticut.

When rock forms around a dead organism, which later disintegrates, a *mold* of that organism remains in the rock. Molds formed in this manner may preserve details of the dead organism with great accuracy. If the mold later becomes filled with mineral deposits, a *cast* is produced. Such a cast is a replica of the external details of the organism.

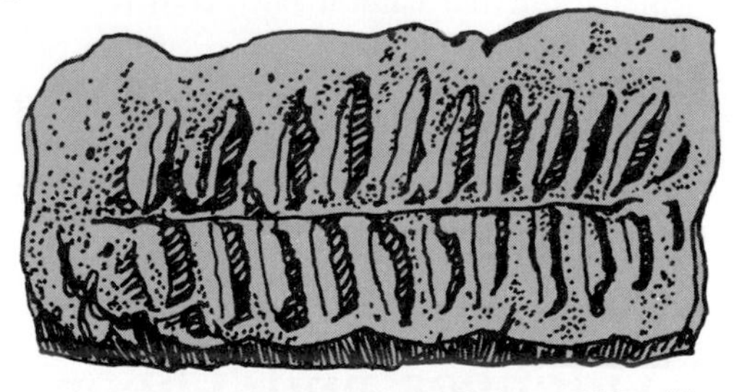

(**a**) An ancient fern left an imprint in coal about 300 million years ago.

(**b**) An insect trapped in amber about 180 million years ago.

Fig. 23–1. Evidence seen in imprints and amber

Another type of fossil is provided by *insects preserved in amber* (see Fig. 23–1). Amber is the hardened gum of resin given off by trees. Small insects were often caught in the sticky gum and preserved as the gum hardened. Some of the insects are so perfectly preserved that the lacy structure of their wings is intact, permitting biologists to compare them with insects that are living today.

Petrification results when the skeletons of animals and the cellulose of plants are covered with water containing large amounts of dissolved minerals such as silica or lime. The cell cavities and intercellular spaces of the hard tissue are filled with the mineral matter, thereby preserving the structure of the original specimen. The Petrified Forest in Arizona has many trees that have turned to stone in this manner.

Coal is the fossilized remains of ancient plants. During the Carboniferous period, about 300 million years ago, deep layers of plant remains accumulated in the hot swampy regions where they grew. Movements of the earth later covered and compressed these plant remains, and coal gradually formed. Today imprints of ancient ferns and mosses are found in coal.

Many ancient animals were trapped and preserved in large pools of gummy asphalt tar. The sabertooth (or saber-toothed) tiger is an example of a fossilized organism recovered from *tar pits* at La Brea in Los Angeles, California. Other fossil specimens taken from the tar pits include mammoths, horses, birds, and camels.

Fossil Formation

Aside from the few special cases such as frozen mammoths and creatures in tar pits and amber, fossils are generally found in sedimentary rock. All rocks of the earth can be classified into three general categories: igneous rock, sedimentary rock, and metamorphic rock.

Igneous rock is formed by the cooling and solidification of molten lava. This may occur either deep in the crust of the earth or on its surface when lava emerges from a volcano. Igneous rock was presumably the original rock of the earth, for it is probable that the earth was entirely molten at some early stage in its history. Any animal or plant that fell into lava would have been destroyed instantly and would not have formed a fossil. Therefore fossils are not found in igneous rock. Examples of igneous rock are granite and basalt.

Sedimentary rock is formed from sediment produced by the breaking up of previously existing rock. When this loose material is subjected to moderate pressure and chemical action, it becomes solid rock. Most sedimentary rocks are formed in layers below bodies of water.

There are several types of sedimentary rock. Sand, washed out of continents into oceans by rivers, becomes *sandstone* after many years. Clay may be changed to a smooth-textured rock called *shale*. Coarse gravel changes to *conglomerate* in which the original pebbles are still easily seen. Many rivers carry calcium carbonate ($CaCO_3$) in solution. This substance settles out when it meets salt water and becomes *limestone*.

The earth's crust is in constant movement. If a bed of sedimentary rock is lifted only an inch a century, it will be raised about one mile after 6 million years—not very long by geological standards.

If an animal or plant dies and falls into limy mud or sand, it may leave an imprint that becomes a mold or cast. Thus, mountain tops built of sedimentary rock may contain fossils of ancient organisms that lived in the sea.

Igneous rock or sedimentary rock may be changed to *metamorphic rock.* How does this occur? Any kind of rock may be subjected to enormous pressure and high temperature due to movements of the earth's crust. If this occurs, the rock may undergo drastic changes in its crystal structure, producing metamorphic rock. Marble is an example of metamorphic rock. Metamorphism destroys almost all fossils.

The Age of Fossils It is estimated that it takes 1,000 years for one foot of sedimentary rock to form. Knowing the thickness of a rock layer and its location between other rock layers above and below, geologists can estimate its age. In some cases, fossils of the same animal are found all over the world. If the animal lived for only a short period of time, it can be used for dating any layer of rock in which it is found. By the use of such *index* fossils, the relative ages of layers of rocks all over the world have been coordinated. Fossils found in lower layers of undisturbed sedimentary rock are older than those found in upper layers (see Fig. 23–2).

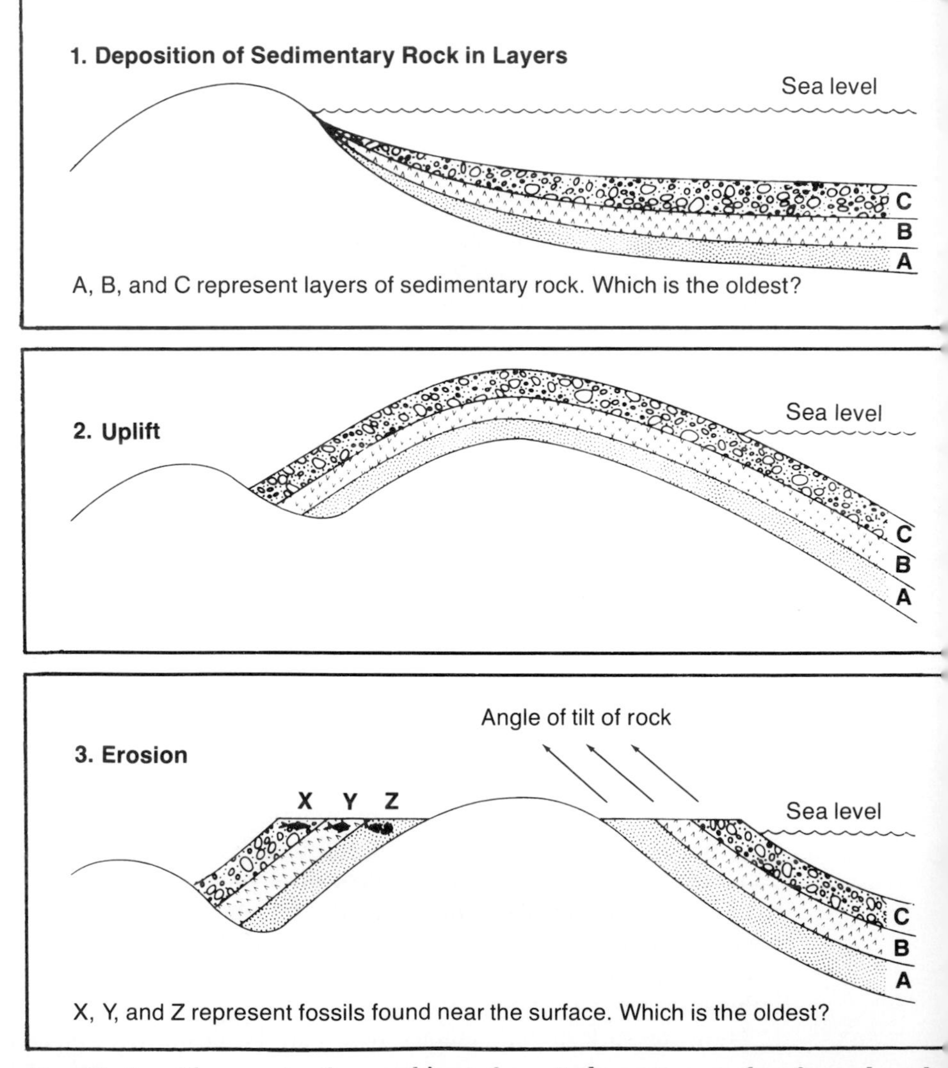

Fig. 23–2. Changes in the earth's surface. Sedimentary rocks, formed under water, are up lifted to form mountains, that are then worn away.

Radioactive Dating The age of rocks and fossils can be more accurately determined by the decay of radioactive isotopes. We shall consider the uranium-lead ratio, the potassium-argon ratio, and the carbon-14 method. To understand how radioisotopes can be used for dating, consider the following story:

In a factory closed for the weekend, a robber entered, and after several wild pistol shots, killed the guard and fled with the contents of a safe. On Monday morning the incident was discovered, and the police soon arrested a suspect. The suspect had a good alibi for his whereabouts on Saturday but not for Sunday. When had the incident occurred?

Now it happens that the factory had a watertank that contained 100 gallons of water. This tank had been pierced by one of the stray bullets, and water was leaking. A rookie policeman noted that the level of water on Monday at 10 AM was at the 52 gallon mark. By placing a container under the leak, he found that the rate of flow was 1 gallon per hour. When was the shot fired? Since 48 gallons had leaked out and the rate of flow was 1 gallon per hour, the shot had been fired 48 hours previously, or Saturday at 10 AM. The suspect was freed.

This story shows that we can date the start of a continuing happening if we know three things: (1) the amount present at the start, (2) the amount present now, and (3) the rate of change. This reasoning is employed in the use of radioisotopes to estimate the age of the earth and the age of rocks and fossils.

When atoms of a radioactive element emit radiations such as alpha, beta, and gamma rays, they may decay to form atoms of a different element. The rate of decay is expressed as its *half-life:* the length of time it takes for half of the atoms in a sample to disintegrate. The rate of radioactive decay is *constant.* It is not affected by physical or chemical changes such as melting or burning. This characteristic is important to the principle of radioactive dating.

Let us examine the idea of half-life in more detail. Phosphorus-32 has a half-life of 14 days. A sample decays so that half the original amount will be present after 14 days. Half of that amount will be present after another 14 days, and so on. When will all of the P-32 be gone? Never, as shown in the graph in Figure 23–3. Since we do not know when all of a sample will decay (its full life), we use the half-life to indicate the rate of decay of radioactive elements.

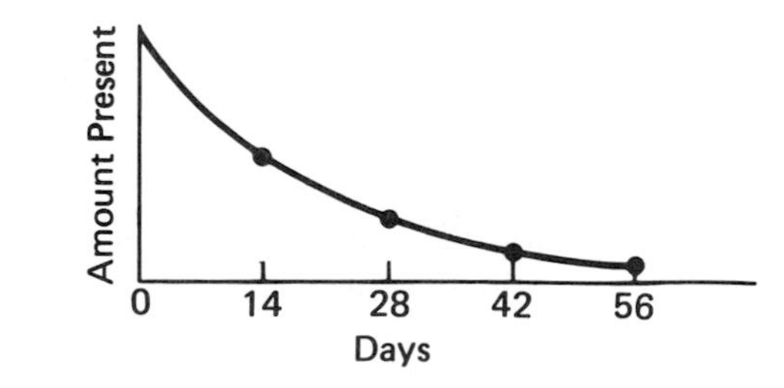

Fig. 23–3. Decay of phosphorus-32, which has a half-life of 14 days.

(1) *The uranium-lead ratio.* Uranium-238 disintegrates to form a series of radioactive elements before reaching the stable isotope, lead-206. The half-life for this series is 4.5 billion years. When scientists want to judge the age of igneous rocks, they first determine the ratio of uranium to lead in the rock. They can safely assume that all the lead-206 came from the decay of uranium-238. Knowing the constant rate at which uranium-238 changes to lead-206, they can then calculate how long it took for that amount of lead-206 to form. This is the age of the rock.

Uranium-lead ratios cannot be used to date sedimentary rocks because the ratio will tell when the material first formed as an igneous rock rather than when sedimentation occurred. However, a lava flow on top of a sedimentary layer can be used. The lava is dated by the uranium-lead ratio, and the sediments just under it cannot be much older. The uranium-lead ratio places the age of the earth at about 4.6 billion years Biologists think this would probably provide sufficient time for the earth to cool and for the evolution of our present forms of life to occur.

(2) *The potassium-argon method.* The half-life for the decay of radioactive potassium-40 to argon is 1.4 billion years. Because potassium-40 is more abundant than uranium in old igneous rock, the potassium-argon method has advantages over the uranium-lead method.

(3) *Radio carbon dating.* Carbon-14 is one of the radioactive isotopes of carbon. Its concentration in the atmosphere has probably remained constant from early times. When taken into living plants as $^{14}CO_2$ during photosynthesis, carbon-14 becomes part of plants and of the animals that eat them. An organism that dies takes in no more carbon. Instead, its carbon-14 decays at a half-life of 5,730 years. By comparing the proportion of carbon-14 assumed to be present in the organism's tissues when it died with the proportion in its fossilized remains, scientists can estimate how long ago the organism stopped living. Radiocarbon dating is considered accurate only for dating fossils that are less than 35,000 years old

As you can see, these dating methods involve a number of assumptions However, they are based upon knowledge from various scientific fields and the data coordinate well.

Fossil History

Marked discontinuities in the succession of rock layers led geologists to divide the earth's history into large units of time called *eras*. Between the eras, great geological changes occurred. Refer to the table, *The Geologic Time Scale*, as you review the eras and their subdivisions. Possibly these changes between rock layers were caused by unusual conditions within the solar system or from beyond, resulting in sudden new conditions on earth. The changes in rock layers were often accompanied by rapid changes or leaps in the forms of life shown in the fossil record.

The Precambrian era. Many of the major animal groups are represented in primitive form in Cambrian rock. Yet, in the earlier era, the Precambrian era, we find fossil remains of only bacteria, simple algae, and a few invertebrates. It is unfortunate that the conditions for forming and preserving fossils of delicate organisms have provided so little concrete

The Geologic Time Scale				
Era	**Period**	**Epoch**	**Events**	**Years Ago Era Began**
Cenozoic (The Age of Mammals)	Quarternary	Recent	Development of human civilization; modern plants and animals	100 thousand
		Pleistocene	Rise of *Homo sapiens.*	1 million
	Tertiary	Pliocene	Early humanlike primates	
		Miocene	Increase in mammals	
		Oligocene	Early primates	
		Eocene	*Eohippus* (early horse)	
		Paleocene	Mammals start to become dominant	75 million
Mesozoic (The Age of Reptiles)	Cretaceous		Dinosaurs become extinct; angiosperms (flowering plants) expand	
	Jurassic		Dinosaurs dominant; first birds and mammals; beginning of angiosperms	
	Triassic		First dinosaurs, land dominated by gymnosperm plants	205 million
Paleozoic	Permian	Age of Amphibians	Great development of reptiles; decline of amphibians; rise of insects	
	Carboniferous	Age of Amphibians	First reptiles and insects; great forests of ferns that became coal	
	Devonian	Age of Fishes	First amphibians and insects; ferns	
	Silurian	Age of Invertebrates	Insects and other invertebrates invade the land; invasion of land by club mosses	
	Ordovician	Age of Invertebrates	Numerous marine invertebrates, including trilobites; first vertebrates (jawless fishes)	
	Cambrian	Age of Invertebrates	Simple marine invertebrates, such as sponges and jellyfish	500 million
Precambrian			Bacteria; simple algae; several invertebrates	4.6 billion

evidence concerning a most interesting subject: the early development of life and the origin of the major phyla.

The discovery of our most ancient fossils was announced in 1980. These were bacteria, discovered in rocks of Western Australia, that were radiometrically dated as 3.5 billion years old. The age of the earth is thought to be 4.6 billion years old. These bacteria, strung along in multicellular units, were far from primitive. Their discovery implies that life, and evolution, must have gone on for quite some time in the billion years between the formation of the earth and these earliest known fossils.

The Paleozoic era. During this era, great changes occurred in plants and animals. Many types of higher marine invertebrates lived at this time—jellyfish, sponges, corals, and snails. In an early period of this era, a major form of life in the sea was a primitive arthropod, the trilobite, which is now extinct. The first jawless fish appeared. Then sharklike and armored fish vertebrates came on the scene and became the predominate marine organisms by the middle of the Paleozoic era. Plant life appeared on land.

During the Paleozoic era, air-breathing organisms such as scorpions and insects appeared. Late in the Paleozoic era, other air-breathing animals, particularly amphibians, appeared in great numbers. The period is also noted for its vast amount of vegetation in the form of mosses and ferns.

The end of the Paleozoic era is noted for its abundance of ferns, which turned into the coal used as fuel today. In addition, primitive reptiles appeared at the end of this era.

The Mesozoic era. During this era the earth was dominated by dinosaurs and other large reptiles (see Fig. 23–4). Some fossils from this era developed heavy protective armor. The first mammals appeared early in the Mesozoic era, and the first birds a little later.

Fig. 23–4. Some dinosaurs of the Mesozoic era

The trees and other plants of this era were quite similar to the plants of today. The ginkgo tree, for example, was about the same then as it is today and for that reason is called a living fossil. The insects of today are very much like those that developed during the Mesozoic era.

The Cenozoic era. The most recent era of life, the *Cenozoic era,* began about 75 million years ago. This era is noted for the many changes produced as great ice sheets moved across the land. The primitive mammals present at the very beginning were eventually replaced by modern mammals. Birds became common; flowering plants appeared and became more common than any other types. Humanlike creatures appeared about 3 million years ago.

Intermediate Forms

When most organisms die, they are either eaten or decayed. Weathering and geologic action also destroy evidences of prehistoric life. Consequently the fossil record is incomplete. It is not possible to construct a tree of evolution showing the exact origin of each branch and twig. Nonetheless, many fossils of intermediate forms have been found.

One of these is the imprint of the fossil bird, *Archaeopteryx* (see Fig. 23–5). This organism had characteristics of both reptiles and birds. Like reptiles, it had a jaw with teeth and a long jointed tail. Birds, on the other hand, lack teeth, have a light beak and a tail consisting only of feathers.

Fig. 23–5. Restoration of *Archaeopteryx*

Archaeopteryx also had claws on its forelimbs, a reptilian characteristic. Why is it then considered a bird? Like birds, it had wings and unmistakable feathers. It is important evidence that supports the theory that birds originated from reptilian ancestors.

Transitional series. More impressive, perhaps, that the intermediate forms are organisms whose fossils show a series of changes. One of the best known is the series that produced the modern horse, Equus. In recent layers of rock are fossils of animals that differ only slightly from Equus. Progressively older layers of rock reveal fossils of horselike animals, each of which differs slightly from the later fossil. This series of horselike animals has been traced, step by step, to *Eohippus* (The Dawn Horse), which lived about 50 million years ago. A comparison of *Eohippus* and *Equus* is given in the following table:

Comparison Between Eohippus and Equus

	Eohippus	Equus
Size	Size of fox	Present day horse (5′-6′ high)
Toes	Four toes on front feet, three on hind feet	One toe; the hoof is homologous with the toenail
Teeth	Short-crowned	Long-crowned

The changes in the legs of fossil horses show that the middle toe became progressively longer and the side toes progressively shorter. All that remains of these side toes in the modern horse are two splint bones, as seen in Figure 23–6.

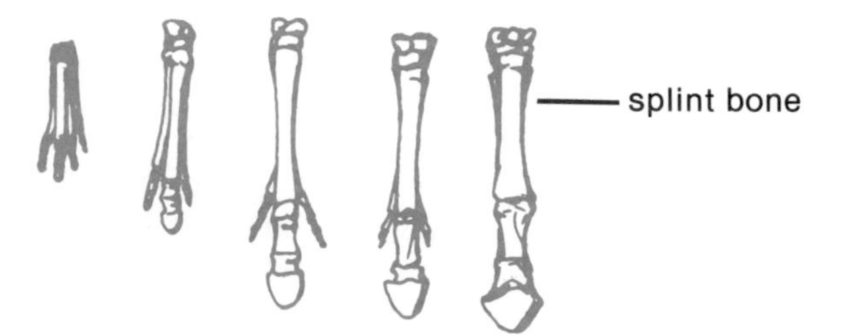

Fig. 23–6. Evolution of the foreleg of the horse.

The fossil record of the horse is less direct than indicated here. Some of the fossils were probably on evolutionary side branches rather than part of a straight-line series of steps.

The Evidences for Relationship

Since it is impossible to observe the changes in all living things over the past 3.5 billion years or so, the fossil evidences for the theory of evolution are necessarily indirect. Yet the diverse kinds of evidence are so compelling that almost all biologists accept this theory of descent with change. The seven sections that follow summarize some of these evidences. Modern theories to explain *how* evolution may have occurred are discussed later.

1. Summary of evidence from rocks and fossils. An examination of rocks and the fossil record indicates that there was: (1) change from simple to complex forms, (2) change from marine to land forms, (3) presence of intermediate forms, (4) presence of transitional series, and (5) sufficient time for evolution to have occurred.

2. Evidence from comparative cytology. The study of cells is called *cytology*. It deals with the various organelles (see Chapter 3). Not only are most organisms similar in that they are composed of cells, but even their organelles are remarkably similar in structure and function. For example, most organisms have a nuclear membrane. The Monera, which do not have a nuclear membrane, are classified in a separate kingdom.

3. Evidence from comparative biochemistry. The study of how organisms function is called *physiology.* Much of our understanding of physiology is based upon our understanding of the chemical reactions in living things, or *biochemistry.* Similarities in the biochemistry and physiology of living things is another evidence for descent from a common ancestor.

The structure of DNA and RNA and the way they function is similar in all living things, from the most simple to the most complex. Many different organisms have similar proteins and enzymes. The chain of amino acids of the protein *cytochrome c* is exactly the same in humans and chimpanzees; but it differs from the cytochrome c of the bread mold, *Neurospora,* by 44 out of 100 amino acids. Molecules of insulin extracted from sheep and pigs are enough like human insulin molecules that they can be substituted in diabetic humans who fail to produce enough of their own insulin. These examples illustrate that the closer the relationship among organisms, the greater their biochemical similarity. This suggests evolutionary relationships.

4. Evidence from comparative anatomy. When you dissect organisms to study their bones and other internal structures, you are studying *anatomy.* In a course in comparative anatomy, you would compare the structures of animals. The evidence from comparative anatomy is based upon the idea that if organisms have similar structures they presumably came from a common ancestor. But biologists distinguish between two kinds of similar structures: *homologous* structures and *analogous* structures. Homologous structures are the only ones used as a basis of classification by today's scientists.

Two structures are *analogous* if they have the same function but different evolutionary origins and different basic compositions. For example, the wing of a fly and the wing of a bird have the same function—both are used in flying. But the wing of a fly is a membrane, and the wing of a bird is bony and covered with feathers. The wing of a fly and the wing of a bird are *analogous* organs because their fundamental structures are so different, in spite of their superficial similarity. Another example can be provided by comparing the horn of a rhinoceros and the antler of a deer. They have the same function, but the horn is hairlike and the antler is bone. These two structures have entirely different origins and are analogous. The presence of analogous organs in two kinds of living things is only a superficial resemblance and cannot be used as a basis for classification.

Two structures are *homologous* if they have the same basic structure and evolutionary origin. They show the same pattern of early growth. Homologous organs evolved from the same ancestral structure. Homologous organs, however, do not necessarily share the same function. For example, the human arm, the wing of a bat, and the flipper of a whale all have the same basic internal bone structure. They are homologous organs even though one is used for writing, another for flying, and the last for swimming (see Fig. 23–7).

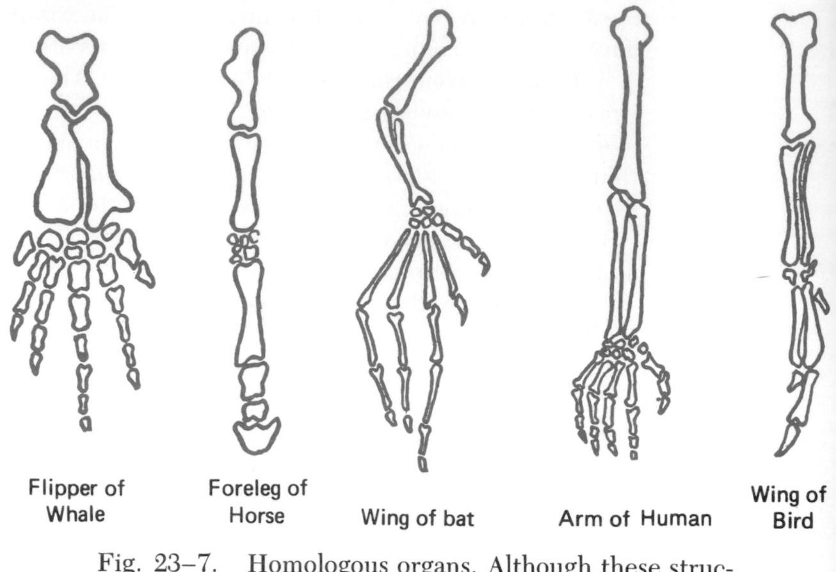

Fig. 23–7. Homologous organs. Although these structures have different functions, their basic similarity in bone structure indicates common ancestry.

Studies of the early development of living things show that the human eustachian tube, which connects the throat with the middle ear, is homologous to one of the gill slits of fish. The three bones in the human middle ear have been traced to certain jaw bones of fishes. The presence of these types of homologous structures is an indication of common ancestry.

Homologies can be traced in every part of the body and indicate close as well as distant relationships. All vertebrates have homologous brains, as can be seen in Figure 23–8.

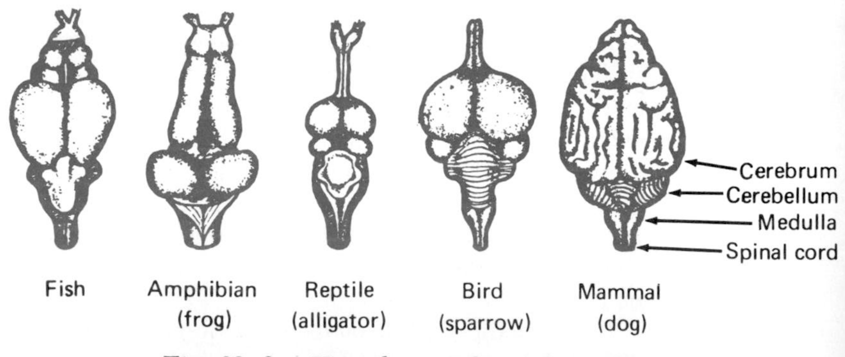

Fig. 23–8. Homologies of vertebrate brains

5. Evidence from immunology. Immunology provides additional evidence of a biochemical nature. Similarities in the blood proteins of various animals can be determined by the Nuttall precipitation technique. In this technique, a series of injections of human blood serum is first made into the vein of a rabbit (see Fig. 23–9). The rabbit's blood then builds chemicals called *antibodies* which can precipitate certain proteins of human blood. These rabbit antibodies are very specific; they will react only with human blood proteins or with proteins that are very similar to human blood proteins.

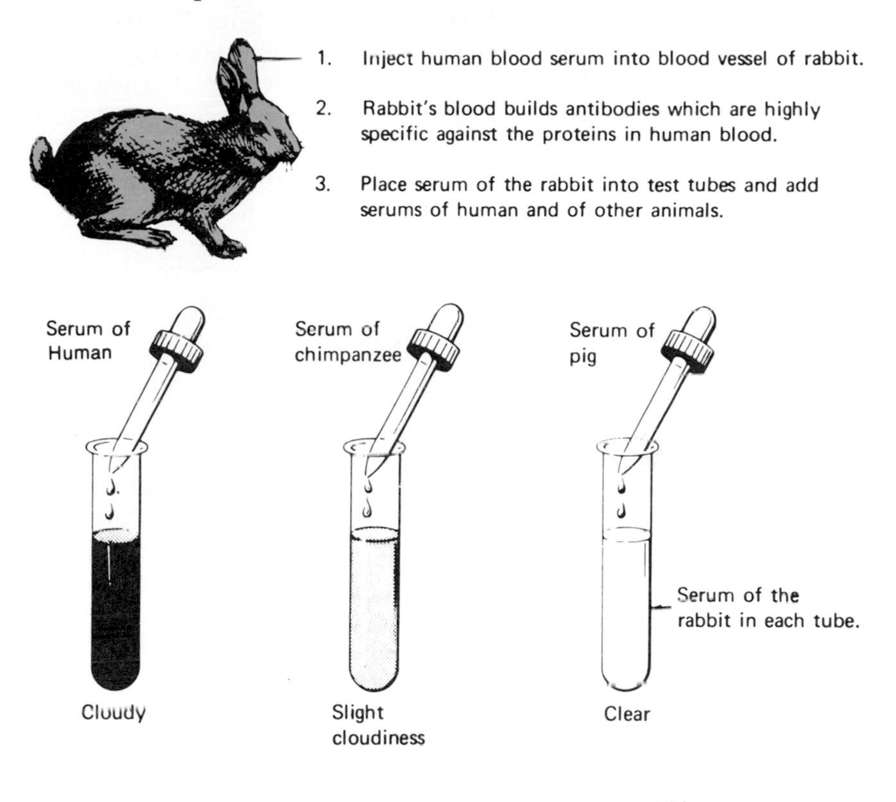

4. The fact that the serum of the chimpanzee produces a slight cloudiness whereas the serum of the pig produces no cloudiness shows that the protein molecules of man resemble those of the chimpanzee more than those of the pig.

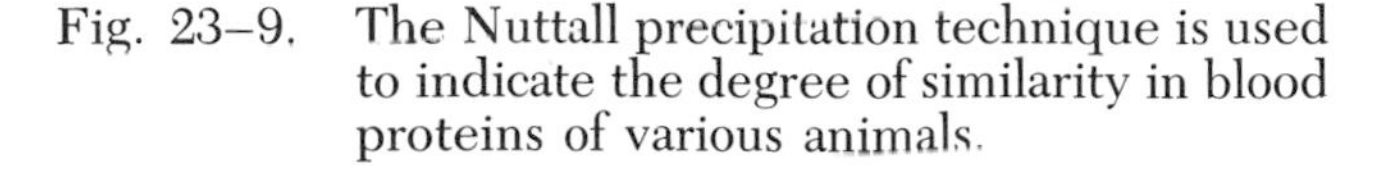

Fig. 23–9. The Nuttall precipitation technique is used to indicate the degree of similarity in blood proteins of various animals.

Some of the rabbit's blood is then drawn off and a liquid portion, called the *serum*, is separated. The rabbit serum is then poured into a series of test tubes. When human serum is added to a test tube of the rabbit serum, a dense precipitate forms. *Chimpanzee* serum forms a less dense precipitate. *Pig* serum forms no precipitate at all. What do these results show? There is greater similarity between the blood proteins of the human and chimpanzee than between the human and pig. To which of these animals is the human most closely related?

The Nuttall precipitation technique has been used to solve many problems in classification. For example, the horseshoe crab has many structural homologies with crabs and with spiders. Which is it most closely related to? The horseshoe crab was finally classified with the spiders after biologists used precipitation techniques. The biologists found that the chemicals in the horseshoe crab's blood were closest to those in the blood of the spider.

6. Evidence from embryology. Figure 23–10 compares the embryos of several vertebrates. Notice the great resemblance of the early embryos. It would be difficult for you to tell them apart. They all have a series of gill slits. Their developing backbone is segmented. They all have a C-shape. Even the human embryo has a tail. This remarkable similarity of their early embryos indicates that these organisms are related, that they had a common ancestor at some time in the past.

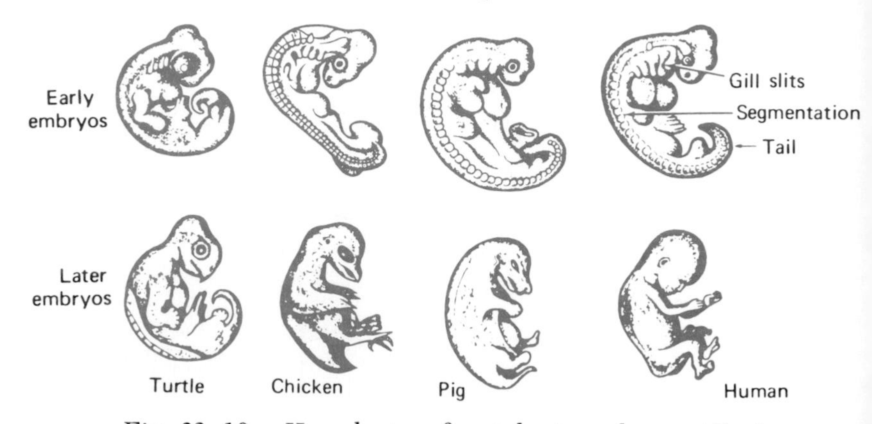

Fig. 23–10. Homologies of vertebrate embryos. All of the late embryos show likenesses, but the early embryos have even greater resemblances.

Structures shared by the early embryos may develop differently in different species. For example, both fish and human embryos have gill slits, but one gill slit of the human embryo develops into the eustachian tube that joins the middle ear and the throat. Another example: Both the reptilian embryo and the human embryo have two small bones in a certain region of the head. In the reptile, these become the bones of the jaw joint, but in the human they become two of the three bones in the middle ear. These two human ear bones are *homologous* to bones of the reptile's jaw. As you can see in Fig. 23–10, late embryos are easy to tell apart.

The heart of a mammalian embryo starts as a pulsating tube. It then becomes folded and partitioned into a two-chambered heart, a three-chambered heart, and finally a four-chambered heart. Significantly, adult fish have a two-chambered heart, adult amphibians and most reptiles have a three-chambered heart, and adult birds and mammals have a four-chambered heart.

Another parallel is seen in the embryonic development of the kidney. Adult reptiles, birds, and mammals have an advanced type of kidney. But during embryonic development, they all pass through two simpler stages: (1) that found in the cartilage fishes, and (2) that found in the true fishes and the amphibians.

Many other systems of the body progress from structures found in adults of early organisms to structures found in adults of more advanced organisms. Such observations let E. H. Haeckel, in the late 19th century, to propose his *Theory of Recapitulation*. This is the idea that the embryonic development of an organism repeats its phylogenetic history. This concept is also stated as "ontogeny recapitulates phylogeny."

Biologists today accept the general idea of recapitulation only in the broadest sense, and Haeckel's precise statement is no longer recognized as valid. At no time does the human embryo swim and breathe like a fish or have scales like a fish. However, the *early embryos* of today's advanced animals greatly resemble the *early embryos* of their probable ancestors. Somehow embryos seem to retain a hereditary memory of some steps from their past history.

7. Evidence from vestiges. *Vestiges* are structures that do not seem to have any use but are the remains of structures that were probably functional in ancestral organisms. The human appendix is an example of a vestige. This is a fingerlike extension of a small pouch of the large intestine where it is joined by the small intestine. The appendix is all that is left of a lengthy pouch that is still used by herbivores, such as the rabbit, for the digestion of food.

At the base of the human spine is a group of bones that are fused to form a single bone called the *coccyx* (see Fig. 23–11). This is the remains of the tail that can still be seen in the human embryo.

Two splint bones in the horse's leg are vestiges of toes that were used when the horse's foot had three or more toes. Several bones embedded in the python's side are the vestige of now useless hips for supporting legs.

Vestiges indicate that organisms have changed. Through evolution, some structures are remodeled, often for new and useful functions; others, apparently useless, persist as vestiges.

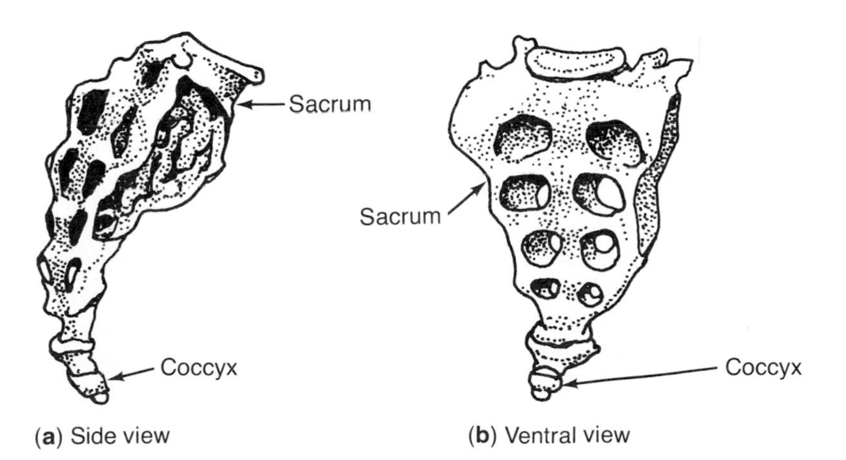

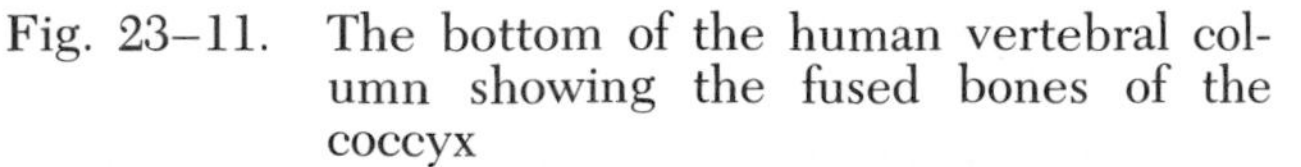
Fig. 23–11. The bottom of the human vertebral column showing the fused bones of the coccyx

Reasoning Exercises

1. Why is the number of fossils limited?
2. Why are no fossils present in igneous rock?
3. How can the relative age of a fossil be determined? How can fossils be used to determine the relative age of a layer of rock?
4. How do scientists use the uranium-lead ratio to determine the age of the earth?
5. What is organic evolution?
6. Distinguish between analogous and homologous structures.
7. What is the nature of the homology between the flipper of the whale and the foreleg of the horse?

B

Lamarck's Theory of Use and Disuse

At various times, going back to the ancient Greeks, people have expressed the concept of evolution. In the 18th and 19th centuries, however, biologists who were busy classifying all the known living things into neat categories generally believed in the *fixity of species*—that species do not change. One of the first of a group of latter-day biologists to reintroduce the idea of evolution was the French biologist, Jean Baptiste Lamarck.

In 1809, Lamarck proposed that living things changed because they had a need to adjust to the environment. His theory was based on two major assumptions:

(1) Use and disuse. Lamarck said that if a living thing used an organ, that organ became more highly developed. For example, a blacksmith's arm becomes powerful with use. On the other hand, an unused organ tends to wither away, or atrophy.

(2) Inheritance of acquired characteristics. Characteristics developed by an organism during its lifetime are *acquired characteristics.* Lamarck said that acquired characteristics are passed on to the next generation.

Lamarck said, for example, that ducks developed webbed feet because these were *needed* for swimming. He explained that, with use, ducks' feet developed slight webs. This acquired characteristic passed on to the offspring which then developed even better webs for swimming, and so on. He suggests that snakes lost their legs because these structures hampered crawling through low and narrow openings. Lamarck's theory is called the *Theory of Use and Disuse.*

Weismann's Criticism of Lamarck

Are acquired characteristics passed on to the next generation? A German biologist, August Weismann, designed an experiment to test Lamarck's assumption that acquired characteristics are inherited.

Weismann cut off the tails of mice and then mated the mice. When the offspring were born, he cut off the tails of the second generation mice and mated these mice. After repeating this process for 20 generations Weismann found that the tails of the last generation were identical in length with those of the first generation. The tails did not shorten or disappear. Weismann concluded that *acquired characteristics are not inherited.*

Weismann's experiment, and observations by other scientists, led to the abandonment of Lamarck's Theory of Use and Disuse. From what you know of reproduction and genetics you would explain that changes in body cells (acquired characteristics) do not affect the genes that are carried by the gametes.

Lamarck, however, introduced the important concept of *adaptation*. This means that evolutionary changes fit a species to its environment.

C The Theory of Natural Selection

Today's theories of evolution are based upon the *Theory of Natural Selection*, presented jointly to an English scientific society in 1858 by Charles Darwin and Alfred Russel Wallace. Darwin's 1859 book, *On the Origin of Species*, presented his evidences and views and was a great influence in many fields of thought in addition to biology.

Life of Darwin

As a youth, Charles Darwin was supposedly preparing for a career in medicine or the ministry, but his major interest was in collecting biological specimens. At the age of 22, this young Englishman obtained the position of naturalist on *H.M.S.Beagle*. In 1831, this sailing vessel started on a five-year voyage around the world to map coastlines and islands.

At various shore places young Darwin found animals and plants not yet known to science. He found many fossils of previously unknown animals. Some of these were fossils of marine organisms that he found on mountain tops. During the long, uncomfortable sea passages Darwin classified his specimens and studied Charles Lyell's *Principles of Geology*. This book showed that the earth is very old and that many rises and falls had occurred in its crust.

At the Galapagos Islands, 600 miles west of South America, Darwin was impressed by the differences in the kinds of finches, tortoises, and snails that inhabited the various islands. For example, finches living in different habitats on the islands occupied different positions in the life of the community and so did not compete with each other. They lived on different kinds of food and had different beaks. One kind carried with it a cactus spine or twig to pry insects from cracks in tree bark—a rare example of the use of tools by animals lower than the primates. Darwin reasoned that the various species of finches had developed from one species that had reached the Galapagos Islands from the mainland.

On his return to England, Darwin spent the next twenty years, often in ill health, searching for additional data and developing his theory of evolution. He studied geology, economics, and statistics as well as biology. One of the books that greatly influenced Darwin's thinking was *Essay on Population* by the Reverend Thomas R. Malthus, an economist. Malthus pointed out that populations grow more rapidly than the food available to feed them.

In 1858, when Darwin was well advanced in writing a summary of his ideas, he received a letter from Alfred Russel Wallace, a fellow naturalist. In this letter, Wallace presented the same ideas on evolution that Darwin had worked a lifetime to formulate! The work of both men was presented together, and the theory is often rightly called the *Darwin-Wallace Theory*.

The Theory of Natural Selection

Darwin's Theory of Natural Selection may be divided into five distinct ideas.

1. Overproduction. One female codfish lays about 9 million eggs a year. If all these eggs were fertilized and the offspring survived, in a few years the ocean would be almost solid with codfish. *Overproduction* means that a species tends to produce too many offspring for the available food and other necessities of life.

2. Struggle for existence. Overproduction causes a struggle for existence. Competition occurs between members of the same species for life needs. This competition need not be a dramatic event such as blood-letting with fang and claw. The competition between two seedlings for water, minerals, and light is as much a struggle for survival as is a battle between two wild stallions for leadership of the herd.

3. Variation. No two individuals are exactly alike—even the peas in a pod vary. They may differ in size, in the ability to produce enzymes, in the efficiency of the cell membrane, and in resistance to disease. Darwin assumed most variations are passed on to succeeding generations.

4. Natural selection. Some organisms in a species have variations that give them an advantage over others. Because of these favorable variations, they are better able to compete in their environment, to survive, and to reproduce their kind. In nature, the fittest survive, others die off without leaving offspring. Since nature selects the organisms that survive, this process is called *natural selection.* By contrast, the selective breeding of plants and animals by breeders is a form of *artificial selection.* Since the fittest survive to reproduce their kind, natural selection is also known as *differential reproduction.*

5. Origin of new species. New species arise by accumulation of variations among the members of a population. When the new population is sufficiently different from the original population, it is a new species.

Weakness of Darwin's theory. A weakness of Darwin's theory is that he did not explain how variations arise. Actually, some of the variations that he described were acquired characteristics. Darwin did not have the benefit of the science of genetics to help him explain the origin of inheritable changes. Mendel's work of the 1860s was not discovered until four decades after the Darwin-Wallace Theory was announced in 1858.

Lamarck and Darwin Compared

How could the evolution of a giraffe's long neck be explained by the theories of Lamarck and Darwin?

Lamarck might have said: (1) Ancestors of the modern giraffe had a short neck. When grass was scarce, they ate leaves from lower branches of trees, stripping bare these branches. The animals of one generation stretched their necks slightly while reaching for the higher branches. (2) This acquired characteristic of a slightly longer neck was passed by heredity to the next generation. These animals also stretched their necks. After many such generations, the descendants of short-necked giraffes had long necks.

Darwin might have said: (1) Among the population of short-necked giraffes more were born than could be supported by the food supply.

(2) These animals competed with each other for food that was on the branches of trees. (3) Some giraffes had necks longer than others of their species. (4) Those with longer necks survived to reproduce and pass this hereditary trait to their offspring. (5) After many generations of this procedure, the giraffes with short necks disappeared and the entire giraffe population had long necks.

D

Modern Evolutionary Theory

Lamarck and Darwin developed theories that explained how life changed or evolved, over a period of time. Darwin's theory became the generally accepted theory of evolution, but there were some questions that Darwin's theory did not answer. One of these is, how did new traits appear in the population of a species?

The major steps of Darwin's theory of evolution are accepted by most biologists. However, as you would expect, many other contributions from the science of genetics have also modified many details of Darwin's century-old concept. The science of genetics began with the study of Mendel's work and has become integrated into evolution theory.

De Vries' Theory of Mutation

An explanation for the origin of variations was proposed by a Dutch botanist, Hugo De Vries. In 1901, De Vries published the results of his experiments on reproduction in the evening primrose plant. De Vries observed that markedly different types sometimes arose in a single generation. These sudden changes were passed on to subsequent generations. He then reasoned that if sudden changes were occuring in his plants, this phenomenon also occurred in other organisms. De Vries introduced the term *mutation* for such sudden changes in heredity.

Mutations, then, resulted in the variation in a species that could be passed on from generation to generation. When a mutation occurs, it is almost always a recessive gene. Therefore, it does not always immediately appear in the phenotype. Also, it is only *germ mutations* which affect sex cells that are passed on to future generations. It is these changes, however, that form the basis for evolution.

When a mutation appears in a species, it can be favorable, unfavorable, or neither favorable nor unfavorable. According to Darwinian explanations, if it is favorable, it will give these members of the population advantages over other organisms of the species. These organisms will then be most likely to survive and produce offspring with the favorable mutation. As nature continues to select offspring with this trait, the mutation becomes integrated into the species.

We now know that De Vries' new plants were not the start of a new species, as he thought, but merely polyploid individuals within the same species. Nevertheless, De Vries is credited with adding to Darwin's theory the concept of mutation. This explained the origin of genetic variations.

Population Genetics

Your earlier study of genetics examined the inheritance of traits by individuals and families. Genetics today is also concerned with inheritance in large groups of sexually-reproducing organisms. The study of these organisms as a reproducing group is known as *population genetics*.

A *species* is a group of organisms that have many genetic characteristics in common and can interbreed. A species may be distributed over a wide geographic area. Those members of a species that inhabit a specific geographic area constitute a *population*. For example, certain frogs from Maine and from Vermont can breed to produce fertile offspring. Both are members of the same species: *Rana pipiens*. But all the *Rana pipiens* around a certain Maine lake constitute the frog *population* of that lake.

Now consider all the alleles of all the frogs in that population. The sum total of all the genes of a population constitutes *a gene pool*. All the alleles of a squirrel population in a certain forest constitute the gene pool of that squirrel population. Modern theories of evolution are based on changes in gene pools. Indeed, evolutionary change is now defined by many geneticists as change in the composition of gene pools, due to differential reproduction.

Change in Gene Pools

What causes change in gene pools? Let us first recall the causes for variability that you have already studied:

(1) *Recombination*. During meiosis, chromosome pairs separate and then recombine during fertilization to form new combinations of chromosomes in the zygote.

(2) *Crossing-over*. During meiosis, portions of chromosomes exchange places to produce new combinations of genes in the chromatids.

(3) *Mutation*. Whether by breakage of chromosomes or by change in DNA composition, mutation results in new hereditary characteristics. Although mutations produced in the laboratory are generally harmful, some mutations are helpful and may be advantageous in a changed environment. Most mutations in nature are small-scale and seem to be neither especially harmful nor beneficial when they occur.

Environmental Change

Change in gene pools is greatly promoted by change in the environment. *Gene frequency* is a number indicating the ratio of a gene to its other alleles in a gene pool. Because of differential reproduction, when a particular environment confers survival value on a gene, its gene frequency increases; when the environment is unfavorable, its gene frequency decreases. A changing environment, therefore, promotes changes in the composition of gene pools—or evolution. If mutations are the raw materials of evolution, environmental change is the guiding force.

Adaptive Radiation

The changes that occur in a population as it responds to environmental change is called *adaptation*. Note that it is the gene pool of a *population* that adapts rather than the genes in a single individual. A small, isolated group within a large population may develop its own gene pool and thus differ in certain traits from the larger population. *Adaptive radiation* is the divergence of a single population into groups having differing traits. With sufficient divergence, a new species may be formed, a process called *speciation*. By adaptive radiation, new species fill available environmental niches—the role of the species in community of organisms.

Geographic Isolation

Darwin found that the finches of the various Galapagos Islands differed from those on the mainland, 600 miles away. They were isolated from the original population by a water barrier. Such isolation of populations by geographic barriers is called *geographic isolation.* Mountains, canyons, rivers, highways, climate, and even other organisms can serve as barriers for various kinds of plants and animals.

When a population becomes divided by a barrier, interbreeding between the two groups is prevented. Genes cannot flow freely between them, and their gene pools may diverge.

Reproductive Isolation

Because of geographic isolation, the two populations tend to become increasingly different. They may have differences in reproductive organs, making breeding impossible. They may have different courtship patterns. Differences in chromosomes may prevent the pairing of chromosomes or fertilization. Females of one population may produce eggs at a time when sperm of the other population are not fertile. Factors such as these constitute *reproductive isolation.*

When the two populations become so different that they can no longer interbreed, they have become two different *species.* When the separate populations of Galapagos Island finches became reproductively isolated, they became thirteen different species.

Geographic Distribution

Fossil evidence indicates that at the time when the evolution of mammals reached the stage of marsupials, the area that is now the continent of Australia was still connected to other land masses. Because of movements of the earth's crust, Australia was then separated from the other continents by an ocean barrier. As a result of this isolation, evolution proceeded differently in Australia than on the other continents. Throughout much of the world, marsupials became extinct and are represented there only by fossil remains. In the United States, the opossum remains as the only native marsupial. Within Australia, however, different kinds of marsupials evolved.

It would be difficult to explain the peculiar geographic distribution of marsupials and their fossils unless evolution had occurred. For such reasons, *geographic distribution* is often cited as an evidence of evolution.

The Hardy-Weinberg Principle

What factors promote stability in a gene pool? Conversely, what factors promote the changes that lead to speciation? This problem was examined mathematically by the English mathematician G. H. Hardy and the German physician W. Weinberg in their study of gene frequencies. The mathematical rules that these men independently proposed in 1908 are known as the *Hardy-Weinberg principle.*

According to this principle, the gene frequencies in a population tend to remain *constant* from generation to generation under these conditions:

- large populations
- absence of mutations
- absence of migration (in or out)
- random mating (no special advantage in mating to any individuals)

Conditions opposite to those specified above promote changes in gene pools.

E

Punctuated Equilibria

In studying the fossil records of organisms such as trilobites and snails that persist through as much as 400 m (¼ mile) of sedimentary rock, paleontologists have found that some species remain essentially unchanged for lengthy periods, millions of years, even. This stasis is then interrupted, or punctuated, by short bursts of rapid change. At such times, many new species appear within brief periods of geological time. Such fossil histories have led Niles Eldredge, of the American Museum of Natural History, and Stephen Jay Gould, of Harvard University, to propose a theory that they call *punctuated equilibria*. This theory proposes that evolution is a process in which long periods of genetic stability are interrupted by short episodes of rapid species formation, within a thousand years or so. (See Fig. 23–12.)

According to punctuated equilibria, the intermediate forms produced during a burst occupy only a minute portion of the evolutionary history of a lineage. Accordingly, the lack of abundant intermediate forms is a genuine result of the evolutionary process rather than of failure of fossils to be preserved.

Do these paleontological studies mean that geneticists must revise their gradualistic views of how species originate? Not yet. A paleontologist's flash of five thousand years represents 20,000 generations of snails to a geneticist. What is one person's burst of punctuated equilibria may be another's evolutionary gradualism. New evidences from various disciplines must continually be incorporated to provide ever new, deeper understandings of the evolutionary process. As shown in Figure 23-12, according to *gradualism*, as types B and C gradually evolve from type A, numerous transitional fossils should be found in this lengthy section of the geological column. According to *punctuated equilibria*, types B and C evolve so suddenly from type A that transitional fossils are difficult to find in this brief portion of the geological column.

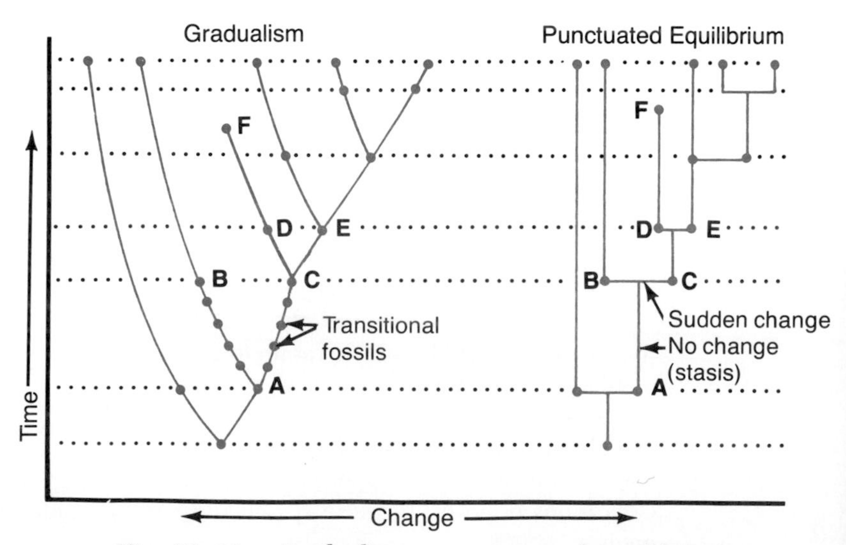

Fig. 23–12. Gradualism vs. punctuated equilibrium

F

Evolution Occurring Today

Is evolution a theoretical process confined to the long distant past or is it also occurring today? New species form too slowly for humans to observe speciation directly. Biologists, however, have several examples of present-day rapid changes in the composition of gene pools.

Insects Resistant to DDT

A village troubled by mosquitoes can spray DDT and soon be rewarded by the elimination of most of these pests. In a short time, however, the mosquitoes again become numerous. Again DDT is sprayed, but this time its effect is negligible. People commonly explain this loss of DDT's effectiveness by saying that the mosquitoes developed immunity to the insecticide. This expression is incorrect. Individual mosquitoes did not develop immunity in the way your body produces antibodies against bacteria. Instead, the mosquito population *evolved* resistance.

Many mosquito generations ago, a mutation occurred in the mosquito population. The mutant allele produced enzymes that neutralize the chemical effects of DDT. But DDT had never been used on this mosquito population. Accordingly, the new gene had no special survival value. But it was carried along with the other genes.

When the mosquito population was exposed to DDT for the first time, most mosquitoes perished, except for those few carrying the resistance-conferring gene. The surviving mosquitoes gave rise to new generations that were resistant to DDT. A new *species* did not develop but, during these few generations, the *gene pool* of a population changed.

Insects and chemists are engaged in a race. As insects evolve new immunities, chemists must continually devise new insecticides. Unfortunately, some of the new chemical compounds may be toxic to other living things in the environment.

Penicillin-Resistant Bacteria

A doctor administers penicillin to a sick child and sees fine improvement. But this improvement may only be temporary; soon the child again develops the disease symptoms. Once more, the doctor injects the antibiotic, but this time there is no improvement. Why not? This situation is similar to that of the mosquitoes and DDT. A strain of bacteria resistant to penicillin *evolved* within the child's body. Such a new, resistant bacterial strain may also spread throughout the neighborhood or within a hospital.

Now you know why your doctor may refuse to give you an antibiotic for a mild illness. He or she may not wish to risk your developing a resistant strain. Biologists must constantly seek new kinds of antibiotics to keep abreast of evolutionary developments with bacterial populations.

The Peppered Moths

Before 1840 most peppered moths *(Biston betularia)* in the woods near Manchester, England, had light-colored wings. Although black moths occurred, these were rare. Within ten years the black moths began to increase in number. By 1895 about 98% of the peppered moths were the black kind. What caused this change in the population of peppered moths?

During this period the Industrial Revolution occurred in England. Tons of soot from factory furnaces darkened the trees of the countryside.

When peppered moths came to rest on a tree trunk, they were seized as food by birds. A researcher in the 1950s observed that the birds take mainly those moths that contrast with the background: from dark tree trunks the birds picked mainly light moths and from light tree trunks they picked mainly dark moths.

Geneticists have found that the dark color of peppered moths is produced by a single dominant allele. In the changed, soot-darkened environment, this gene favored the survival and the subsequent differential reproduction of the dark variety. *Biston betularia* is still *Biston betularia;* a new *species* did not develop within a single century. But the history of the peppered moths shows natural selection at work *altering gene frequencies* within a population.

The shift toward darker color in response to industrial pollution is called *industrial melanism.* This phenomenon has been observed in more than 150 other species of moths in Europe and the United States. As factories in England shift from coal to gas furnaces, how may the future population of peppered moths be affected?

G

Origin of Life

Spontaneous Generation

Until the 17th century, most people believed in *spontaneous generation.* This is the idea that living things can arise from nonliving things. For example, people thought that frogs and eels arise from mud and that roundworms develop from horsehairs in a rain barrel. In the mid-1600s, Francesco Redi, an Italian physician, proved that maggots do not develop from decaying meat. (See Fig. 23–13.) He showed that the maggots come from eggs that live flies deposit on the meat. When bacteria were later discovered, however, the controversy over spontaneous generation arose anew. Could these microscopic organisms arise spontaneously from the nonliving food present in a flask?

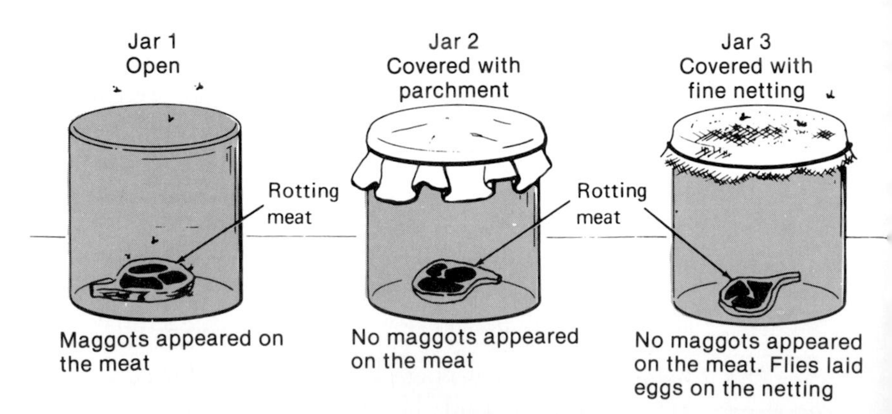

Fig. 23–13. Redi's experiment

In 1861, Louis Pasteur of France proved that even microorganisms arise only from previously living things. One of Pasteur's experiments is shown in Figure 23–14. As this drawing shows, one flask of sterilized food had a curved neck. Its S-shaped neck allowed air to enter but kept living bacteria from reaching the food. No bacteria developed in the S-necked flask. But in flasks of sterilized food, where live bacteria could enter, bacteria did grow profusely. Is this experiment well controlled?

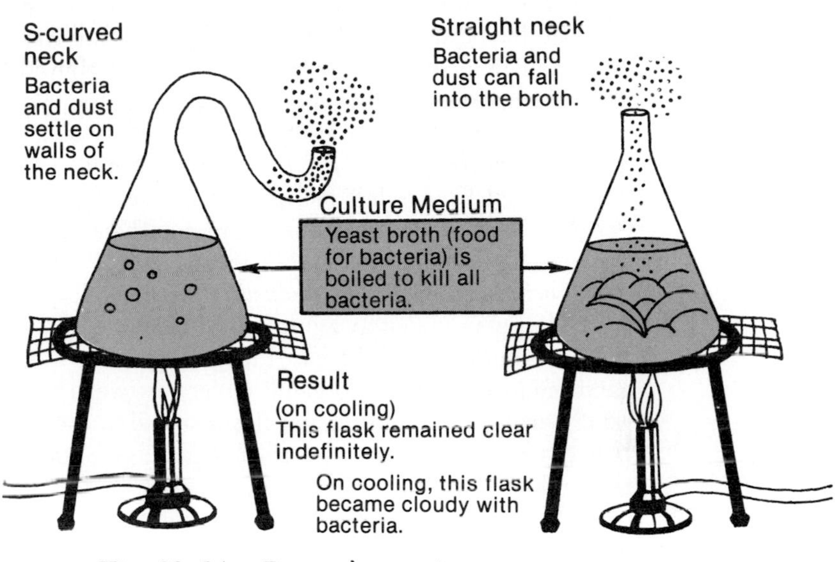

Fig. 23–14. Pasteur's experiment on spontaneous generation. Both flasks had the same conditions. Even fresh air could enter both flasks. But bacteria developed only in the flask where live bacteria could reach the food.

Biogenesis means the production of life from living things. *Abiogenesis* (*a* means "without") means the production of life from nonliving things (or spontaneous generation). Biologists are convinced that living things today arise only by biogenesis—only from other living things. If this is so, how did the very first living things arise?

The Heterotroph Hypothesis

Although evolution is a well-supported scientific *theory*, explanations for the origin of the very first life have less supporting evidence and are called *hypotheses*. But these educated guesses are not dreamed up out of thin air. Scientists base these hypotheses upon knowledge of conditions on other planets, on the study of primitive organisms living today, and on established principle of physics and biochemistry.

Autotroph or heterotroph? Inasmuch as animals today depend upon plants for needed food and oxygen, it would seem reasonable to assume that the autotrophic (plant) way of life originated first. But although an *autotroph hypothesis* seems attractive at first glance, it fails to recognize the complex biochemistry of photosynthesis that you have studied. A primitive living thing that could make its own food would already be complex, it could hardly have been the first form of life on earth. For this and other reasons biologists developed the *heterotroph hypothesis.*

According to this hypothesis the first living things obtained food and energy by taking in organic material from their environment, not by making it photosynthetically. According to this hypothesis, the first living things were heterotrophs.

The main outlines of the heterotroph hypothesis were presented by the English biologist J.B.S.Haldane in 1929, the Russian biologist A.I. Oparin in 1936, and by the American chemist Harold Urey in the 1950s. The assumptions of this hypothesis are given below.

1. *The presence on the primitive earth of an atmosphere that differed greatly from the atmosphere of the earth today.* In its early stages, the earth cooled from a hot molten mass. The ancient atmosphere lacked oxygen and nitrogen. The gases present in the atmosphere were probably the ones shown in the table below.

2. *Formation of organic molecules in the atmosphere and in the seas.* With energy provided by lightning, by X-rays, and by unfiltered ultraviolet rays from the sun, the gases in the primitive atmosphere formed organic molecules. These organic molecules were carried to the seas by rain. Further linkages of molecules resulted in the first proteins and carbohydrates. This accumulation of organic compounds made the ocean resemble a sterile *hot, thin soup.* Support for this assumption has been provided by laboratory studies duplicating the conditions assumed to prevail on the primitive earth.

In 1953, Stanley Miller, a pupil of Harold Urey at the University of Chicago, circulated water vapor, hydrogen, ammonia, and hot methane past a strong electrical spark for one week. (See Fig. 23–15.) Miller found that this simulation of possible primitive Earth conditions resulted in the production of several amino acids.

Gases in the Primitive Atmosphere

Gas	Formula
water vapor	H_2O
hydrogen	H_2
ammonia	NH_3
methane	CH_4

In 1957, Sidney Fox, of Florida State University, heated a dry mixture containing amino acids and obtained polypeptides. Laboratory experiments by other scientists showed that forms of energy probably present on the primitive Earth could cause linkages yielding sugars, purines, and pyrimidines. These are components of DNA. By simulating the conditions probably present in early days, scientists demonstrated that conditions on the primitive earth could have produced the molecules that are used by today's simplest organisms for energy release, enzyme action, and heredity.

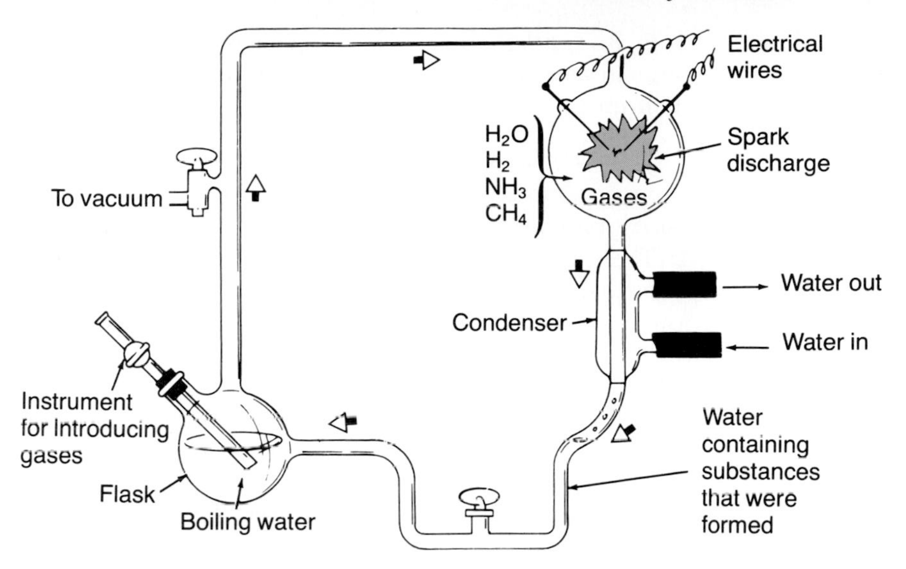

Fig. 23–15. Diagram of Stanley Miller's apparatus

3. *Formation of aggregates.* In college laboratory lessons, students of physical science study large accumulations of proteinlike molecules having a boundary of electrically attracted water molecules. These accumulations are called *aggregates* (also known as "coacervates"). Aggregates have the capacity to attract other molecules.

It is assumed that such "sticky" aggregates developed in the primitive seas and attracted other molecules. In time, the aggregates became larger, more complex, and developed a boundary membrane. They developed the ability to take and use energy-rich molecules from the sea, to grow, and to reproduce with the aid of their purines and pyrimidines. At this stage, these primitive heterotrophic systems could be considered to be a living protocell. Throughout this process, natural selection sorted out the more efficient systems from the less efficient ones.

4. *Rise of the anaerobes.* Inasmuch as free molecular oxygen was presumably absent from the earliest atmosphere, the first forms of life must have obtained energy by anaerobic respiration. Anaerobic respiration releases energy by chemical oxidation without using free molecular oxygen. An example of anaerobic respiration (fermentation) is:

$$\text{glucose} \xrightarrow{\text{enzymes}} \text{alcohol} + CO_2 + \text{energy}$$

Thus anaerobic respiration could have added CO_2 to the atmosphere.

5. *Rise of the autotrophs.* With CO_2 now available, the first primitive autotrophs could arise. These photosynthetic organisms utilize CO_2 and water to produce their own food.

$$CO_2 + H_2O + \text{light} \xrightarrow{\text{enzymes}} \text{glucose} + O_2$$

This process probably added oxygen to the atmosphere.

6. *Rise of the aerobes.* The oxygen now available in the atmosphere was used in respiration by both heterotrophs and autotrophs. Aerobic respiration uses molecular oxygen to release energy by chemical oxidation.

$$\text{glucose} + O_2 \xrightarrow{\text{enzymes}} CO_2 + H_2O + \text{energy}$$

As previously stated, aerobic respiration is more efficient than anaerobic respiration for releasing energy.

These hypothetical steps resulted in early forms of one-celled organisms that could carry on autotrophic nutrition as well as some that could carry on heterotrophic nutrition. These living things could obtain energy by aerobic or anerobic methods. Examples of such unicellular organisms still existing today are:

heterotrophs—yeasts, molds, protozoa, some bacteria
autotrophs—algae, some bacteria

Although the heterotroph hypothesis provides an explanation for the rise of living things from lifeless matter, this form of abiogenesis could not occur under today's conditions. If primitive heterotrophs should somehow originate in today's oceans, they could not compete with modern heterotrophs that would use them as food.

Most biologists accept the broad outlines of the heterotroph hypothesis, but there is much divergent opinion concerning details. Moreover, recent bursts of information from astronomy concerning the origin and early history of galaxies, stars, and other planets are providing new ideas about the probable early events on planet Earth.

Reasoning Exercises

1. According to the Hardy-Weinberg principle, what factors could promote evolution?
2. How does the theory called punctuated equilibria modify Darwin's idea of evolution?
3. Explain the meaning of adaptive radiation.
4. Give three examples of evolution occurring today.
5. List four gases that were probably present in the primitive earth's atmosphere.
6. Why is it unlikely that the first organism was an autotroph?

Completion Questions

A

1. The hardened resin of trees forms . . . . . .
2. An impression of an extinct organism found in a rock is called a(n) . . . . . .
3. La Brea, Los Angeles, is famous for the fossils that are found in . . . . . .
4. Hot molten material in the interior of the earth cools to form . . . . . . rock.
5. Fossils are most often found in . . . . . . rock.
6. Scientists estimate the age of the earth by the ratio of . . . . . . in rocks.

7. Present scientific estimates of the age of the earth place it at about . . . . . . years.
8. Dinosaurs were dominant during the . . . . . . era.
9. In its evolutionary history, the horse showed a decrease in the number of toes but an increase in . . . . . .
10. Similar structures in different organisms that may have the same function but different origins are said to be . . . . . . structures.

B-C

11. Lamarck's theory is called the Theory of . . . . . .
12. Weismann criticized Lamarck's theory by showing that . . . . . . are not inherited.
13. The Darwin-Wallace Theory is called the Theory of . . . . . .
14. Darwin studied finches and tortoises found on the . . . . . . Islands.
15. The book in which Darwin first explained his theory is entitled . . . . . . and was published in the year . . . . . .

D

16. De Vries said that inherited variations arise by . . . . . .
17. The study of inheritance in large groups of sexually reproducing organisms is called . . . . . .
18. Scientists think that the guiding force in evolution is . . . . . .
19. The divergence of a population into two groups that occupy different niches is called adaptive . . . . . .
20. The separation of a population into groups that can no longer mate with each other is called reproductive . . . . . .
21. The only living marsupial that is native to the United States is the . . . . . .
22. According to the Hardy-Weinberg Principle, random mating leads to (constancy, change) . . . . . . in gene frequencies.

E

23. According to the theory of punctuated equilibrium, we should expect to find (many, few) . . . . . . examples of transitional fossils.
24. Genetic shift is a change in gene frequencies because of . . . . . . factors.

F-G

25. The darkening of the wings of moth populations is called industrial . . . . . .
26. The belief that mice can arise from filth illustrates the idea of . . . . . .
27. Pasteur let air into his flasks but kept out bacteria by using flasks with a(n) . . . . . . neck.
28. The concept that living things arise only from previous living things is called (biogenesis, abiogenesis) . . . . . .
29. According to the hypothesis of Haldane and Oparin, the first living things had the . . . . . . type of nutrition.
30. The accumulation of organic compounds in the oceans probably made it resemble a hot, thin . . . . . .

Multiple-Choice Questions

A

1. The age of organic remains less than 40,000 years old can be measured by the proportion of carbon-14 found in them because (1) there was less carbon-14 in the air in former times, (2) there was more carbon-14 in the air in former times, (3) the half-life of carbon-14 changes at a known rate, (4) carbon-14 undergoes radioactive decay at a known rate.

2. Petrification is best defined as the process by which (1) organic materials are converted into humus, (2) minerals are dissolved and carried down through the topsoil, (3) the molecules of organisms are gradually replaced by minerals, (4) stone is weathered into soil.
3. Many homologous structures found in pigs, frogs, and snakes indicate that these organisms originated from a(n) (1) protist, (2) invertebrate, (3) fixed species, (4) common ancestor.
4. Although the arm of a human and the flipper of a dolphin serve different functions, there is great similarity in their structures and developments. This similarity is known as (1) homology, (2) analogy, (3) embryonic similarity, (4) biochemical similarity.

B-C

5. Which scientist most strongly supported the idea that evolutionary changes occurred because there was a need for them? (1) De Vries, (2) Lyell (3) Lamarck, (4) Darwin
6. Weisman's experiments with mice produced results that helped to (1) support Darwin's assumption of a struggle for survival, (2) disprove Lamarck's theory of the inheritance of acquired characteristics, (3) disprove De Vries' concept of evolution, (4) support Lamarck's theory of use and disuse.
7. About how many years ago did Darwin propose his theory of evolution? (1) 50, (2) 125, (3) 300, (4) 3,300
8. Malthus contributed to Darwin's idea of (1) variation, (2) overproduction, (3) adaptation, (4) inheritance of variations.
9. The scientist most closely associated with the theory of use and disuse is (1) Darwin, (2) Lamarck, (3) Miller, (4) Watson.
10. "The eyes of a cave animal either lose their function or disappear because eyes are not needed in the darkness."
    This statement would most likely have been written by (1) Mendel, (2) Morgan, (3) Lamarck, (4) Malthus.
11. Which idea is *not* basic to Darwin's ideas of evolution? (1) Mutations cause changes in living things. (2) Nature selects the most fit organisms to survive. (3) Variations are inherited by organisms. (4) Organisms increase in number faster than their food supply.
12. A construction worker explained that his muscles had become well-developed by the type of work he did and therefore his son had inherited this trait. This observation would have been most strongly supported by (1) Watson, (2) Lamarck, (3) Nuttall, (4) Haeckel.

D

13. In his theory of evolution, Darwin did not explain (1) natural selection, (2) overproduction, (3) survival of the fittest, (4) the source of variations.
14. De Vries believed that the major source of the variations associated with evolution was (1) mutations, (2) mitosis, (3) use and disuse, (4) acquired traits.
15. Which is an example of a population? (1) all the animals in the world, (2) all the animals in a certain location, (3) all the birds in a certain location, (4) all the robins in a certain location
16. Application of Mendelian principles to the study of genes in populations is known as (1) adaptive radiation, (2) population genetics, (3) gene frequency, (4) variations.

17. The percentage of occurrence of a particular gene in a population is known as the gene (1) pool, (2) frequency, (3) total, (4) number.
18. The gene pool of a population tends to remain stable if (1) mating is random, (2) there is extensive migration, (3) the populations involved are small, (4) there are frequent mutations.
19. Which factor has the *least* effect on the development of new species? (1) variations, (2) natural selection, (3) changing environmental conditions, (4) constant environmental conditions.
20. Which is *not* considered a major force in organic evolution? (1) changes in the DNA of somatic cells, (2) natural selection, (3) mutations, (4) competition within a population
21. The total of all the alleles of a population constitutes the (1) genetic distribution, (2) dominant genes, (3) gene pool, (4) recessive genes.
22. According to the Hardy-Weinberg principle, which of the following would most likely change the gene pool of a population? (1) maintenance of a large population, (2) absence of mutations, (3) random mating, (4) migration
23. Two species of frogs live in the same location but cannot breed and produce fertile offspring. This is an example of (1) adaptive radiation, (2) reproductive isolation, (3) population migration, (4) geographic isolation.

E

24. Evolution took place by sudden changes which interrupted long periods of stasis. This is the theory of (1) use and disuse, (2) abiogenesis, (3) gradualism, (4) punctuated equilibrium.
25. The theory of punctuated equilibrium was developed by (1) Haldane and Oparin, (2) Eldredge and Gould, (3) Hardy and Weinberg, (4) Watson and Crick.

F

26. Which best suggests that evolution is still taking place? (1) volcanic activity, (2) fossil discoveries, (3) melting of polar icecaps, (4) changes in the gene pools of peppered moths.

G

27. The assumption that life comes only from preexisting life is called (1) the heterotroph hypothesis, (2) biogenesis, (3) abiogenesis, (4) spontaneous generation.
28. According to the heterotroph hypothesis, which substance was missing from the atmosphere prior to the origin of life? (1) ammonia molecules, (2) methane molecules, (3) hydrogen molecules, (4) oxygen molecules
29. Which is a basic assumption of the heterotroph hypothesis? (1) More complex organisms appeared before less complex organisms. (2) Living organisms did not appear until there was oxygen in the atmosphere. (3) Large autotrophic organisms appeared before small photosynthesizing organisms. (4) Autotrophic activity added molecular oxygen to the environment.
30. Energy for the formation of organic molecules during primitive earth conditions probably included heat, ultraviolet rays, and (1) enzymes, (2) X-rays, (3) ATP, (4) chlorophyll.

Chapter Test

1. Evidence of common ancestry based on similarities of blood proteins is obtained from studies of comparative (1) anatomy, (2) biochemistry, (3) embryology, (4) cytology.
2. In its fossil history, the horse showed (1) an increase in size and a decrease in number of toes, (2) a decrease in size and a decrease in number of toes, (3) a decrease in size and an increase in number of toes, (4) an increase in size and an increase in number of toes.
3. When several strata of rock are found one above the other, scientists usually conclude that the oldest stratum is the one that is (1) horizontal, (2) lowest, (3) thickest, (4) topmost.
4. The theory that characteristics acquired during one generation will be transmitted to the next was proposed by (1) Darwin, (2) Lamarck, (3) Eldredge and Gould, (4) Hardy and Weinberg.
5. Mutations provide a basis for (1) abiogenesis, (2) reproduction, (3) formation of aggregates, (4) evolution.
6. Which is the best evidence that two organisms have a common ancestor? (1) Their fossils were formed at the same time. (2) They have the same enzymes and hormones. (3) They eat the same type of food. (4) They live in the same type of environment.
7. The earliest known mammalian ancestor of the horse was about the size of a (1) mouse, (2) dinosaur, (3) fox, (4) cow.
8. A vestigial structure is one that (1) is more useful than another similar structure, (2) is in the process of becoming useless, (3) has apparently lost its usefulness to the species, (4) is found only in organisms of no value to humans.
9. The flipper of a whale is homologous to the (1) arm of a human, (2) trunk of an elephant, (3) wing of an insect, (4) tail of a fish.
10. *Eohippus* is an early ancestor of the modern (1) pigeon, (2) horse, (3) human, (4) hippopotamus.
11. If fossils of two different organisms are found in two layers of rock that lie one above the other, it is most probable that the (1) two forms are closely related, (2) upper form lived before the lower one, (3) lower form descended from the upper one, (4) lower form is older than the upper one.
12. According to the heterotroph hypothesis, which was *not* a source of energy for the formation of the first organic molecules? (1) lightning, (2) respiration, (3) radioactivity, (4) heat
13. The theory of punctuated equilibrium explains why (1) simpler organisms appeared before more complex ones, (2) fewer transitional fossils have been found than one might expect, (3) living things originated in the warm oceans, (4) evolutionary change is slow and gradual.
14. Certain strains of bacteria that were susceptible to penicillin in the past have now become resistant. The probable explanation is that (1) the mutation rate increased, (2) the strains became resistant because they needed to do so for survival, (3) a mutation was retained and passed on to succeeding generations because it had high survival value, (4) the principal forces influencing the pattern of survival in a population are isolation and mating.

15. Darwin observed that different but closely related species of finches filled the diverse environmental niches on the different Galapagos Islands. The filling of these environmental niches is known as (1) acquired characteristics, (2) blending inheritance, (3) common ancestry, (4) adaptive radiation.
16. Which occurs as a result of adaptive radiation during the evolution of new animal species? (1) no mutations appear, (2) available environmental niches are filled, (3) natural selection ceases, (4) random mating between species increases
17. Which statement would most likely have been made by Charles Darwin? (1) X-rays and other forms of energy produce changes in genes. (2) Giraffes have long necks due to a series of mutations. (3) The individuals that survive are the ones best fitted to exist in their environment. (4) Species are fixed and unchanging.
18. The concept that most organisms tend to produce more offspring than can possibly survive is part of the (1) theory of use and disuse, (2) theory of natural selection, (3) heterotroph hypothesis, (4) principle of dominance.
19. Subsequent to the publication of Darwin's theory, evolutionists developed the concept that (1) a species produces more offspring than can possibly survive, (2) the individuals that survive are those best fitted to the environment, (3) favorable variations are retained in a species, (4) mutations are partially responsible for variations within a species.
20. Which factor has the *least* important role in the formation of new species? (1) use and disuse, (2) natural selection, (3) reproductive isolation, (4) mutation
21. In the process of evolution, the effect of the environment is to (1) prevent the occurrence of mutations, (2) act as a selective force on variations that appear, (3) provide conditions favorable for the formation of fossils, (4) provide stable conditions favorable to the survival of all species.
22. A gas that was probably absent from the primitive earth's atmosphere is (1) methane, (2) oxygen, (3) ammonia, (4) hydrogen.
23. The concept of mutation as an inherited kind of variation was introduced by (1) Weismann, (2) Eldredge, (3) De Vries, (4) Lamarck.
24. A scientific theory must (1) deal with the supernatural, (2) be falsifiable, (3) be unchangeable, (4) be kept secret from scientists in other countries.
25. A person who believes in abiogenesis would most likely make the statement that (1) maggots develop from fly's eggs, (2) the autotrophic way of life originated first, (3) roundworms develop from horsehairs in a rain barrel, (4) the mosquito population developed a resistance to DDT.

Chapter 24 Human Evolution

When did the first human appear? The answer depends upon what you mean by human. If walking upright on two feet, or *bipedalism,* is your sole criterion, then the first humanlike primates lived 3.5 million years ago. These were Lucy and her kin, fossils discovered by Donald C. Johanson in Ethiopia in 1974. The name Lucy comes from "Lucy in the Sky with Diamonds," a Beatles song that was played incessantly during the celebration on the night of the discovery. The skeleton of Lucy, only three and one-half feet tall, was almost complete, and 13 additional fossils of this species were found nearby in a group a year later.

Lucy appeared to be quite human, especially from the neck down. But her brain was too small really to consider her a human. Moreover, her jaw was the wrong shape and there was no indication that her group used stone tools. So Johanson and his colleagues decided against classifying Lucy and her kin in the genus *Homo*. Instead, they classified these fossils in the already established genus *Australopithecus* (Australo = southern, and pithecus = ape; given this name because the first fossils of this genus were found in South Africa). Because Lucy and her relatives were found in the Afar region of Ethiopia they were named *Australopithecus afarensis*.

So the 3.5 million-year-old Lucy was not the first human. The earliest hominid to be classified as *Homo* is *Homo habilis,* who lived in Africa about two million years ago. The earliest fossils of our own species, *Homo sapiens*, date back to about 80,000 years ago in Europe.

(A) Anthropology

Anthropology is the study of humans—their origins, their races, their physical characteristics and their cultures. *Paleo*anthropologists trace the evolution of ancient humans and humanlike creatures by finding and studying fossils. Sometimes these scientists must reconstruct the entire body from fragments of skeleton, such as pieces of skull, broken jaw bones, teeth, and hip bones. Some extinct hominids, however, left numerous complete skeletons. Scientists determine how long ago a fossil lived by radioactive dating of surrounding layers of volcanic ash, using the potassium-argon method.

A famous family of English paleoanthropologists and geologists are the Leakeys—Louis Leakey (deceased), his wife, Mary, and their sons, Jonathan and Richard. This family made many important fossil finds in Tanzania, East Africa, especially at Olduvai Gorge.

Human Characteristics

Since fossils do not come branded with their name, the classification and naming of extinct hominids is a matter for discussion—and disagreement—among anthropologists. In judging how to classify a hominid fossil, the following characteristics are considered human:

(1) Bipedalism. The shape of the pelvis is an important indication of whether the creature walked upright like a human being. (See Figure 24-1.)

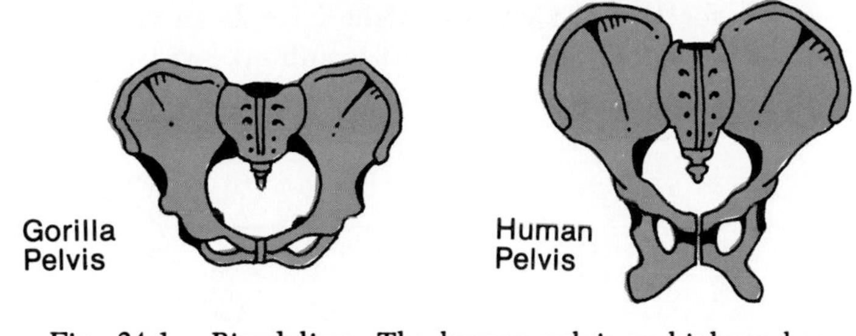

Fig. 24-1. Bipedalism. The human pelvis or hipbone has proportionately a greater surface than that of the gorilla for supporting large muscles that are used in walking upright. It is also better adapted for supporting the internal organs of an animal that is erect. Thus, a pelvis shaped like that of a modern person is an indication that the fossil animal had a two-legged, upright posture.

(2) Brain size. The size of the brain is determined by measurements of the skull. Some approximate brain capacities are: chimpanzee, 350 cm^3; *Australopithecus*, 450 cm^3; *Homo habilis*, 725 cm^3; *Homo sapiens*, 1,500 cm^3.

(3) Teeth and jaws. Humans have large front teeth and small molars but this situation is reversed in apes. The human jaw has a rounded, U-shape but the ape jaw is V-shaped.

(4) Use of tools. Early tools used by humans were stones that seem to have been smashed together to produce sharp edges, but later tools were skillfully chipped away to serve specific purposes. When you pick up a hammer or a book, your thumb is opposite to your other fingers. This *opposable thumb* occurs also in other primates but is highly adapted in humans for the skillful use of tools and delicate instruments.

(5) Culture. Estimates of primitive societies are based on items found where the people lived. For example, animal bones found in caves of early humans show whether their diet included meat as well as vegetable matter. The presence of bones of large animals indicate that these people engaged in cooperative, group activity—for the hunt. Charred bones show that these people knew how to use fire for cooking and keeping warm. By piecing together this kind of information, anthropologists picture the social and cultural patterns of extinct people.

(B)

A Phylogenetic Tree

A phylogenetic tree is a diagram that indicates the probable pathway of evolution. Figure 24-2 is a phylogenetic tree for the evolution of humans. The overall picture shown here is accepted by most anthropologists but there are differences of opinion concerning details.

In studying Figure 24-2, notice the fork in the evolutionary road about 12 million years ago. This is when humanlike animals (hominids) are thought to have separated from the ape lineage. Contrary to a common misunderstanding, anthropologists do not suggest that humans descended from monkeys, chimpanzees, or gorillas. The common ancestor for the two groups might have been a long-extinct creature such as *Ramapithecus*. Some paleoanthropologists, however, no longer consider *Ramapithecus* as part of the human lineage but as part of the orangutan lineage.

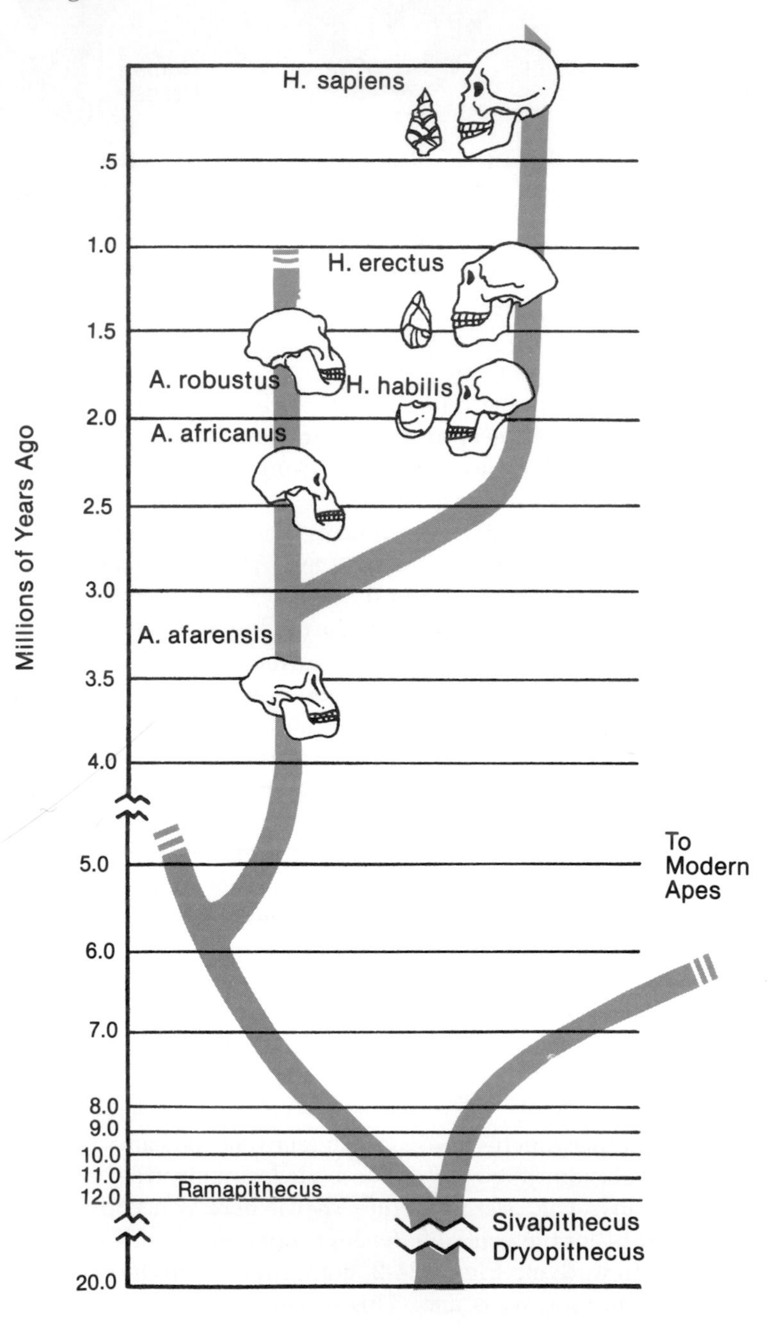

Fig. 24-2. **A phylogenetic tree of human evolution based on recent fossil evidence.**

The evidence for a common ancestry of modern humans and apes is provided by three kinds of homology on the molecular level: (1) Humans and chimpanzees show similar immunological reactions (See Nuttall precipitation procedure in chapter 23); (2) Many of the proteins of both groups—hemoglobin for example—are more than 99 percent identical in their amino acid structure; and (3) Both groups have great similarity in the sequence of nucleotides in their DNA molecules.

Ramapithecus. The earliest primate fossil that is generally considered somewhat humanlike is *Ramapithecus*. The only remnants of these creatures are fragments of humanlike jaws and teeth. Scores of these jaws indicate that *Ramapithecus* lived in Africa and Eurasia from about 15 million years ago to 8 million years ago. Nobody knows what its head looked like nor whether it walked on two legs or four.

Australopithecus afarensis. The fossils of Lucy and her kin show that their hips and knees were clearly built for fully-erect, striding bipedalism. Their footprints, preserved in hardened volcanic ash, look quite modern. Their heads, however, are quite primitive and their brains, at 400 cm^3, were not much bigger than that of today's chimpanzee. Because 13 male and female skeletons, including those of children, were found in one place, *A. afarensis* might have lived in family groups. Their discoverer, Donald D. Johanson of the Cleveland Museum of Natural History, thinks that two lineages developed from these creatures: One lineage was the later forms of *Australopithecus*, which died out. The other lineage produced humans, including us. Johanson, thus, regards *A. afarensis* as an ancestor of modern people. Mary and Richard Leakey, however, do not view *A. afarensis* as an ancestor of ours. They think the *Homo* line branched off much further back in antiquity, perhaps directly from a creature such as *Ramapithecus* — 6 million years ago.

Other Australopithecines. Members of the australopithecine and human lineages shown in Fig. 24-2 should not be considered as rungs on a ladder leading to a definite end. Rather, these species are like a many-branched system with an unknown origin.

Appearing later than *A. afarensis* were *A. africanus* and then *A. robustus*. *A. africanus* was more delicate or "gracile" in appearance than the "robust" *A. robustus*. The latter was taller, had a heavier brow, and a skull crest to anchor its powerful jaw muscles. Both species seem to have been vegetarians, with wide molars used for grinding coarse matter. They did not make tools but probably used pebbles and bones as ready-made implements. Anthropologists think these australopithecines lived in family groups on the African plains.

Homo habilis. The earliest creature that scientists classify as clearly human is *Homo habilis* (meaning "handy man" or tool user). These people lived about 2 million years ago and seem to be the first hominids to make and use stone tools. Some of these tools were merely fist-sized stones that were smashed together to form sharp edges. But some stone tools were made by striking flakes off a large stone until a sharp cutting edge remained. These could be used to butcher a carcass or cut wood.

The *Homo habilis* people were slightly larger than their australopithecine contemporaries. Significantly, they had a larger brain, ranging from 500 cm^3 to 700 cm^3. Microscopic scratch marks on their teeth indicate that prehistoric people had a well-balanced diet, with plenty of vegetables. For food they mainly gathered eggs, roots, and berries. But the presence of large bones in places where they lived indicates that these early people hunted in groups, and thus had social organizations.

Homo erectus. *Homo erectus* appeared on the scene about 1.5 million years ago. By that time the brain size of early humans had increased to more than 800 cm^3. This is double the brain size of chimpanzees and more than half that of today's people. At the same time, the jaw receded to make the face look flatter in profile. *H. erectus* has this name because, at the time of its discovery, it was the earliest upright (bipedal) hominid known. Fossils originally called Java man (*Pithecanthropus erectus* or "ape man") and Peking man (or Peking woman) are now classified as *H. erectus*.

The brain capacity of *H. erectus* increased over the next million years. Its fossil locations show this to be the first human to move out of Africa into Eurasia. These people made superior stone tools for hunting and butchering and they were the first to use fire. Since the kind of thought required to conceive and design a fine tool is similar to that needed for language, anthropologists think that *H. erectus* had at least a simple kind of language.

The Neanderthals. The earliest hominids to be classified together with today's people in the species *Homo sapiens* are the Neanderthals. The first fossil of these people was found in a cave in the Neander Valley of Germany, in 1856. More than 50 fossils found later show that the Neanderthals people lived in Europe, the near East, and Central Asia. They first appeared about 80,000 years ago and became extinct about 40,000 years ago when they were replaced by more modern people.

The conventional picture of the Neanderthal as a stooped, hulking, dull-witted brute derives from the first fossil that was found. Because this individual happened to be arthritic and unusually robust, the Neanderthals were originally considered to be half-way between apes and humans. The modern concept of the Neanderthals, however, is that of an intelligent, fully-erect individual with powerful muscles in the shoulders and chest. Many had a low forehead with heavy brow ridges and a large nose, but there was a wide variety of skeletal features. It is often said that a Neanderthal on a subway or bus today would attract little attention.

The Neanderthal brain was about the same size as ours. These people made stone tools, used fire, and hunted the wooly mammoth and rhinoceros. Because Neanderthalers buried their dead with sacrifices, anthropologists think they had some kind of spiritual sense. Why did they disappear? Were they driven to extinction by invasions of more modern people who had evolved elsewhere? Were they absorbed into more modern people by interbreeding? Scientists do not yet have an answer.

Cro-Magnons—Modern People. Anthropologists separate the Neanderthals from today's people by classifying the two groups into separate subspecies. The Neanderthals are *Homo sapiens neanderthalensis* and we are *Homo sapiens sapiens*. Included within our subspecies are prehistoric representatives called the *Cro-Magnon people*.

The first fossils of these people were found in 1868 in a cave near Cro-Magnon, France. Compared with the Neanderthals, the Cro-Magnons were modern in appearance. Gone was the heavy skull, protruding brow ridge, slanting forehead, and coarse, thick jaws. The chin was better developed and the forehead higher. Numerous fossils found in France and Spain indicate that the Cro-Magnons appeared suddenly in Europe about 40,000 years ago. They seem to have migrated from southern Africa or southern Asia, but nobody knows where fully modern people first appeared. When the Cro-Magnons settled in Europe, they coexisted for a time with the Neanderthals.

Early Cro-Magnons, probably with all the intelligence of people of today, spent much of their time as hunters and gatherers of food. Later, they learned to domesticate animals and then plants. Their first permanent settlements date to about 9,000 years ago and their first cities to about 3000 B.C.

Cro-Magnons produced excellent tools, including stone knives, spear points, bows and arrows. These prehistoric people seem to have enjoyed such a surplus of food that they could afford to set some individuals aside as skilled artists. Between 20,000 and 10,000 years ago they produced cave paintings—of the animals they hunted—that by today's standards are considered splendid works of art. The Cro-Magnons ushered in a culture called the New Stone Age, which led to the Age of Metals and then to people of historical times and written records.

Ⓒ

Human Races

Many people confuse race with nationality, language, or religion. There are no Italian or Spanish races—these are nationalities. Aryan, Semitic, and Slavic are *language groups*, not races. Christian, Jewish, and Moslem are *religions*, not races.

Homo sapiens sapiens can be divided into a number of sub-groupings called races. A *race* consists of a regional group of individuals who have many genes in common. These different gene pools arose long ago during periods of isolation. Today, however, there is no such thing as a "pure race." This is because of migration and interbreeding.

Races, as categories, are human inventions. Characteristics employed to arrange people into racial groups include skin color, hair texture, facial appearance, and blood type. Many scientists classify people into these major races: Caucasoid, Mongoloid, Negroid, Australoid, American Indian, and Polynesian. Other scientists, however, make breakdowns of from 3 to 30 races.

No race has been shown to be more intelligent than others. Racial groups in this country may have had different opportunities for education and advancement. It is therefore difficult to make a controlled test of their inborn abilities. Even if one race were found to have a higher *average* ability in study, athletics, mechanics, music, or dance, there is much overlap among *individual* members of the groups. With equal opportunities, each person's achievement will depend upon his or her merit.

Reasoning Exercises

1. Describe three physical characteristics used in classifying a fossil as human.
2. State three kinds of molecular homology between modern humans and modern apes.
3. Was Lucy (*Australopithecus afarensis*) an ancestor of ours? Give two views on this subject.
4. How can anthropologists make estimates of the social characteristics of extinct hominids?

Multiple-Choice Questions

1. The common ancestor for the hominid and ape lineages may have been a creature such as the 12 million-year-old (1) Neanderthals, (2) *Ramapithecus*, (3) *Australopithecus afarensis*, (4) *Homo habilis*.
2. Bipedalism in a fossil is indicated by the (1) presence of stone tools, (2) size of the teeth, (3) shape of the jaw, (4) shape of the pelvis.
3. The prehistoric humans noted for their artistic cave drawings were (1) the Cro-Magnons, (2) the Neanderthals, (3) Lucy and her kin, (4) *Homo erectus*.
4. The classification of human races is based upon (1) language, (2) nationality, (3) gene pools, (4) religion.
5. Studies of fossils indicate that the first *Homo sapiens* lived about (1) 12 million years ago, (2) 3.5 million years ago, (3) 80,000 years ago, (4) 6,000 years ago.

Chapter Test

1. A characteristic that is considered to be *human* is (1) a V-shaped jaw, (2) an opposable thumb, (3) a brain capacity of 400 cm^3, (4) a smaller pelvic surface.
2. A *hominid* is (1) a humanlike ape, (2) an apelike human, (3) in the genus *Homo*, (4) a human.
3. The earliest *Homo sapiens* was probably (1) Cro-Magnon, (2) *Homo sapiens sapiens*, (3) Neanderthal, (4) Java man.
4. A *race* has the folowing in common: (1) religion, (2) language, (3) nationality, (4) gene pool.
5. If the name given a species has the word root "pithecus" in it, the animal is thought to have been (1) a human, (2) an ape, (3) from southern regions, (4) delicate in appearance.

Unit 6 Evolution

Portfolio Project

Make a time line of evolution using the geologic time scale. Show the different stages of life forms that have arisen and gone extinct on earth. Indicate ancestors and descendants of each life form, if known, that you depict on your time line. Your depiction of the various life forms may be based on illustrations or photos of fossils that scientists have discovered.

UNIT SEVEN ENVIRONMENT

In this book, you have studied the living things that inhabit our planet. All the different species of plants, animals, and other life forms are interconnected with one another in a complex web of life. In addition, organisms interact with the earth itself—the atmosphere, the soil, and bodies of water. All the materials that are needed for life are found in our environment and are reused again and again. The only item that is added to the system daily is energy in the form of sunlight. Because the earth is a system with only solar energy added from outside, our planet has been compared to a spaceship that gets its energy from solar cells.

Just as none of you would be able to manage a spaceship without training, you cannot understand Spaceship Earth with its many interacting systems without training. You can consider this unit your Spaceship Earth Training Manual. You have studied the living things that inhabit the planet. These species can be compared to the pieces of a jigsaw puzzle. This training manual will show you how those pieces fit together in the biosphere—the part of earth that contains and sustains life. With the information you learn here, you should be able to understand the earth and its living things more fully, and thus be able to make better decisions about how we should care for our planet.

Chapter 25 Ecology

We are confronted today with many problems that threaten our natural environment. These problems can be solved only if we understand the complexity of that environment. *Ecology* is the branch of science that studies the environment—what it consists of and how it works. The word ecology is derived from two Greek words that mean "the study of our house." The environment is "our house," so ecology is the study of the environment. This science concerns the living and nonliving things around us as well as the many interactions that occur in the living systems that exist on our planet. A person who studies ecology is called an *ecologist*.

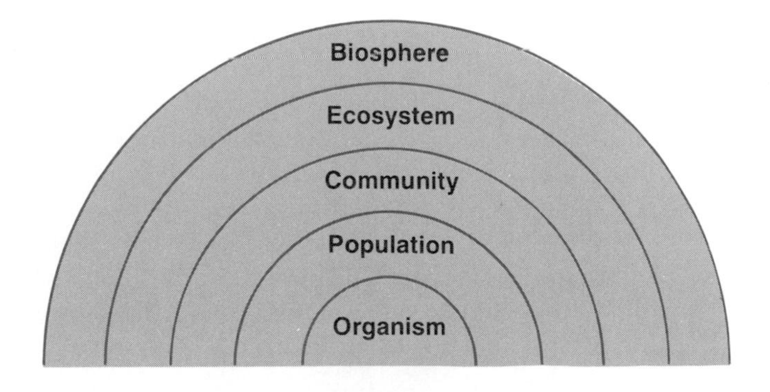

Fig. 25–1. Levels of ecological organization.

A

Ecological Organization

So far you have studied organisms and the way in which they are organized into cells, tissues, organs, and systems. Biological organization does not stop with organisms, but continues with larger categories that are studied in the field of ecology. Ecologists have identified four levels of ecological organization beyond the organism level. They are the population, the community, the ecosystem, and the biosphere.

A *population* is all the members of one species in a given area at a particular time. All the moose in the Adirondack Mountains during the summer make up a population. All the birds in New York do not make up a population because they include many different species. All the striped bass in the Hudson River make up another population. Another example of a population of organisms is all the humans in New York City.

In a given area, there are many different kinds of living things, so there are many populations. All of these populations make up an ecological *community* by interacting with one another. The community of organisms in Lake Ontario includes populations of organisms such as algae and different kinds of fish, while the community in the Catskill Mountains contains populations of trees, mice, deer, and other forest organisms.

The members of the community are as dependent on the nonliving environment around them as they are on the other members of the community. The community plus this physical environment constitutes an *ecosystem*. The term ecosystem refers not only to all the living and nonliving things, but also to the many interactions that occur between these components. The two most important types of interactions in an ecosystem are those involving the flow of energy through living things and the cycling of materials through both the living things and the physical environment. These and certain other ecosystem interactions will be discussed later in the chapter.

Natural ecosystem boundaries are difficult to determine because ecosystems tend to overlap and blend into one another. A pond is an easily defined ecosystem, yet it interacts with the soil and with the organisms of the surrounding ecosystems that come to drink from it or to catch food. A marsh, a forest, and a meadow can each be considered an ecosystem. A farm field is also an ecosystem, one that is largely influenced by humans. A balanced aquarium that can sustain itself is actually a small, simple ecosystem. Natural ecosystems tend to be large and complex, and they overlap and interact with other ecosystems.

The largest level of organization on earth is the *biosphere*. The biosphere includes all the earth's ecosystems interacting with each other. This includes all areas on earth in which living things exist, from the depths of the ocean and the ground where organisms burrow to the tops of mountains and the heights of the atmosphere where birds and insects may fly. In relation to the entire earth, the biosphere is a thin zone of life around the planet, somewhat comparable to the leather cover on a baseball.

For many years, ecologists have concentrated their studies on the population, community, and ecosystem levels of organization. The biosphere is so large and complex that it is difficult to study. In recent years, however, problems such as acid rain and depletion of the earth's ozone layer (see Chapter 26) have forced ecologists to study the biosphere level more intensely.

Population Ecology

We have defined a *population* as all the members of one species in a given area at a particular time. Most people think of a number when they think of population. The number of organisms is just one characteristic used to describe a population. Other characteristics of a population include population density and growth rate.

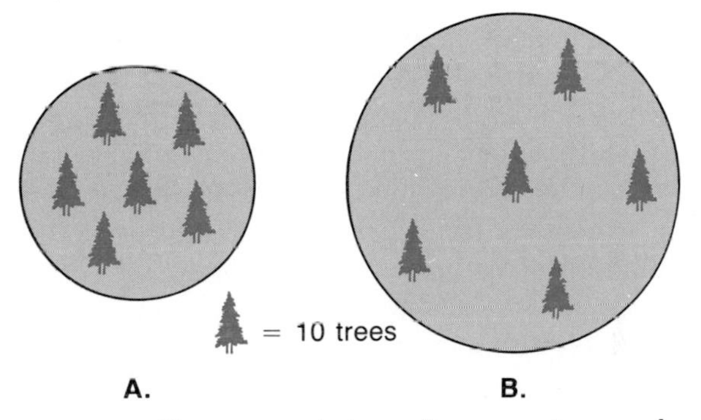

Fig. 25–2. Different populations of one species may have different densities. In which area is the population more dense, A or B?

The size of a population is an important population characteristic. It is of special importance when a species becomes endangered or when a species becomes too abundant. With too few lynx in New York's mountains, people have decided to release more of them in the Adirondacks. With too many gypsy moth caterpillars in our forests, we risk losing many trees whose leaves get eaten. The existence of too few California condors has prompted scientists to capture the entire population of these birds and breed them in captivity to prevent the species' extinction.

Size alone is not very informative in studying most populations. The *density*, or number of organisms per given area, is more informative. One thousand grizzly bears may seem like a large population until you realize that the bears are spread over several hundred million acres in the Rocky Mountain states. Densities are usually stated in number of organisms per square mile or acre (hectare in metric). Density data may give information concerning the chances of reproduction occurring, or of the availability of nest sites or feeding areas. All of these factors, in turn, influence the future size and density of that population. In other words, they influence the growth rate.

Population Growth. The *growth rate* of a population is the change in size of the population over a period of time. A population's growth rate may be positive (increasing the size of the population), negative (decreasing the size), or zero (indicating a stable population whose size is not changing). Four factors contribute to the population growth rate. They are birth rate, death rate, immigration, and emigration.

Birth rate is the rate at which individuals are being added to the population by reproduction. Death rate is the rate at which individuals are being lost from the population through death.

Movement of organisms from area to area is another factor affecting growth in many populations. The movement of organisms into an area of a population, called immigration, will contribute to the growth rate by increasing the size of the population. The movement of individuals out of the area, called emigration, will decrease the growth rate. The growth rate can be calculated by adding the birth and immigration rates and subtracting the death and emigration rates.

Populations are affected very much by the availability of food, water, shelter, nesting sites, and space. The members of a population compete for these resources, and this competition leads us to the conclusion that there is a limit to the size of any population that can be sustained in a given area. The maximum size of a population that can be sustained in an area over a long period of time is that area's *carrying capacity.* The food supply is usually the factor that determines the carrying capacity for a population of animals in a given area.

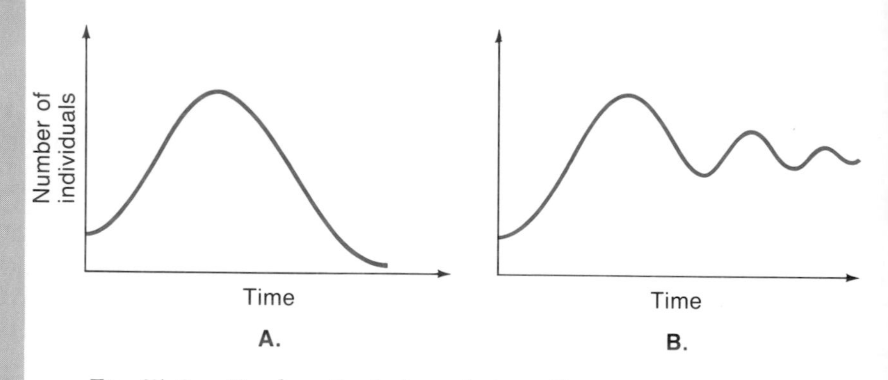

Fig. 25–3. Two hypothetical populations of bacteria in separate Petri dishes: In A, the starting food supply is used up, and no more is provided. In B, a food supply remains available.

An environmental condition that limits the growth of a population is called a *limiting factor.* Availability of food or nest sites, predation, temperature, rainfall, or amount of nutrients in the soil or water are all examples of potential limiting factors. The size of a population of bacteria living in a petri dish is limited by the amount of food in the dish. When first introduced to the dish, the population begins to grow rapidly, but then it levels off and eventually decreases as the food is used up. If nutrients are added to the dish, the bacterial population may be sustained.

B

The Ecosystem

Populations interact with their physical environment as well as with other populations. In order to better understand the way all the components of the environment work together, it is necessary to study ecosystems. An *ecosystem* is all the living things (the community) and the physical environment interacting in a self-sustaining relationship. First we will look at the components that make up an ecosystem, then we will study the ways in which they interact.

Ecosystem Components

The components that make up an ecosystem can be divided into two major categories: living and nonliving. Living things are called biotic factors, while nonliving things in the physical environment are abiotic factors.

Biotic Factors

Biotic factors are the living organisms in an ecosystem. In Chapter 2, you learned how organisms are classified into kingdoms and phyla. Ecologists classify organisms according to their role in the ecosystem. Ecologists have defined three major roles in ecosystems: producer, consumer, and decomposer.

Producers are organisms that can make their own food from simple substances. Green plants and algae are the main producers in most ecosystems. They contain chlorophyll and can perform photosynthesis. In this process, simple abiotic substances (carbon dioxide and water) are converted to complex food molecules that are used by the plants and directly or indirectly by all other organisms. Sunlight is the energy source for photosynthesis. Since producers can make their own food, they are called *autotrophs* (meaning self-feeders).

The total amount of photosynthesis carried out by the producers in an ecosystem is called the *productivity* of that ecosystem. Deserts and deep oceans have low productivity, while tropical rain forests and estuaries have very high productivity levels.

While most producers perform photosynthesis, a few autotrophic bacteria perform a similar process called chemosynthesis. They too produce food molecules from simple abiotic substances, but the energy source for this process is chemical energy. This process was known to occur but thought to be unimportant to ecosystems until deep-water ecosystems were discovered in the late 1970s. These ecosystems form around volcanic vents in the sea floor, and chemosynthesis is vital for their survival because sunlight cannot penetrate to these depths. Chemosynthetic bacteria are the producers, and an array of tube worms, clams, crabs, and small fish survive on the food produced by these bacteria.

Many organisms cannot produce their own food and must rely directly or indirectly on producers to supply them with nutrients. Organisms that rely on other organisms for food are called *heterotrophs* (meaning other feeders). There are two kinds of heterotrophs in ecosystems: consumers and decomposers.

Consumers are animals or microscopic organisms that feed on other organisms. Consumers are further classified according to what they eat. Consumers that eat producers are called *herbivores*. Examples of herbivores are cows and caterpillars. Herbivores are also called first-level consumers. A consumer that eats other consumers is called a *carnivore*. Although carnivore means "flesh eater," we can use this term in ecology to refer to all animals that eat other animals, even if they are not actually eating flesh. Examples of carnivores are spiders and sharks. Scavengers are animals that eat dead and decaying animal matter. Some animals, such as the raccoon and the black bear, eat both producers and other consumers. They are called *omnivores*. What kind of consumer are you?

The other category of heterotrophic organisms is the decomposers. *Decomposers* are organisms that consume dead organisms. Bacteria and fungi are the most common types of decomposers in ecosystems. Various

Fig. 25–4. An ecological consumer: This leaf-eating caterpillar functions as an herbivore in its ecosystem.

Fig. 25–5. This eastern bluebird has caught a caterpillar. In most ecosystems, some consumers eat other consumers.

types of worms and insect larvae are among other types of decomposers. These decomposers feed on dead organisms, bringing about decay. This process recycles the molecules of the dead organism, returning nutrients to the soil. The term *saprophyte* is sometimes used to describe the plant decomposers such as mushrooms.

biotic Factors

Abiotic factors in an ecosystem include any matter, energy, or characteristic of the physical environment that is not living. Substances like air, water, rocks, and minerals are part of the abiotic environment. Organisms often use some or all of these substances, making them part of the living environment. Oxygen, carbon dioxide, water, and nitrogen are examples of substances that move between both the physical environment and the biotic community. Such substances move in cycles that will be discussed later in this chapter.

Climate. Climate is another abiotic factor that is important to ecosystems. Climate includes amount of rainfall and sunlight and the temperature range of the region.

Rainfall helps to determine the amount of moisture available to organisms. Along with temperature, amount of water available is one of the major factors that influence the types of organisms that can survive in an ecosystem. Plants that live in the desert have adaptations for preventing water loss, such as spines instead of broad leaves. They also have large root systems to reach water and absorb it quickly after an infrequent rain. The kangaroo rat excretes very little water as a waste and is able to survive without drinking by using the water produced by cellular respiration (oxidation of food). Most desert animals rest underground or in the shade during the hottest part of the day to avoid overheating and water loss.

Temperature has an enormous impact on the types of organisms that can live in an ecosystem. Ectothermic (cold-blooded) animals do not have a constant body temperature. Their temperature varies with the temperature of their environment, so they have difficulty surviving in extremely cold climates. There are few reptiles and amphibians in the Arctic. Most arctic animals are endothermic (warm-blooded). They maintain a constant body temperature with heat generated from within their bodies. They have thick coats of fur or feathers and insulating layers of fat. Many migrate to warmer climates for the winter.

Availability and intensity of sunlight is another abiotic factor that affects organisms. Plants capture the energy in sunlight to make food. Light penetrates less than 200 meters into the ocean, so algae cannot survive at greater depths. The floor of a mature forest receives only a small amount of sunlight because of the dense canopy of leaves, so relatively few plants survive there. The leaves of trees are arranged for maximum light absorption, and the trees compete for space in the canopy so they can have a large share of direct sunlight.

The photoperiod, or amount of light per day, is a factor relating to light that has profound effects on an ecosystem. Diminishing day length in autumn is the primary cause of the changes of leaf coloration and a major factor in stimulating animal migration. Reproduction is triggered in many animals by the changing length of the photoperiod in different seasons.

Fig. 25–6. Sunlight in a tropical forest: the treetops are sunlit, but they make dense shade at ground level.

The geology of a region also has an impact on the ecosystem. The type of soil present in an ecosystem will help determine the types of plants that can survive, which in turn affects the animals. The climate of the northeastern U.S. generally supports a deciduous forest, but the sandy soils of the Long Island Pine Barrens help to create a different kind of ecosystem. The geology of the surrounding area also has a great influence on aquatic ecosystems. The pH of the water and its ability to resist acid rain is directly related to the amount of natural limestone in the surrounding soil.

Even the topography, or shape of the land, affects organisms. Deep ravines with much water and little sunlight will support a stand of hemlock trees, while the surrounding areas may have few hemlocks. Altitude, because it affects temperature, also influences ecosystems. Some mountains in the Adirondacks have ecosystems near their peaks that are similar to those found in northern Canada and the Arctic.

Ecosystem Interactions

There are numerous relationships and interactions occurring between the abiotic and biotic components of an ecosystem. In this section, we will discuss the major interactions of energy flow along with other ecosystem interactions.

Energy Flow

Just as all organisms require energy to stay alive, ecosystems need a flow of energy to be self-sustaining. Sunlight provides the energy for most ecosystems, so it must be added to an ecosystem regularly to sustain it. Energy does not recycle within any ecosystem.

The fuel that provides energy for living organisms is food. Producers capture sunlight and use it to make food molecules through photosynthesis. This is the first step in the path of energy flow in an ecosystem. Producers use some of this food to meet their own energy requirements. This food energy is consumed during cellular respiration. The remainder is used for growth or stored for later use. Heterotrophs (consumers and decomposers) cannot trap sunlight energy to make food, so they are dependent on producers for their food supply.

Food chain. The pathway in which energy flows from organism to organism is called a *food chain*. Here are some examples of food chains:

Algae ⟶ Zooplankton ⟶ Krill ⟶ Blue Whale
Grass ⟶ Grasshopper ⟶ Frog ⟶ Snake ⟶ Hawk
Grass ⟶ Cow ⟶ Human

The general pattern of a food chain is always the same. Sunlight provides a producer with energy. Energy trapped by the producer then flows to successive consumers. Though decomposers are not shown in the food chains above, it is understood that some energy flows to the decomposers when any organism dies. Here is a generalized food chain:

Producer ⟶ Consumer 1 ⟶ Consumer 2 ⟶ Decomposer

With this general pattern, you can understand the role of any organism in a food chain, even if you do not know what that organism is. For example, in the food chain

Grass ⟶ Oryx ⟶ Lion

you may not know what an oryx looks like, but you know it grazes on grass and is food for lions.

Pyramid of Energy. Each step in the food chain represents a transfer of energy. Consumers do not eat all the new growth built by plant photosynthesis, because some of it is always unavailable to them. Part of the material they do consume is not digested, and part is burned during respiration to meet their basic energy needs. Only a fraction of the material consumed provides energy for growth and reproduction. Energy transfer from one group of consumers to a higher group of consumers gives similar results.

These relationships tell us that there is a step-like decrease in energy as one moves along the food chain from producer to the last consumer. The energy burned up in respiration is lost to the ecosystem. Only the energy used for growth and reproduction can be harvested by other organisms. Therefore each level of consumers contains less energy than the level just below it.

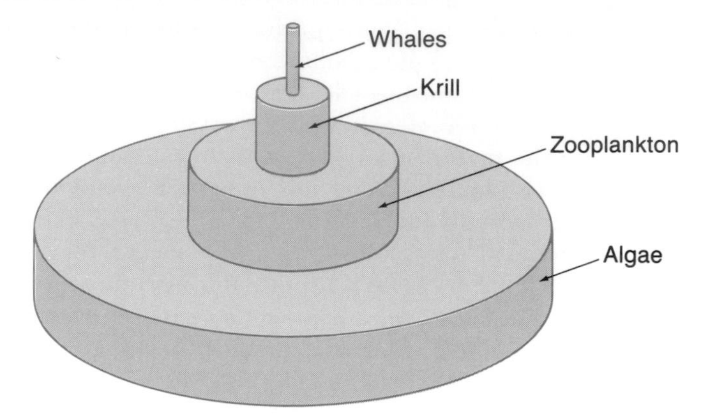

Fig. 25–7. A pyramid of energy: Each level represents the amount of energy contained in the bodies of the organisms.

A diagram of the amount of energy stored at each feeding level looks like a pyramid. The pyramid of energy diagram shows that there is far more energy stored in the algae of this ecosystem than in the whales.

Since a feeding level with more energy generally supports a greater number of organisms, a pyramid of energy can also represent a pyramid of numbers. There must be more krill than whales in Fig. 25–7, or the whales would starve. Sometimes, though, a pyramid of numbers may look upside down. For example, a tree (one organism) can support many insects that feed on it because the tree is so large. In this case a pyramid of *biomass* looks more like the energy pyramid than does a pyramid of numbers. The biomass (amount of organic matter) of the tree is larger than the total biomass of all the insects feeding on it.

Some people believe or say that we could feed more of the world's hungry humans if we did not feed so much grain to livestock, and then eat

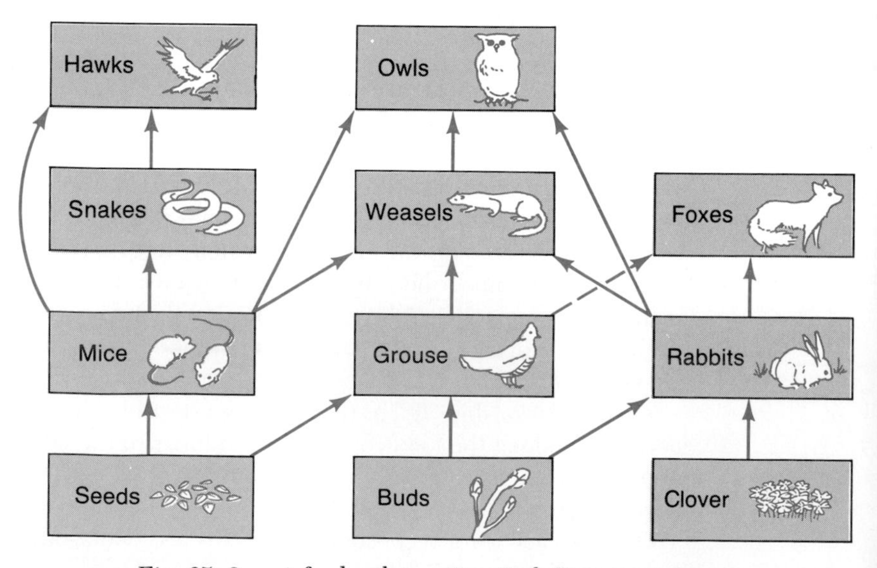

Fig. 25–8. A food web in a New York State environment.

the livestock. They point out that the world's human population could obtain more total food energy directly from the world's grain crops than from eating consumer organisms.

Food webs. So far we have discussed feeding relationships as simple food chains. Food chains are useful models, especially for studying energy-flow relationships, but they are not accurate representations of the true feeding relationships in an ecosystem. In reality, each organism is part of several or many interconnected food chains. This complex array of interconnected food chains is called a food web.

The arrows in a food web diagram represent the flow of energy just as they do in a food chain. You can pick out individual food chains within the food web (Fig. 25–8) by following the arrows from a producer to the various consumer levels.

Symbiosis and Competition

Another form of ecosystem interaction is the way different species of organisms relate to each other in the environment. They may form cooperative relationships that help one another. Some of these relationships benefit one species at the expense of others. And sometimes the relationship is one of competition.

Competition. *Competition* means that two or more organisms are striving for the same limited resource. Organisms compete with members of their own species for resources such as food, water, territory, and mates. Two white oak trees growing next to each other in a forest may compete for nutrients and water from the soil, and for sunlight in the forest canopy. Organisms also compete with members of other species, especially for food or nest sites. Competition for nest sites between bluebirds and starlings is thought to have reduced bluebird populations in the 1900s. A large effort to supply bluebirds with nest sites by building nest boxes has helped the native bluebird population to recover.

Symbiosis. Many organisms are involved in relationships with members of other species in which at least one of the two benefits from the arrangement. These interactions are called *symbiotic relationships.* The word symbiosis means living together. In a symbiotic relationship, organisms of two species are living in close association with each other.

Mutualism is a kind of symbiotic relationship in which both species benefit. Bees obtain food from flowers and in turn pollinate the flowers to help them reproduce. Both bees and flowers benefit in this mutualistic relationship. Termites lack the enzymes to digest the woody materials they eat. A species of protist that lives in termite stomachs can digest the wood. Both benefit because they both get nourishment when the termite chews up the wood and the protist digests it.

In *commensalism*, one organism benefits while the other is unaffected. Orchids growing on trees in tropical rain forests demonstrate commensalism. The orchid benefits by finding a place to grow. The tree is not affected since the orchid takes nothing from the tree. It gets its nutrients directly from the air around it.

Parasitism is another symbiotic relationship. In this relationship, one organism, the parasite, takes its nourishment directly from a living host. The parasite benefits while the host is harmed. Ticks, fleas, and leeches

Fig. 25–9. Two lions chase a very young gnu. This is an interaction of predators and prey.

are examples of parasites that live on the outside of their host. Most parasites live within their hosts. Tapeworms live in their hosts' intestines. Many types of worms, fungi, and microorganisms are internal parasites.

Predation. One last interaction is *predation*. In predation, one organism kills and eats another. Wolves feeding on caribou is an example of predation. The wolf is the predator and the caribou is the prey species. It is easy to see that the wolf benefits and the individual caribou that is eaten is harmed. Yet the caribou herd benefits because predation is a form of natural selection. The weak or diseased caribou will be more easily captured than strong, healthy ones, so predation removes most of the weaker individuals. In some cases, predation may also sometimes prevent overpopulation of the prey species.

C

Material Cycles

While energy that flows through an ecosystem is lost, materials are recycled. Every use of a substance by a living organism is part of a cycle of that substance. The substance passes through organisms by way of the food chain, but its flow is not just one way as is the case with energy. Materials are used again and again. The same atoms of carbon, hydrogen, and oxygen that are cycling through the biosphere today were present at the time of the dinosaurs (and even before). It is possible that an oxygen molecule you just breathed in was once part of a stegosaurus.

Decomposer organisms are essential to material cycles. Materials would stay locked up in dead organisms if decomposers did not break them down. Decomposers also help break down the waste products of animals. The biosphere does not need any landfills because in nature there is no waste. Everything is recycled.

The Water Cycle

Perhaps the most familiar material cycle is the water cycle. Water is essential to all living things and is also abundant in our environment. In the environment, most water is in liquid form in oceans, rivers, lakes, and streams. Water can also be found underground. In addition, water can exist as a gas in the atmosphere, or as ice.

Most of the water on earth is in the oceans, so we will begin tracing the

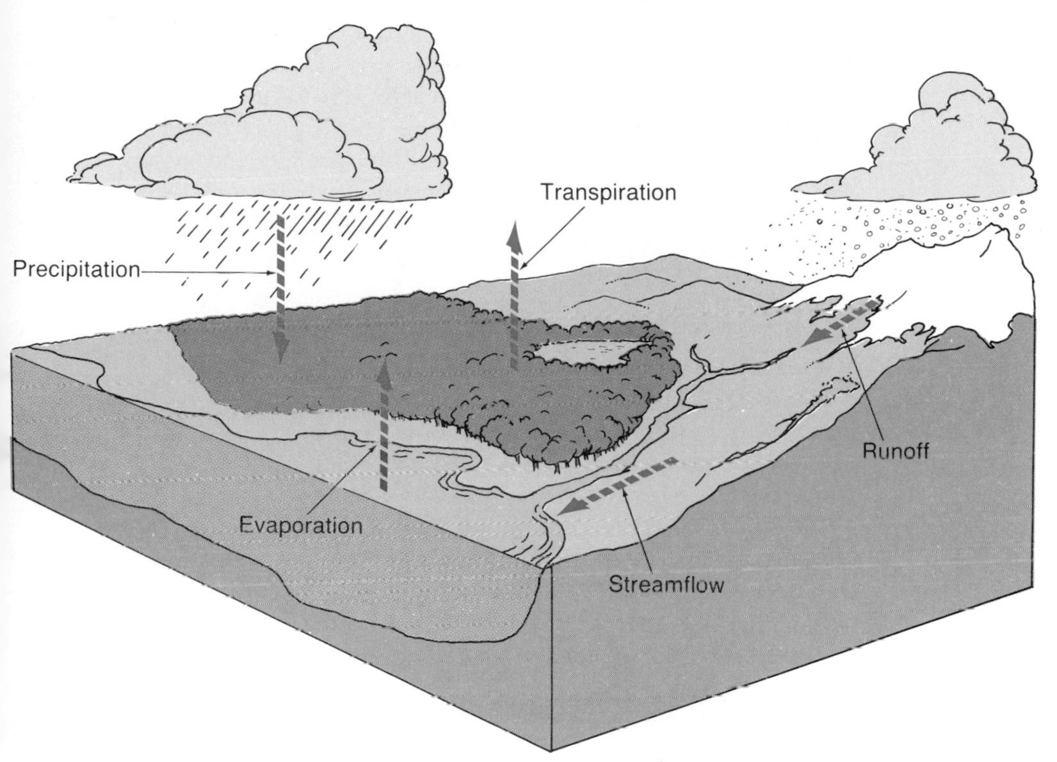

Fig. 25-10. The water cycle.

water cycle there. Sunlight supplies the energy to evaporate water from the oceans. *Evaporation* is changing of a substance from a liquid to a gas, or vapor. Through evaporation, ocean water is changed to water vapor in the atmosphere. This moisture is responsible for the formation of clouds when the atmospheric water vapor condenses, or changes from a gas back to a liquid. Eventually clouds produce precipitation in the form of rain, snow, or sleet.

Some precipitation falls back into the ocean. If the water falls on land, it can enter many other parts of the water cycle. On land it can become runoff and flow into lakes and streams. Animals or plants can take in this water. Some of it is excreted (given off as a waste product) from organisms. This water returns to the physical environment to continue through the cycle.

Water that falls on soil may soak in to become groundwater or may be taken up by the roots of plants. Plants take in large quantities of water and much of it moves right through the plant and escapes from the leaves. This process, called transpiration, releases water back into the atmosphere. Some of the water used in the process of photosynthesis becomes part of molecules made by the plant.

All water eventually returns to the oceans, even though it may take thousands of years. This water is then ready to begin a new journey through the water cycle. You should have noticed from this example that material cycles are not simple circles. They are complex pathways with many alternate routes, but the material eventually does recycle.

Other material cycles share some characteristics with the water cycle. Like the ocean in the water cycle, there is generally a large reservoir of the material. There is also a pool of the material that is cycling through both the physical environment and the living organisms of the biosphere. In addition, energy is needed to drive the cycle. Sunlight energy supplies the power to run the water cycle. Wind energy also helps move water around the atmosphere. Directly or indirectly, sunlight provides most of the energy required to power material cycles.

The Carbon Cycle

We can begin this cycle with a producer performing photosynthesis. A plant absorbs water from the soil and carbon dioxide from the atmosphere and uses them as the raw materials for making sugar molecules in photosynthesis. Those sugar molecules, containing carbon, hydrogen, and oxygen, are used as food by the plant, or are converted to other molecules needed for growth or reproduction. The plant gives off oxygen to the atmosphere as a by-product.

The cycles of carbon and oxygen are intertwined by the processes of photosynthesis and respiration. Carbon is present in the atmosphere in carbon dioxide. Oxygen is an abundant gas, making up nearly 20 percent of the atmosphere. It is also part of carbon dioxide and water.

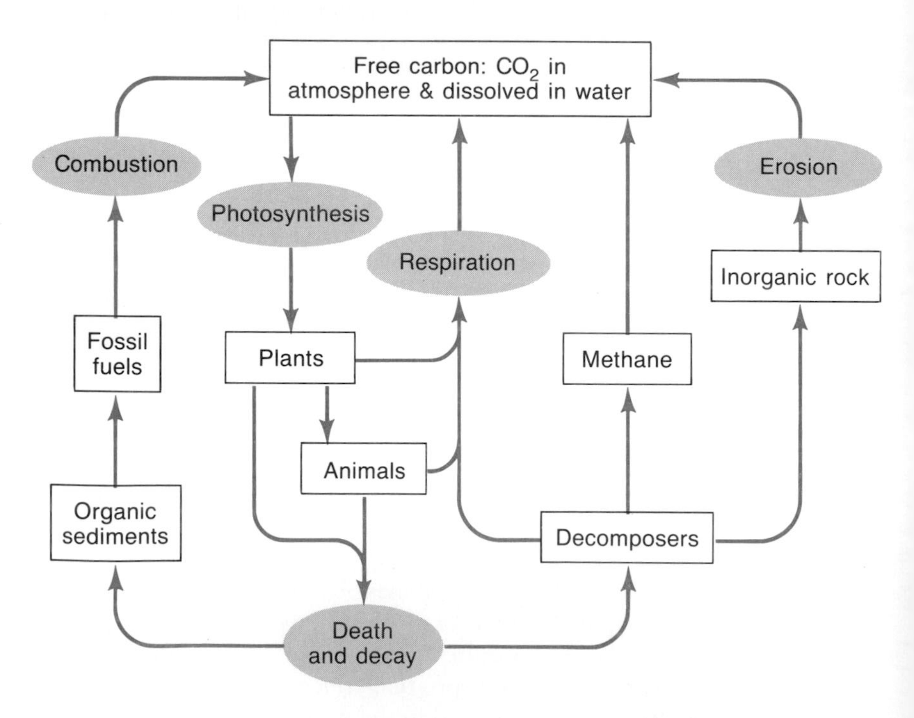

Fig. 25–11. The carbon cycle: Different pathways require very different amounts of time. The cycle from CO_2 to plants and back may take only a day; the cycle from CO_2 to fossil fuel and back requires millions of years.

In the process of respiration, organisms take in oxygen and use it to break down food molecules and release energy. An animal may breathe in oxygen and eat a plant. The animal uses those plant molecules containing carbon and oxygen as food, and, to release energy, combines them with the oxygen it has breathed in. Carbon dioxide and water are the waste products given off. Figure 25-11 shows the many pathways of the carbon cycle.

The Nitrogen Cycle One of the most complex cycles in the biosphere is the nitrogen cycle. Nitrogen is an important element in living organisms because it is needed to build proteins, nucleic acids, and certain other vital substances. Nitrogen is the most abundant gas in the atmosphere, accounting for nearly 80 percent of the air we breathe. Yet this large reservoir of nitrogen is not useful to most plants and animals. It must be converted to other compounds of nitrogen before it can be used. While decomposers and other bacteria are involved in all material cycles, they play a starring role in the nitrogen cycle.

Though plants and animals cannot use atmospheric nitrogen directly, certain kinds of bacteria can convert nitrogen gas to nitrates in the soil. This process is called nitrogen fixation. Some of these bacteria live freely in the soil. Others live on the roots of legumes (plants such as clover, peas, and soybeans), and fix large amounts of nitrogen in the soil. It is good to rotate legumes with other kinds of crops, since legumes restore the nitrogen supply in the soil. Lightning also converts some atmospheric nitrogen to nitrates.

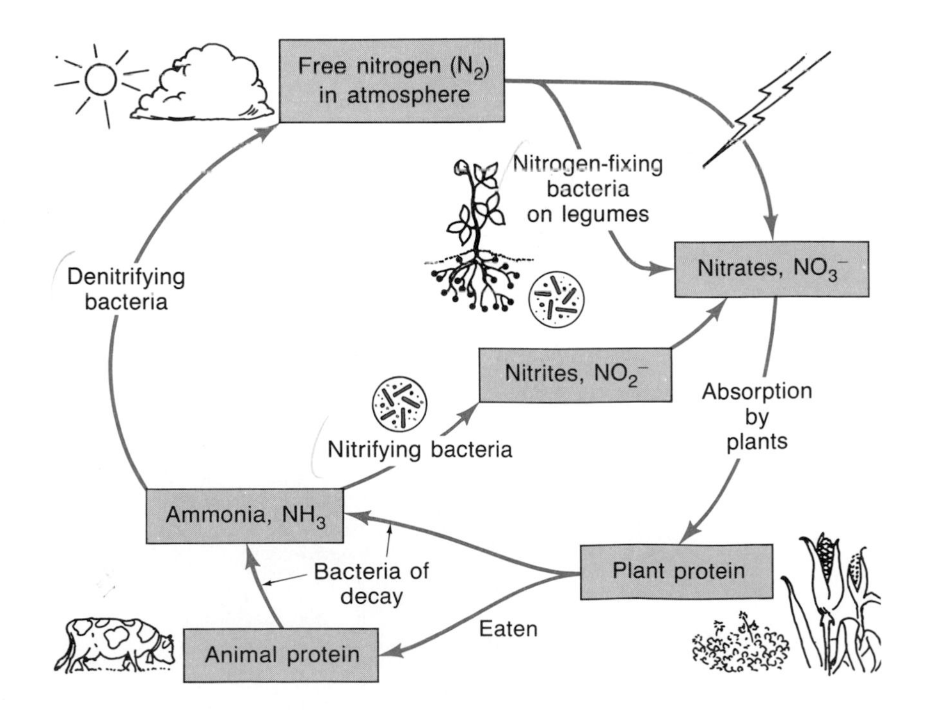

Fig. 25–12. The nitrogen cycle.

Nitrates are taken up by plants and used to build proteins. Animals eat the plants and use the plant proteins to build their own proteins. Some nitrates also dissolve in water and become nutrients in aquatic food chains. As plants and animals die, decomposers recycle the nitrogen, returning it to the soil as ammonia, which can be converted once again to nitrates. In addition, animals excrete large amounts of nitrogen in their waste products. These also reenter the soil and can enter the food web again when absorbed by plants. Completing the cycle are denitrifying bacteria, which can convert soil nitrates back to atmospheric nitrogen.

(D)

Ecosystem Change

An important characteristic of ecosystems is their diversity, or variety, of species. It has long been assumed that the greater the diversity of an ecosystem, the more stable the ecosystem would be. Stability here is defined as the ability to resist damage from a natural problem such as an outbreak of a disease within that ecosystem. It is not certain that greater diversity always leads to greater stability. It may be that a stable physical environment is good for the development of a diverse ecosystem.

A diverse, natural forest can resist catastrophic change better than a tree plantation of one species can. Eastern U.S. forests were attacked by chestnut blight in the last century. Almost every living chestnut tree in the eastern forests was killed. Even though the chestnut was one of the most common trees, the forests themselves were not destroyed, since there were many other kinds of trees that were not affected by the blight. A tree plantation of just one species would be completely wiped out by a disease of that species. As a result, pesticides are often used to prevent diseases on tree plantations.

Farming usually replaces natural, diverse ecosystems with large fields

Fig. 25–13. Succession on land: A meadow, at far left, is gradually changing to forest (far right) as new plants invade, grow, and take over.

of only one or a few crops. The wheat fields of Kansas and corn fields of Iowa are not diverse and are therefore unstable. Farmers must provide care for them all the time. Large amounts of pesticides and fertilizer are often used on such farms.

Succession

Certain kinds of natural events destroy even diverse ecosystems and set the stage for the development of new ecosystems. Fires, floods, and volcanic eruptions may destroy ecosystems. Logging and clearing of fields for farming are among the human activities that destroy existing ecosystems. Each of these events will be followed by the development of a new ecosystem to take the place of the one that is destroyed.

The development of a new ecosystem follows a pattern called ecological *succession*. In the process of succession, one biotic community is gradually replaced by another, then another, until a final, stable community develops. This final community is called the *climax community*, and it will remain in place until a human or natural disturbance destroys it. At that time, succession will begin again.

The kind of climax community that develops depends on abiotic factors such as climate and soil type. In New York and the other northeastern states, the climax community on land is usually a deciduous forest of trees such as oaks, maples, and birches. A field of grass left untended for many years would change to a wild meadow and then become wooded. Ponds also undergo succession, eventually filling in with sediment and becoming a terrestrial ecosystem.

Succession takes a long time to reach the climax community stage. An abandoned farm is one of the best places to observe the slow but steady

Fig. 25–14. This scene near the volcano Mount St. Helens in Washington shows that plants are growing in an area where the 1980 eruption killed all the living organisms.

process of succession. A typical pattern of succession on an abandoned farm in New York would proceed from grasses to shrubs to small, deciduous trees and conifers, to the climax forest of oaks and other hardwoods. This process would probably take well over 100 years to reach the stable, climax forest. Some of the ancient forests of the Pacific Northwest are up to 800 years old.

It is also possible to observe succession when a volcanic eruption destroys an ecosystem, soil and all, or when a volcanic eruption forms a new island in the ocean. *Pioneer organisms* such as lichens are the first to grow in such an area. These lichens begin to produce a soil and prepare the way for other organisms such as mosses. No one really knows how long this process takes, but studies at Mount St. Helens in Washington State have surprised ecologists. The volcano erupted in 1980, and already a community is developing. Part of the area has been protected as an ecological study zone for research on succession.

(E)

The Biosphere—Biomes

The abiotic factors in a given area of the biosphere determine what type of producers and consumers make up the climax community of an area. Over large expanses of the earth, similar climax communities develop in areas with similar physical conditions. These large geographic areas with similar climax communities are called *biomes*.

The most important factors determining the major plant types in a land biome are photoperiod, rainfall, and temperature. Extremely cold temperatures and short growing seasons will prevent the growth of trees. Lack of rainfall will have the same effect. Broad-leaved trees grow in tropical or temperate (four-season) climates, while conifers grow in colder regions. Altitude has the same effect as latitude. Traveling north, you would notice a change from deciduous to coniferous trees, then to a scrubby, treeless vegetation. Climbing a high mountain you would pass through the same zones.

Terrestrial (Land) Biomes

The Tundra. The tundra is a treeless biome located in or near the arctic regions of the biosphere. It is a biome of cold temperatures and little rainfall. Winters are long, dark, and very cold. Summers are cool and short, although in parts of the tundra there are 24 hours of daylight in this season. Only the top few inches of soil thaw during the brief summer. Underneath is a layer of permanently frozen ground called permafrost. Mosses, lichens, and grasses are the main plants here. Animals include caribou, musk oxen, wolves, and arctic hares. In summer, many birds migrate to the tundra to breed.

Forest Biomes. Just south of the tundra and covering much of Canada is the taiga, or northern coniferous forest. Spruce and fir trees are the largest producers. Among animals, moose, pine martens, red squirrels, and beavers are typical of this biome. Geese and other waterfowl breed in the many lakes of the taiga. The waterfowl and most of the small birds of the forest migrate south for the winter.

A large part of the eastern United States was once covered by a temperate deciduous forest. Although much of it is gone, this is the natural biome of this part of North America. In the deciduous forest biome, winters are cold and summers are hot. There is a moderate amount of rainfall, so trees can grow well here. The trees are deciduous, which means they lose their leaves, an adaptation for surviving the winter. Before they fall, the leaves take on a beautiful array of colors in autumn.

There is a greater diversity of trees in the temperate deciduous forest than in the taiga. Oaks, maples, beeches, and birches are among the more abundant. A few conifers are scattered through the forest as well. White-tailed deer, black bear, raccoons, foxes, rabbits, and gray squirrels are typical animals. Songbirds are abundant, although some migrate south in winter. The climate here is also warm enough to support some ectothermic (cold-blooded) reptiles and amphibians.

In the tropics, the most diverse of all terrestrial forest biomes exists. This biome is called the tropical rain forest. The predominant plants are broad-leaved trees that thrive on abundant rainfall and constantly warm temperatures. Many vines also grow in this forest. Animal life abounds. There are more kinds of birds found in some tropical forest ecosystems than in all of North America. The tropical rain forests cover less than 7 percent of the earth, but more than half of all the different species on earth

Fig. 25–15. The tropical rain forest biome: The leaves of tall trees and climbing vines blot out the sky and shade the ground all year.

live in this biome. The number of amphibians, reptiles, and insects is staggering. You can see why there is so much concern today about saving the rain forests from destruction.

Grasslands and Deserts. In temperate regions where there is not enough rainfall to support the growth of trees, grasslands or deserts develop. Grasslands cover much of the central part of the U.S. and southern Canada. These grasslands are ideal for farming, so little remains of the natural biome. Growing here is a diversity of grasses and herbs that are adapted to drought and fire, which are common in natural grasslands. Bison, pronghorn antelopes, and prairie dogs are among the characteristic mammals. Today, wheat and corn, cattle and sheep have replaced the natural species.

Fig. 25–16. The temperate grassland biome: In North America, herds of bison once roamed vast prairies.

A desert biome develops in regions of extremely low annual rainfall. Temperatures are often hot during the day and cool at night. Some deserts are cold in winter. It is lack of rainfall, not temperature, that creates the desert biome. Various species of cactus, tough shrubs like sagebrush, and some scattered grasses make up the sparse vegetation of the desert. Some extremely dry deserts have almost no vegetation. Lizards, jackrabbits, and small rodents are among desert animals. They are active mainly at night.

Terrestrial Biomes			
Biome	**Characteristics**	**Climax Flora**	**Climax Fauna**
Tundra	permanently frozen subsoil	lichens, mosses, grasses	caribou
Taiga	long, severe winters; summers with thawing subsoil	conifers	moose, black bear
Temperate-Deciduous Forest	moderate precipitation; cold winters, warm summers	trees that shed leaves (deciduous trees)	gray squirrel, fox, deer
Tropical Forest	heavy rainfall; constant warmth	many varieties of broad-leaved plants	snakes, monkeys, leopards
Grassland	low total annual rainfall or uneven seasonal occurrence of rainfall	grasses	pronghorn antelope, prairie dog, bison
Desert	sparse rainfall; extreme daily temperature fluctuations	drought-resistant shrubs and succulent plants	kangaroo rat, lizards

Aquatic (Water) Biomes

Water covers more than 75 percent of the earth's surface. Water-covered parts of the biosphere are divided into two biomes: the marine, or saltwater, biome, and the freshwater biome.

Marine Biome. The oceans are the largest biome on earth. Ecologists divide the marine biome into the intertidal zone, estuaries, and the ocean. The *intertidal zone* is the shoreline area that is underwater at high tide, but exposed to air at low tide. Crabs, mussels, and barnacles live in this zone. These animals are adapted to exposure to air during the day and withstanding the force of the waves. Crabs burrow into sand and mussels and barnacles cling to rocks and have protective shells.

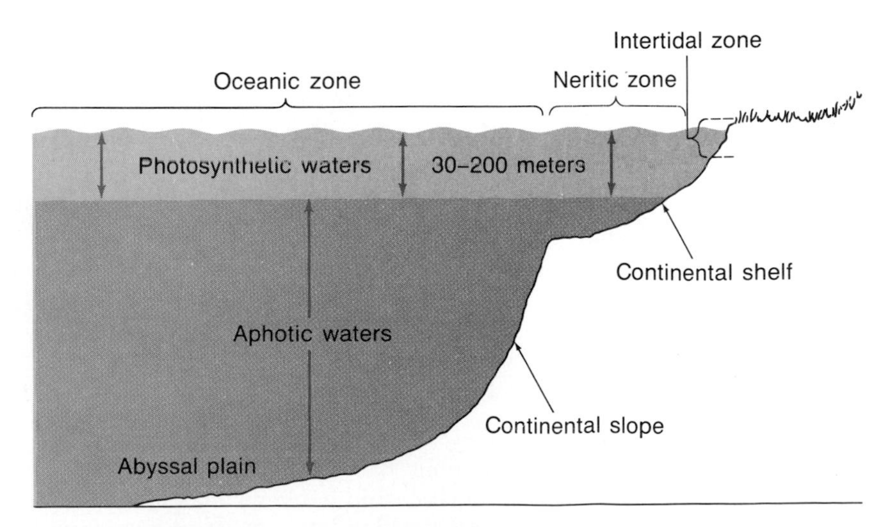

Fig. 25–17. Zones within the marine biome.

The ocean is divided into two zones. The *neritic zone* is the shallow ocean area near land. This is the part of the ocean where most commercial fish populations live, along with whales, dolphins, and sea turtles. The *oceanic zone* is the open ocean. Most of the deep parts of the oceanic zone have little life in them because sunlight does not penetrate more than about 200 meters below the ocean's surface. Algae can perform photosynthesis only near the surface. In both the neritic and oceanic zones, large numbers of floating microscopic organisms called *plankton* live near the surface. There are many different kinds of planktonic organisms. Floating algae are called phytoplankton (phyte = plant), and they are the producers in this biome. They are eaten by the microscopic animals, or zooplankton. Plankton is the basis of the food chain for all the ocean's larger creatures.

Perhaps the most critical part of the marine biome is its *estuaries*. An estuary is an arm of the ocean that extends to the mouth of a river. In an estuary, freshwater and saltwater mix. The waters in estuaries are rich in nutrients and are very productive. Estuaries are the breeding grounds for many of the ocean's fish. They are threatened by pollution from cities and industries that often grow up around them.

Freshwater Biome. The freshwater biome is made up of many smaller ecosystems. Lakes and ponds, rivers and streams are all part of the freshwater biome. One of the most important abiotic factors in freshwater biomes is the amount of oxygen dissolved in the water. Running water tends to have more oxygen than still water, and colder water has more than warm water. The amount of oxygen, along with the nutrients available, determines the life forms that live in a freshwater ecosystem. Trout, for example, need cool, clean water with much oxygen.

Nutrients are generally in short supply in aquatic biomes. This lack of nutrients is the limiting factor for the growth of algae. The existence of a limiting factor is good because rapid algal growth can choke off aquatic ecosystems, killing the fish and destroying the natural ecosystem. Human sewage and fertilizer runoff from farms add nutrients to the water and stimulate harmful explosions of algal growth.

Lakes and ponds have phyto- and zooplankton populations that form the basis of the food chain. Some plants, like water lilies, are rooted in the soil at the bottom of ponds or the shallow parts of lakes. Large rivers may also have plankton and plants in them. Small streams, however, depend mainly on leaves or other organic matter falling into them to supply nutrients for the ecosystem. Insect larvae feed on this decaying material and in turn provide food for crayfish and fish.

Reasoning Exercises

1. Define ecology.
2. Define ecosystem.
3. What is the relationship between a population and a community?
4. What is the relationship between a community and an ecosystem?
5. What is the relationship between the biosphere and an ecosystem?

6. What is the relationship between the biosphere and the earth?
7. Select any two different species of living organisms near your home and describe the differences between their populations.
8. What might be a limiting factor for each of the populations you describe in the previous question.
9. What is the difference between population density and population size?
10. Describe the difference between producers and consumers in an ecosystem.
11. Select two abiotic factors and describe how they affect living organisms.
12. What is the difference between ectothermic and endothermic animals?
13. What function is served by decomposers in a food web?
14. Why does the amount of energy in a food chain take the shape of a pyramid?
15. What is meant by "eating high on the pyramid of energy?"
16. What is the difference between symbiosis and competition?
17. Describe two examples of symbiotic relationships.
18. Describe a similarity between the water cycle and the nitrogen cycle.
19. Why doesn't a climax community normally change?
20. What is the difference between a biome and a climax community?
21. Select any two land biomes and describe the main differences between them.
22. Which ocean zone(s) produce the most food? Why is this so?
23. If a swarm of mosquitos bites a human to get blood for food, and a little brown bat eats mosquitos in the swarm, does this mean that the human and the bat are part of the same food chain? Why or why not?

Completion Questions

A

1. The study of the relationships between living things and their environment is called . . . . . .
2. All the organisms of the same species living together in a region are known as a(n) . . . . . .
3. Populations of different species in a given location constitute a(n) . . . . . .
4. Three characteristics of a population are . . . . . . , ... , and . . . . . .
5. The living communities of a region, together with the nonliving environment, constitute a(n) . . . . . .
6. Ecosystems are found in the earth's zone of life, also called the . . . . . .
7. Something in the environment that can prevent the growth of a particular population is called a(n) . . . . . .
8. Two factors that decrease the growth rate of a population are . . . . . . and . . . . . .
9. Two factors that increase the growth rate of a population are . . . . . . and . . . . . .
10. Population density can be expressed as . . . . . . per given area.

B

11. A photosynthetic plant in an ecosystem has the role of a(n) . . . . . .

12. In a food chain, a deer is known as a(n) . . . . . .
13. Bacteria act as . . . . . . in a food chain.
14. The entire group of organisms in a community through which food energy flows is called a(n) . . . . . .
15. A heterotrophic organism in an ecosystem has the role of a(n) . . . . . .
16. Two examples of abiotic factors in an ecosystem are . . . . . . and . . . . . .
17. A plant that uses dead organisms to provide nutrients is sometimes called a(n) . . . . . .
18. Animals that can eat both plants and animals are called . . . . . .
19. Most ecosystems derive their energy from . . . . . .
20. The role of humans in a food chain is that of a(n) . . . . . .
21. There is . . . . . . (more, less) stored energy in all of the secondary consumers of a community than in all of the producers.
22. The symbiotic relationship between a large tree and a small plant that lives on one of the tree limbs may be called . . . . . .
23. A fungus and an alga living together for each other's benefit have a symbiotic relationship called . . . . . .
24. The form of symbiosis in which one organism harms its host is called . . . . . .
25. The relationship between termites and protists in their digestive systems may be called . . . . . .

C

26. Most of the water in the biosphere is in . . . . . .
27. The biosphere's reservoir for nitrogen is . . . . . .
28. Nitrogen-fixing bacteria live in . . . . . . on the roots of plants in the group known as . . . . . .
29. An example of a plant with root nodules is . . . . . .
30. Denitrifying bacteria change the ammonia to . . . . . .
31. Before carbon from the atmosphere can enter a sugar molecule in a living organism, it must enter the process of . . . . . .

D

32. A fire or flood that destroys a climax community can set in motion the process of . . . . . .
33. The first organisms to grow in a new environment are called . . . . . .
34. In New York, succession would gradually change a wild meadow into a . . . . . .

E

35. The land biome with the greatest diversity of organisms is the . . . . . .
36. The most productive part of the ocean is the . . . . . .
37. The ocean water from the surface to the depth of maximum light penetration is called the . . . . . .

Multiple Choice Questions

A

1. The living organisms and the nonliving environment in a specific area function together as a(n) (1) population, (2) community, (3) ecosystem, (4) species.

2. In order to be self-sustaining, an ecosystem must have (1) a large number of organisms, (2) a warm, moist climate, (3) a source of energy, (4) organisms that compete.
3. All the members of one species living in a given location are (1) a population, (2) an ecosystem, (3) a biome, (4) an organism.
4. The portion of the earth where ecosystems support life is known as (1) the biome, (2) the community, (3) the biosphere, (4) the atmosphere.
5. An example of an ecosystem would be (1) the waters and organisms of Long Island Sound, (2) the trout in the upper Delaware River, (2) all birds in New York City, (4) all the rocks in Lake Champlain.
6. An example of a population would be (1) all the fish in Long Island Sound, (2) all the people in New York State, (3) all the trees in New York State, (4) deer ticks and meadow mice in a cow pasture.
7. Organisms of different species that interact with one another in a pond make up (1) an ecosystem, (2) a community, (3) a population, (4) a symbiotic relationship.
8. Two factors that increase population size are (1) birth rate and death rate, (2) death rate and emigration, (3) energy flow and parasitism, (4) birth rate and immigration.

B

9. Organisms of different species and abiotic factors that interact with one another in a pond make up (1) an ecosystem, (2) a community, (3) a population, (4) a symbiotic relationship.
10. Which one of the terms that follow includes all the others? (1) parasitism, (2) commensalism, (3) symbiosis, (4) mutualism.
11. Norway rats eat food that people discard. On this basis, the rats and people have a relationship that can best be described as (1) parasitism, (2) predator—prey, (3) commensalism, (4) mutualism.
12. Which biotic role for an organism is *not* shown in the following representation of a food chain?

    ryegrass → grasshopper → toad → snake → hawk

    (1) herbivore, (2) decomposer, (3) producer, (4) carnivore.
13. In the food chain shown above, the most numerous organism is likely to be the (1) ryegrass, (2) grasshopper, (3) toad, (4) snake.
14. Identify the top—level consumer in the food chain shown above. (1) hawk, (2) snake, (3) toad, (4) grasshopper.
15. A consumer—producer relationship is best illustrated by (1) foxes eating mice, (2) leaves growing on trees, (3) rabbits eating clover, (4) tapeworms living in foxes.
16. The symbiotic relationship between a human and the fungus that causes athlete's foot is an example of (1) predation, (2) commensalism, (3) parasitism, (4) saprophytism.
17. If bacteria living in a cow's digestive tract perform a function useful to the cow, then the relationship between the two organisms would be called (1) parasitism, (2) phototropism, (3) mutualism, (4) saprophytism.
18. Nodules containing nitrogen—fixing bacteria are found on the roots of plants in the legume family. The relationship between the bacteria and the plants is called (1) mutualism, (2) parasitism, (3) decomposition, (4) commensalism.
19. Barnacles often become attached to whales and receive free transportation to many parts of the ocean. This relationship is

an example of (1) parasitism, (2) mutualism, (3) commensalism, (4) competition.

20. Bread mold sometimes spoils the bread in the homes of people. The relationship between people and bread mold could be called (1) predator—prey, (2) parasitism, (3) competition, (4) energy flow.
21. In the food chain below, which organism provides the main source of energy?
    shrubs → insects → lizards → snakes → hawks
    (1) hawks, (2) shrubs, (3) insects, (4) lizards.
22. In the food chain above, the least numerous organisms are likely to be the (1) insects, (2) lizards, (3) snakes, (4) hawks.
23. Which of the following is *not* a predator—prey relationship? (1) hawks eating snakes, (2) lizards eating insects, (3) snakes eating lizards, (4) insects sucking sap from a shrub.
24. In a natural community, the producer organisms may include (1) bacteria, fungi, and protists, (2) deer, rabbits, and squirrels, (3) grasses, trees, and ferns, (4) trout, algae, and water lilies.
25. An ecosystem's initial supply of energy is converted into a biologically useful form by the process of (1) mutualism, (2) symbiosis, (3) population growth, (4) photosynthesis.
26. A set of abiotic factors in Lake Ontario would be (1) water temperature, depth, and oxygen concentration, (2) water temperature, depth, and algae concentration, (3) water temperature, bass reproduction, and dissolved ions, (4) oxygen concentration, photosynthesis, and respiration.
27. Between which organisms would competition for food or energy be likely? (1) lions and zebras, (2) grasshoppers and bees, (3) snakes and frogs, (4) clover and ryegrass.
28. Between which organisms would competition be most intense? (1) lions and zebras, (2) whales and trout, (3) foxes and weasels, (4) mushrooms and maples.

C

29. Atmospheric nitrogen is converted to usable nitrates by (1) nitrogen-fixing bacteria, (2) nitrifying bacteria, (3) denitrifying bacteria, (4) decay bacteria.
30. From plant and animal protein, bacteria of decay produce (1) free nitrogen, (2) nitrites, (3) ammonia, (4) nitrates.
31. When water in the soil returns to the atmosphere by way of the roots, stems, and leaves of plants, the process is called (1) transpiration, (2) respiration, (3) evaporation, (4) erosion.
32. A realistic sequence of events in the water cycle would be (1) precipitation-transpiration-runoff, (2) precipitation-runoff-stream flow, (3) transpiration-evaporation-stream flow, (4) stream flow-transpiration-evaporation.
33. Understanding the carbon cycle shows that (1) waste products always build up faster than they are recycled, (2) the waste product of one process can be the raw material of another process, (3) the main carbon reservoir is in the bodies of dead animals, (4) the carbon content of the atmosphere must always increase.

D

34. In a succession that begins with lichens growing on bare rock, the lichens are the (1) pioneers, (2) climax, (3) herbivores, (4) scavengers.

35. One aspect of a climax community is (1) constant change in plant populations, (2) the presence of stable plant populations, (3) constant changes in productivity of autotrophs, (4) a lack of energy.

(E) 36. Three important abiotic factors that affect land biomes are (1) photoperiod, rainfall, and temperature, (2) photoperiod, competition, and pH, (3) photosynthesis, sunlight, and cloud cover, (4) altitude, predation, and material cycling.

For each of the statements in questions 37–40, select the number of the biome that best fits the statement. Choose from this list of biomes:
(1) Tundra, (2) Temperate deciduous forest, (3) Tropical rain forest, (4) Grassland, (5) Desert, (6) Marine, (7) Freshwater

37. In this biome, frozen ground prevents the growth of trees.
38. This biome contains the greatest number of different species.
39. This biome is found where there is a lack of precipitation.
40. This biome is the largest on earth.
41. Photosynthesis does not occur (1) in a cold stream, (2) at the bottom of the open ocean, (3) in the intertidal zone, (4) in a desert biome.

Chapter Test

Base your answers to questions 1 and 2 on the following diagram and on your knowledge of biology. The diagram illustrates the relationships between the organisms in a certain pond.

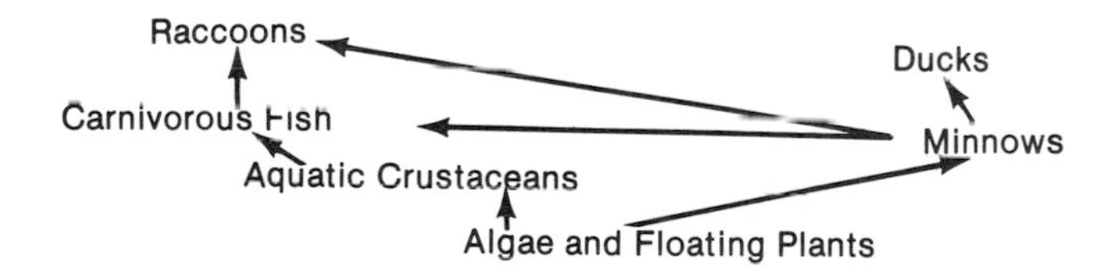

1. In addition to sunlight, another factor needed to make this a self-sustaining ecosystem would be the presence of (1) producers, (2) primary consumers, (3) decomposers, (4) higher order consumers.
2. In this pond community, which organisms are secondary consumers? (1) aquatic crustaceans and raccoons, (2) carnivorous fish and aquatic crustaceans, (3) ducks and minnows, (4) ducks and carnivorous fish
3. A species of mold growing on a slice of bread secretes digestive enzymes onto the bread. The mold would be classified as (1) a lichen, (2) a herbivore, (3) a saprophyte, (4) an omnivore.
4. All the red-winged blackbirds living in a marsh are (1) a community, (2) a succession, (3) an ecosystem, (4) a population.
5. A temperate deciduous forest is the predominant natural climax condition occurring in (1) southwestern United States, (2) northeastern United States, (3) central Canada, (4) the Great Plains region.

6. A molecule of nitrogen which you are now breathing in may have been part of a plant which lived thousands of years ago. This is an illustration of the principle that (1) dead organisms may be reincarnated, (2) molecules of cytoplasm may be replaced by inorganic salts, (3) nitrogen does not combine readily with other elements, (4) bacteria of decay return elements into circulation.

For each *statement in these questions, select the type of nutritional relationship,* chosen from the list below, *that exists between the organisms described by that statement.*

Nutritional Relationships: (1) Commensalism, (2) Mutualism, (3) Parasitism, (4) Saprophytism, (5) Scavenger.

7. An alga and a fungus live together as a lichen.
8. Fleas are found in the fur of certain dogs.
9. When attached to whales, barnacles are transported to new feeding grounds.
10. Slime molds grow on rotting logs.
11. Of the following populations in an ecosystem, the most numerous organisms would be (1) insects, (2) mice, (3) earthworms, (4) grasses.
12. Which sequence illustrates a generalized food chain in a natural community? (1) autotroph → herbivore → secondary consumer, (2) autotroph → herbivore → autotroph, (3) heterotroph → herbivore → secondary consumer, (4) secondary consumer → autotroph → carnivore.

Base your answers to questions 13 through 15 on the information below and on your knowledge of biology.

An aquarium container is filled with water and colonies of aquatic plants and animals. Various protists are added and the aquarium is then sealed and placed on a window ledge. After a period of time the aquarium appears to reach a state of balance.

13. The oxygen content of the tank is maintained by the (1) autotrophs, (2) heterotrophs, (3) fungi, (4) carnivores.
14. The energy needed to maintain this ecosystem originates from the (1) fish, (2) green plants, (3) water, (4) sun.
15. Which group of organisms in the aquarium contains the largest amount of energy? (1) primary consumers, (2) secondary consumers, (3) producers, (4) herbivores

Chapter 26 People and the Biosphere

Thousands of years ago, humans learned how to grow crops and raise animals for food. This knowledge led to the growth of cities and civilization as we know it today. The remarkable advances of technology throughout history have been made possible, at least in part, by agriculture and its ability to feed us. As time has passed, most of us no longer are involved in food production and the cycles of nature. This has led to a lack of understanding of both our role in the biosphere and our dependence on ecosystems for the resources we need for survival. Humans have destroyed many natural ecosystems, released huge amounts of pollution, and caused the extinction or decline of many species of plants and animals.

Recently, many people have realized that to insure our survival, we must take care of the biosphere so it can take care of us. We are not separate from nature. We must live in a way that does not damage or destroy the earth for future generations.

A

Human Population Growth

If humans are to live on the earth without destroying the biosphere, we must limit our numbers. Human population growth is rising dangerously. There are now more than five billion people on the planet, and it is projected that there will be nearly a billion more by the year 2000. Feeding six billion people and preventing them from destroying the life support systems of the biosphere will be a major challenge in the years ahead.

Populations in nature seldom, if ever, grow without limit. Review Figure 25–3 in the preceding chapter. It shows two common models of population growth. Note that in one, the population levels off after a period of rapid growth. In the other, rapid growth is followed by a rapid decline. How does human population growth in the world compare?

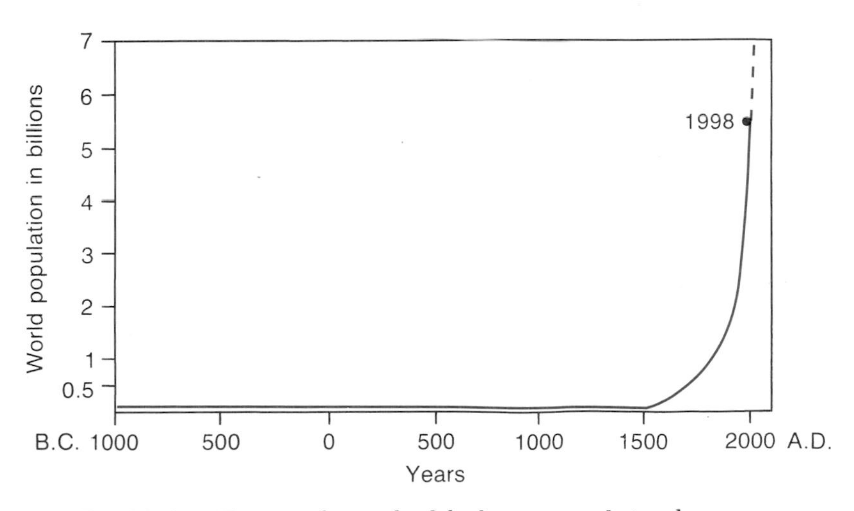

Fig. 26–1. Estimated growth of the human population during the last 3000 years. The dotted line projects future growth if current trends continue.

The human population growth curve is shown in Fig. 26–1. As you can see, there was a long period of slow growth until the last 400 years. Since then, we have been in a rapid growth phase. Will this rapid growth slow down? The answer to that question depends on how much food our farmlands, rangelands, and the oceans can continue to produce. It also depends on whether or not we can stop the rapid population growth with voluntary birth control. Sooner or later, the rapid growth will end. We do not know if earth's human population will level off because of birth control, or crash because of starvation and disease.

Throughout most of human history, death rates were very high and average life spans were much shorter than they are today. As a result, population growth was very slow, even though the birth rate was quite high. With advances in medicine and food production in the last few centuries, human death rates have declined dramatically. People live longer and fewer infants die. Because the birth rate has changed very little as the death rate has declined, humans are experiencing a period of rapid population growth.

According to scientific estimates, it took all of human history for the population size to reach the first one-half billion level in about 1650 A.D. It took about 200 years—until around 1850—to add the next half billion and double the population. The population again doubled, to two billion, by about 1930. By 1970, the population again doubled, to four billion, a doubling time of only 40 years. The present doubling time is calculated to be a little less than 40 years. There may be more than 10 billion people on earth by the year 2030. Can we limit our population growth so it does not

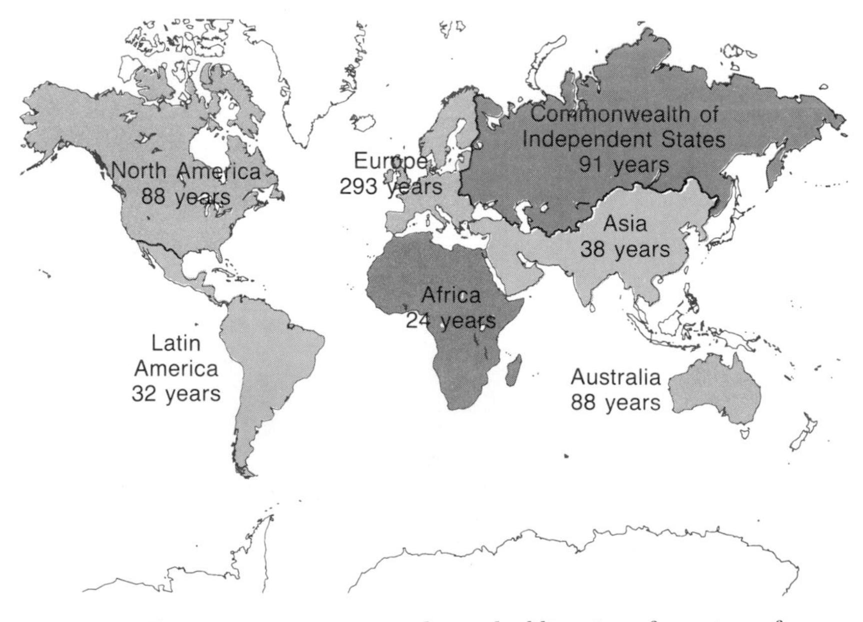

Fig. 26–2. Human population doubling times for regions of the earth. The numbers are doubling times in years.

exceed the carrying capacity of the biosphere? That question is one we cannot answer with certainty.

Many governments and private organizations are trying to cope with human population growth. Most of the nations in the industrialized world have already reduced their population growth rates. The growth rate in the United States is less than 1 percent per year, and some of the increase in population is caused by immigration rather than births. Many European nations actually have reached zero population growth.

Two-thirds of the world's people live in less-developed nations rather than in the richer industrial ones. The birth rates in these countries are still very high, while medical treatment has decreased the death rates. Most of these countries are in Asia, Africa, and Latin America. The growth rates are so high that in many countries the population will double in less than 30 years. Many of these countries can barely feed their present populations.

As human populations explode, more and more land is needed for the growing numbers of people. More living space is required as well as more land for agriculture. Population growth also puts more pressure on forests because firewood is an important fuel source in poor countries. In their struggle to survive, people in these countries are destroying the natural ecosystems around them. This leaves less room for wildlife and fewer resources for future generations, when there will be so many more people that need them.

Limiting population growth will take a concerted effort on the part of both rich and poor countries alike. Education efforts in countries with rapidly growing populations must be successful in convincing adults to have fewer children. Industrial nations must support such education and provide funds and materials for birth control.

During the 1970s, the human population growth rate declined from 1.9 to 1.7 percent per year, and many people were optimistic that human population growth was finally coming under control. But an increase to 1.8 percent in the 1980s has shown that vigorous efforts must continue if human population growth is to be slowed voluntarily before we cause further damage to our environment.

Depletion of Natural Resources

The depletion of natural resources is not just a problem of poor countries. The resources of the biosphere are under tremendous pressure from the populations of rich and poor countries alike.

The oceans were once thought to have an unlimited supply of fish. The collapse of the anchovy population off the coast of Peru in the 1970s was the first major sign that ocean resources were being depleted. Stocks of some kinds of tuna, Alaska king crab, and cod have also declined dramatically. The world fish catch has increased greatly since 1950, but there are signs that catches of many species are declining.

As fish populations decline, modern fishing fleets have been using more effective methods for catching the fish that remain. Driftnets that are miles long and drift in the open ocean catch large numbers of seabirds and marine mammals along with the fish and squid they are intended to catch. Tuna fishing involves techniques that net and kill dolphins along with the tuna the dolphins tend to swim near. Shrimp fishing kills many sea turtles. In their attempt to continue to make a living from fishing, humans are using techniques that not only harm other species, but in many cases will contribute to the decline of future stocks of their target fish.

If the biosphere is to continue to sustain us, we must protect it from the abuses of overconsumption.

B

Destruction of Ecosystems

Humans are damaging or destroying many of the ecosystems that are vital to the health of the planet. Examples of this damage to the biosphere include destruction of forest ecosystems, loss of vital wetland ecosystems, the transformation of grasslands into deserts because of overgrazing, and loss of topsoil from farmlands through erosion.

Forests Perhaps the most serious and well known example of ecosystem destruction is the clearing of tropical rain forests. Poor people in Latin America, Africa, and Asia are clearing land for farming or cutting trees for fuel. They cut the trees, then burn them to clear land for farming. Their actions are destroying large amounts of tropical forest. But the tropical soil is poor and becomes exhausted in a few years, so the farmers have to move on and clear more forest. The peasants cannot be blamed for this activity. They are simply trying to survive.

Tropical forests are also being cut for profit. Poor tropical nations with large debts are selling their forests to timber companies to raise much-needed money. The lumber is used mainly to make cheap plywood. Some Asian tropical forests are being cut and turned into disposable chopsticks for fast-food restaurants in Japan. And rain forests were also being cleared to provide grazing land for cattle. For years these cattle provided an inexpensive source of beef for fast-food restaurants in the United States. Recently, some chains of fast-food restaurants have announced that they will no longer buy beef from ranches in cleared rain forest lands.

Why is the loss of the rain forests such a threat to the biosphere? One important reason is that destruction of this habitat can affect climate. It can do so in two ways: First, rain forests normally release much water into the air through transpiration. Without this process, the climate may become drier in some places. Second, forests absorb large quantities of carbon dioxide for photosynthesis. When people cut and burn forests, we release large amounts of carbon dioxide. The increase of carbon dioxide in earth's atmosphere may lead to gradual warming of the global climate. People simply don't know the long-range consequences of global warming.

Preservation of biodiversity is an equally important reason for conserving tropical forests. While the tropical rain-forest biome covers only about 6 percent of the land in the biosphere, it is probably home to more than half of the world's known species. According to some biologists, so many different species live in tropical forests that we have discovered and classified only a fraction of them. Every time biologists study a section of tropical forest that was not studied before, they discover many new

Fig. 26–3. Each year, the cutting and clearing of the world's tropical forests destroys an area larger than New York State.

species of plants and insects and other invertebrates. The health of our biosphere may depend on this diversity.

The rain forests are being cleared at a staggering rate. We are losing many of these forests before we have a chance to study them. We are also destroying the homes of numerous tribes of people who live in rain forests. Some of these people live much like their ancestors did for thousands of years. As their cultures disappear, so does their knowledge of the plants and animals of the rain forest. Some scientists have gone to live with rain-forest people in the hope that we cannot only learn from them but also save their cultures, as well as the wild species of the forest.

Clearing tropical forests is causing the extinction of many species. There are many reasons why it is extremely important to prevent mass extinctions of species. One reason is that many of our medicines come from plants. A plant called the rosy periwinkle, which grows only in Madagascar, produces a natural chemical that scientists have turned into a drug to fight leukemia, a blood cancer. This plant nearly disappeared before we knew of its value in producing a cancer-fighting drug. Another reason is that all of our food crops come from wild strains of plants. If these wild strains become extinct, we will lose the genes that may be needed in the future to breed resistance to drought or disease into our domestic crops. The most important reason is that every species is part of the fantastic web of life that exists in the biosphere. We can lose some species without harming the web of life, but if we wipe out too many, we may damage the web beyond repair.

Logging companies are at work cutting the remaining temperate rain forests on the west coast of the U.S. and Canada. These ancient forests of fir and spruce are a rich and diverse ecosystem. The very recent discovery of a cancer-fighting drug, named taxol, in the Pacific yew tree helped

Fig. 26–4. A marsh in its natural state supports populations of fish, shellfish, birds, and many other organisms.

emphasize the importance of preserving the biodiversity of this ecosystem.

Wetlands

Another North American ecosystem that is very much endangered is our wetlands. Wetlands include marshes, swamps, bogs, and temporary ponds called potholes. Over half of all the wetlands that existed in North America before the European settlers arrived have been drained, filled in, or destroyed in other ways. Cities grew up near many of the coastal marshes along bays or estuaries. These marshes were considered wastelands. They were used as dumps or were filled in to provide land for development. The New Jersey meadowlands are an example of a marsh ecosystem that has been damaged by development. The Everglades, a huge expanse of wetland in southern Florida, are shrinking because of human activities. The populations of wading birds that made the Everglades famous have declined by an estimated 90 percent.

Wetlands are valuable for many reasons. They absorb large amounts of rain and prevent flooding. They help maintain a good supply of groundwater. They serve as a purification system for water that runs off the land. And they are the nurseries or breeding grounds for many species of fish, waterfowl, and other wildlife species.

Grasslands

Grasslands are also threatened by human activity. In North America, nearly the entire grassland biome has been converted to agriculture. This area produces more food than any other area on earth. Only a few remnants of the natural grassland remain.

Fig. 26–5. Marshes have been destroyed to make marinas, harbors, housing developments, landfills, airports, and industrial sites.

Large parts of the dry grasslands in the western U.S. are used primarily as grazing land for cattle and sheep. Much of this land is owned by the government, and government land is severely overgrazed. Overgrazing can contribute to destruction of grasslands.

Another problem associated with our attempts to produce food is soil erosion. The use of larger farm equipment, along with shrinking profits, has led many farmers to farm in ways that cause increased erosion. Many farmers clear streamside vegetation and plow right up to the streambank. Large tractors cannot be easily moved around strips of trees or shrubs, called fencerows, or along the edges of wetlands, so the fencerows are cut down and the wetlands drained. In tropical countries, peasants are clearing mountainsides to try to grow food. When the rainy season comes, the hillside soil washes away. Erosion of the red soil on Madagascar is so bad that astronauts in outer space can see a reddish ring in the ocean around this island nation.

What is being done about all the problems that threaten ecosystems? People are trying to learn how to farm in the tropics in less destructive ways. They are also developing projects that emphasize the value of the forests in local economies. Many rain-forest products, such as Brazil nuts and rubber, can be harvested and sold without destroying the trees that produced them. Tourism is another way the rain forests can generate income for tropical countries.

In many parts of the developing world, it is too late for protection of the forests because they have already been cut. Many poor people in these

Fig. 26–6. The planting of tree seedlings helps restore land where clearing of forests has taken place.

countries depend on trees for fuel. In these places, reforestation is necessary. Some reforestation efforts have already been successful in places like India, Kenya, and China.

We can help the biosphere by protecting and restoring wetlands. A law passed in 1985 in the United States prevents farmers who drain wetlands from receiving federal aid. Many wetland areas have been purchased and protected as wildlife refuges. They were saved mainly to protect waterfowl, but they also protect the fish and other wildlife that live there.

The same law that helps prevent drainage of wetlands on U.S. farms also contains provisions by which farmers are paid to set aside land that is subject to a high degree of erosion. This project alone has significantly reduced erosion on U.S. farms. Better farming techniques can also help. Leaving a buffer zone of trees along streams helps trap soil that would otherwise wash away. Plowing with the natural contour of the land, instead of straight up hillsides, is an old erosion-control method that has been ignored on many farms. And planting fencerows can reduce wind erosion to a large extent.

Fig. 26–7. Erosion of the soil severely damages agricultural land.

Fig. 26–8. Contour planting of crops greatly reduces soil erosion.

All these efforts to conserve our ecological resources have proven to be effective, although many of them are costly. The destruction of ecosystems, on the other hand, will be far more costly in the long run. If we expect the biosphere to support us, we must treat it with care.

C Pollution and Solid Waste

Human activities release large amounts of chemical wastes into the environment. These wastes are called pollutants. A pollutant may be a natural substance or an unnatural one. Natural substances are part of material cycles in the biosphere. If humans release them in small enough quantities, the surrounding ecosystems can absorb them without harm. If, on the other hand, large amounts of these substances are released in one place, they overwhelm nature's ability to absorb them and thus become pollutants. Unnatural pollutants come from consumer products. Chlorofluorocarbons (CFCs) are synthetic chemicals used as propellants in aerosol spray cans, as refrigerants in air conditioners and refrigerators, and for a variety of industrial purposes. They are not part of a natural cycle so they do not break down quickly. Instead, they remain in the atmosphere for many years and destroy the molecules of ozone in the upper atmosphere that protect us from the ultraviolet rays of the sun.

Air pollution

Motor vehicles and industry are the major sources of air pollution. Most air pollution comes from the burning of fossil fuels—coal, oil, and natural gas—to produce energy. Many of the pollutants caused by burning fossil fuels can actually be trapped before they escape into the atmosphere. The catalytic converters on motor vehicles prevent many harmful pollutants from reaching the atmosphere. One waste product of fossil-fuel burning that cannot be trapped is carbon dioxide.

Nitrogen oxides and sulfur dioxide are two natural substances that normally occur in small quantities in the atmosphere. Power plants and automobiles emit larger quantities of these substances than the biosphere can handle. They end up as pollutants that fall back to earth as acid rain. Acid rain sterilizes lakes and streams. Hundreds of lakes in the Adirondack Mountains no longer support fish populations because of their high levels of acidity. Acid rain also contributes to the decline in forest growth and damages the surfaces of cars and buildings. Pollution control devices on cars can prevent the release of nitrogen oxides, while scrubbers on smokestacks can remove the sulfur dioxide from smokestack emissions. These pollution-control techniques are costly, however, and their use leads to increases in the prices of cars and other products.

The United States has made great strides in protecting air quality. The Federal Clean Air Act has required scrubbers on many smokestacks, and the 1990 version of the act requires large reductions in future sulfur emissions. Laws requiring catalytic converters and better gas mileage have decreased the amount of pollution created by motor vehicles. But we still have unsafe air in many cities. Laws requiring stronger pollution controls, conservation measures, and use of alternative fuels are needed to continue the progress that has been made. Protecting air quality is expensive but vital, because our health and the health of the biosphere are at stake.

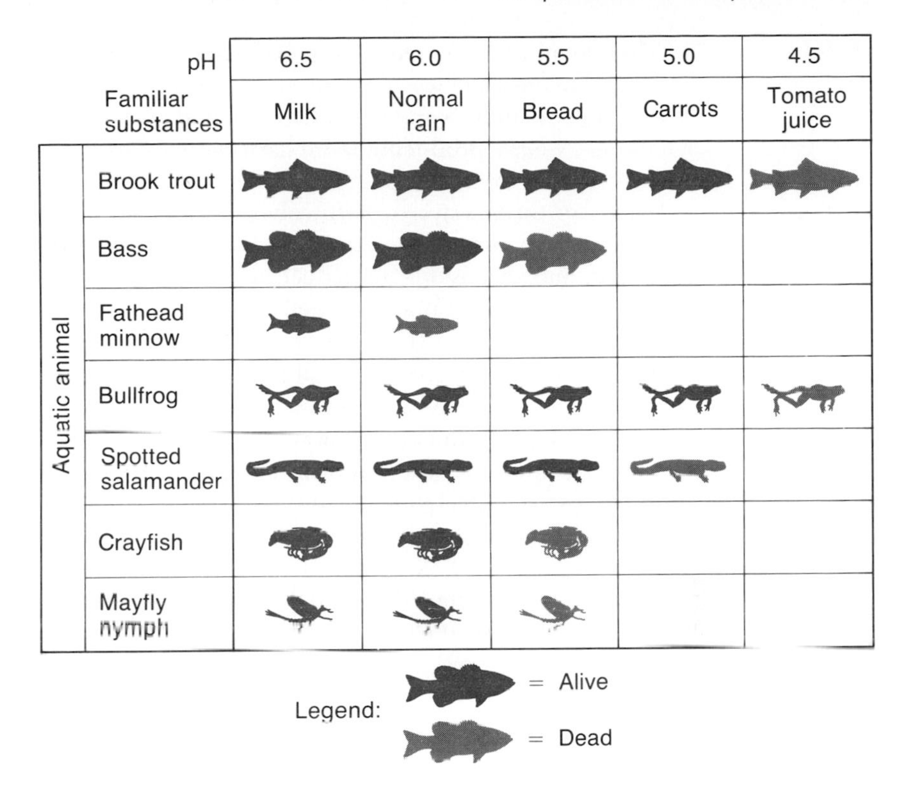

Fig. 26–9. Acid rain can make bodies of water unfit for aquatic organisms. Various levels of acidity affect organisms in different ways. As the pH of the water decreases, more organisms die off.

Water pollution

Water pollution is another area where laws have made a big impact on pollution. Industries and cities once used lakes and rivers as dumps for their wastes. The Clean Water Act has required towns and cities to build sewage treatment plants. Industries too must treat their wastes before they are released into rivers or lakes. Fish have returned to many lakes and streams since passage of this federal law in 1972. Lake Erie was nearly dead in the 1960s, but it has recovered and today is an important fishing and recreation area.

One source of water pollution that has not been controlled by the Clean Water Act is runoff of fertilizers and pesticides from farmland. Pesticides poison the water supply and make it unsafe for fish and other wildlife, as well as humans. Fertilizer runoff adds nutrients to the water, promoting the growth of algae. In many places, the explosive growth of algae has damaged aquatic ecosystems.

Many rivers were so polluted in the 1960s that they could not support fish or be used for recreation. The Cayuhoga River in Cleveland was so polluted that the waste on its surface once caught fire. Today, because of cleanup efforts, the Cayuhoga has been restored enough that it is again used for recreation.

Solid waste Solid waste, or garbage, has caused problems that we are just beginning to face. Most of our solid waste is buried in landfills. But we are running out of space in our landfills and it is difficult to find places for new ones. At the same time, we are producing more garbage than ever. America produces garbage at the rate of five pounds of solid waste per person each day.

There are three ways to *help* solve the solid-waste crisis that exists today. First, we must reduce the amount of waste we produce. Excessive packaging and disposable items account for a large percentage of our garbage. Buying reusable products instead of disposable ones would reduce what is known as the waste stream. Soft drinks and beer can be sold in reusable bottles. While disposable diapers are convenient, cloth diapers do not add to the waste stream.

The next step in reducing the flow of solid waste is to recycle. Wherever reusable products are not practical, we should use recyclable materials. Some states, such as New Jersey and Pennsylvania, have mandatory recycling laws. All communities must have a recycling program and residents must participate. New York and eight other states have "bottle bills," laws that require deposits on all beer and soft drink containers. The deposit encourages people to return the containers for refilling or recycling.

Part of the solution to the solid-waste problem is to carefully dispose of any waste that cannot be eliminated by waste reduction or recycling. Some communities have turned to incineration to reduce the amount of waste that eventually needs to be buried. Even with incinerators, some landfills are still necessary. And there are doubts about the safety of the ash incinerators produce.

Pest Control The control of "pests" such as weeds that compete with crops or insects that damage them is important to food production. Without pest control, the amount of food we grow would be diminished.

The most common method of pest control since World War II has been the use of biocides, chemicals that kill living things. These chemicals are generally called pesticides, but *biocides* is really a more accurate name because they often kill many organisms in addition to the targeted pest. The best known pesticide is DDT. Its widespread use in agriculture and mosquito control in the 1950s and '60s led to contamination of the biosphere. It entered food chains and killed many higher-level consumers, especially birds. In addition, it caused reproductive failures in fish-eating birds such as ospreys and bald eagles. And it was found to be present in the fatty tissues of most humans.

The way in which DDT was harming higher-level consumers was through a process called bioconcentration. The DDT entered small non-pest organisms in small quantities. Larger organisms ate the smaller ones, receiving many small doses of DDT and storing them in their bodies. By the time it reached the highest-level consumers, such as large birds of prey, the DDT had accumulated to high concentration levels. This caused harm to the metabolism of eagles and other birds, including failure to reproduce. Investigations led to the discovery of the bioconcentration of DDT in the food chain. As a result, DDT was banned in 1973.

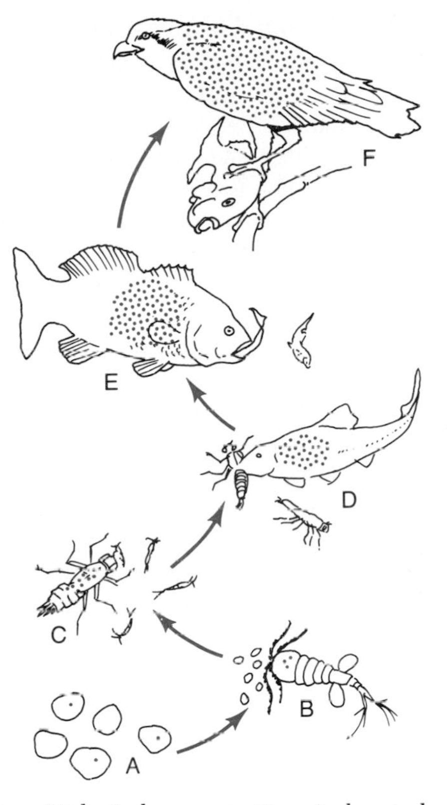

Fig. 26–10. Biological concentration: A chemical pollutant is represented by blue dots in organisms A-F. When ingested by animals, pollutants in an ecosystem become more concentrated as they move up the food chain from producers to top-level consumers.

Complete reliance on chemical pesticides has led to problems for farmers as well. Pest insects can often become resistant to the pesticides and the farmer must increase the amount used. This form of pest control has become very expensive. And the pesticides are dangerous to farm workers as well as to pests.

Biologists have been working to solve the problem of pest control with a system called integrated pest management, or IPM. With this approach, the farmer uses a variety of pest-control measures. Pest-resistant strains of crops are being developed by geneticists. Biological methods of controlling pests are also being developed. And finally, small amounts of chemical pesticides are still used when necessary.

The most promising part of IPM is the development of biological control methods. Some of these controls involve the use of other insects, bacteria, fungi, or viruses that attack the pest species. Because these biological agents are rather specific for their targets, they do not kill many other forms of life along with the intended target. Nor do they accumulate in the food chain to cause problems for higher-level consumers. An example is B.t. (*Bacillus thuringensis*), a bacterium that kills only leaf-eating caterpillars. It has been effective in controlling tent caterpillars and gypsy moths on ornamental trees, in orchards, and in cities and towns.

Another biological control method involves the use of pheromones, or sex attractants. Female insects secrete pheromones when they are ready to mate. These chemicals are signals that lead the males to the fertile females. Using pheromones to confuse the males can lure them to traps or cause them to exhaust themselves and die searching for females before the females are ready to mate.

Other biological controls include natural predators of the pest species. Ladybird beetles (ladybugs) are known to be voracious predators that eat many harmful aphids and other garden pests. Some garden product catalogs offer these insects for sale to gardeners by mail.

With integrated pest management, resistant strains of crops and biological controls are used first. Chemicals are used sparingly and only when necessary. More and more farmers are turning to these methods. They are safer than using chemicals, and sometimes cost far less. The competition between humans and their pests for food will always be a struggle. Biologists are constantly researching new ways to compete more successfully with plant and insect pests without damaging the environment.

D

Wildlife Conservation

Wildlife is a resource that will continue to renew itself if provided with the proper habitats and left undisturbed. The habitat of a species is the type of ecosystem it needs to survive. Polar bears need a very different habitat than bison, and trout need a different habitat than whales. Some species have very specific habitat requirements. The koala of Australia needs a habitat where certain types of eucalyptus trees grow. The snail kite can survive only if its prey species, the apple snail, is abundant. Other species can adapt to many different habitats. Coyotes are predators that eat many different kinds of small prey animals and are thriving throughout the United States.

Hunting. A major threat to wildlife is overhunting. In the past, market hunting almost eliminated the bison from the prairies. It did cause the extinction of the passenger pigeon, one of North America's most abundant birds in the 1800s. Many large wading birds, such as herons and egrets, nearly became extinct about 100 years ago when they were hunted to supply feathers that were used in ladies' hats. Even the largest animals on earth, the great whales, were endangered by whaling until a few years ago.

Illegal hunting still threatens animals, especially in other countries. Poaching in Africa threatens elephants and rhinos. Most of the world's spotted cats are endangered because of hunting or trapping for their fur. Much of this illegal hunting is done to supply illegal items for black-market trade in wildlife products. Rhinoceros horns are sold to make dagger handles for wealthy men in Yemen, a country in the Middle East. Bear gall bladders are sold for medicinal purposes in oriental countries. Ivory from elephant tusks are now banned from international commerce. But during the 1980s, hundreds of thousands of African elephants were

Fig. 26–11. The State of New York was the first state to pass a law banning ownership or sale of any wild bird captured in the wild.

slaughtered for their tusks. And many wild birds, especially parrots and other colorful tropical birds, are caught and sold as pets.

Laws. Laws to protect wildlife species have helped. The U.S. Endangered Species Act of 1973 is one of the toughest such laws in the world. It has been instrumental in saving many endangered species from extinction. Examples of success stories include the recovery of the whooping crane, the bald eagle, the peregrine falcon, and the American alligator. Perhaps the most famous current examples of species protected by the law are the California condor and the Northern spotted owl.

New York was the first state to pass a law banning the sale of wild-caught birds. The law prohibits possession or sale of wild birds except in very special cases and is being used as a model for other state laws. The United States Congress is also using it as a model for a proposed federal law that would ban nearly all trade in wild birds.

Exotic Introductions. Another threat to wildlife species is the introduction of foreign species into the habitat. The gypsy moth and Japanese beetle, both pest animals mentioned before in this chapter, are introduced species. Starlings and house sparrows, which compete with native birds such as bluebirds and tree swallows for nest sites, are also introduced species in North America. The fungi that caused Dutch elm disease and chestnut blight, which wiped out those two species in the eastern U.S., are both introduced pests. Even the common pest of cities, the Norway rat, is not native to North America.

Most of these species were introduced accidentally. Chestnut blight arrived with some Asiatic chestnut trees, which it does not harm. Norway rats arrived, most likely, on ships. Others were brought here purposely; the gypsy moth, for example, was brought in an attempt to start a silk

Fig. 26–12. National parks, wildlife refuges, and wilderness areas are intended to conserve wildlife.

industry. Inspections and quarantines help prevent accidental introductions that may be harmful to native plants and animals, and importation of organisms is strictly controlled. But some exotic animals are still accidentally introduced to non-native habitats.

Parks and Refuges

The single most important step in saving wildlife is preserving habitat. Setting aside parks and wildlife refuges is an important step that many countries have taken. The U.S. has been a leader in this form of wildlife protection. Yellowstone National Park, established in 1872, was the first national park. Many other nations have since designated parks. The United Nations also helps, with its Biosphere Reserve Program. This project designates internationally important wildlife habitats as biosphere reserves and urges the country or countries governing the area to preserve it. The Everglades National Park is an example of a designated biosphere reserve.

Setting aside reserves is difficult, especially in poor, overpopulated countries. Poor peasants who face starvation are not likely to stay out of a wildlife park when they need its land or wildlife to survive. The poachers who kill African elephants or rhinos are often very poor people who can survive by poaching. The poor people who capture the birds for the pet trade, like the poachers, get little for their efforts, while dealers make huge profits selling wildlife items or pets to wealthy customers.

While setting aside parks and refuges is important to preserving habitat for many species, preserves alone cannot save our wildlife. Most wild creatures live outside parks and refuges on privately owned land, or on public land that is used for other purposes. If healthy populations of wildlife are to survive, we must learn to manage these non-park lands so that people can use the land to supply their own needs without destroying the habitat for wildlife. These lands must be managed with a "multiple-use" philosophy of balance between human use and conservation of wildlife.

National forests and grazing land managed by the United States government are examples of large tracts of land that are not part of parks or preserves. These forests can provide us with wood and provide habitat for wildlife if carefully managed. In fact, well-managed forestry can actually benefit certain species of wildlife, such as moose and deer. The grasslands of the West can support cattle for human consumption and provide room for wildlife.

At one time, farms in the United States were good places for wildlife. There were small woodlots and wetland areas left untouched. Fencerows of trees and shrubs that divided fields provided cover for animals. Many large modern farms have no fencerows or woodlots, and the wetlands in them have been drained to provide more land for crops. These farms do not support much wildlife.

Some scientists working to save the tropical rain forests from destruction are researching ways for people to live off the forests without destroying them. They are trying to find ways to farm that will not exhaust the soil and lead to clearing still more land. They are also encouraging harvesting fruits, nuts, and other products from the forests for sale to support the people who live in and around the forests. And they are trying to find ways to cut trees for lumber without destroying the forests. One possible way is to cut narrow strips of forest that will be reseeded quickly by the surrounding mature trees. Such approaches can help poor people survive without destroying the forests and their wildlife.

The fate of all the living things on Spaceship Earth lies in the hands of human beings. We now recognize that our fate is tied to the earth and to all its inhabitants. Modern humans have finally learned the wisdom of the great Native American, Chief Seattle, who said, "If all the beasts were gone, men would die from loneliness of spirit, for whatever happens to the beasts, happens to man. All things are connected. Whatever befalls the earth, befalls the sons of earth."

Reasoning Exercises

1. What is the difference between an S-shaped growth curve and a J-shaped growth curve?
2. How can industrialized countries help stop destruction of the tropical rain forest biome?
3. What is slash and burn agriculture?
4. Give four reasons why wetlands are important?
5. How can farmers help reduce the amount of land erosion?
6. Describe the greenhouse effect.
7. What is bioconcentration?
8. List and describe the variety of pest control measures a farmer uses with integrated pest management?

Completion Questions

A

1. In the United States, most of the growth rate is caused by . . . . . . rather than births.
2. Two-thirds of the world's people live in . . . . . . countries, rather than in the richer industrial ones.
3. The industrialized nations use the vast majority of the world's . . . . . .
4. The collapse of the anchovy population off the coast of Peru in the 1970s was the first major sign that . . . . . . resources were being depleted.

B

5. The most important reason for preserving the tropical rain forests is . . . . . .
6. Clearing tropical rain forests is causing the . . . . . . of many species.
7. If wild strains of plants inhabiting the tropical rain forest become extinct, we lose a resource of . . . . . . that may be needed in the future.
8. The anticancer drug . . . . . . was recently discovered in the Pacific yew tree in the United States.
9. The New Jersey meadowlands is an example of the destruction of a great salt . . . . . . ecosystem.
10. Prairie potholes are small ponds that fill up in the spring and dry up by late . . . . . .
11. Wetlands absorb large amounts of rain and prevent . . . . . .
12. Almost the entire grassland biome in North America has been converted to . . . . . .
13. Larger farm equipment has led to farming practices that cause increased . . . . . .
14. Reforestation efforts are especially important in countries that depend on trees for . . . . . .

C

15. Harmful chemical substances released into the environment by humans are called . . . . . .
16. Coal, oil, and natural gas are . . . . . . fuels.
17. The only way to prevent a buildup of carbon dioxide in the atmosphere is to burn less . . . . . .
18. Solar power and wind power are two types of renewable . . . . . . sources.
19. The Clean Water Act has required towns and cities to build . . . . . . treatment plants.
20. Most of our solid waste is buried in . . . . . .
21. DDT is a . . . . . .

D

22. The U.S. Endangered Species Act of 1973 has saved many species from . . . . . .
23. The single most important step in saving wildlife is preserving . . . . . .
24. The Everglades National Park is an example of a . . . . . . Reserve.
25. African elephants are an . . . . . . species because their tusks are valuable in the ivory trade.

Multiple Choice Questions

1. The human population size is now about (1) 5 million, (2) 2 billion, (3) 5 billion, (4) 10 billion.
2. The human population is currently in which growth phase? (1) rapid-growth phase, (2) slow-growth phase, (3) equilibrium, (4) S-phase.
3. More than half of the world's known species live in (1) grasslands, (2) tropical rain forests, (3) wetlands, (4) deserts.
4. Wetlands include marshes, swamps, bogs, and (1) potholes, (2) bays, (3) estuaries, (4) streams.
5. Fencerows are (1) temporary ponds, (2) rainforest products, (3) strips of trees, (4) water purification systems.
6. The ozone layer is being destroyed by (1) acid rain, (2) CFCs, (3) carbon dioxide, (4) nitrogen oxide.
7. High levels of nitrogen oxides and sulfur dioxide in the atmosphere cause (1) global warming, (2) destruction of ozone molecules, (3) the greenhouse effect, (4) acid rain.
8. Pollutants from motor vehicles react with sunlight to produce the hazy mixture of harmful chemicals called (1) biocides, (2) acid rain, (3) smog, (4) ozone.
9. Fertilizer runoff adds nutrients to the water raising the limiting factor for the growth of (1) fish, (2) weeds, (3) algae, (4) insect pests.
10. Chemicals that kill living things are called (1) fertilizers, (2) biocides, (3) pheremones, (4) IPMs.
11. The type of ecosystem a species needs to survive is called its (1) habitat, (2) biome, (3) niche, (4) community.
12. Which of the following organisms is *not* an introduced species in North America? (1) gypsy moth, (2) Norway rat, (3) bluebird, (4) housesparrow.

Chapter Test

Base your answer to question 1 on Fig. 26-1 on page 475.

1. The shape of the curve in the graph shows that the human population is (1) in a period of little or no change, (2) going to change soon from a slow growth rate to a rapid growth rate, (3) in a period of rapid increase, (4) in a period of steep decline.
2. The rosy periwinkle, a plant found in the tropical rain forest in Madagascar, produces a drug used to fight (1) arthritis, (2) allergies, (3) AIDS, (4) leukemia.
3. The biggest threat to wetlands today is drainage for (1) industrial use, (2) housing development, (3) landfills, (4) farmland.
4. Dry grassland areas in the western United States are used primarily for (1) farming, (2) logging, (3) grazing, (4) breeding.

5. The major sources of air pollution are (1) motor vehicles and industry, (2) sewage treatment plants, (3) farmlands, (4) aerosol spray cans.
6. A melting of the polar ice caps may result from (1) acid rain, (2) a rise in sea level, (3) photosynthesis, (4) the greenhouse effect.
7. The "Bottle Bill" laws in some states help encourage (1) recycling, (2) waste reduction, (3) incineration, (4) landfilling.
8. Which of the following is the most promising method of insect control? (1) stronger insecticides designed to kill higher percentages of insects, (2) physical barriers to insect pests, (3) interference with insect reproductive processes, (4) draining marshes and other insect habitats.
9. Overhunting caused extinction of the (1) passenger pigeon, (2) bison, (3) whooping crane, (4) California condor.
10. Which of the following is *not* a wildlife conservation method? (1) passing laws to limit the hunting season, (2) establishment of wildlife refuges, (3) reforestation, (4) poaching.

Unit 7 Environment

Portfolio Project

From fighting pollution to saving endangered species, people working in environmental jobs solve problems using a variety of skills. Prepare a poster advertisement for environmental careers. You will have to do some research to find out the types of careers available and the skills needed. Include in your advertisement a description of the environmental careers, the kinds of problems that people in each career try to solve on the job, and the skills and training required.

APPENDIX

Review of Laboratory Skills

Your biology course has emphasized laboratory work in order to help you develop laboratory skills. The process of acquiring these skills will give you firsthand experience in understanding the nature of scientific inquiry and will provide a foundation in laboratory techniques for any future science courses you may take. Many of the manipulative skills, safety precautions, ways of handling data, and procedures for testing hypotheses, will be useful in your daily life.

The New York State Syllabus in Regents Biology identifies 16 laboratory skills that you should acquire during the laboratory portion of your biology course. These skills are subject to testing in the Regents examination. The following section of this book is designed to help you review and organize your laboratory experiences in terms of these 16 lab skills.

The 16 laboratory skills are summarized in the following list:

1. Formulate a question or define a problem and develop a hypothesis to be tested in an investigation.
2. Given a laboratory problem, select suitable lab materials, safety equipment, and appropriate observation methods.
3. Distinguish between controls and variables in an experiment.
4. Identify parts of a light microscope and their functions and focus in low and high power.
5. Determine the size of microscopic specimens in micrometers (microns).
6. Prepare wet mounts of plant and animal cells and apply staining techniques using iodine or methylene blue.
7. Identify cell parts under the compound microscope such as the nucleus, cytoplasm, chloroplast, and cell wall.
8. Use and interpret indicators such as pH paper, Benedict's (Fehling's) solution, iodine (Lugol's) solution, and bromthymol blue.
9. Use and read measurement instruments such as metric ruler, Centrigrade thermometer, and graduate cylinder.
10. Dissect plant and animal specimens for the purpose of exposing major structures for suitable examination. Suggestions of specimens include seeds, flowers, earthworms, grasshoppers, etc.
11. Demonstrate safety skills involved in heating materials in test tubes or beakers, use of chemicals, and handling of dissection instruments.
12. Collect, organize, and graph data.
13. Make inferences and predictions based upon data collected and observed.
14. Formulate generalizations or conclusions of the investigation.
15. Assess the limitations and assumptions of the experiment.
16. Determine the accuracy and repeatability of the experimental data and observations.

These 16 laboratory skills can be divided into three basic areas:

(1) Pre-lab skills	Numbers 1-3	Those pertaining to the planning of an experiment.
(2) Laboratory activities	Numbers 4-12	Those that are mainly manipulative or procedural skills.
(3) Post-lab skills	Numbers 13-16	Those that pertain to analysis of results and drawing of conclusions.

Many of the laboratory skills and procedures have already been described as exercises at appropriate points in the text. Some of these sections are again reproduced here along with additional material. The chart below correlates the Regents lab skills with our exercises.

Correlation of Regents Lab Skills with *Concepts in Modern Biology*

Chapter	New York State Regents Laboratory Skill Number(s)	Laboratory Exercises in *Concepts in Modern Biology*	Page(s)
1	1, 2, 3	Gather, Process, and Record Data	3
3	4	The Compound Microscope: Parts and Function	42
3	5, 9	Microscopic Measurement	46
3	7	Identifying Cell Organelles	53
3	11	Using Dissection Equipment Safely	54
3	6, 7	Using Staining Techniques	54
3	11	Handling Chemicals Safely	54
5	1, 3, 13, 15	Formulate a Question and Devise an Experiment	90
5	10	Earthworm Dissection	108
5	11	Safety Dissection Procedures	109
11	8, 13	Use and Interpret Indicators in Tests for Nutrients	198
11	11	Safety in Heating Materials in the Laboratory	199

In the following review of laboratory skills, the first group to be considered will be the laboratory activity skills 4-12, followed by the pre-lab skills and the post-lab skills.

Laboratory Skill 4:

- Identify parts of a light microscope and their functions.
- Focus in low and high power

The compound microscope (Figure 1) contains a combination of a two-lens system. The *eyepiece* (or ocular) is a system of lenses at the top of the body tube. The *objective* is the system of lenses at the lower end of the tube. (Note: There are two objectives shown in Figure 1, high power and low power.) The objective produces a magnified image of the specimen, and this image is further magnified by the eyepiece.

The compound microscope commonly used in the high-school laboratory has two interchangeable objectives. The shorter objective is low power in its magnification, and the longer one is high power. The magnifying power is always marked on the objective. To determine the total magnification, you multiply the magnifying power of the two lenses that are in use. The objectives are fastened to the nosepiece, which may be rotated to bring either of the two objectives into position below the eyepiece.

The specimen to be observed is usually placed on a glass *microscope slide* and covered with a *coverslip*. The microscope slide is placed over the opening in the *stage* and held in place by *stage clips*.

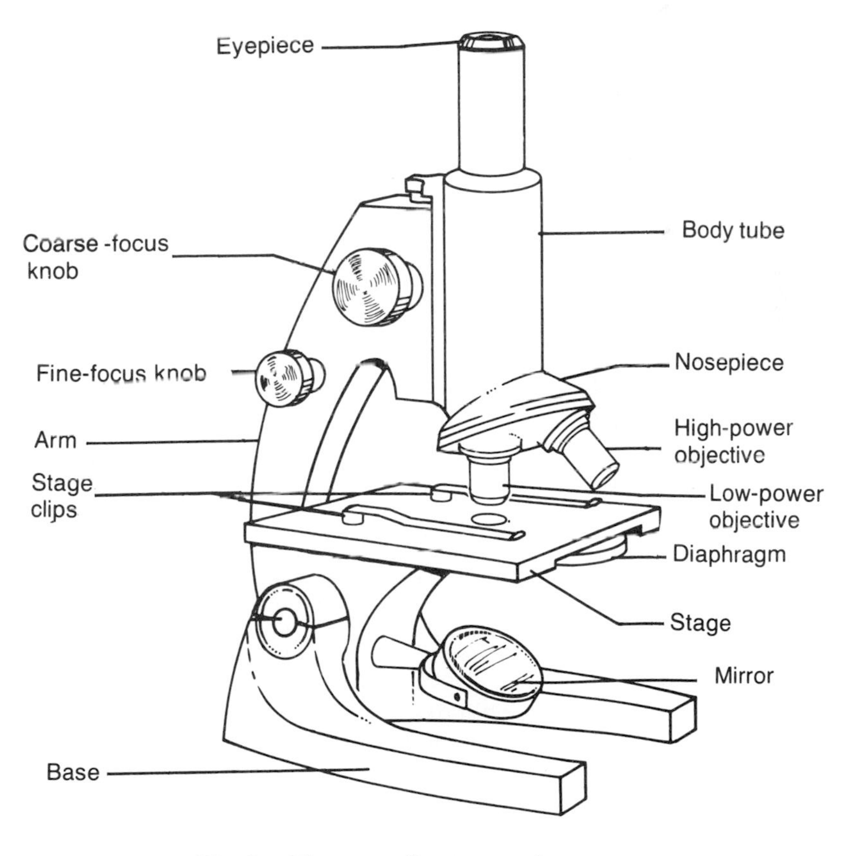

Fig. 1. The parts of a compound microscope.

Light must pass through the specimen on the slide and travel up through the objective, the body tube, and the eyepiece to the eye of the observer. In some microscopes, light from a window (but not direct sunlight) or from a light fixture, is reflected into the lens system by a *mirror*. Other microscopes have an electric light attached below the stage to provide the required illumination. This is called a *substage illuminator*. *Switching from low power to high power reduces the brightness of the field.* You can often obtain more light by adjusting the diaphragm or the mirror.

A *diaphragm*, mounted below the stage, regulates the light reaching the objective lens. A smaller diaphragm opening often provides a sharper image, but reduces the brightness of the field. Try various settings of the diaphragm to obtain the image having the best overall clarity.

The heavy *base* supports the microscope and is attached to the *arm* which holds the body tube and acts as a carrying handle. A *coarse-focusing knob* and a *fine-focusing knob* can be turned to vary the distance between the objective and the specimen in order to produce a sharp image. For the object to be in focus under high power, the objective lens must be closer to the object than under low power.

A microscope reverses and inverts the image of an object seen through the lens system. Therefore, a microorganism viewed under the microscope will appear to move in the opposite direction from which it is actually moving.

Using the microscope.

- Carry the microscope by its arm while holding one hand under the base.
- *Never focus downward* while looking through the eyepiece for you might push the objective into the microscope slide. Instead, while looking at the objective from the side, lower this lens until it is very close to the slide. Then return your eye to the eyepiece and focus *upward*.
- Do not use direct sunlight for this is too bright and could injure your eye.

Laboratory Skill 5:

- Determine the size of microscopic specimens in micrometers (microns).

Objects seen under the microscope are so small that they are measured in a special unit. This unit is the *micrometer* (μm), formerly called the *micron* (μ).

Estimating the size of a specimen under the microscope can be done in the following way: Place a transparent plastic metric ruler in the field of your *low-power objective* as shown in Figure 2. Then estimate the diameter of the field in millimeters. For example, 1.3 mm. Finally, convert the millimeters to micrometers: 1.3 mm = 1300 μm. The diameter of the low-power field, therefore, is 1300 μm.

An object that is about one-half the length of the diameter of the field as seen under low power, has an approximate length of 650 μm.

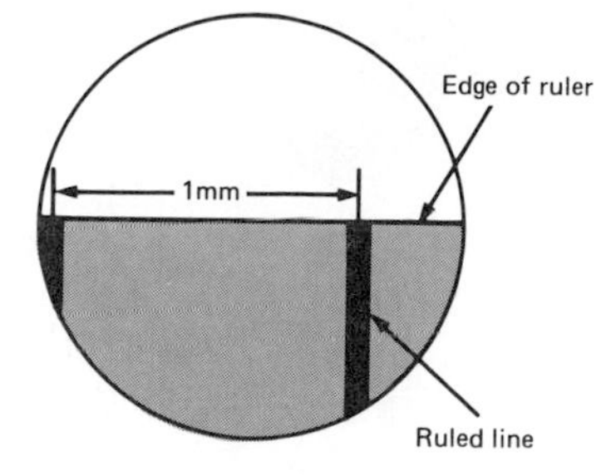

Fig. 2. The field of view under low power measured with a transparent ruler.

Laboratory Skills 6 and 7:

- Prepare wet mounts of plant and animal cells.
- Apply staining techniques using iodine or methylene blue.
- Identify cell parts under the compound microscope, such as the nucleus, cytoplasm, chloroplasts, and cell wall.

The preparation of a permanent microscope slide is a lengthy process which results in a preserved and stained specimen that is sealed to the slide with a coverslip. For most observations you will be doing in the laboratory and for viewing living specimens, a temporary preparation called a *wet mount* can be used.

Preparing a wet mount. In a wet mount, the specimen is immersed in a thin layer of water on the slide and covered by a removable coverslip. The water provides a mounting medium of uniform optical density which is not very different from that of the specimen. The water also prevents tissues and microorganisms from drying up and permits the observation of specimens while they are alive. Swimming protozoa, beating cilia on a clam's mantle, and cyclosis can be observed in a wet mount.

Applying stain to a wet mount. To distinguish cellular components more clearly, specimens in a wet mount may be stained by use of water-soluble stains such as *Lugol's iodine solution* and *methylene-blue solution*. Lugol's iodine cannot be used for staining living specimens as it kills cells. However, methylene blue is a *vital stain* and may be used to stain living specimens such as protozoa and algae. It can also be used to stain the cells from the inner lining of your cheek. Cyclosis in *Elodea* can be observed only in the living state; therefore, methylene blue must be used.

Note: *In observing a wet mount, do not tilt the stage of your microscope as the coverslip and specimen might run off the slide.*

Preparing a wet mount of onion tissue. It is easy to study a piece of onion skin under the microscope because this tissue is thin enough for light to pass readily through it. The "skin" that is used is not the dead outer layer of an onion but is taken from one of the thick leaves inside the onion. (See Figure 3.)

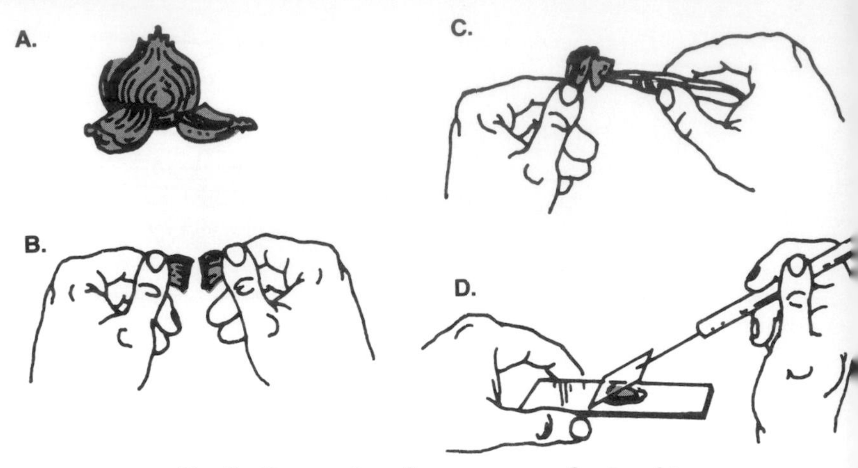

Fig. 3 Preparation of a wet mount of onion skin

1. Cut a wedge from an onion and remove one of the thick, juicy leaves (Figures 3-A, 3-B). From the inner, concave layer of this leaf peel off the thin membrance, using a forceps or a scalpel (Figure 3-C). This is the "onion skin" that is to be observed. Cut out a square that is about half a centimeter on each side.
2. Using a medicine dropper, place a drop of water in the center of a clean microscope slide. Transfer the onion skin specimen to this drop of water using forceps, the edge of a scalpel, or a dissecting needle.
3. Lower a clean coverslip over the drop *at an angle* as shown in Figure 3-D. Support the upper edge of the coverslip with a dissecting needle or forceps as you slowly lower it onto the slide. This procedure will squeeze out extra water and reduce the chance of air bubbles forming under the coverslip. Air bubbles that do form may be pushed out by gently tapping the coverslip with the handle of a dissecting needle.

Preparing a wet mount of cheek cells. A sample of animal cells can be observed under the microscope by preparing a wet mount of epithelial cells scraped from the inside of your cheek. The procedure, using a toothpick, is shown in Figure 4.

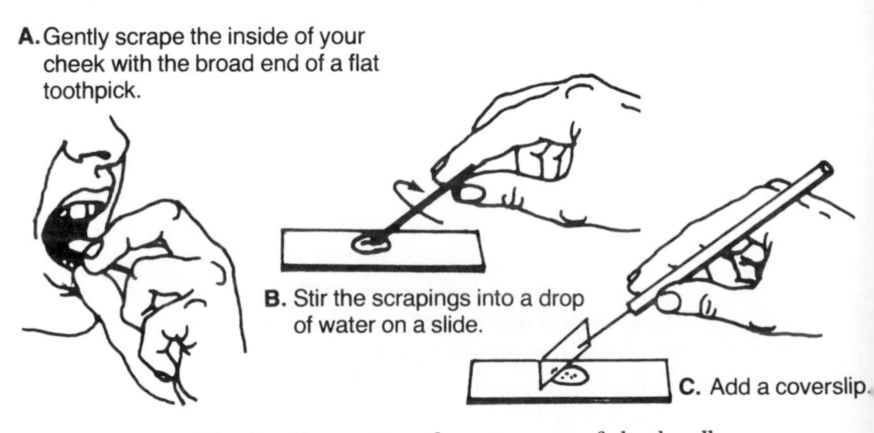

Fig. 4. Preparation of a wet mount of cheek cells.

Preparing a wet mount of an *Elodea* leaf. The onion skin cells that you have observed grow below ground and lack chloroplasts. To observe plant cells that do have chloroplasts, the leaf of the *Elodea* plant is commonly used. *Elodea* is a green plant about 15 centimeters long that grows submerged in ponds and streams. It is often used in home aquariums. Thin, delicate leaves taken from the tip of a stem have only two layers of cells. Thus, the leaf specimen is thin enough to be studied with a compound light microscope. Thicker, plant specimens would have to be sliced very thin with a special instrument.

If the plant has been growing in the light, and if the slide is gently warmed, you can see *cyclosis*—the streaming of cytoplasm that moves the chloroplasts.

Preparing a wet mount of cork cells. Robert Hooke introduced the word "cell" when he observed thin slices of cork under his microscope. You can follow his procedure by following the directions in Figure 5.

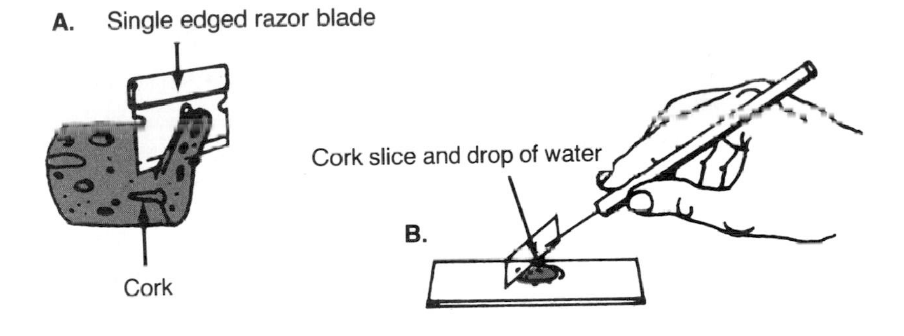

Fig. 5 Preparing a wet mount of a cork slice.

Staining wet mounts. Specimens for a wet mount may be stained by including a water-soluble stain such as Lugol's iodine or methylene blue in the drop of mounting water. Another procedure is to draw the stain under the coverslip after the coverslip has been added. As shown in Figures 6-A and 6-B, place a drop of the stain at one edge of the coverslip. Then draw the stain under the coverslip by touching a piece of paper towel to the opposite edge.

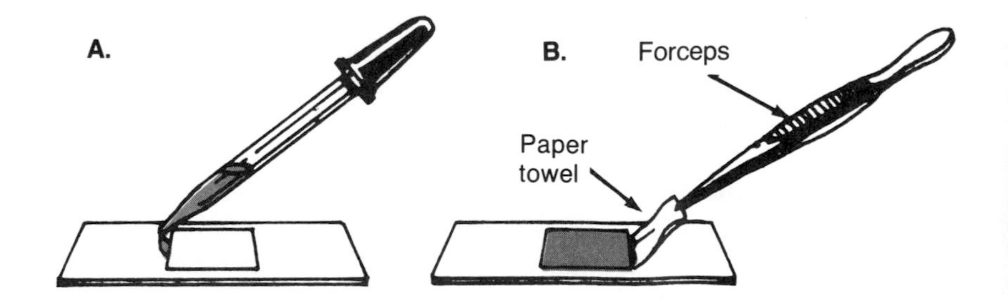

Fig. 6. Drawing stain under a coverslip

Laboratory Skill 8:

- Use and interpret indicators such as pH paper, Benedict's (Fehling's) solution, iodine (Lugol's) solution, and bromthymol blue.

An *indicator* is a substance that indicates the presence, and sometimes the concentration, of a substance in a compound or a mixture.

Test for sugar. You will recall that glucose and other simple sugars are monosaccharides. To test a food for the presence of simple sugar, place the food in a test tube and add enough clear blue Benedict's solution to cover it. Heat to boiling. An orange-red cloudiness or precipitate indicates the presence of glucose; a green color indicates the presence of a trace of glucose. In the absence of simple sugar, Benedict's solution retains its clear blue color. This test does not work with a disaccharide, such as sucrose.

Test for starch. To test a food sample for starch, add iodine solution to the sample. The iodine solution turns blue-black if starch is present.

Test for protein. A test for protein can be demonstrated by placing some raw egg white in a test tube. Add one drop of a 1% solution of copper sulfate and five drops of a 10% solution of sodium hydroxide. The formation of a purple color indicates the presence of protein. This is called the *Biuret test.)*

Test for fat. For a simple test for fat, rub a food sample on a piece of unglazed paper, such as from a brown paper bag. Warm the sample moderately in order to allow any water present to dry. Then hold the paper to the light. If the paper becomes translucent, fat is present.

Test for water. To test a food for water, gently heat a sample in a dry test tube. If droplets of water condense at the cooler top of the test tube, water was present in the food sample.

Test for vitamin C. Although tests for most vitamins are complex, the test for ascorbic acid (vitamin C) is relatively simple. In this test, use *indophenol;* it forms a clear blue solution when dissolved in water. Ascorbic acid causes this solution to become colorless.

To perform the test, first add 10 drops of blue indophenol to a test tube. Then add, one drop at a time, a solution of the food sample being tested. Shake the tube each time a drop is added. Keep an accurate count of the drops needed to turn the indophenol colorless. The greater the number of drops needed, the *lower* the concentration of ascorbic acid present in the food sample.

You can use this test to compare the amounts of vitamin C in fresh, canned, and frozen fruit juices. How could you find out if letting a glass of freshly-squeezed orange juice stand around for a day has any effect on its vitamin C content?

Laboratory Skill 9:

- Use and read measurement instruments such as a metric ruler, a Celsius (Centigrade) thermometer, and graduated cylinder.

The metric ruler. The basic unit of length in the metric system is the *meter* (m). This is about three inches longer than the yard of the English system. A meter stick is one meter long and is divided into 100 *centimeters* (cm). Each centimeter is divided into 10 *millimeters* (mm). There are 1000 millimeters in a meter (Figure 7).

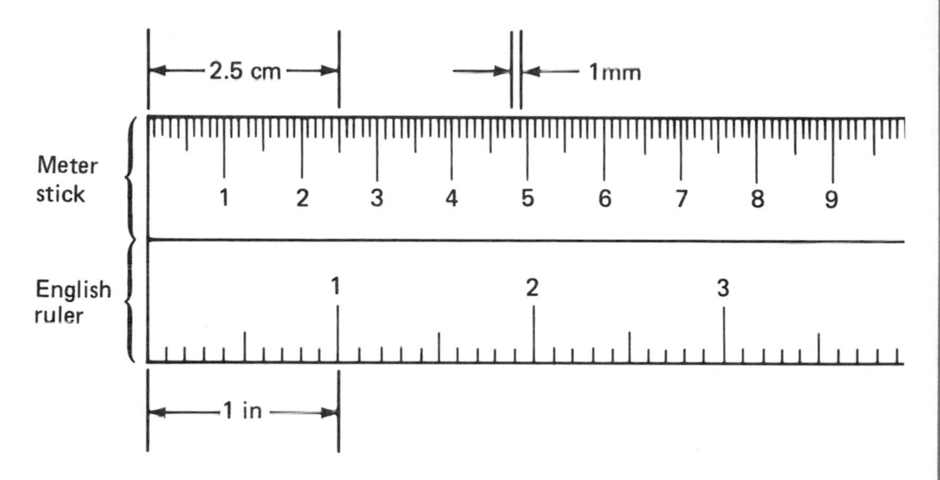

Fig. 7. A section of a meter stick (actual size) showing a centimeter and a millimeter. Compare the meter stick with the English system ruler

Make your determinations with a metric ruler only to the nearest millimeter. Do not try to estimate decimal portions of a millimeter by the naked eye. For example, the length of the object in Figure 8 may be recorded as 7.8 cm.

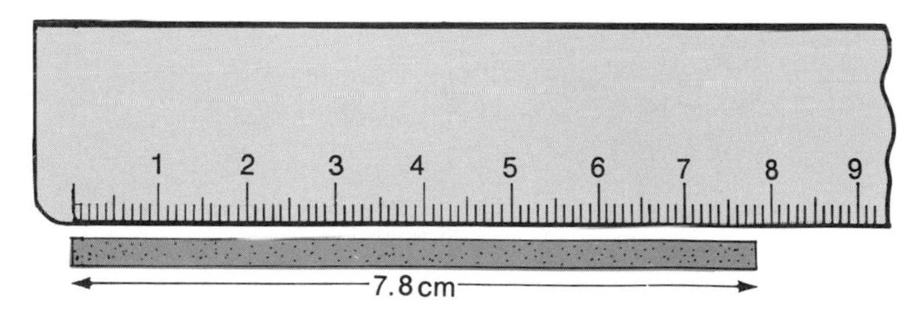

Fig. 8. Measuring in centimeters

For convenience, metric rulers used in the laboratory are of short lengths such as 15 cm. Note that the metric ruler in Figure 8 does not use the ends for measurement since these edges may become rounded through use. If your ruler does not have this feature, start measuring from the 1-cm mark instead of from the zero mark. But do not forget to subtract 1 cm from your final reading.

The Celsius thermometer. The liquid metal mercury is used in most laboratory thermometers because it expands at a uniform rate when heated. You can tell a mercury thermometer by the silver color of the metal. The scale on the thermometer is based on the *freezing point* and *boiling point* of water (Figure 9).

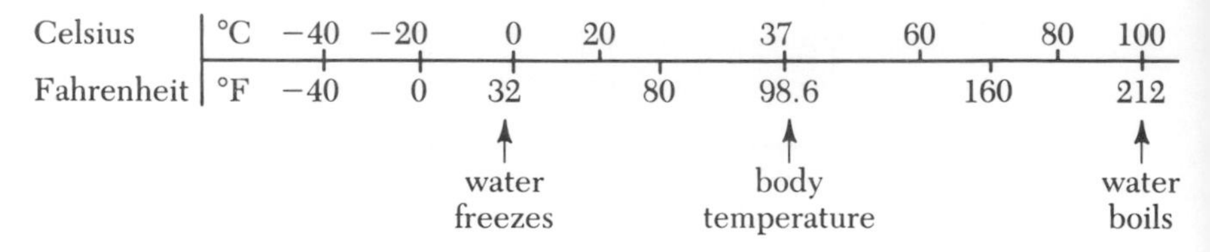

Fig. 9. Comparison of Celsius and Fahrenheit scales.

On the Celsius scale, the freezing point is marked 0 degrees Celsius and the boiling point is marked 100 degrees Celsius. The distance between these two points is then divided into 100 equal divisions called degrees. On the Celsius scale these are called *degrees Celsius* (°C). The Celsius scale is named after Anders Celsius (1701-1744). The Celsius scale is the scale used in the metric system.

The most commonly used thermometer scale in this country is the Fahrenheit scale. On the Fahrenheit scale there are 180 divisions between the freezing and boiling point of water. The Fahrenheit scale is named for Gabriel D. Fahrenheit (1687-1736).

In reading a thermometer, you should first study the markings to determine how many degrees are represented by each scale unit. In Figure 10, each Celsius scale unit represents 2 degrees. The point marked x is read as

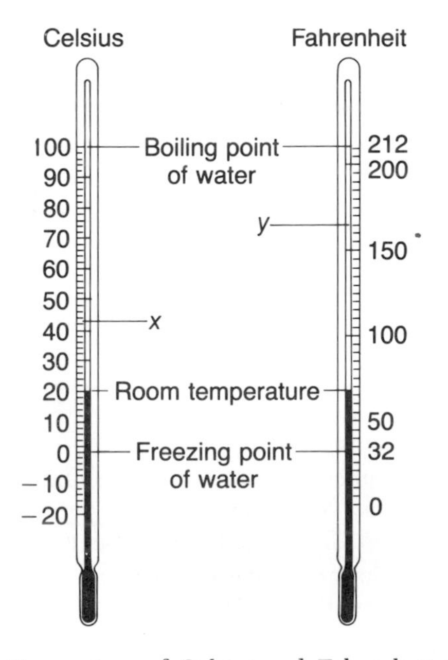

Fig. 10 Comparison of Celsius and Fahrenheit thermometers (x is 43°C; y is 165°F)

43°C. On the Fahrenheit scale shown in Figure 10, how many degrees are represented by each scale unit? (Subtract 100° from 150° and divide by 10 units.) What is the reading for point *y*?

The graduated cylinder. The basic unit for liquid measurement in the metric system is the liter (l or L). A liter is a little more than a quart in the English system. One thousandth of a liter is the milliliter (ml or mL). The milliliter occupies a volume of a cube that is one centimeter on each side, or one cubic centimeter (1 cm^3). One milliliter equals one cubic centimeter. Most liquid measurements that you will make in the biology laboratory are in milliliters and most laboratory glassware is marked in milliliters.

The *graduated cylinder* is one of the instruments used to measure the volume of liquids. The graduated cylinder consists of a glass or plastic cylinder having markings which indicate the volume when the cylinder is filled to various levels (Figure 11).

Water molecules adhere to glass more strongly than they cohere to each other. As a result, water wets glass surfaces and rises slightly along the sides of a glass tube to form a curved surface. The curved surface of the liquid in a tube is called the *meniscus*. Water, and similiar liquids, form a meniscus that curves upward. By common agreement, when the meniscus on a graduated cylinder curves upward, the volume is read at the *bottom* of the meniscus (Figure 11-A)

Molecules of mercury cohere to each other more strongly than they adhere to glass surfaces. As a result, mercury does not wet glass and therefore forms a meniscus that curves downward. The volume for such a liquid is read at the *top* of the meniscus (Figure 11-B).

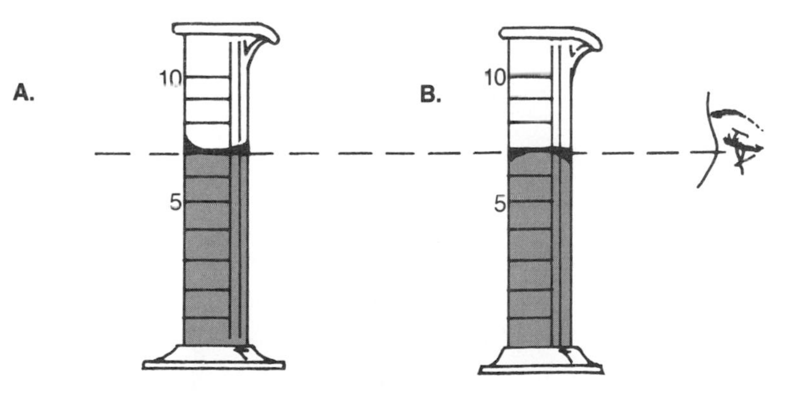

Fig. 11. Reading the meniscus. **A.** When the meniscus curves upward, read the bottom. **B.** When the meniscus curves downward, read the top. In both graduated cylinders, the volume is 7.0 ml. In making the reading, the meniscus should be at eye level.

Carefully examine the scale graduations to determine the value of eac division. Figure 12 presents several examples. Do not select a graduate cylinder that is much larger than you need. To measure a volume of 8 ml for example, use a 10 ml graduated cylinder rather than a 100 ml one. Th smaller one has finer graduations and thus provides a more accurate mea surement.

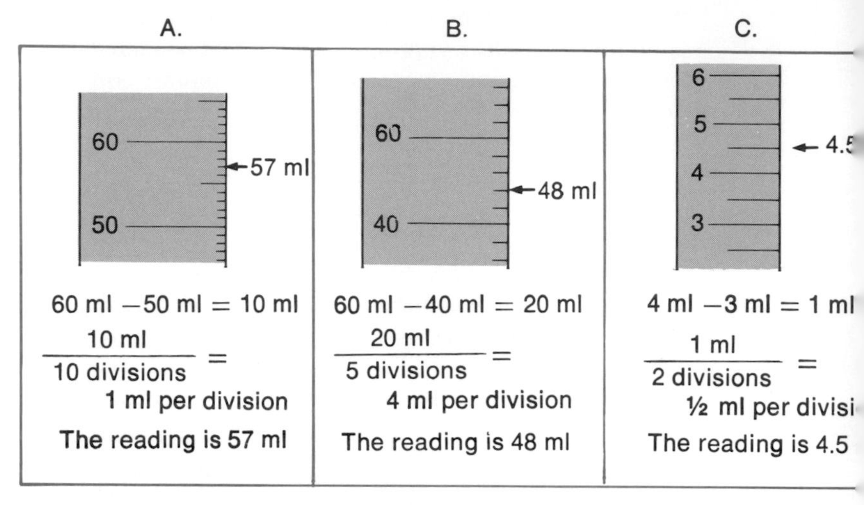

Fig. 12. Scale graduations on gradulated cylinders.

Laboratory Skill 10:

- Dissect plant and animal specimens for the purpose of exposing majc structures for suitable examination.

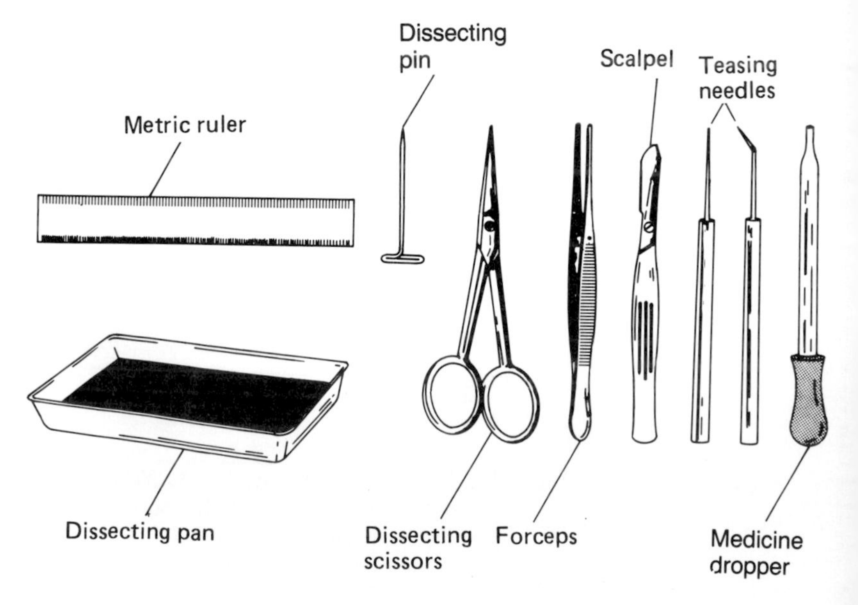

Fig. 13. Dissecting instruments

In your laboratory sessions that are devoted to the dissection of plant and animal specimens, you learned such skills as:

- to explore anatomy that is new to you by following directions in a dissection guide
- to make labeled drawings of what you observe
- to use instruments that are appropriate for the various tasks called for in each dissection
- to probe with a dissecting needle before making cuts with scalpel or scissors. A dissecting needle is used to tease tissues gently apart

The dissecting instruments that you used are included among the drawings of laboratory apparatus shown in Figure 13.

Figure 14 shows a typical flower. For other plant dissections, review your text:

Sample types of flowers Figs. 19-1, 19-2	Page 321, 322
Dicotyledon seed (lima bean) Fig. 19-7	Page 325
Monocotyledon stem Fig. 6-8	Page 126
Dicotyledon stem Fig. 6-9	Page 127

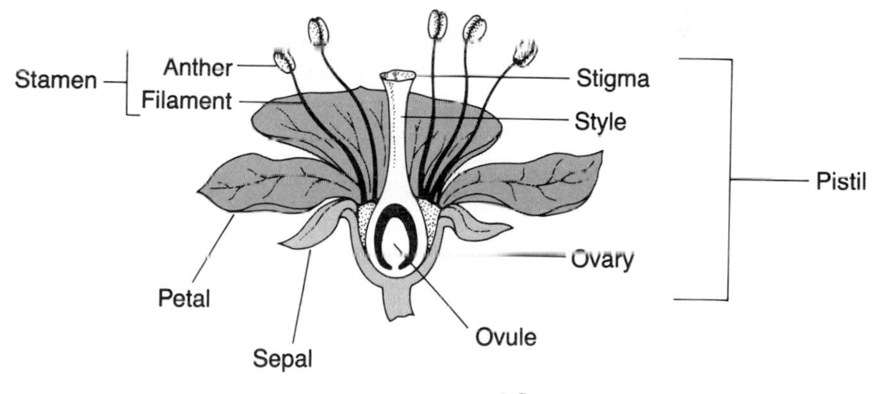

Fig. 14. A typical flower

Review the structures you have observed in your dissection of the earthworm and the grasshopper by examining the following figures:

For the earthworm dissection, see:

Digestive system Figs. 5-16, 5-17	Page 109
Circulatory system Fig. 6-18	Page 135
Excretory system Fig. 8-2	Page 162
Nervous system Fig. 9-8	Page 175

For the grasshopper dissection, see:

Digestive system Fig. 5-18	Page 111
Circulatory system Fig. 6-19	Page 136
Excretory system Fig. 8-3	Page 163
Nervous system Fig. 9-9	Page 175

Laboratory Skill 11:

- Demonstrate safety skills involved in heating materials in test tubes o beakers, use of chemicals, and handling of dissection instruments.

General safety rules.

1. Follow the general outline of the laboratory lesson using chemicals an apparatus that have been set out, unless special permission is obtained t deviate from the direction sheets.
2. Do not wear loose clothing. Tie back long hair that may interfere wit vision or catch on fire. Wear a laboratory apron to protect clothing.
3. Wear safety goggles whenever you heat anything in the laboratory o when you expect chemical reactions to produce spattering.
4. Know the location of safety equipment such as the fire extinguisher, fir blanket, and the laboratory shower if provided.
5. Report all accidents to the instructor no matter how trivial they may seen
6. The laboratory is not the place for horseplay.
7. Do not eat food in the laboratory.
8. Do not taste anything in the laboratory even if directed to do so i printed laboratory directions.
9. At the end of the laboratory session, sponge the laboratory table an then wash your hands thoroughly.

Safety in heating materials.

1. To light a Bunsen burner, first turn on the gas and then apply a burnin match or a spark from a flint lighter to the top of the barrel. A improperly adjusted burner may strike back; that is, burn at the bottom o the barrel, and melt the rubber tubing. In such an event, turn off the ga promptly and obtain assistance from your instructor.
2. Not all test tubes are made of heat-resistant Pyrex glass. Heat a sof glass test tube in the cooler part of the flame before placing it in the hotte part of the flame. The hottest part of the flame is at the top of the inner blu cone, as shown in Figure 15.
3. Do not include an obstructive mass such as a lump of bread within liquid that you are heating in a test tube. Steam accumulating below suc an obstruction may expel it with considerable force.

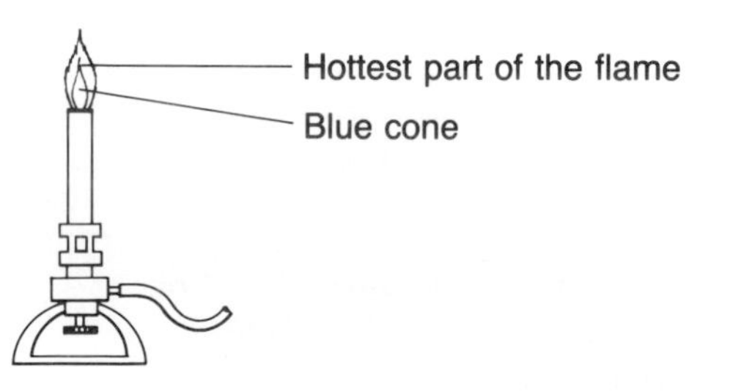

Fig. 15. The hottest part of the Bunsen burner flame is at the tip of the inner blue cone

4. When heating a test tube over a Bunsen burner, hold the test tube with a test-tube holder. Because the contents may shoot out of the tube, tilt the test tube so that its opening points away from you and nearby students. (See Figure 16.)

Fig. 16. Tilt the test tube so its opening does not face you or other students. Wear safety goggles

5. When it is necessary to boil alcohol—for example, to remove chlorophyll from a leaf—prevent the alcohol vapors from exploding by one of these procedures:

- Use an electric hot plate or an electric immersion heater instead of a flame.
- Use a hot-water bath. First, all students in the class should boil water at the same time in large beakers using a Bunsen burner with tripod or ring stand. (See Figure 17.) Then, students turn off all flames in the room. Students can now pour alcohol into a small beaker, add a leaf, and insert the small beaker into the large beaker of boiled water.

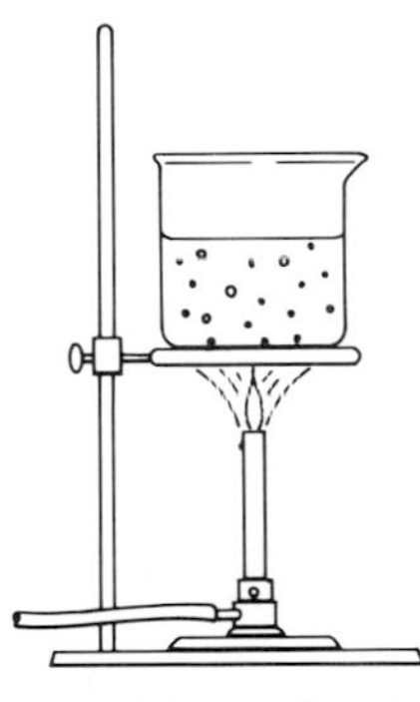

A. Boil large beaker of water.

B. Turn off flame.

C. Place small beaker of alcohol with leaf into large beaker of boiled water.

Fig. 17. Hot water bath for heating alcohol

Inasmuch as the temperature of the boiled water is close to 100°C and alcohol boils at 78°C, the alcohol soon starts to bubble and turn green from the chlorophyll that is extracted from the leaf.

6. Do not use an open flame in a room where flammable materials are exposed. Vapors from such volatile and flammable substances as alcohol, ether, gasoline, and benzene form explosive mixtures that may be ignited by the flame.
7. To heat liquids in a beaker or flask, use a ring stand or tripod as shown in Figure 18. The wire gauze prevents spot heating of the beaker by distributing the heat over a wider area.
8. If clothing catches fire, smother the flames with a fire blanket, if available, or use a fire extinguisher.

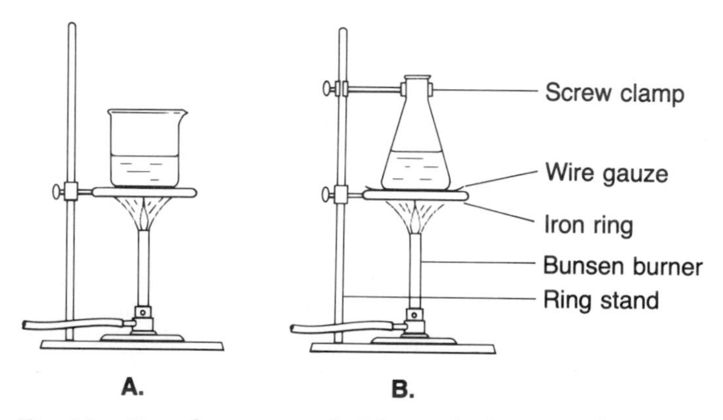

Fig. 18. Use of a ring stand. When a beaker (A) is heated instead of a flask (B), the clamp is not used

Safety in the use of chemicals.

1. Use only chemicals that have been set out for the specific exercise or experiment that you are doing and follow the oral or written directions that have been given by your instructor. Request permission if you wish to deviate in any way from the directions. Random mixing of chemicals may cause explosions or the production of toxic fumes.
2. Do not use chemicals from containers that are unlabeled or not clearly labeled. If the label has deteriorated or has fallen off, notify the instructor.
3. To transfer dry chemicals, use a spatula, spoon, or wood splint. Do not touch any chemical with your bare fingers.
4. To transfer liquids, pour carefully using a funnel if necessary. Do not place the wet glass stopper of a reagent bottle on the table where it may deposit a caustic chemical. Instead, hold the stopper between your fingers while pouring as shown in Figure 19. Measured amounts of liquids may be transferred by use of a glass graduate cylinder or a medicine dropper.
5. Unless you know otherwise, assume that solutions are caustic, toxic, infectious, or otherwise dangerous. Biuret reagent, for example, which is used to test for proteins, contains sodium hydroxide, a caustic base. Other caustic substances are potassium hydroxide, sulfuric acid, nitric acid, and hydrochloric acid.

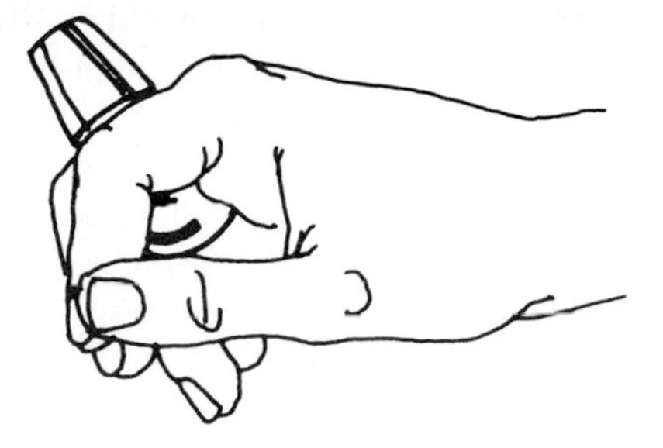

Fig. 19. Hold the stopper from a bottle between your fingers when pouring a chemical

6. If the laboratory is equipped with a fume hood, use it when so directed. This is a glass-fronted enclosure containing a fan that vents vapors through the roof of the building. If the decomposition of mercuric oxide is performed, for example, this procedure should be done under a hood because highly toxic mercury vapor is released. Since mercury is toxic, do not handle mercury from a broken thermometer since it can readily be absorbed through the skin.
7. Concentrated acid may not be made available to you in the biology laboratory. If, however, you should be required to make a dilution of concentrated acid, you should slowly *add the acid to the water* while stirring. (See Figure 20.) If you add water to concentrated acid, heat is suddenly released which may cause hot acid to spatter on you. (Heat is produced because the combination of concentrated sulfuric acid with water is not simply a physical process of dilution. Rather, this is a chemical reaction which releases heat. A small amount of acid in a large volume of water yields only a small amount of heat at a time.)

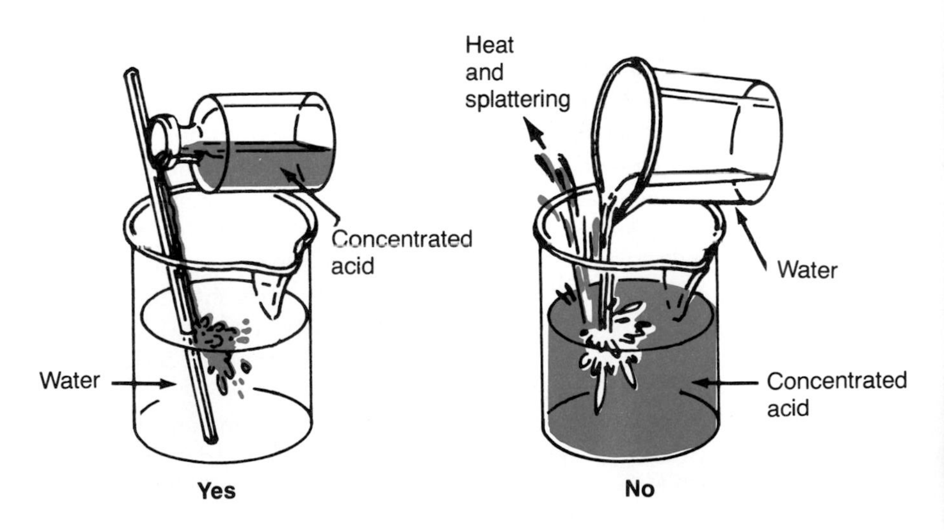

Fig. 20. Add concentrated acid to water, not the water to the acid

8. Do not return unused chemicals to their storage container. Contamination might result. Accordingly, avoid removing more chemicals from the container than you will need.
9. Strong acids and bases are caustic substances that can burn your skin and clothing. Handle them with special care. In the event of an accident, the first thing to do is flush the area with large amounts of water.
10. Use caution in smelling substances. First use your hand to waft a bit of the vapor to your nostrils and sniff gently.

Safety in handling dissecting instruments.
1. Recognize that scissors, scalpels, and dissecting needles have sharp edges and pointe so they should be handled with care (See Figure 13.) Not only can these instruments cause cuts and punctures, but they may carry infectious microorganisms from the specimen being dissected. Even the numerous dissecting pins that are used to pin the spcimen to the wax of the dissecting tray may cause infection. In wrapping the specimen in paper toweling for discard at the end of the laboratory session, be careful that the dissecting pins do not protrude from the toweling and puncture your skin.
2. Preserved animals that are provided for dissection may have their body cavity filled with the preservative formaldehyde. At the first incision into the body cavity, this chemical may shoot into your eyes causing a painful and dangerous burn. (In such an event, wash immediately with water.) Preserved specimens should be washed in running water before use. Make the first incision into the body cavity with special care.

Laboratory Skill 12:

• Collect, organize, and graph data.

Collecting data. In performing an experiment, each fact you collect is a *datum* and a mass of them constitutes *data*. Your experiment should be designed so that the data collected is *objective* rather than *subjective*. Objective data is free from personal feelings, whereas subjective data involves personal judgments by the experimenter. For example, using a finger to judge which of two liquids is warmer is a subjective evaluation; but using a thermometer to measure the temperature of the liquids is an objective evaluation. Much ingenuity goes into the design of scientific instruments to increase their objectivity so that each user will obtain the same reading. Learn to operate each instrument correctly to increase the accuracy of your observations.

Recording data. Collecting objective information often provides a host of data that is in numerical form. To be useful, data must be recorded, organized, and presented in a meaningful way. A *data table* should be prepared to record the information as it is collected. For example, a student who is investigating the rate of growth of bamboo stems might have a data table that looks like this:

Age in weeks	Height in meters
1	0.7
2	1.6
3	2.4
4	4.0
5	6.2

Data tables should have columns for the different kinds of information that will be collected. Each column should be headed with the kind of observable variable and the unit used, such as age in weeks, height in meters, weight in grams, or bubbles per minute.

Example: A student performed an experiment to determine the effect of temperature on the activity of the enzyme catalase. This enyzyme breaks down hydrogen peroxide (H_2O_2) yielding bubbles of oxygen. Using a constant concentration of both the peroxide and the catalase, and varying only the temperature, the student obtained data that was recorded in the table below. (The number of bubbles of oxygen produced per minute is an indication of the rate of enzyme activity.)

Temperature (°C)	Bubbles of oxygen/minute
0	2
10	24
20	36
30	54
40	68
50	2

Graphing data. The raw data recorded on the data table may be treated in a variety of statistical manners. One way organized data may be presented is in the form of a graph. Graphs are often superior to tables as a method of presentation because they show relationships in a vivid, pictorial manner. Three commonly used graphs are the line graph, the bar graph, and the circular graph.

The line graph. The raw data from the catalase experiment is presented as a line graph in Figure 21. Note the following:

1. The graph has a precise heading.
2. There is a horizontal (X-axis) and a vertical (Y-axis). The horizontal axis

has values for the *independent variable.* This variable consists of the varying temperatures provided by the experimenter. The vertical axis has values for the *dependent variable.* This consists of the varying number of bubbles produced by the enzyme and depends on the temperature.
3. The values for both axes start at zero at the lower left and values increase going to the right or going up.

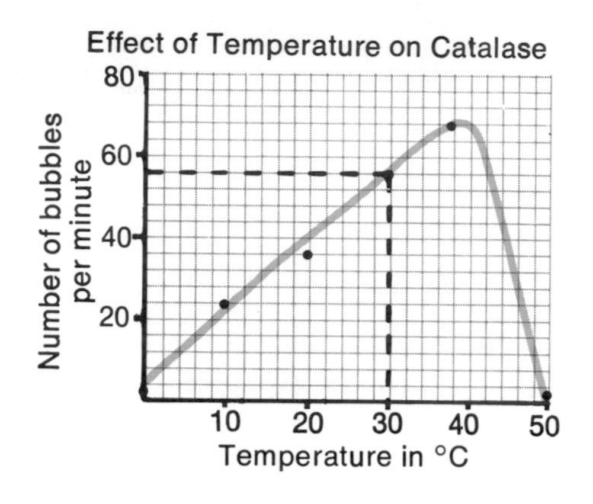

Fig. 21. Line graph of the catalase experiment

4. The numerical values have been selected so that they will fit on the paper. Each space on a line graph should represent a unit that is easy to work with. For example, 1, 2, 4, 5, 10, 100. (How many units are represented by each space on the vertical axis of Figure 21?) The units are not made so large that the graph runs off the paper nor is it so small that the graph is difficult to read.
5. After the points for the data were plotted, a smooth line was drawn that passes through most of the points. It is assumed that the changes in nature are smooth and that some of the data that diverges from a smooth line may be slightly in error.
6. Each point on the graph is located by two pieces of data from the data table. The dotted line shows you how to locate the point for 30°C.

A line graph may disclose a number of relationships which may not be readily apparent in a table. It shows whether the dependent variable goes up or down as the independent variable increases. A flat line indicates little change and a steep slope indicates a rapid change. In Figure 21, note there is a sudden decrease in enzyme activity at 40°C. Such a sudden change in the slope of a curve signals that a new phenomenon is occurring. It challenges the experimenter to develop a hypothesis for what is happening at this point and to investigate further.

The bar graph. The bar graph is used to compare data rather than to show relationships or gradual changes over a period of time. Figure 22 shows several graphs of pupil attendance in a certain school. The bar graph has no scale along the horizontal axis. The vertical bars can be of any width and spacing that is convenient and pictorially effective.

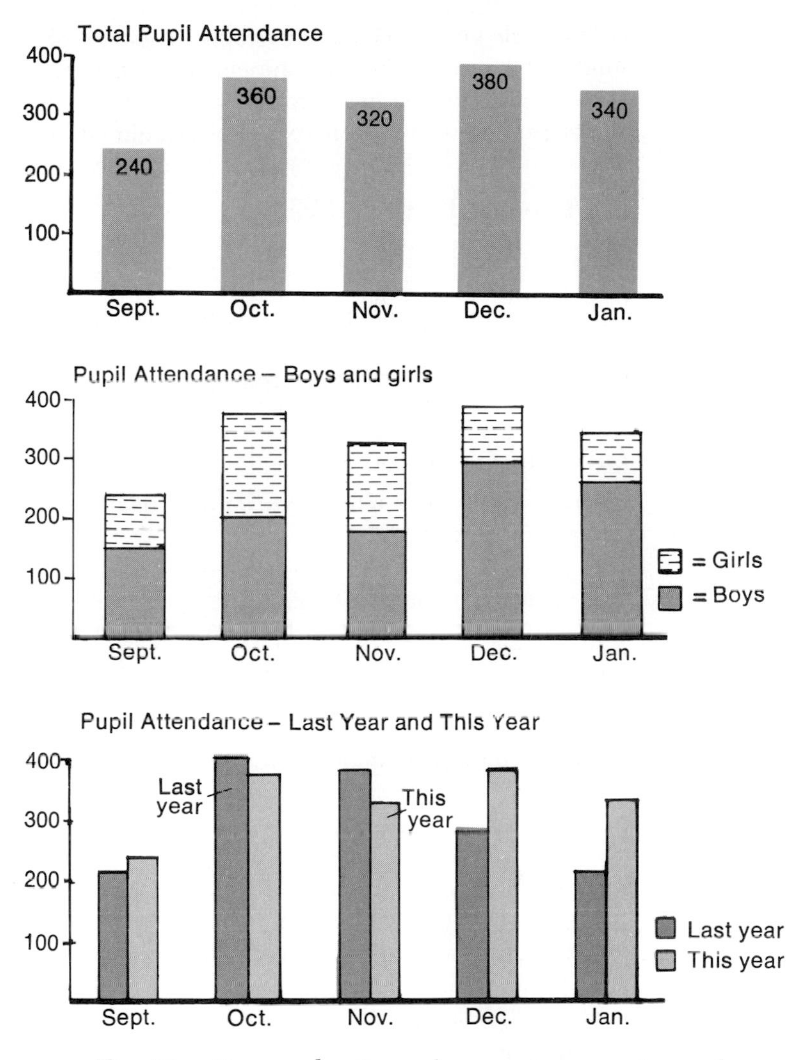

Fig. 22. Bar graphs. Several comparisons can be made in a single graph.

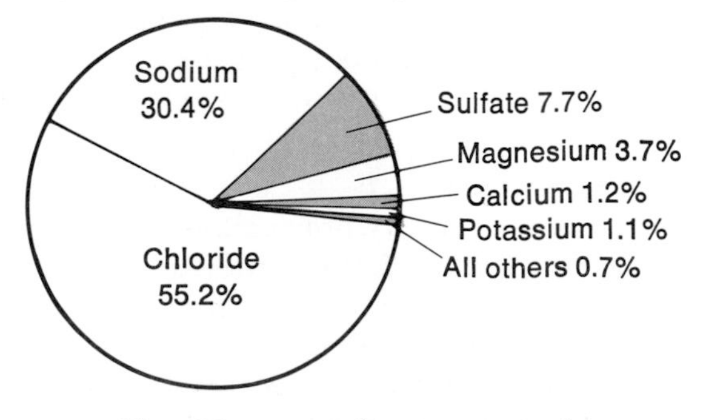

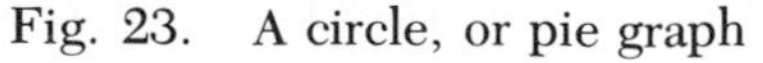
Fig. 23. A circle, or pie graph

The circle graph. The circle graph, or pie graph, is an effective way show the numerical relationship of the parts of anything to the whol Percentages appear as wedges, like pieces of a pie. Figure 23 is an examp of a circle graph. All the percentages should add up to 100%.

Pre-Lab and Post-Lab Skills

The pre-lab and post-lab skills are not strictly manipulative skills but rath are broad considerations related to the general philosophy and logic scientific experimentation. The "scientific method" is an organized ap proach scientists use in solving problems. These pre-lab and post-lab skil identify many aspects of this method.

Laboratory Skill 1:

- Formulate a question or define a problem and develop a hypothesis to b tested in an investigation.

This means that you should have a clear idea of what you are trying to te before you start your work. A *hypothesis* is a creative or imaginative leap explain some phenomenon. It must be stated in a testable form that subject to being disproved by observation and experimentation. Hypo theses can never be proven right in all infinitely possible situations, but the gain in credibility as they pass more and more tests. When generally ac cepted, they gain the status of theories, or even laws. Each of the followin laboratory experiments attempts to answer a question or test a hypothesis

Experiment 1. Is light needed for photosynthesis? Pin disks of cork t opposite sides of a geranium leaf. Keep the plant in the sunlight for severa hours. Remove the leaf from the plant and unpin the corks. Boil the leaf i alcohol to remove its chlorophyll, then cover the leaf with Lugol's iodin solution. The uncovered part of the leaf turned blue-black; the covered par remained the color of the iodine solution.

Experiment 2. Does a green plant use CO_2 during photosynthesis? I you exhale through a straw into a dilute solution of bromthymol blue, th CO_2 in your breath turns the indicator yellow. In the absence of CO_2 i turns blue again. Use *Elodea*, a green plant that grows underwater, fo your experiment.

Experiment 3. Do green plants in the sunlight give off a gas? Use sprig of *Elodea* in test tubes of water. What gas is probably present in th bubbles that arise from the plant?

Laboratory Skill 2:

- Given a laboratory problem, select suitable lab materials, safety equip ment, and appropriate observation methods.

Based on what you have learned in laboratory skills 4 through 12, selec materials (Figure 24) and methods for investigation of experiment 2 above Does a green plant use CO_2 during photosynthesis?

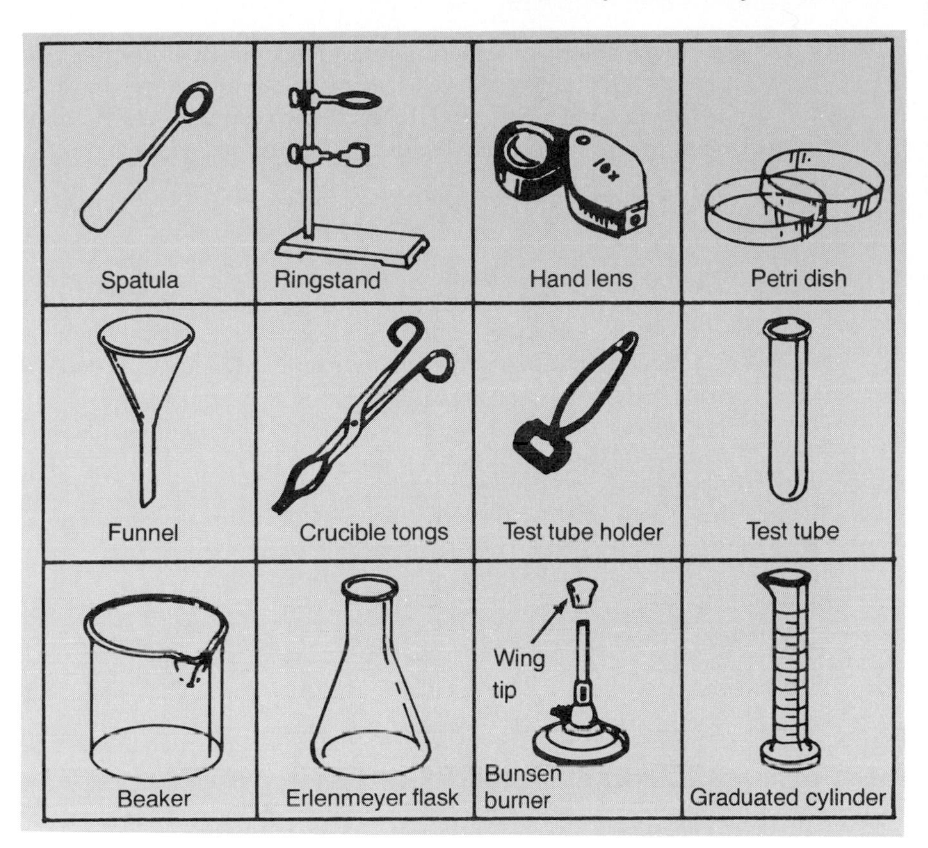

Fig. 24. Apparatus used in a biology laboratory

Laboratory Skill 3:

- Distinguish between controls and variables in an experiment.

An experiment has two parts—the experiment itself and the control, or check. Both parts should be exactly alike in all respects except for the condition being tested. That is, there should be only a single *variable* between the experiment and the control.

In the above experiment "Is light needed for photosynthesis to take place in a green plant?", the question should be easy to answer. This seems to be a well-controlled experiment; actually, it is not. (See pages 90-91 for a discussion.)

Laboratory Skills 13 and 14:

- Make inferences and predictions based upon data collected and observed.
- Formulate generalizations or conclusions of the investigation.

Draw conclusions that flow logically from the data. Beware of drawing conclusions that are more sweeping than warranted by the evidence. From an experiment conducted on corn seedlings, for example, do not make predictions or conclusions concerning all plants.

Figure 25 shows an experiment which indicates that the enzyme urease promotes the breakdown of urea at body temperature. In this experiment, the liberation of ammonia (NH^3) is detected by the use of red litmus paper. Ammonia forms a base which turns red litmus paper blue.

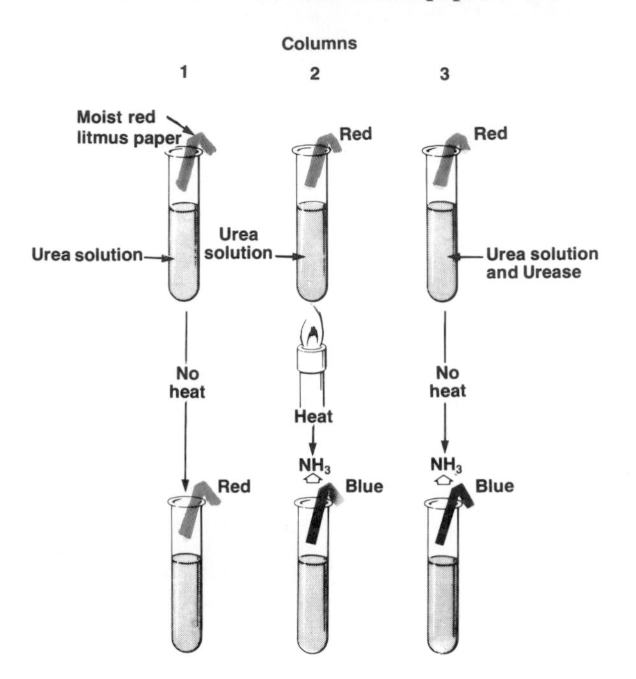

Fig. 25. This experiment shows that the enzyme urease promotes the breakdown of urea at body temperatures.

The following observations were made: Column 1 shows that a urea solution by itself does not liberate a gas which turns the red litmus paper blue. Column 2 shows that when the urea solution is heated, a gas is liberated which turns the red litmus paper blue. The gas is assumed to be ammonia because urea contains the amino group, NH_2. Column 3 shows that when the enzyme urease is added to the urea solution, the effect is the same as when the solution is heated; that is, the red litmus paper turns blue again. It is again assumed that the gas released is ammonia. Based on the observations, it can be concluded that the enzyme urease breaks down the urea solution at body temperature. Do you see any serious flaws in this demonstration?

Laboratory Skill 15

Assess the limitations and assumptions of the experiment.

In the above experiment, several assumptions are stated. It is assumed that room temperature is body temperature. Also, that the gas liberated is ammonia. The procedure is also limited by the need for additional trials.

When writing up a report of an experiment, you should point out such assumptions and limitations.

Laboratory Skill 16

- Determine the accuracy and repeatability of the experimental data and observations.

Data and observations are *valid* if they measure what they are supposed to be measuring. They are *reliable* if repeated trials give the same results. Statistical procedures are available to indicate the reliability of a set of observations. *Accuracy* is a general term which includes both validity and reliability of a set of observations.

Laboratory Skills Review Questions

Pre-lab Skills 1-3:

1. A student placed ten radish seeds of the same variety on moist paper in each of three Petri dishes and placed the dishes in the following environments:
   Dish No. 1—Refrigerator, 5°C
   Dish No. 2—Room temperature, 20°C
   Dish No. 3—Incubator, 37°C
   Which factor is the variable in this investigation? (1) temperature, (2) kind of seeds, (3) moisture, (4) number of seeds
2. Which would be best suited for tranferring a *Hydra* from a culture jar to a microscope slide? (1) cotton swab, (2) beaker, (3) medicine dropper, (4) forceps
3. In order to test the hypothesis that irradiating radish seeds slows down their rate of germination, which of the following experimental designs would be best to use? (1) Plant 25 irradiated radish seeds and 25 irradiated bean seeds and examine the results of both plantings. (2) Plant 50 irradiated radish seeds and examine the results of this planting. (3) Plant 50 irradiated radish seeds and 50 normal radish seeds at the same time and examine the results of both plantings. (4) Plant 25 normal seeds and one week later, plant 50 irradiated seeds. Examine the results of both plantings.
4. A student performed the following experiment: a dry piece of white bread was tested with iodine solution; the bread turned blue-black. Another piece of white bread was chewed and then tested with Benedict's solution; the mixture turned red. The student therefore concluded that when a piece of bread is chewed starch is changed to sugar. One error in the student's procedure was that he did *not* (1) test the chewed piece of bread for starch, (2) test the dry piece of bread for sugar, (3) consider the age of the bread, (4) use nitric acid.

Skill 4:

5. The *X* in the circle below indicates the position of an object in the field of your microscope. To get this object in the center of the field you should move the slide (1) to the left and up, (2) to the left and down, (3) to the right and up, (4) to the right and down.

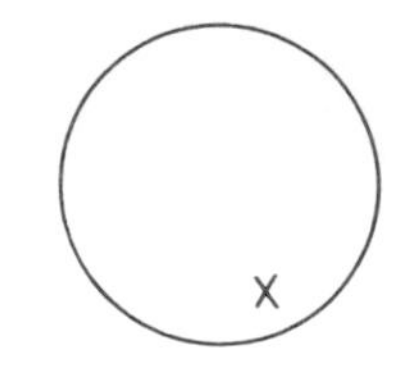

6. Changing from a 10X objective to a 43X objective is accomplished by (1) rotating the nosepiece, (2) adjusting the diaphragm, (3) turning the fine-focus knob, (4) turning the coarse-focus knob.
7. After switching to a higher-power objective, it is often necessary to (1) lower the eyepiece, (2) raise the eyepiece, (3) open the diaphragm slightly, (4) close the diaphragm slightly.

Skill 5:

Base your answers to questions 8 through 10 on the drawing below and on your knowledge of biology.

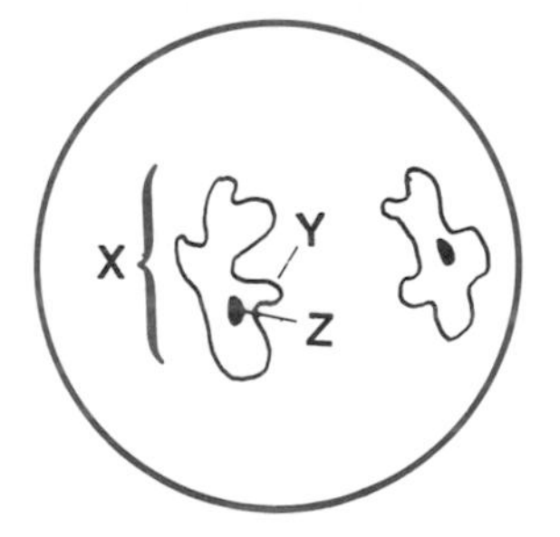

8. If the field of view shown in the drawing is 1.8 millimeters, what would be the approximate length of the organism, as indicated by bracket *X*? (1) 60 micrometers, (2) 600 micrometers, (3) 180 micrometers, (4) 1,800 micrometers
9. To which kingdom does the organism indicated by *X* in the drawing belong? (1) Monera, (2) Protista, (3) Animalia, (4) Plantae
10. If the organism indicated by *X* were viewed under a higher magnification, the actual length of the organism would (1) decrease, (2) increase, (3) remain the same, (4) increase then decrease.
11. The left side of the drawing on the next page (top) shows a plastic metric ruler as seen under the low power of your microscope. The drawing that is at the right side shows a strand of *Spirogyra* cells under low power of the same microscope.

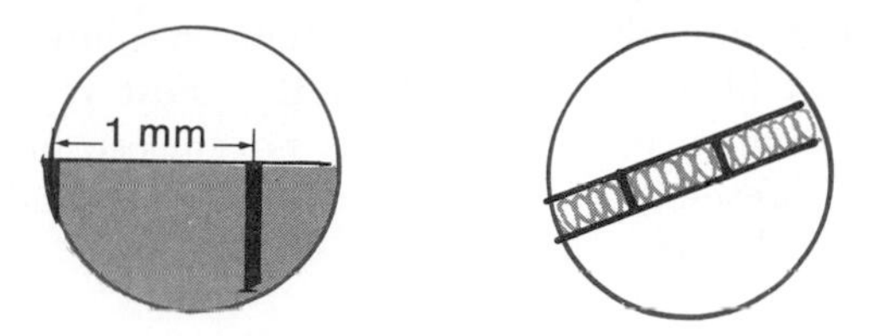

The length of each cell is approximately (1) 54 μm, (2) 43mm., (3) 430 μm, (4) 30 mm

Skills 6 and 7:

Base your answers to questions 12 through 15 on the statement below and on your knowledge of biology.

A leaf from the growing tip of *Elodea* is mounted in a drop of aquarium water for examination under the microscope.

12. The slide is gently warmed before being placed under the microscope. This is done in order to show (1) the nucleus, (2) osmosis, (3) cyclosis, (4) the cell wall.
13. Several drops of a strong salt solution are added to the water on the slide. A cell structure which will be better observed, after several minutes, as a result of this treatment is the (1) cell membrane, (2) cell wall, (3) nucleus, (4) chloroplast.
14. Proper illumination for viewing the leaf under the microscope may be obtained by adjusting the mirror, the light source, or the (1) eyepiece, (2) body tube, (3) nosepiece, (4) diaphragm.
15. To observe nuclei better without killing cells, a drop of the vital stain that may be drawn under the coverslip is (1) methylene blue, (2) iodine, (3) bromthymol blue, (4) Benedict's solution.

Skill 8:

16. Which of the following can best be used to determine whether a solution is an acid or a base? (1) Benedict's solution, (2) litmus paper, (3) iodine, (4) ethyl alcohol.
17. An indicator that would be useful in determining if germinating seeds give off carbon dioxide is (1) methylene blue, (2) bromthymol blue, (3) Lugol's iodine solution, (4) Benedict's solution.
18. If the apparatus shown below is placed in a moderately warm location, within a few hours the (1) molasses solution will turn yellow, (2) molasses solution will turn blue, (3) solution in the beaker will turn yellow, (4) solution in the beaker will turn blue.

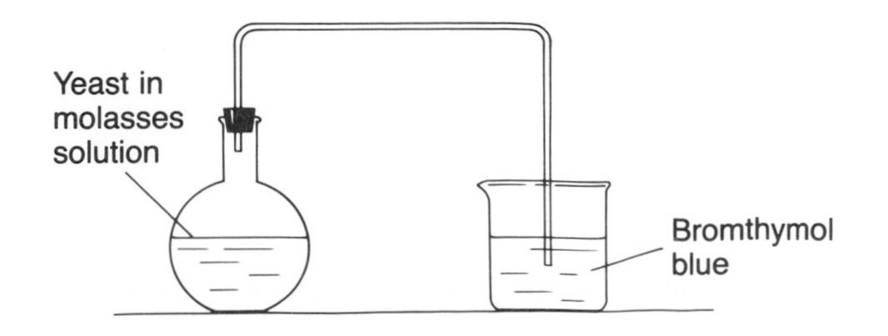

19. The result of testing an unknown solution with Benedict's solution was a blue color. Which is the most reasonable conclusion from this evidence? (1) There was no glucose present. (2) There was protein present. (3) The unknown solution contained starch. (4) The unknown solution contained fatty acids.

Skill 9:

20. In order to measure and pour 10 milliliters of Benedict's solution into a test tube, which of the following is the best procedure to ensure the accuracy of the measurement? (1) Use a graduated cylinder. (2) Measure the required amount with a metric ruler. (3) Weigh out 10 milliliters directly on a metric balance. (4) Fill a medicine dropper ten times.
21. Part of a meter stick is shown below. Which letter indicates a measurement of six millimeters?

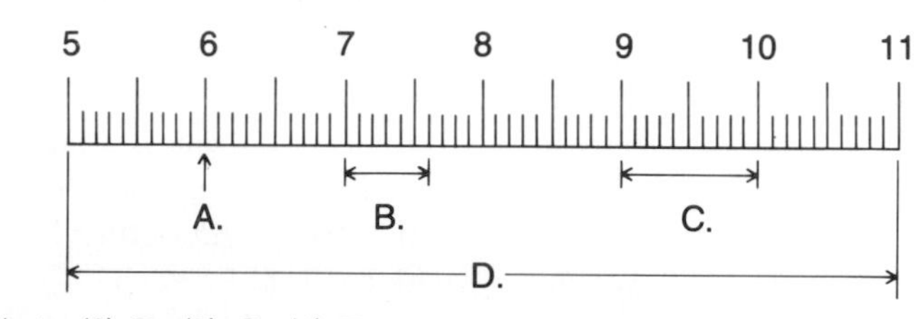

(a) A, (2) B, (3) C, (4) D

22. The drawing at the right shows a portion of a 100-ml graduated cylinder. What is the volume of the liquid? (1)42 ml, (2) 44 ml, (3) 48 ml, (4) 50 ml

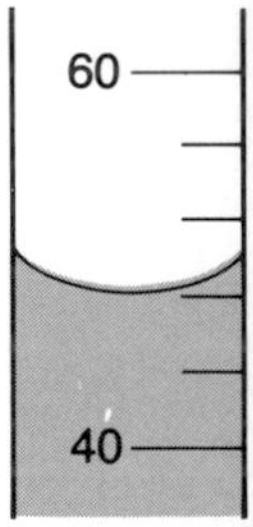

Skill 10:

23. In the drawing of a dissected lima bean seed, a cotyledon is represented by the letter (1) A, (2) B, (3) C, (4) D.

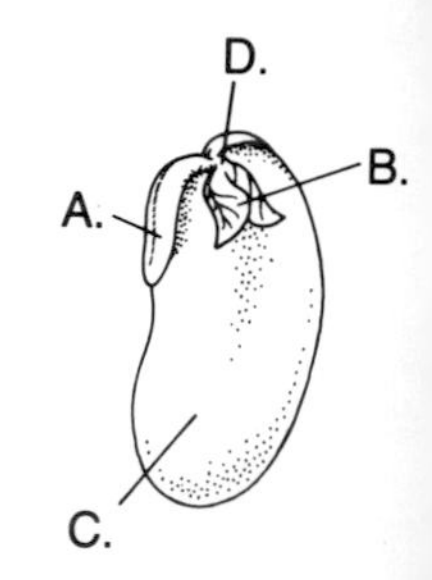

24. What is the *best* use for the dissection instrument illustrated in the diagram below?

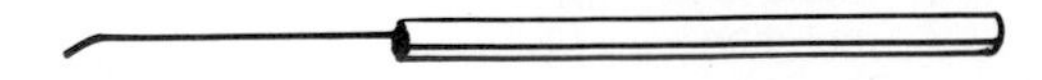

(1) cutting through bones, (2) cutting through thick muscles, (3) teasing apart muscle tissue, (4) removing plasma

Skill 11:

25. Which procedure should *not* be used during the heating of substances in a test tube? (1) Point the test tube away from you and others. (2) Stopper the test tube to prevent spills. (3) Wear safety goggles and a protective apron. (4) Use a test tube holder to avoid burns.

Skill 12:

Base your answers to questions 26 through 30 on the information below and on your knowledge of biology.

A laboratory investigation was performed to determine the length of time necessary to digest protein (egg white). Five grams of egg white taken from a hard-boiled egg, 15 milliliters of pepsin solution, and 2 milliliters of hydrochloric acid were added to a test tube. The percentage of protein digested was recorded over a 24-hour period, as shown in the data table below.

Time (in hours)	Total Percentage of Protein Digested
0	0
4	5
8	15
12	50
16	75
20	80
24	90

26. According to the data, during which four-hour time period did the greatest amount of protein digestion occur? (1) 0-4 hours, (2) 4-8 hours, (3) 8-12 hours, (4) 20-24 hours.
27. According to the data half the egg white is digested after (1) 24 hours, (2) 12 hours, (3) 16 hours, (4) 8 hours.
28. On a graph of this data, the vertical axis would read (1) Time, (2) Data table, (3) Percentage of protein digested, (4) Milliliters.
29. On a graph of this data the horizontal axis would read (1) Time, (2) Data table, (3) Percentage of protein digested, (4) Milliliters.
30. The most appropriate graph to represent the above data would be a (1) line graph, (2) bar graph, (3) circle graph, (4) pie graph.

Post-Lab Skills 13-16:

Base your answers to questions 31 through 34 on the following graph and accompanying information.

Equal weights of a yeast culture were placed in water solutions of four different sugars of the same concentration. Under the same conditions, the volume of CO_2 liberated at the end of various periods of time is indicated on the graph at the top of the next page:

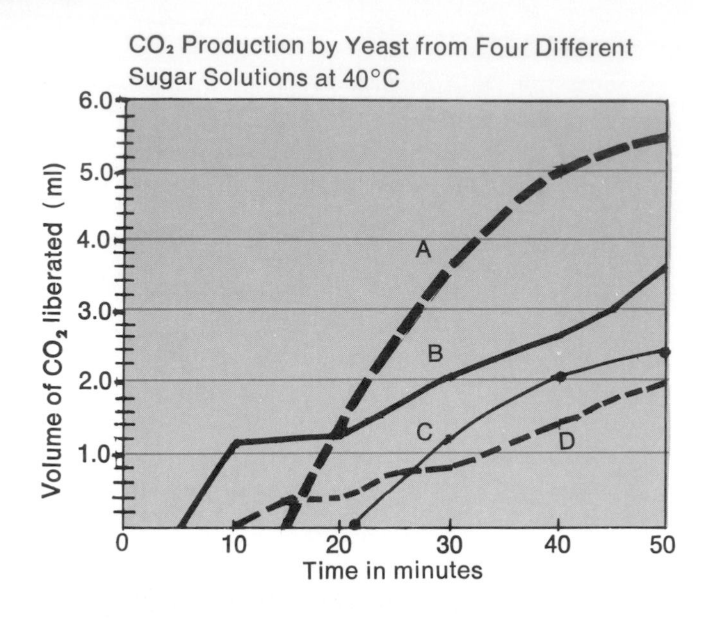

31. What was the volume of CO_2 liberated from sugar B after 30 minutes (1) 2.1 microns, (2) 2.1 milliliters, (3) 2.1 millimeters, (4) 2.1 liters.
32. From which sugar was CO_2 liberated first? (1) A, (2) B, (3) C, (4) D.
33. From which sugar was the most CO_2 liberated at the end of 3 minutes? (1) A, (2) B, (3) C, (4) D.
34. If the temperature is increased from 40°C. to 80°C., the volume of CO liberated from sugar C after 40 minutes will be (1) 2.0 ml, (2) 3.0 ml, (3) 4.0 ml, (4) impossible to determine from the information given.

Base your answers to questions 35 through 37 on the graph below and you knowledge of biology.

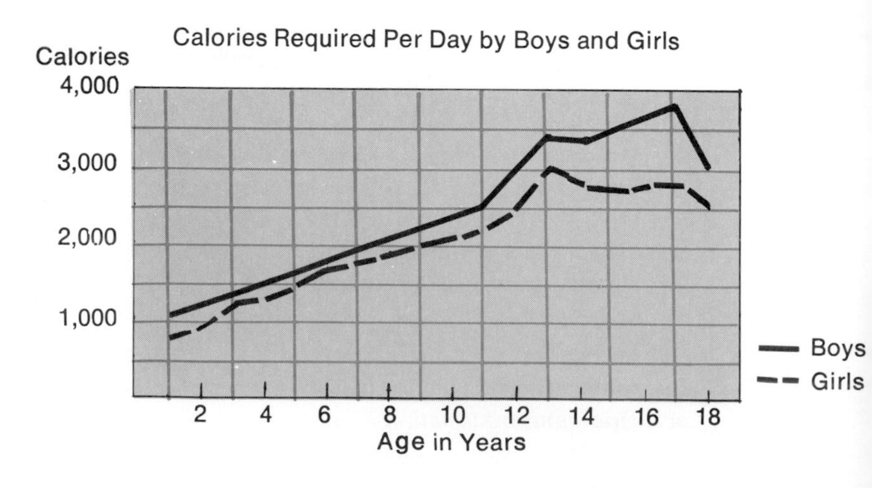

35. Approximately how many more Calories per day are required by boys than by girls at age 17? (1) 800, (2) 1,000, (3) 2,500, (4) 3,500.

36. On the basis of the graph it may be assumed that, in general, Calorie requirements for boys and girls (1) are quite similar until age 17, (2) are wholly dissimilar, (3) reach their peak at about the same age, (4) have a simliar rate of increase until about the age of 13.
37. If there is a direct relationship between physical growth and Calorie intake, the graph indicates that most girls will have completed their physical growth about (1) the same time as boys, (2) 1 to 2 years sooner than boys, (3) 4 years sooner than boys, (4) 6 years sooner than boys.

Base your answers to questions 38 through 40 on the experiment described below.

A group of 24 frogs was separated into two equal groups. Group A was placed in an environment in which the temperature was a constant 35°F. Group B was placed in a similar environment, except that the temperature was a constant 65°F.

Equal amounts of food were given to each group at the start of the experiment and every 24 hours thereafter. Immediately before each daily feeding the excess food from the prior feeding was removed and measured. Thus, it was possible to determine the daily consumption of food by each group. Each day the frogs in each group were checked for heartbeat rate and breathing rate.

At the end of the experiment, the following bar graphs were prepared:

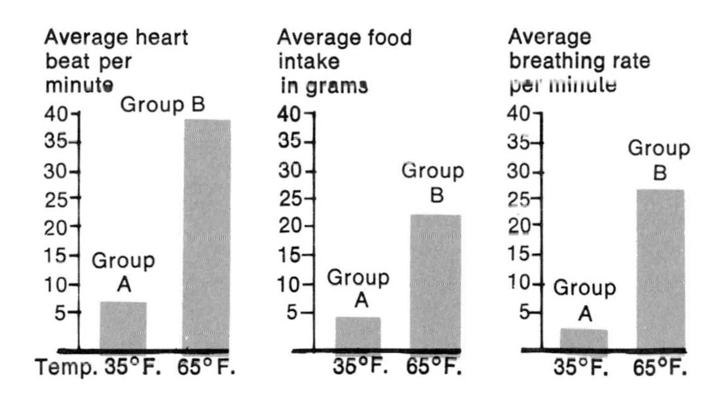

38. The specific question which the scientist was probably studying in this experiment was (1) how do living things adapt to a change in temperature, (2) in what ways do frogs adapt to a change in temperature, (3) how much oxygen does a frog need when the temperature changes, (4) how much blood is circulated through the heart of a frog when the temperature changes.
39. One could reasonably assume after an examination of the three graphs that at low temperatures the frogs (1) became more active, (2) produced less carbon dioxide, (3) required more food, (4) required more oxygen.
40. The experimental variable in this experiment was the (1) heartbeat rate, (2) breathing rate, (3) temperature, (4) amount of food consumed.

A Classification of Organisms.

The classification presented here provides details of the five-kingdom system that is in general use today. The five kingdoms may be organized into two super groups: the *prokaryotes*, whose cells lack a nuclear membrane, and the *eukaryotes*, whose cells have a true nucleus. Members of the kingdom Monera are prokaryotes; all members of the four other kingdoms are eukaryotes.

Classification of organisms is always subject to change by biologists. This change comes about for several reasons. One is that the discovery and description of new species changes the ways in which biologists group related organisms. Another is that new information that emerges about the biology of organisms changes biologists' views of the evolutionary relationships among groups of organisms.

Kingdom Monera

PHYLUM SCHIZOPHYTA. True bacteria: *Spirochaeta, rickettsia.*
PHYLUM CYANOPHYTA. Blue-green algae: *Nostoc, Oscillatoria.*

Kingdom Protista

The Protozoa
PHYLUM SARCODINA. Move by pseudopodia. Rhizopoda (*Ameba, Entameba)*, foraminifera, radiolaria.
PHYLUM SPOROZOA. Lack power of locomotion; reproduce by spores. *Plasmodium, Monocystis.*
PHYLUM MASTIGOPHORA. Move by flagella. *Trypanosoma, Astasia.*
PHYLUM CILIOPHORA. Move by cilia. *Paramecium, Stentor, Vorticella.*
The Algae
PHYLUM EUGLENOPHYTA. Photosynthetic flagellates not possessing a rigid cell wall. *Euglena.*
PHYLUM CHLOROPHYTA. Have a rigid cell wall; one-celled, multicellular, and colonial forms. Grass-green algae: *Spirogyra.*
PHYLUM PYRROPHYTA. Flagellated unicellular organisms conspicuous in the oceans; produce poisonous red tides which kill fish. Dinoflagellates.
PHYLUM CHRYSOPHYTA. Golden algae: diatoms.
PHYLUM PHAEOPHYTA. Brown algae: rockweeds, kelps, *Fucus, Laminaria.*
PHYLUM RHODOPHYTA. Red algae: *Chondrus crispus* (Irish moss).
The Slime Molds
PHYLUM MYXOMYCOPHYTA. Very simple organisms with both plant and animal characteristics. The spreading-mass stage is the plasmodium which contains hundreds of nuclei and no cell boundaries. Slime molds: *Lycogala, Physarum, Stemonitis.*

Kingdom Fungi

PHYLUM EUMYCOPHYTA. Single celled or composed of hyphae; lack chlorophyll; reproduce by spores.

CLASS PHYCOMYCETES. Produce spores in a sporangium; lack cross-walls in the hyphae. *Rhizopus.*

CLASS ASCOMYCETES. Spores produced in a sac-like cell, the ascus; hyphae with cross-walls. The sac fungi: *Saccharomyces*, yeast, *Neurospora*, *Aspergillus*, *Morchella*.

CLASS BASIDIOMYCETES. Spores borne on club-shaped structures called basidia; cross-walls present in hyphae. The club fungi: mushrooms, shelf-fungi, puffballs, truffles, rusts, smuts. *Puccinia*, *Ustilago*, *Psalliota*.

CLASS DEUTEROMYCETES. Fungi whose method of sexual reproduction is not known. They therefore cannot be properly classified. The imperfect fungi: *Penicillium*.

The Lichens

Mutualistic combination of an alga and a fungus. The alga is usually a blue-green or a grass-green alga; the fungus is usually an ascomycete. Rock tripe, reindeer moss, goblet lichen.

Kingdom Plantae (Plants)

PHYLUM BRYOPHYTA. Small plants without true roots, stems, or leaves, but which look like higher plants; gametophyte the dominant generation; sporophyte reduced in size and often parasitic on the gametophyte; no well-developed conducting tissue.

CLASS HEPATICAE. Low-lying plants which are often liver-like in shape, thin leathery leaves which grow flat on the moist soil or ground. Liverworts: *Marchantia*, *Riccia*.

CLASS MUSCI. Plant body is an erect shoot that bears tiny spirally arranged leaflets; no specialized water-conducting vesssls. Mosses: *Sphagnum*, *Polytrichum*.

PHYLUM TRACHEOPHYTA. The vascular plants, containing specialized water-conducting vessels; sporophyte is the dominant generation; gametophytes often microscopic and parasitic on the sporophyte.

SUBPHYLUM LYCOPSIDA. Small spirally arranged leaves which resemble those of mosses; spores borne in club-shaped strobili. Club mosses: *Lycopodium*, *Selaginella*.

SUBPHYLUM SPHENOPSIDA. Leaves arise in whorls from the main branch. Horsetails and scouring rushes; *Equisetum*.

SUBPHYLUM PTEROPSIDA. Possess relatively large leaves with many veins.

CLASS FILICINEAE. Underground stem (rhizome) gives rise to leaves (fronds); numerous sporangia often clustered on lower leaf surface. Ferns: *Marsilea*, *Azolla*, *Polypodium*.

CLASS GYMNOSPERMAE. Seeds not enclosed in a fruit ("naked"); many are evergreens. Cone-bearing plants: pines, spruces, firs, hemlocks, cedars, redwood, *Ginkgo*, cycads.

CLASS ANGIOSPERMAE. Seeds enclosed in a fruit ("hidden"). Flowering plants.

SUBCLASS DICOTYLEDONEAE. Embryo with two cotyledons; floral parts in groups of fours or fives; net-veined leaves; stems with a cylinder of vascular tissue. Dicots: buttercup, snapdragon, carnation, magnolia, rose, bean, parsley, honeysuckle, oak, maple, dandelion.

SUBCLASS MONOCOTYLEDONEAE. Embryo with one cotyledon; floral parts in groups of threes; leaves parallel-veined; stem with scattered vascular bundles. Monocots: lily, onion, palm, orchid, iris, tulip, and grasses such as wheat, rice, and corn.

Kingdom Animalia (Animals)

PHYLUM PORIFERA. Pore-bearing; two cell layers. Sponges (*Grantia*, bath sponge).

PHYLUM COELENTERATA. Hollow-bodied; two cell layers; tentacles with stinging cells. *Hydra*, jellyfish, sea anemone, coral.

PHYLUM PLATYHELMINTHES. Flattened bodies; three cell layers; mostly parasitic. Flatworms: tapeworm, liverfluke, *Planaria* (free-living).

PHYLUM NEMATODA. Long, cylindrical, unsegmented bodies; tubular digestive system with mouth and anus; parasitic and free-living. Roundworms: *Ascaris*, *Trichina*, hookworm.

PHYLUM ANNELIDA. Body segments very similar; complex organ systems. Segmented worms: earthworm, bloodworm, leech.

PHYLUM MOLLUSCA. Soft-bodied, many protected with shell. Mollusks: snails, slugs, clams, mussels, squid, octopus.

PHYLUM ARTHROPODA. Jointed appendages; exoskeleton; segments often fused to form definite regions of body; respiration by gills or trachea; ventral nerve cord.

CLASS CRUSTACEA. Lobster, crayfish, crabs, shrimp, barnacles, pillbug, *Daphnia*.

CLASS CHILOPODA. Centipedes.

CLASS DIPLOPODA. Millipedes.

CLASS ARACHNIDA. Usually has a fused head and thorax (cephalothorax); four pairs of legs. Spiders, scorpions, ticks, mites, horseshoe crab.

CLASS INSECTA. Three pairs of legs; body usually divided into head, thorax, and abdomen. Silverfish, grasshoppers, cockroaches, termites, lice, aphids, bugs, dragonflies, butterflies, moths, flies, mosquitoes, beetles, bees, ants.

PHYLUM ECHINODERMATA. Skin usually spiny; adults with radial symmetry; water vascular system. Spiny-skinned animals: starfish, sea urchin, sand dollar.

PHYLUM CHORDATA. Notochord; hollow dorsal tubular nerve cord; gill slits; segmentation. (The first three subphyla may be grouped as the Protochordates.)

SUBPHYLUM HEMICHORDATA. Acorn worms.

SUBPHYLUM UROCHORDATA. Tunicates.

SUBPHYLUM CEPHALOCHORDATA. Lancelets (*Amphioxus*).

SUBPHYLUM VERTEBRATA. Vertebrae form backbone; enlarged brain; appendages in pairs; olfactory organs, ears, and eyes.

FISH (NOT A TAXONOMIC DIVISION). Aquatic; breathe by gills; cold-blooded; air bladder; two-chambered heart; scales. (The fish consists of the next three classes, the jawless fishes, cartilage fishes, and bony fishes.)

CLASS AGNATHA. Jawless fishes; lamprey eel.

CLASS CHONDRICHTHYES. Cartilage fishes: sharks and rays.

CLASS OSTEICHTHYES. Bony fishes: perch, flounder, trout.

CLASS AMPHIBIA. Moist, smooth, scaleless skin; larvae usually aquatic and adults usually terrestrial; three-chambered heart; cold-blooded. Frog, toad, salamander, mud-puppy.

CLASS REPTILIA. Breathe by lungs from birth; scaly skin; three-chambered heart or four-chambered heart. Snake, lizard, alligator, crocodile, turtle.

CLASS AVES (BIRDS). Feathers; warm-blooded; skeleton with hollow bones, eggs with shell. Robin, penguin, ostrich, *Archaeopteryx*.

CLASS MAMMALIA. Mammary glands; give birth to living young; hair; warmblooded; four-chambered heart.

ORDER MONOTREMATA. Egg-laying nonplacental, primitive mammary glands. Duckbilled platypus, spiny anteater.
ORDER MARSUPIALIA. Nonplacental; young born immature and carried in marsupium (brood pouch). Opossum, kangaroo.
ORDER INSECTIVORA. Shrews, moles.
ORDER CHIROPTERA. Bats
ORDER EDENTATA. Anteaters, armadillos.
ORDER RODENTIA. Rats, mice, beavers, squirrels, guinea pigs, hamsters.
ORDER LAGOMORPHA. Differ from rodents in having an extra pair of incisor teeth. Rabbits and hares.
ORDER CETACEA. Whales, dolphins, porpoises.
ORDER CARNIVORA. Dogs, cats, bears, seals.
ORDER PROBOSCIDEA. Elephants.
ORDER SIRENIA. Manatees.
ORDER PERISSODACTYLA. Odd number of toes. Horse, zebra, hippopotamus.
ORDER ARTIODACTYLA. Even number of toes. Pigs, sheep, deer, cattle.
ORDER PRIMATES. Much enlarged brain; usually stand erect; thumbs opposing the other fingers; eyes on front of head; fingers with nails instead of claws. Monkeys, apes, humans.

Bibliography

UNIT I: Unity and Diversity Among Living Things

Attenborough, David. *Life on Earth.* Little, Brown & Co., 1981

Becker, Wayne M. *The World of the Cell.* Benjamin-Cummings, 1986.

Bender, Lionel. *Birds and Mammals.* Watts, 1988.

Berger, Jim. *Clear and Simple Chemistry.* Simon and Schuster, 1986.

Breslow, Ronald. *Enzymes.* Carolina Biology Reader, Carolina Biological Supply Co., 1986.

Buchsbaum, Mildred, *et al. Living Invertebrates.* Blackwell Publications, 1987.

Carolina Arthropods Manual. Carolina Biological Supply Co., 1982.

De Duve, Christian. *A Guided Tour of the Living Cell.* W. H. Freeman & Co., 1985.

Evslin, Bernard. *Thy Hydra (Monsters of Mythology).* Chelsea House, 1989.

Flint, S. Jane. *Viruses.* Carolina Biology Reader, Carolina Biological Supply Co., 1988.

Margulis, Lynn, and Karlene Schwartz. *Five Kingdoms,* 2nd ed. W. H. Freeman & Co., 1987.

Minelli, Giuseppe. *Amphibians.* Facts on File, 1987.

Minelli, Giuseppe. *Reptiles.* Facts on File, 1987.

Teasdale, Jim. *Microbes.* Silver Burdett, 1985.

UNIT II: Maintenance in Living Things

Harrington, W. F. *Muscle Contraction.* Carolina Biology Reader. Carolina Biological Supply Co., 1981.

Miller, Kenneth. *Energy and Life.* Carolina Biology Reader, Carolina Biological Supply Co., 1988.

Nakatani, Herbert Y. *Photosynthesis.* Carolina Biology Reader, Carolina Biological Supply Co., 1988.

Nicholls, P. *The Biology of Oxygen.* Carolina Biology Reader. Carolina Biological Supply Co., 1982.

Pritchard, J.J. *Bones,* 2nd ed. Carolina Biology Reader, Carolina Biological Supply Co., 1979.

Ralston, Diane D., and Henry J. Ralston III. *The Nerve Cell.* Carolina Biology Reader, Carolina Biology Supply Co., 1988.

Ross, Dennis W. *Blood.* Carolina Biology Reader, Carolina Biological Supply Co., 1988.

Wilkins, Malcolm. *Plantwatching: How Plants Remember, Tell Time, Form Partnerships, and More.* Facts on File, 1988.

UNIT III: Human Physiology

Arehart-Treichel, Joan. *Immunity: How Our Bodies Resist Disease.* Holiday House, 1976.

Elting, Mary. *The Macmillan Book of the Human Body.* Aladdin (Macmillan), 1986.

Restak, Richard. *The Brain.* Bantam Books, 1985.

Sproule, Anna. *Bodywatch: Know Your Insides.* Facts on File, 1987.

UNIT IV: Reproduction and Development

Flanagan, Geraldine Lux. *The First Nine Months of Life.* Simon and Schuster, 1982.

John, B., and K. R. Lewis. *Somatic Cell Division.* Carolina Biology Reader, Carolina Biological Supply Co., 1980.

Parker, Gary. *Life Before Birth.* Master Books, 1987.

Stone, Doris. *The Lives of Plants.* Scribner, 1983.

UNIT V: Genetics

Arnold, Caroline. *Genetics: From Mendel to Gene Splicing.* Franklin Watts, 1986.

Asimov, Isaac. *How Did We Find Out About DNA?* Walker, 1985.

Fox, L. Raymond, and Paul R. Elliott. *Heredity and You,* 2nd ed. Kendall-Hunt, 1983.

Gribbon, John. *In Search of the Double Helix.* Bantam Books, 1987.

UNIT VI: Evolution

Ayala, F. J. *Origin of Species.* Carolina Biology Reader, Carolina Biological Supply Co., 1983.
Berry, R. J., and A. Hallam, eds. *The Encyclopedia of Animal Evolution.* Facts on File, 1987.
Fox, Sidney. *The Emergence of Life: Darwinian Evolution from the Inside.* Basic Books, 1988.
McLoughlin, John C. *The Tree of Animal Life.* Dodd, Mead and Co., 1981.
Miller, Jonathan. *Darwin for Beginners.* Pantheon, 1982.
Taylor, Kenneth N. *What High School Students Should Know About Evolution.* Tyndale, 1983.
Woese, Carl R. *The Origin of Life.* Carolina Biology Reader, Carolina Biological Supply Co., 1984.

UNIT VII: Plants and Animals in Their Environment

Attenborough, David. *The Living Planet.* Little, Brown and Co., 1984.
Moore, Peter D. *The Encyclopedia of Animal Ecology.* Facts on File, 1987.
Pringle, Laurence. *Restoring Our Earth.* Enslow Publishers, 1987.
Sagan, Dorion, and Lynn Margulis. *Biospheres: From Earth to Space.* Enslow Publishers, 1989.
Smith, Howard E., Jr. *Small Worlds: Communities of Living Things.* Macmillan, 1987.
Wallace, David Rains. *Life in the Balance.* Harcourt Brace Jovanovich, 1987.

Glossary

Glossary

absorption The diffusion of water and dissolved materials into cells.

acetylcholine A neurotransmitter that functions in the transmission of an impulse across a synapse.

acids Compounds that ionize to form hydrogen ions, H^+

acquired characteristics Characteristics that are developed by an organism during its lifetime.

active immunity Immunity to a disease from having had the disease in a strong or mild form. (The body builds its own antibodies.)

active transport The process by which molecules move against the concentration gradient. (It is called active because energy must be contributed by the cell in order for it to occur.)

adaptation A change in a species that better fits it for survival in its environment.

adaptive radiation The production of a number of different species from a single ancestral one.

adenosine diphosphate (ADP) The molecule that is formed when one phosphate is removed from ATP.

adenosine triphosphate (ATP) Complex molecule in which the energy of cellular respiration is released.

adhesion The force of attraction between unlike molecules.

adrenaline A hormone which is secreted by the adrenal medulla that helps the body to meet emergency needs.

adrenocorticotrophic hormone (ACTH) The hormone that stimulates the adrenal cortex to liberate the hormone cortisol.

aerobic Occurring with the use of oxygen.

agar An extract from red algae which is used in culture media.

agglutinins Antibodies that cause clumping of large particles such as bacteria or blood cells.

algae A photosynthetic group of protists. (The algae include more than one phylum.)

alimentary canal The tube through which ingested material moves in vertebrates.

alleles The alternative genes for a trait (for example, in the case of the trait of height, the genes for tallness and shortness). Alleles occupy the same site on a chromosome.

alternation of generations A life cycle in which asexual stages alternate with sexual stages.

alveoli The functional units of the lungs where the exchange of gases between the external air and the blood occurs.

amino acids Compounds that have at least one amino group (NH_2) and one carboxyl group (COOH) bonded to a central carbon atom. (Amino acids are the building blocks of proteins.)

ammonia A highly toxic substance with the formula NH_3.

amniocentesis The withdrawal of a sample of amniotic fluid from a pregnant woman. The amniotic fluid contains embryo cells which are then examined.

amnion A thin membrane forming a closed sac around the embryos of some organisms.

Amphibia The class of chordates that consists of animals that go through a metamorphosis involving a water-dwelling stage followed by a land-dwelling stage; frogs and toads are amphibians.

anaerobe An organism that uses only anaerobic respiration—respiration, not requiring oxygen.

analogous structures Structures that have the same function but different basic compositions and different evolutionary origins.

angiosperms Flowering plants that reproduce by seeds hidden within a fruit.

Annelida The animal phylum that consists of segmented worms such as the earthworm.

anterior Front end or head of an animal.

antibodies Proteins produced in the blood as a reaction to the presence of antigens in the body.

antigen Protein foreign to the body which induces it to form antibodies.

antitoxin An antibody that neutralizes a specific toxin.

anus An opening at the posterior of an alimentary canal.

aorta A large artery leading from the heart.

aortic arch In the earthworm, one of the five pairs of lateral pumping arteries (sometimes called hearts).

artery Vessel that carries blood from the heart.

arteriole Small artery

Arthropoda The animal phylum that consists of "joint-legged" animals which includes lobsters and insects.

asexual reproduction Reproduction in which there is no fusion of nuclei.

assimilation The incorporation of digested molecules into the makeup of an organism.

atom The smallest particle of an element that can take part in a chemical reaction.

atomic mass or **mass number** The total number of protons and neutrons in the nucleus.

atomic number The total number of protons in the nucleus of an atom. (The atomic number also indicates the number of electrons in the shells.)

ATP-ase The enzyme that regulates the hydrolysis and synthesis of ATP.

atrium The thin-walled upper chamber of the heart that receives blood from the veins—also called the auricle.

autonomic nervous system The regulatory system that controls involuntary activities of the body; the system has two divisions: the sympathetic nervous system, and the parasympathetic nervous system.

autotrophs Organisms that can produce their own food from simple materials (*auto* = self; *trophe* = nourishment).

auxins Chemicals that inhibit or promote cell growth (also called plant hormones).

Aves (birds) A class of chordates characterized by feathers, a highly efficient lung system, a four-chambered heart, and hollow bones for flight.

axon The long portion of the neuron which transmits impulses away from the cell body.

bacteria (*sing.* = bacterium) A group of monerans, mostly heterotrophs, that have various shapes (bacillus, coccus, spirillum). Some cause disease and many are involved in the process of decay.

bacteriophage Virus that attacks and destroys bacteria.

bilateral symmetry Having a right side and a left side which are alike.

binary fission A type of asexual reproduction in which one cell splits into two cells of about equal size.

binomial nomenclature The two-name system for naming organisms in which the first name is the genus name and the second name is the species name.

biodegradable Capable of being broken down by natural biological processes.

biogenesis The theory that living things originate only from previous living things.

biology The study of living things.

biome A climax community of plant and animal life that is typical of a broad region with one kind of climate.

biosphere The portion of the earth in which ecosystems operate.

biotic Refers to life or living.

biotic environment The part of the environment which is living and directly or indirectly affects an organism.

bipedalism Walking on two feet.

bone A living tissue consisting of bone cells and a matrix containing calcium phosphate.

Bowman's capsule A double-walled cup at one end of a kidney tubule.

bronchi (*sing.* = bronchus) Two cartilage-ringed tubes that extend from the lower end of the trachea into the lungs.

bronchioles Subdivisions of the bronchi that branch into the lungs.

bryophyte One of the two plant phyla; divided into two classes: liverworts and mosses.

budding A type of asexual reproduction in which a new individual is produced as an outgrowth of the parent.

calorie The unit by which the energy value of food is measured; a (large) calorie is the amount of heat required to raise the temperature of one kilogram of water one degree Celsius.

cambium Plant tissue with the ability to carry on cell division. Differentiates into xylem and phloem.

capillary Thin-walled blood vessel where exchange of materials between the blood and the cells takes place.

carbohydrate An organic compound containing the elements carbon, hydrogen, and oxygen with the hydrogen and oxygen in a 2:1 ratio.

cardiac muscle A type of muscle found only in the heart.

carnivore A meat-eating animal.

catalyst A substance that affects the speed of a chemical reaction without itself being used up.

cell A unit of structure and function in organisms.

cell differentiation The development of special tissue characteristics by a cell that is unspecialized when first formed.

cellulose A carbohydrate present in the cell walls of plant cells.

cell wall A rigid envelope of nonliving material that surrounds the cell membrane of plant cells.

central nervous system The brain and the spinal cord.

centrioles Cylindrical particles in the centrosome which function in the division of animal cells.

centrosome A tiny spherical structure found mainly in the cytoplasm of animal cells near the nucleus. It functions during reproduction of animal cells.

cerebellum The part of the brain that coordinates and controls all voluntary and some involuntary activities and maintains balance.

cerebrum The enlarged forebrain that receives and interprets impulses from the sense organs and controls the higher functions such as reasoning, memory, and emotion.

chemical bond Force of attraction that links atoms together in molecules.

chemosynthesis The process by which organisms obtain energy by the oxidation of sulfur, iron, or other simple material.

Chilopoda A class of wormlike arthropods that have one pair of walking legs for each body segment.

chloroplast Plastid containing chlorophyll.

Chordata The phylum of animals that have notochords, stiff supporting rods of cartilage, in the dorsal (upper) parts of their bodies; includes the vertebrates.

chromatid One of the strands of a double-stranded chromosome formed by replication during cell division. The two chromatids are joined by a centromere.

chromosomes Structures within the nucleus that carry heredity and are more easily seen during the steps of mitosis.

cilium (*pl.* = cilia) A short outward projection from the cell membrane that functions in locomotion of some one-celled organisms and moves liquids and objects past stationary cells in multicellular organisms.

circulation The transport of materials within cells or between parts of a many-celled organism.

cleavage The early stages in the development of the embryo characterized by a rapid division of cells.

climate The general atmospheric and weather conditions of a region.

climax community A stable, self-perpetuating community in which populations exist in balance with each other and with the environment. Usually the last stage of ecological succession.

clone A line of genetically identical cells originating from one cell.

Coelenterata The phylum of the animal kingdom that includes *Hydra*, jellyfish, sea anemones, and coral; the bodies of coelenterates consist of a cuplike digestive sac with a wall composed of two layers of cells.

coenzyme A molecule which assists an enzyme in its action.

cohesion The force of attraction between like molecules.

cold-blooded animal One that has the same body temperature as the environment.

commensalism A symbiotic food relationship in which one organism benefits without harming the other one.

community Populations of different species in a given location, interacting with each other.

complete protein A protein that contains all the essential amino acids.

compound Two or more elements that are combined chemically.

conjugation A type of sexual reproduction found in simpler organisms in which isogametes fuse. The term is also applied to the exchange of nuclear materials in *Paramecium*.

consumer An herbivore that feeds directly on a producer.

contractile vacuole The vacuole associated with the regulation of water balance in protozoans.

coronary Pertaining to the heart; for example, the coronary circulation.

cotyledon Within the seed, the seed food supply to the developing embryo.

covalent bond The chemical bond that results from sharing electrons.

crossing-over The breaking of linkage groups and the exchange of these linkage groups between homologous chromosomes (Crossing-over occurs during meiosis.)

cross-pollination Transfer of pollen from an anther of one plant to a stigma of a plant of a different kind.

crustaceans A class of arthropods that are mainly aquatic—for example, lobsters and crabs.

cyclosis The circular movement of cytoplasm through a cell.

cytoplasm The protoplasm of a cell between the nucleus and the cell membrane.

dark reactions The reactions of photosynthesis which do not directly use light as a source of energy. (This is the synthesis phase of photosynthesis.)

deamination The removal of an amino group ($-NH_2$) from an amino acid.

decomposers Organisms that feed upon dead organic matter, returning inorganic materials to the environment where they are used again by other living things.

dehydration synthesis The combination of two molecules to form a larger molecule; in this process a molecule of water is released.

dendrites The branched extension of the cyton, or cell body.

denitrifying bacteria Those bacteria that convert the nitrogen of ammonia to free nitrogen.

deoxyribonucleic acid (DNA) Nucleic acid whose nucleotides contain deoxyribose sugar. DNA carries the genetic information and controls cellular metabolism.

deoxyribose A 5-carbon sugar having one less oxygen atom than ribose.

depletion The removal of organic matter and minerals from the soil.

dermis The inner layer of skin, below the epidermis, which consists mainly of connective tissue.

diaphragm A sheet of muscle that separates the thoracic (chest) cavity from the abdominal cavity which functions in breathing.

diastolic pressure The blood pressure resulting from the relaxation of the left ventricle (diastole).

diatom A single-celled organism with a hard silica cell wall.

dicot A plant that produces seeds having two cotyledons.

differentiation The process of forming different kinds of cells from the similar cells of the early embryo.

diffusion The migration of materials because of random molecular motion. (The net movement is from the region of higher concentration to the region of lower concentration of these molecules.)

digestion The process of breaking down large organic molecules into smaller, soluble ones by chemical and physical means.

dihybrid An organism that is hybrid for two traits.

dipeptide Two amino acids linked together by a peptide bond.

diploid number The number of chromosomes in the double set of homologs found in all body cells.

Diplopoda A class of wormlike arthropods that have two pairs of walking legs for each body segment.

disaccharide A double sugar formed by the union of two simple sugar molecules. Sucrose is a disaccharide.

DNA *See* deoxyribonucleic acid.

dominant gene A gene that exerts its full effect no matter what effect its allelic partner may have.

dominant species The species in each stage of ecological succession which exerts control over the other species present.

dorsal Having to do with the upper surface of an animal. In chordates, the same surface as the backbone. Toward the upper, or back, surface.

Echinodermata The animal phylum that consists of spiny-skinned animals; the starfish is a common example of this phylum.

ecology The study of relationships among living things and their interaction with the environment.

ecosystem A system containing a living community and its nonliving environment.

ectoderm Outer layer of cells in an embryo or simple animal.

effector Part of the body that responds to the stimulus received by a receptor.

egestion The removal of undigested food.

egg An ovum. The female gamete.

electron Negatively charged particle of an atom.

element The basic form of matter. A pure substance that cannot be decomposed or changed to another substance by chemical means. A sample of an element has atoms of only one kind.

elimination The removal of undigested food.

embryo An organism in an early stage of development.

emulsion A mixture composed of droplets of one liquid suspended in another.

endocrine gland Ductless gland that secretes hormones into the blood.

endoderm Inner layer of cells in a simple animal body or embryo.

endoplasmic reticulum Network of tubelike structures within the cytoplasm that forms a transport system for the cell.

endoskeleton An internal skeleton, composed of cartilage or bone, present in chordates such as fish, frogs, reptiles, birds, and mammals.

environment All of the substances, forces, and organisms that affect an organism during its life.

enzyme Protein produced by living things that acts as a catalyst in biochemical reactions.

epidermis The thin outer layer of skin.

epiglottis A cartilaginous flap which diverts food and liquid toward the esophagus and prevents it from entering the larynx.

erosion The action of wind and water that removes the soil.

esophagus The food tube connecting the pharynx and stomach; also known as the gullet.

eukaryotes Cells with a distinct nucleus.

evolution *See* organic evolution.

excretion The removal of harmful wastes of metabolism.

exoskeleton An external skeleton composed of chitin, present in such arthropods as crabs, spiders, lobsters, millipeds, and insects.

extensor A muscle that pulls on a bone so as to spread apart the opening at a joint.

external fertilization Fertilization that occurs outside the body of the female.

fat An organic molecule composed of three fatty acids and one glycerol.

fatty acid Organic acid in which the R group is a long hydrocarbon chain; part of a fat molecule.

feedback The automatic reversal or slowing of a process which occurs when its speed exceeds the limits imposed by the system.

female An organism that produces ova (or egg cells).

fermentation Anaerobic oxidation of a carbohydrate.

fertilization Sexual reproduction by the union of dissimilar gametes (heterogametes); for example, the fusion of a sperm nucleus and an ovum nucleus.

fetus A human embryo when it becomes recognizable as a human.

fibrinogen A protein in the plasma which functions in the clotting of blood.

filtration The removal of suspended impurities from a liquid by passing it through substances such as paper, porcelain, or charcoal.

flagellum (*pl.* flagella) A long whiplike projection used by some simple organisms for locomotion.

flexor A muscle that pulls on a bone so as to narrow the opening at a joint.

flower The organ for sexual reproduction in angiosperms.

food pyramid A representation of energy at various feeding levels of a community.

food web Interconnected food chains in an ecosystem.

fossil Any remains, impression, or trace of an organism that lived in the geologic past.

fraternal twins Twins that result when two ova, produced simultaneously, are fertilized by different sperm cells.

fruit A mature ovary with its seeds and any parts of the flower that remain attached.

FSH (follicle-stimulating hormone) A hormone that affects the ovaries by stimulating the growth of the follicle, and testes by stimulating sperm production.

Fungi A kingdom that consists of a group of plantlike organisms that lack chlorophyll.

gamete A cell that unites with another cell in sexual reproduction (a sex cell such as the sperm or ovum).

gametophyte The gamete-producing stage in an alternation of generations.

gamma globulin A fraction of the blood protein which includes the antibodies.

ganglion Cluster of neurons which may serve as a relay center for directing impulses in several directions.

gastrula The stage of the developing embryo which marks the beginning of differentiation and which consists of an inpushing of a hollow sphere to form a sac.

gene That part of the DNA molecule which holds a unit of genetic information.

gene frequency The ratio of an allele to its other alleles in a gene pool.

gene pool The sum total of all the genes collectively present within a given population.

genetics The study of the process of heredity.

genotype The genetic makeup of an individual.

genus A group of closely related species having a common ancestor in the recent past.

germination The growth of a new plant from the seed.

gill Respiratory organ in fish and other aquatic organisms.

glucagon A hormone secreted by the pancreas which helps to change glycogen to glucose.

glycerol An alcohol with three hydroxide (OH) groups.

glycogen A polysaccharide which is a major storage product in animals.

Golgi body Cell organelle which appears as a stack of flattened discs; seems to be involved in the packaging of molecules for secretion from the cell.

gonads Sex organs; ovaries and testes.

gymnosperms Class of seed plants that produce "naked seeds" on the scales of cones rather than protected in fruits; includes pine, spruce, and fir.

habitat The place where a species lives.
half-life The length of time it takes for half the atoms in a radioactive element to decay.
hemoglobin An iron-containing protein compound which helps to transport oxygen and carbon dioxide. (It gives blood its red color.)
hemophilia A hereditary condition in which the blood clots very slowly.
herbivore A plant-eating animal.
heredity The code combination received through the gametes of the parents.
hermaphrodite An organism that has both male and female sex organs.
heterotroph An organism that takes, as food, preformed high-energy molecules obtained from dead or living things (*hetero* = other; *trophe* = nourishment).
heterozygous Having two different alleles for a trait (hybrid).
homeostasis Maintenance of an organism's constant internal environment (*homeo* = same; *stasis* = condition).
homologous structures Structures (in various animals) that are fundamentally similar and have the same evolutionary origin. (They may have different functions.)
homologs The two chromosomes of a pair that carry genes for the same set kinds of traits.
homozygous Having a pair of identical genes for a trait (pure).
hormone Chemical secreted by the endocrine glands and carried by the bloodstream to target organs.
host The living organisms from which a parasite takes its food.
humus The organic portion of soil.
hybrid An organism in which the alleles of a pair are not alike (heterozygous).
hydrocarbon A compound containing only hydrogen and carbon atoms.
hydrolysis The splitting of large molecules into smaller units by the addition of water molecules.
hyperglycemia An excess of blood glucose.
hyperthyroidism An oversecretion of thyroxin which increases the rate of metabolism.
hypoglycemia A deficiency of blood glucose.
hypothalamus A structure located at the base of the brain which produces brain hormones that flow to the pituitary gland.
hypothyroidism An undersecretion of thyroxin which lowers the rate of metabolism.

identical twins Twins that result from a single fertilized egg.
immunity The resistance of an organism to disease.
impulse Electrical and chemical changes that travel along a nerve fiber.
inbreeding The mating of organisms of the same strain.
incomplete dominance A type of heredity in which the hybrid is intermediate between the purebred dominant and recessive parents.
incomplete protein A protein that lacks one or more of the essential amino acids.
index fossil A fossil of an organism which can be used to determine relative ages of other fossils and rocks.
insulin A hormone secreted by the pancreas that helps to convert glucose to glycogen.
intercellular fluid (ICF) Tissue fluid consisting of water and dissolved materials that carries food, oxygen, and other materials from the capillaries to the cells and returns CO_2 and other materials to the capillaries.
interferon A defensive protein produced by living cells that have been entered by a virus.
internal fertilization Fertilization inside the body of the female.
ion An atom (or group of atoms) that has gained or lost one or more electrons.
ionic bond The chemical bond that results from the transfer of electrons.
ionization A process by which a compound is separated into ions.
isomers Compounds with the same empirical formula but different structural formulas.
isotopes Atoms that have the same atomic numbers but different atomic masses.

lacteal A projection of the lymph system into the villus. The lacteal absorbs the end products of fat digestion (fatty acids and glycerol).
lactic acid A 3-carbon organic acid which is formed during anaerobic respiration from pyruvic acid. (Lactic acid has the formula $CH_3-CHOH-COOH$.)
larva An immature stage in the metamorphosis of an insect.
larynx The voice box, situated just above the trachea in humans. (Air enters the trachea through the larynx.)
lichen A combination of an alga and a fungus

which exists in a relationship of mutualism.

life cycle A term used to describe the life history of an organism which has different life forms at different stages.

ligament Strong, fibrous tissue that connects bones to other bones at joints.

light reactions The reactions in photosynthesis which directly require light as a source of energy. (This is the "photo" phase of photosynthesis.)

linkage The sticking together of genetic traits that occurs because their genes are present on the same chromosomes.

lipid Organic compound composed of fatty acids and glycerol. Lipids are the fats, oils, and waxes.

locomotion The ability to move from place to place.

lung An organ for breathing air found in higher animals.

lymph A colorless fluid found in tissue spaces and in lymph vessels. (Also called tissue fluid or intercellular fluid.)

lymphatics Lymph vessels.

lymphocytes White blood cells that help the body develop immunity against foreign proteins.

lysosomes Small, oval bodies of the cell that contain chemicals used in digestion.

male Organism that produces sperm cells.

Mammalia The class of chordates distinguished by three main characteristics: they give birth to living young; they have mammary glands to supply their young with milk; and they have hair on their bodies.

mammary gland Gland that secretes milk.

matrix Material between cells. (Also called intercellular material.)

matter Anything that has mass and occupies space.

medulla The posterior part of the brain which is the control center for various involuntary activities.

meiosis A kind of cell division in which the number of chromosomes is reduced to half.

menstruation Periodic discharge of the lining of the uterus when an embryo is not implanted.

meristem Undifferentiated cells in a plant (for example, cambium).

mesoderm Middle layer of cells in a simple animal body and developing embryo.

metabolism The sum total of all the life processes.

metamorphosis A series of changes from an egg to an adult.

micron (micrometer, μ) A microscopic unit of measurement equal to 1/1000 of a millimeter.

microorganism Any organism so small that it can be seen only under the microscope.

mitochondria Organelles in which most of the reactions of cellular respiration occur—the powerhouses of the cell.

mitosis The exact duplication of the nucleus of a cell so as to form two identical nuclei during cell division.

mixture A substance in which several kinds of molecules are associated physically without being combined chemically.

molecular formula A representation of a molecule that indicates the number of each kind of atom but does not describe the arrangement of atoms.

molecule A combination of two or more atoms joined by chemical bonds.

Mollusca An animal phylum including clams, snails, and squid, that consists of soft-bodied, unsegmented animals that have three layers of tissue and well-developed organ systems; the bodies of many mollusks are protected by shells of calcium carbonate.

molting The discarding of an exoskeleton during metamorphosis.

Monera A kingdom that comprises bacteria and blue-green algae—organisms distinguished by the fact that they lack a distinct membrane-bound nucleus.

monocot A plant that produces seeds having one cotyledon. Corn is a monocot.

monohybrid An organism that is hybrid for only one trait.

monoploid number The number of chromosomes in a single set of homologs. (This is the number found in sperm and ova.)

monosaccharide Single sugar or simple sugar. The basic unit of complex carbohydrates; glucose, fructose, and galactose are monosaccharides.

motile Capable of locomotion.

mucus A slippery, largely protein, substance secreted by living cells that provides lubrication.

mutation A genetic change which can be inherited.

mutualism A relationship in which two organisms live together to the advantage of both.

Nematoda (roundworms) One of the three phyla of wormlike animals. Nematode bodies are round in cross section.

nephron Microscopic tubelike structure in the kidneys that removes wastes from the blood.

nerve A bundle of axons covered with connective tissue.

nerve net The simple network of nerve cells found in *Hydra*.

neuron The nerve cell that is the basic unit of the nervous system.

neuropeptides Small chains of amino acids that bind to receptors of the brain.

neurotransmitter A chemical, secreted by the ends of nerve cells, which carries impulses across the synapse from neurons to other neurons or to muscle and gland cells. Two common neurotransmitters are acetylcholine and noradrenaline.

neutralization The union of hydrogen ions and hydroxide ions from an acid and a base to form water and a salt.

neutron A subatomic particle with a mass number of 1 and no charge. (It acts as though it were composed of a proton and electron.)

niche The role a species plays in the life of the community.

nitrifying bacteria Bacteria that oxidize ammonia to nitrates or oxidize nitrites to nitrates.

nitrogen-fixing bacteria Bacteria that produce nitrogen compounds by combining other elements, such as oxygen, with free nitrogen.

nonbiodegradable Chemical substances which are *not* broken down by natural biological processes.

nondisjunction Failure of the chromosomes to separate from each other after synapsis.

notochord A stiff supporting rod in the dorsal part of the body found at some stage in the life of a chordate.

nucleic acid Compound consisting of nucleotides linked in a chain. (Examples are DNA and RNA.)

nucleolus A structure contained within the nucleus of a cell composed mainly of RNA and involved in the passage of RNA to the cytoplasm.

nucleotide A building block of nucleic acids composed of three elements: a nitrogen base, a phosphate, and a 5-carbon sugar.

nucleus The spherical body which contains the chromosomes. The nucleus of an atom is the central mass which contains the protons and neutrons.

nutrients The useful portion of foods; there are six main groups of nutrients: carbohydrates, proteins, fats, vitamins, minerals, water.

nutrition Those activities of an organism by which it takes food materials from its environment and makes them usable.

oogenesis The series of cell divisions and other changes by which a diploid primary egg cell produces a monoploid ovum.

organ A group of specialized tissues performing one main function. Examples: stomach, kidney.

organ system A group of organs which carry one one of the major functions of the body. (For example, the digestive system.)

organelles Specialized microscopic structures within the cell.

organic chemistry The study of carbon compounds in living and nonliving things.

organic evolution The theory that existing living things developed by a process of change from earlier forms of life.

osmosis The diffusion of water molecules through a membrane.

ovaries The gonads of the female animal that produce ova.

ovulation The discharge of mature ova from the ovaries.

ovule Structure in the ovary of a flower which develops into the seed.

ovum A female gamete; egg cell.

oxidation The loss of hydrogen or of electrons in a chemical reaction, resulting in the release of energy.

parasite An organism that lives on or in a host from which it takes its food.

parthenogenesis The development of an egg into a new individual without its being fertilized by a sperm cell.

passive immunity Immunity that an individual has to a disease as the result of being inoculated with antibodies.

passive transport Diffusion of molecules from a region of high concentration to a region of low concentration. (It is called passive because it occurs without energy being added to the process.)

peptide Short chain of amino acids.

peptide bond The bond between two amino acids in a polypeptide or protein.

peripheral nervous system Includes spinal nerves to and from the spinal cord and the autonomic nervous system.

peristalsis A series of wavelike muscular contractions and relaxations by which food is moved through the alimentary canal.

phagocytes White blood cells that engulf and destroy bacteria.

phagocytosis The engulfing of bacteria particles by white blood cells; the process by which pseudopods of a cell flow around matter and engulf it forming a food vacuole.

pharynx The cavity at the back of the oral cavity where the adenoids and tonsils are located—the throat.

phenotype The observable appearance or characteristics of an individual resulting from its genotype.

phloem Thin-walled plant cells that primarily transport food downward in the stem.

phospholipids Phosphorus and oxygen attached to lipid molecules. Phospholipids make up the two layers of the cell membrane.

photolysis The decomposition of water into hydrogen and oxygen by light energy during the light reactions of photosynthesis.

photosynthesis The process by which green plants use energy from sunlight to make their own food from simpler materials.

phylum A large division of classification below the kingdom.

pinocytic vesicle Saclike enfolding of the cell membrane which takes in large molecules.

pinocytosis The process by which large molecules, such as proteins, enter the cell by means of pinocytic vesicles.

pioneer organisms The first organisms to populate a barren region.

Pisces (fish) A class of chordates with gills and two-chambered hearts. Pisces move by means of paired fins.

placenta The structure by which the mammalian embryo is attached in the uterus of the mother and through which nutrients and wastes pass while the embryo develops.

plankton The mass of minute organisms floating near the surface of the sea.

plasma The liquid part of the blood.

plasmolysis The shrinking of the cell contents due to loss of water by outward osmosis.

plastids Small structures found in the cytoplasm of cells of higher plants and some one-celled organisms. Chloroplasts are plastids that contain chlorophyll.

platelets Fragments of the cytoplasm of certain giant bone cells that function to initiate the complex series of biological reactions that cause blood to clot.

Platyhelminthes (flatworms) The simplest of the three phyla of wormlike animals; their bodies are flat in cross section, show bilateral symmetry, and are composed of three layers of cells.

pollen Grains that contain the male sex cells of a flowering plant.

pollination Transfer of pollen from an anther to a stigma.

polypeptide A large number of amino acids linked by peptide bonds. (Polypeptides combine to form proteins.)

polyploidy A condition in which the cells have extra sets of chromosomes, beyond the diploid number. (Polyploid individuals may have $3n$, $4n$, $5n$, $6n$, etc. chromosomes.)

polysaccharide Carbohydrate having more than two monosaccharide units.

population All members of a species inhabiting a given location.

Porifera The phylum of the animal kingdom characterized by bodies having many pores (sponges).

posterior The rear portion of an animal.

predator An animal that kills another organism (the prey) and then eats it.

producer An organism that uses the sun's energy in the manufacture of food from simple raw materials.

proglottid One of the segments of the tapeworm.

prokaryotes Cells without a distinct nucleus.

proteins Tissue-building organic compounds composed of numerous amino acids linked by peptide bonds. (The main elements present are C, carbon; H, hydrogen; O, oxygen; N, nitrogen; and S, sulfur.)

Protista A kingdom that includes a number of microscopic organisms that cannot be definitely classified as plants or animals; examples are *Euglena*, algae, protozoa, slime molds, and viruses.

proton A particle in the nucleus of an atom that has a mass number of 1 and a positive charge.

protoplasm A term used to designate all the substances that collectively form the living contents of a cell.

protozoa A group of simple animal-like protists. (The protozoa include more than one phylum.)

pseudopod Outpushing of protoplasm used in locomotion and food getting, as in *Ameba* and white blood cells.

pulmonary Pertaining to the lungs.

Punnett square A checkerboard method for determining the probability of obtaining various results in genetic crosses.

pyruvic acid A 3-carbon molecule that is produced during the anaerobic phase of cellular respiration.

R group In an organic compound, a general expression for any of a number of combinations which can substitute for a hydrogen atom.

race A regional group of interbreeding individuals who have many genes in common.

radial symmetry Having parts of the body radiate from a central axis. (An organism having radial symmetry can be divided into two identical halves by any plane passing through the central axis.)

radioactive isotope Isotope that changes to another atom upon emitting radiations consisting of particles or electromagnetic waves.

radio-carbon method A method for dating fossils not much older than 40,000 years, based on the decay of carbon-14.

reabsorption The process by which materials are absorbed again. For example, the reabsorption of water from the large intestine back into the blood system.

receptor A site that consists of specialized nerve tissue sensitive to a specific stimulus.

recessive Pertaining to the gene that is masked in the F generation if the allelic gene is dominant.

recombination The formation of new linkage groups during crossing-over.

red corpuscles The blood cells which contain hemoglobin.

reduction A gain of electrons or a gain of hydrogen atoms by an atom or molecule—the opposite of oxidation.

reflex An inborn, automatic act.

regeneration The ability of an organism to grow back a missing part. Also, the ability of one of the parts to develop into an entire animal.

regulation The control and coordination of the various activities of an organism; in higher animals regulation is carried on by the nervous system and the endocrine system.

renal Pertaining to the kidney.

replication The process by which the DNA molecule makes an exact copy of itself.

reproduction The process by which organisms produce new individuals of the same kind.

Reptilia A class of chordates that includes turtles, lizards, snakes, crocodiles, and alligators and is characterized by the female laying large eggs on land from which hatch land-living creatures.

resolution The ability of an optical system to distinguish clearly and in detail between two lines that are very close to each other.

respiration The process by which energy is released from food molecules by oxidation.

response The movement, or secretion resulting from a stimulus.

rhizome A thickened, woody underground stem.

ribonucleic acid (RNA) Nucleic acid containing nucleotides in which the sugar is ribose. RNA works with DNA in performing the instructions of the genetic code.

ribosomes Tiny dense particles composed of ribonucleic acid (RNA) and protein that are attached to the wall of the endoplasmic reticulum or that move freely in the cytoplasm. Sites of protein synthesis in the cell.

RNA *See* ribonucleic acid

roughage Food substances that cannot be digested and pass out of the body unused; generally cellulose.

saprophyte A heterotrophic plant that obtains food from dead organisms.

scavenger An organism that feeds upon the bodies of dead animals or plants.

scientific theory Coordinated ideas (based upon verified data, controlled experimentation, and logical thought) providing a meaningful, overall explanation that is subject to testing.

scion The portion of a stem grafted onto a rooted stock.

secretion A chemical substance synthesized by an organism for its metabolism. Also, the production of secretions.

seed A ripened ovule containing an embryo.

selectively permeable membrane A membrane that permits some materials to pass through readily but not others.

self-pollination Transferal of pollen from an anther to a stigma of a flower on the same plant.

serum Plasma without fibrinogen and other clotting factors.

sessile A term that describes organisms that cannot move from place to place.

sexual reproduction Reproduction by fusion of the nuclei of two cells.

skeletal muscle Striated muscle that moves the bones of the skeleton and is controlled voluntarily by the nervous system.

smooth muscle Unstriated muscle consisting of spindle-shaped cells, controlled involuntarily by the nervous system.

solution A uniform mixture of the molecules of a solute and a solvent.

somatic nervous system The part of the nervous system that controls the voluntary muscles of the skeleton.

speciation The process by which a single species can separate into two or more species.

species A group of organisms that breed together to form fertile offspring. The basic unit in taxonomy.

sperm A male gamete.

spermatogenesis The production of monoploid sperm from diploid sperm mother cells.

spinal cord In vertebrates, a dorsal tube containing bundles of nerve fibers and serving as a center for reflex action.

spontaneous generation The belief that living things can originate from nonliving matter.

spore An asexual reproductive cell which can give rise to a new organism.

sporophyte The spore-producing stage in an alternation of generations.

staphylococcus A mass of cocci (spherical bacteria).

stimulus A change in the environment that causes a response in an organism.

stock The rooted portion of a plant to which the scion from another plant is grafted.

structural formula A representation of a molecule that uses dashes to show the bonds between atoms.

substrate The material acted upon by an enzyme.

succession The orderly process by which one biotic community is replaced by another.

symbiosis A nutritive relationship in which organisms of different species live together. The relationship may be mutualism, commensalism, or parasitism.

synapse The microscopic gap between the terminal branches of one neuron and the dendrites of the next neuron.

synapsis The pairing of homologous chromosomes during meiosis.

synthesis The chemical reactions by which small molecules combine to form larger molecules.

systolic pressure The blood pressure resulting from contraction of the left ventricle (systole).

tagged atom or **tracer** An isotope used to trace an element within a series of chemical reactions.

taxon A category of classification; in order from highest to lowest the taxons are: kingdom, phylum, class, order, family, genus, species.

taxonomy The science of classification of presently existing and extinct organisms.

tendon Tough, inelastic, fibrous cord that attaches muscles to bones.

testes The gonads of the male animal.

tetrad A group of four chromatids formed during synapsis of meiosis.

theory (*See* scientific theory.) A general statement that unifies many isolated facts into a broad idea to explain a phenomenon.

thyroxin The hormone secreted by the thyroid gland that increases the general rate of metabolism in the body [also, in frogs].

tissue A group of cells that perform the same function.

toxin Poisonous chemical produced by a microorganism. (Toxins cause disease.)

trachea The large tube, commonly called the windpipe, that extends from the larynx to the bronchi.

tracheophyte A plant of the phylum Tracheophyta that has a vascular system of tubes for conducting water; the more advanced tracheophytes have true roots, stems, and leaves.

transpiration The process by which a plant gives off water.

transport The process by which materials are carried across membranes or distributed within an organism.

tropism The growth of part of a plant toward a stimulus (positive tropism) or away from a stimulus (negative tropism).

uranium-lead ratio A method which is used for dating ancient igneous rocks based on the radioactive disintegration of uranium.

urea A nontoxic and soluble nitrogenous waste that is present in urine and perspiration.

ureters The tubes that carry urine from the kidneys to the urinary bladder.

urethra The tube that carries urine from the bladder out of the body.

vacuole Spherical, bubblelike storage sac found in many cells.

vascular bundle Conducting tube in plants, consisting of xylem, phloem, and cambium.

vegetative propagation A method of asexual reproduction in which a new plant develops from roots, stems, or leaves.

vein Vessel that carries blood to the heart. Also, conducting tube in leaves.

ventral Pertaining to the under surface of an animal.

ventricle Muscular chamber of the heart that pumps blood into arteries.

vertebrates Chordates which have backbones.

virus A disease-causing microorganism composed of an outer coat of protein and an inner coil of DNA or RNA.

visceral muscle Unstriated, involuntary muscle found primarily in the organs of the body. Also called smooth muscle.

vitamins Organic compounds necessary in small amounts for proper metabolism. Some are parts of coenzymes. Most are taken in with food, but vitamin D is synthesized in the skin with the aid of sunlight.

warm-blooded animal One that maintains the same body temperature despite variations in the temperature of the environment.

white blood cells Colorless blood cells that act to defend the body against disease.

X chromosome The sex chromosome present doubly in diploid cells of the human female and singly in the human male.

xylem Thick walled plant cells which provide support and which conduct materials upward through the stem.

Y chromosome In humans, the sex chromosome present only in males.

zygote The cell that is formed as the result of the union of two gametes. A fertilized egg.

INDEX

E

F

H

M

R

Photo Credits

41 – Dr. Jonathon Eisenback/Phototake
93 – James Dennis/Phototake NYC
188 – (left) © New York Zoological Society
188 – (right) © New York Zoological Society
297 – Bob Schuchman/Phototake NYC
302 – © New York Zoological Society
305 – (top) © Edward S. Ross/Phototake NYC
305 – (bottom) © CBC/Phototake NYC
388 – New York State Department of Health
393 – Photo Researchers
452 – (top) Grant Heilman
452 – (bottom) Grant Heilman
458 – Photo Researchers
463 – Earth Scenes
465 – Earth Scenes
466 – Grant Heilman
479 – Earth Scenes
480 – Grant Heilman
481 – Grant Heilman
482 – Earth Scenes
483 – (top) Grant Heilman
483 – (bottom) Grant Heilman
489 – Douglas Falk
490 – Douglas Falk